THE DESIGN AND ANALYSIS OF
INDUSTRIAL EXPERIMENTS

THE
DESIGN AND ANALYSIS
OF
INDUSTRIAL EXPERIMENTS

EDITED BY

OWEN L. DAVIES, M.Sc., Ph.D.

AUTHORS

GEORGE E. P. BOX, B.E.M., B.Sc., Ph.D.

LEWIS R. CONNOR, M.Sc.

WILFRED R. COUSINS, B.A., B.Sc.

OWEN L. DAVIES, M.Sc., Ph.D.

FRANCIS R. HIMSWORTH, B.Sc., Ph.D.

GEORGE P. SILLITTO, B.Sc., Ph.D.

PUBLISHED FOR

IMPERIAL CHEMICAL INDUSTRIES LIMITED

BY

OLIVER AND BOYD
LONDON AND EDINBURGH

HAFNER PUBLISHING COMPANY
NEW YORK

1967

First edition - - - - - - - - - 1954
Second edition, revised   - - - - - 1956
Second edition, reprinted -   1960, 1963, 1967

AUTHORS' PREFACE

Imperial Chemical Industries Ltd. has long recognised that statistical methods have an important part to play in industrial research and production. To encourage the use of such methods and to give publicity to them within its own organisation it arranged for the publication of a book in 1947.* In this book no attempt was made to deal with the design of experiments which was considered to be such a big subject that it should be dealt with in a separate book. In this field statistical methods have a major contribution to make to industrial research, because the use of such methods enables clear and unambiguous conclusions to be drawn from the minimum number of experiments and therefore for the minimum cost. In this volume, therefore, the design and analysis of industrial experiments are dealt with in considerable detail.

The present volume, though complete in itself, is a sequel to the first book. The first book is a useful introduction to the second, because it sets out in a simple way the elements of statistical analysis which it is essential to understand before the design of experiments can be undertaken. In the second book frequent references are made to the first, and such references are designated by the letters "*S.M.*"

Most books which have been written on the design of experiments have been based on experience gained in agricultural research, and this experience is not easily translated into terms and examples which can readily be understood by research workers in other fields, e.g. the chemical industry. More important, however, is the fact that experimental designs which are suitable for one field of research work are not necessarily the best for others. While a knowledge of the designs used in agricultural research is basic to the design of industrial experiments, the former designs are inadequate to the very important problem of finding the best operating conditions of a process. Suitable designs have only recently been introduced, and a full treatment of the methods and examples of their application in practice are a special feature of this book.

As in the first book, the authors have been allowed to draw freely on information in I.C.I.'s possession, so that almost every example represents a problem which has been met in actual practice and for which full working details are given. Although the examples are chemical, the basic principles are explained in general terms and are capable of extension and application to other fields of industrial activity. Each new principle is illustrated by one or more practical examples. The authors, however, have confined themselves

---

* *Statistical Methods in Research and Production* (*Third Edition*), edited by Owen L. Davies. Oliver & Boyd (Edinburgh and London, 1957).

to those methods which in their experience have proved of value and have avoided including abstract theoretical matter which has little relevance to the problem under discussion.

The book has been written principally for the research worker in the chemical industry with a limited knowledge of mathematical statistics, but it is hoped that it will appeal to other readers. For example, it is hoped that lecturers in universities and technical colleges who require further information on practical applications, and students of statistics who intend to enter industry, will find it of use. Those concerned with management who may wish to assess the value of these methods to their particular field of activity may also find it helpful.

The authors intend to keep this book up to date, and any helpful suggestions and criticisms from readers will be welcomed.

Acknowledgments are due to members of I.C.I. staff and others who have supplied data, discussed matters of theory and application and commented on the drafts, and to the Biometrika Trust, Professor G. A. Barnard, the editor of *Research*, the McGraw-Hill Book Company, and the publishers of this volume for permission to use copyright matter.

* * * * * *

Sections, tables in the text, formulae, figures and references are numbered on the "decimal" system, but no attempt is made to keep these various systems of numbers in alignment, e.g. Table 3·4 falls in § **3·311** and Formula (*3·1*) in § **3·21**. Sections are numbered in bold type, formula numbers in italics, and other numbers in roman type.

References to literature are enclosed in square brackets, thus [2·1] *simpliciter* means "Refer to Sir Ronald A. Fisher's *Design of Experiments*."

In addition to tables in the text, sixteen general tables of functions have been inserted at the end of the volume and numbered A, A·1, A·2, B, . . ., N

* * * * * *

Changes in the second edition are mainly corrections to printers' errors and occasional improvements in wording. More important changes are additions to the list of references to Chapter 11 indicating recent developments in the subject, alteration of *S.M.* to refer to the appropriate sections in the third edition, and correction to a formula in Appendix 4A.

CONTENTS

Principles of Planning illustrated by a Simple Experiment—Reasoning behind the Significance Test—Need for Randomisation—Taking the Specimens in Pairs—Choice of Experimental Error—Advantages and Disadvantages of making the Experiments Self-contained—Reliability of Mean Difference—Single- and Double-sided Tests—Comparison of Means, σ known (Normal Curve Test), σ estimated from Sample (t-test)—Comparison of Proportions—Comparison of Variances (χ^2- and F-tests)—Confidence Limits for Variances and Ratio of Variances—Controlling the risks of Errors of the Second Kind—Number of Observations required—Operating Characteristic Curve—The Number of Observations required in the Comparison of Means, Proportions, and Variances—Assumptions made in Statistical Tests—Transformation of Data to obtain Approximate Normality—Tests based on the Randomisation Distribution

APPENDIX: 2A. The Assumption that the Errors are Normally Distributed

The Sequential Test—Testing for a Difference in Mean Value, σ known—Single-sided Alternative Hypothesis—Operating Characteristic Curve—Number of Observations—Double-sided Alternative Hypotheses—Testing for a Difference in Mean Value, σ estimated from Sample—Barnard's Sequential t-test—Testing for a Difference in Proportions, in Frequencies and in Variances—Summary of Sequential Tests

APPENDICES: 3A. Sequential Tests of Simple Hypotheses—3B. The Operating Characteristic Curve, or Power Curve—3C. The Average Sample Number

Objects of Experiments—Interaction—Replicate Analyses—Errors of Chemical Analysis—Analysis of Experiment with b Batches and k

LIST OF EXAMPLES

CHAPTER 1

INTRODUCTION

Object of the handbook

1·1. This handbook deals with the rational design of experimental work; it is a sequel to *Statistical Methods in Research and Production* (1947 revised 1957), which dealt mainly with the use of statistical methods for extracting information from pre-existing data. It is not intended as a general treatise on industrial research; it deals with one aspect of it, namely the arrangement of the individual items composing a complex experiment designed for a given purpose, and the statistical analysis of the results. It does not consider the methods by which the experiments are performed or the general organisation of scientific research. The use of statistical methods for analysing and interpreting the results of experiments will in this volume be considered mainly in relation to the experimental design.

Most chemists and physicists graduate without a knowledge of statistical methods, and are often unaware of the value of such methods in their work. An early reaction when they are introduced to the subject is that statistical methods are in some way an alternative to whatever methods they would normally have used—an alternative which is applied by enthusiasts and which is entirely optional. It is worth stressing, therefore, that whenever a problem involves the use of data which are subject to appreciable experimental errors, statistical methods offer the only sound and logical means of treatment; there is no question of any alternative which is equally satisfactory. When an experimenter relies on his own judgment to assess the results of his work, he applies, or should apply, criteria similar to those which might have formed the basis of a statistical test but without the numerical discipline imposed by the test. As long as he is dealing with effects which are large compared with the random variations such a procedure may be satisfactory; when, however, these random variations become considerable compared with the effects, such mental judgments may become misleading and cannot be considered to be satisfactory alternatives to rigid statistical tests. In universities students of science carry out closely controlled experiments of high accuracy with materials of great purity. These ideal conditions are frequently unattainable in industrial process work, and even where they can be achieved, the results obtained will often not be directly applicable to the more complex situations occurring in practice. Statistical methods therefore should be regarded as part of the technique which scientists in industry should learn in order to deal effectively with the problems of industrial work.

It will in general be assumed that the reader is familiar with the simpler statistical techniques described in the previous book, references to the appropriate sections of which will frequently be made. Those wishing to refresh their memories of the subject are particularly advised to re-read Chapters 4, 6, and 9, where they will find a full description of most of the statistical tests used in the present volume.

Those readers who are not already conversant with the subject may find it advisable to omit Chapters 3 and 6 of this book at their first reading, since the matter contained in them is not required for the understanding of the subsequent chapters. On the other hand, Chapter 2 contains much of the basic reasoning used throughout the book, and it should be carefully studied and, if need be, referred to frequently.

Nature and value of experimental design

1·2. Experimental work in the chemical industry is extremely diverse, but the following types of investigation cover a considerable portion of it.

(a) *Physical or physico-chemical investigations.* These usually involve the precise determination of fundamental constants or properties of substances. In this work, which is closely allied to the kind of research carried out at the universities, the design of the experiments is usually imposed by the nature of the work and does not often require the use of statistical methods, though these may be required in the assessment of the errors involved.

(b) *Routine analysis of products, raw materials, etc.* In chemical analysis the errors involved are more often systematic than random. These systematic errors will usually be different for different analysts or for the same analyst at different times. In such circumstances the replication of a test by the same analyst will do little to increase the accuracy of the result and is usually only resorted to in order to detect mistakes. In addition to the errors of the actual analysis, the operations of taking a sample and subdividing it into portions suitable for analysis introduce further errors which may be of considerable magnitude. It is important, therefore, in considering any scheme of sampling and analysis to know the magnitudes of the errors involved. Investigations into such errors require careful design; the use of statistical methods both in choosing the pattern of the experiments and in interpreting the results is essential if reliable estimates are to be obtained.

(c) *Testing materials.* When testing the mechanical and other properties of materials, such as the tensile strength of rubber, or when estimating less clearly defined properties such as corrosion resistance or durability, the individual observations are often subject to considerable random error, so that to obtain reliable estimates it is necessary to take the average of a number of observations. Whenever investigations involve tests of this sort there is need for rational design on statistical lines.

(d) *Laboratory investigations into chemical processes.* Nearly all new chemical processes and most improvements of old ones start from small-scale laboratory investigations. In the early stages these may consist of simple and *ad hoc* experiments offering little scope for design, but sooner or later a stage is reached at which it becomes necessary to examine systematically the effects on the process of various changes in conditions or materials. For systematic investigations of this sort statistics offers the research worker valuable guidance in choosing the most suitable design.

(*e*) *Investigations into the operation of chemical plants and manufacturing processes.* These investigations may involve the determination of process efficiency or the study of process operation under normal working conditions, or of the effect of various changes in operating conditions, raw materials, etc. Such experiments may be expensive and may require the co-operation of a considerable number of people. They should therefore be carefully planned to ensure that the most suitable design is used.

In investigating any given problem, particularly of types (*d*) and (*e*), there are usually two possible methods of approach: the investigator may either set out to study the fundamental relationships affecting the particular process under investigation or he may adopt a more empirical method and study directly the effects of various changes in the process. In the fundamental approach the experimenter may study, for example, the rates and equilibrium constants of the various chemical reactions concerned in the process, together with the mass transfer coefficients, permeabilities, and other physical quantities which enter into it; on the basis of these he will try to predict the best conditions for operating the process and the effect of changes in any of the conditions. If, however, he adopts the empirical approach he will measure directly the effects of various changes in conditions without necessarily concerning himself with the exact mechanisms leading to the effects he observes. The latter approach has often to be used in industrial research when problems are so complex that to study the underlying causes of all the many effects observed would involve a prohibitive amount of work. In such cases empirical investigations using experimental designs based on statistical principles offer economical means of obtaining the necessary practical information. Even where a fundamental study has been undertaken it will often be found that, since this has been based on a simplification of the actual system, the final adjustment of a full-scale process to its optimum conditions must be performed empirically.

A good experimental design is one which furnishes the required information with the minimum of experimental effort. To do this three things are required: first, the questions to be answered by the experiments must be correctly formulated; second, a correct choice of experimental method must be made in the light both of the accuracy required and of the various experimental pitfalls which are likely to be encountered; and third, the general pattern of the experiments, i.e. the number, spacing, and interrelation of the individual observations, must be correctly chosen. It is with this general pattern comprising the number and interrelation of the individual items in a set of observations that the statistical theory of experimental design deals. Using mathematical theory it is possible to obtain measures of the quantity of information provided by an experimental arrangement, which can then be used to compare different arrangements to assess their suitability for any given problem. From studies of this sort, combined with practical experience in their use, there has grown up a body of knowledge about the properties of various types of design which is now available to guide the experimenter in the choice of a design suitable for his particular problem.

Any set of observations is a pattern or arrangement in the conditions that are being investigated. If the results are obtained haphazardly during the course of the work the final arrangement is likely to be unbalanced and irregular, and it will usually be found on examination that the use of a proper design would have yielded the same amount of information with less work. A function of statistics in this field is to provide criteria by which the experimenter may judge the efficiency of a proposed design and to provide him with certain standard types of design which have been shown on both theoretical and practical grounds to be particularly useful in dealing with certain types of problem. An incidental advantage of the statistical planning of experiments is that it forces all experimenters who use it to consider in advance what they are seeking and what steps must be taken to find it. They will also be forced to consider the likely magnitude of all the possible sources of error. A preliminary consideration of this sort is itself of great value, since it often leads the experimenter to recognise and avoid possible pitfalls and fallacies which otherwise might have been discovered only at a later stage of the work, if at all.

An important function of statistics is to provide a rational basis for deciding the number of observations to be made. Since all measurements are subject to random errors to some degree, it is frequently necessary to combine the results of a number of observations in order to obtain the required information with sufficient precision. In industrial work these random errors may be appreciable, and in an investigation designed for a given purpose a certain minimum number of observations is required to give the necessary precision. If more observations than this are made, experimental effort which might be better employed on other work will be wasted. This is equivalent to what engineers would call over-design, and in industrial research it can often be as expensive as it would be in the design of a piece of industrial equipment. If, however, the experiment is under-designed, so that too few observations are made, false conclusions may be drawn. Unless the research worker has some definite criterion by which he can judge the correct number of experiments to make, over-design or under-design of this sort is inevitable. It has been shown by experience that the combined effect of the correct type of design and of the use of the right number of observations leads to substantial economies in the amount of experimental work required for a problem. These economies far outweigh the extra time and thought required in planning the experiments. Since the main expense in any investigation is nearly always the expense due to the experimental work, a reduction in this is immediately reflected in the cost of the work as a whole.

In order to obtain the best and most economical design for an experiment we require prior knowledge of the errors involved and of the magnitude of effect it is required to detect. At first sight this may appear to raise a grave difficulty, but in practice a worker is seldom called on to perform experiments of such a novel character that there does not exist any prior information on the errors involved. The information may sometimes be sketchy and uncertain, but even where this is so, the design obtained by its use, though possibly not as efficient as one based on full knowledge, will invariably be better than an unplanned experiment. Where rational design of experimental work is regularly practised a fund of knowledge of the sort required rapidly accumulates, on which later workers draw in planning similar experiments. One of the main features of rational design, when properly carried out, is that it encourages the worker to make full use of all knowledge and experience at his disposal in order to assist him in planning his work.

In addition to the knowledge available at the start, further information may accrue in the course of the work. In chemical research, for instance, the results of individual tests or preparations usually come in singly or a few at a time, so that in the course of an experiment the results of earlier tests are available before the later ones are started. Where this occurs, use can be made of the information so provided to decide either the experimental design or the number of further tests that are required. The idea of using information from the early parts of a series of observations to design the later work is termed the Sequential Approach to a problem. In its simplest form it may consist merely of doing a small pilot experiment to provide approximate information on the errors or on the general nature of the effects, which can then be used in designing the full experiment. The advantages of this sequential approach are more marked when it can be applied in a systematic manner.

Statistical tests of significance are often required in interpreting the results of experiments. In such tests it is usual to postulate that the effect sought does not exist, and to see whether on this hypothesis the observed differences can reasonably be attributed to chance. If the probability of obtaining a difference as great as that found is small, e.g. less than 1 in 20, the hypothesis is considered disproved and the effect is said to be Significant. If the probability is greater than that regarded as defining significance, all that can be said is that there is insufficient evidence to show that an effect exists.

Significance tests must of course be used and interpreted with discretion. Although most of the designs in this book were originally developed for use with tests of significance, their value is not in general dependent on such tests, which can often be omitted without detracting from the value of the designs. When the variability of the individual tests is large compared with the effects sought, as frequently happens in experiments dealing with natural materials or living organisms, it is necessary to have a large number of observations before firm conclusions can be reached. In these circumstances a test of significance is advisable before any of the effects found are accepted as genuine, and since the result of the test may depend markedly on the magnitude of the random errors it is advisable to use a design which will allow these errors to be estimated from the actual experiment.

Deciding the number of observations required

1·3. In general the objects of scientific experiments involve either determining certain quantities with a given precision, or deciding whether or not some quantity differs from a standard value or from some other quantity by more than a specified amount. Where the individual observations are subject to appreciable random errors it may be necessary to combine the results of a number of separate observations in order to obtain a mean result of greater precision. If we have no knowledge of the errors involved we cannot, of course, forecast the number of experiments required. If, however, as is frequently the case, we know the magnitude of the errors to be expected in the various measurements involved, it is relatively easy by elementary statistical theory to forecast the number of observations required to determine any quantity with a given precision. When we wish to test the existence of a difference the problem is more complex. By applying the appropriate test of significance as described in the previous book we can ensure that we will run only an acceptably small risk of asserting that a difference exists when in fact it does not. It is frequently forgotten however that in carrying out a statistical test of this type we run the risk of a second kind of error, that of asserting that no difference exists when in fact there is a difference of sufficient magnitude to be of practical importance [Chapter 2]. In industrial research it is often quite as important to avoid missing genuine differences as it is to avoid asserting differences which have no real existence. If, for example, a number of new catalysts are being tested in a chemical process and compared with the catalyst in normal use, an error by which a particular catalyst was said to be an improvement when in fact it was no better than the normal one would as a rule soon be corrected by further experimental work and no great loss would result. If, on the other hand, an improved catalyst was reported as no better than the normal, work on this catalyst would probably cease and the process might continue for a long time to use the less efficient catalyst, involving an unnecessary loss which might be quite out of proportion to the relatively small cost incurred by reporting an improvement which did not exist. In planning an experiment of this type, therefore, due consideration must be given to both kinds of risk, and the size of the experiment should be sufficient, but only just sufficient, to reduce both risks to acceptable levels. The magnitude of the risks which may be tolerated obviously depends on the probable costs of errors of either kind and of carrying out a larger experiment. If large expenditure, e.g. on building a new plant, may result from the experiment, the risks of being wrong must be reduced to very small levels, but if the result of the experiment will be to plan further experiments much greater risks may be taken.

Sequential tests

1·4. When it is not practicable or convenient to examine the results of each trial before carrying out the next and the whole experiment must be performed at one time, the above method must be followed. When, however, the observations are made one after another or in small groups, it may be more economical to use Sequential Tests of Significance. An appropriate test is applied to the series of results as each comes to hand and the experiment is stopped as soon as there is sufficient evidence to indicate either that a difference exists or that any difference which might exist is not greater than some given value [Chapter 3]. In a test of this sort the experiment continues until one or the other of two alternative hypotheses is accepted. Theoretically there is no defined upper limit to the number of observations required, and although on the average the number is about one-half of what would be required for an experiment of fixed size, occasional experiments will occur which require greater numbers of observations. This uncertainty about the number of observations which will be required is not as serious as might be thought, since in practice the number of observations required to reach a decision is seldom more than double that required for an experiment of fixed size, and the occasional occurrence of large numbers is more than compensated by the high proportion of sequential experiments that end quickly. Any sequential experiment can, of course, be terminated after a given number of observations, but this will involve increasing slightly the risks of erroneous conclusions. Criteria are available to arrive at a decision in these circumstances.

Investigations of sampling and testing methods

1·5. Since most chemical experiments involve the sampling and testing of materials, the errors introduced by these procedures are particularly important. The methods used to investigate sampling and testing errors are moreover relatively simple and form a useful introduction to the more complex types of experiments and to the related statistical techniques. For these reasons a separate chapter [Chapter 4] is devoted to the consideration of the investigation of the errors of sampling and testing. Such investigations are usually carried out to improve the existing methods of sampling and analysis, to test and compare new methods, or to find the most economical routine testing scheme for some particular material. The information yielded by such investigations is often of great assistance in estimating the errors likely to be encountered in any subsequent experiment and thus in deciding the best experimental design to use.

Randomised blocks and Latin Squares

1·6. Theoretically, to obtain the highest precision in comparative trials, the trials should be carried out under identical conditions apart from the conditions being compared. In practice, particularly when the number of trials required is large, it is often difficult to ensure such uniformity owing to the natural variability of the materials and processes involved. Even if the variability could be eliminated it is doubtful whether it would be wise to try, since such variability broadens the basis of comparison and so renders the results more generally applicable. It is often possible, however, to split up a set of trials into smaller groups within which such variations are likely to be less than in the set as a whole. Thus pieces cut from the same sheet of rubber are expected to be more alike in their properties than pieces cut from different sheets, and samples taken from a plant over a short period vary less than those taken over a longer period. Where these conditions hold, the precision of the experiment can be increased by dividing it into Blocks, within each of which the random variations are likely to be smaller than in the experiment as a whole. In the simple examples discussed in Chapter 5 each block contains all the treatments (i.e. sets of experimental conditions) concerned, while the use of several blocks ensures that the number of observations is sufficient to give the required precision to the experiment as a whole. Where the block is too small to accommodate all the treatments, recourse may be had to the more complex Incomplete Block Designs discussed in Chapter 6.

Although the variability within any block is likely to be less than that in the experiment as a whole, there may be a systematic variation within the individual blocks. Thus pieces from the centre of a sheet of rubber are likely to differ systematically from those cut from the edge of the sheet. If therefore the treatments are introduced in the same relative positions in successive blocks, spurious effects due to the systematic variations associated with position within a block are likely to be introduced into the results. To overcome this the arrangement of the treatments must be different in each block, the actual positions of the treatments within any block being chosen by an adequate random process. Where the number of blocks is equal to or a multiple of the number of treatments it is possible to improve on the random arrangement by using a design in which each treatment appears an equal number of times in each position in a block, the treatments being then distributed randomly among the various sets of positions. Such designs are known as Latin Square designs. They are also of use in giving economical designs for examining the effect of two or three sets of factors when the effects of these factors can be assumed to be additive and independent of changes in the other sets of factors. The uses and limitations of these designs are discussed in Chapter 5.

Factorial designs

1·7. Frequently in scientific investigations, particularly where an empirical approach has to be adopted, problems arise in which the effects of a number of different factors on some property or process require to be evaluated. Such problems can usually be most economically investigated by arranging the experiments according to an ordered plan in which all the factors are varied in a regular way. Provided the plan has been correctly chosen, it is then possible to determine not only the effect of each individual factor but also the way in which each effect depends on the other factors (i.e. the Interactions). This makes it possible to obtain a more complete picture of what is happening than would be obtained by varying each of the factors one at a time while keeping the others constant [Chapter 7]. Designs of this sort, moreover, lend themselves well to statistical analysis and can if required provide their own estimates of experimental error. In this field the design and the analysis of the results are closely linked, and unplanned experimental work is liable to confuse the effects sought in such a way that much of the information which would otherwise be available is sacrificed.

Factorial designs have been in use for a great many years in agricultural and biological research, in which the experimental errors are usually large compared with the effects being investigated and the cost of the individual observations is not very great. Elaborate designs with much replication are therefore frequently used. In industrial investigations the experimental errors may be smaller in proportion to the effects sought and the cost of the individual experiments may be considerable. Moreover it is sometimes possible to state on theoretical grounds which factors are likely to interact and which may safely be assumed not to interact. The results are normally available quite quickly, and the experimenter is naturally averse to doing a large number of experiments according to a fixed plan without having an opportunity of revising his plan in the light of the results obtained. If therefore a series of experiments in industrial research were planned like an agricultural experiment it would frequently be found that the resulting design was so large and cumbersome that it would be rejected out of hand by the experimenter, and that if it were used a large proportion of the experimental effort would be wasted in evaluating unimportant interactions and in determining the experimental error with an unnecessary degree of precision. On this account considerable attention is given in this volume to Fractional Factorial Designs [Chapter 10], which enable the size of an experiment to be reduced to a fraction of that of a full factorial experiment while still providing all the important information.

Sequential methods in experimental design

1·8. In addition to its use in sequential experiments for simple comparative trials, the sequential approach can also be employed in a less formal way in the general strategy of experimental design. An investigation may proceed as a series of small experiments instead of as a single comprehensive experiment, so that the information obtained in the earlier experiments may be used in the later ones. Industrial research offers a particularly favourable field for the application of methods of this sort. Frequently the observations are made either singly or in sets of a few at a time, and the results are available quickly. The random errors of the observations are usually not very great, so that only a moderate degree of replication is required. Altogether in industrial work an experimenter is well placed to take advantage of the economy and flexibility of sequential methods, and it will be found that such methods fit in well with the natural inclinations and training of the research chemist. In agricultural work, for which many of the existing statistical techniques were developed, it is common for the experimenter to have to wait some time, usually a whole season, before he obtains the results of his experiment and can begin another one. It is natural, therefore, to use large complex designs, covering as many aspects of the problem as practicable at one time. In industrial work what is required is numbers of smaller experiments which give a high degree of flexibility.

One of the most important problems in industrial research is the discovery of the optimum conditions for operating any given process. In some cases it is possible to calculate the optimum conditions on theoretical grounds; much more often, however, only an empirical approach is possible, and even when the theoretical optimum can be calculated it seldom corresponds exactly to the true optimum because of the effect of various unforeseen factors such as the presence of impurities. This search for optimum conditions moreover has in many cases to be carried out on a scale where not only is experimentation costly but the experimenter is under the severe limitation that nothing he does must cause any serious drop in plant efficiency. Considerable thought has been given to this problem, as a result of which methods have been evolved which enable the search for optimum conditions to be carried out with the minimum of experimental effort while at the same time allowing the efficiency of the plant to be progressively improved as the work proceeds [Chapter 11].

CHAPTER 2

THE PLANNING OF SIMPLE COMPARATIVE EXPERIMENTS

THE fundamental principles involved in the planning of experiments are discussed in terms of simple comparative investigations. The application of these principles ensures that the conclusions drawn from the experiment are valid, and similar considerations enter into the planning of the more complex experiments described in later chapters. The basic ideas underlying the significance tests and confidence limits which are used in interpreting experimental data are explained. It is shown, by using these ideas, that the number of observations necessary to ensure a conclusive result may be derived. The assumptions made in statistical tests are discussed.

Introduction

2·1. In this chapter the planning of simple comparative experiments is discussed. It is assumed that the circumstances are such that it is necessary or convenient to plan the experiment completely in advance, an appropriate statistical test being applied when all the observations have been taken. Such tests are called Non-sequential, to distinguish them from the Sequential tests discussed in the next chapter which are applied to the data as each observation is made. The principles which emerge from the discussion of these simple tests are generally applicable, and their consideration will serve as an introduction to the wider subject of experimental planning.

The object of the methods discussed is to obtain the best return for a given amount of effort. To do this, attention must be focused both on the planning of the experiment and on the analysis of the results obtained from it. These two phases are closely interlinked. The plan should ensure that when the experiment is completed it answers efficiently and unambiguously those questions it is intended to resolve. The analysis should be such that it extracts all the information from the data, and its form is largely determined by the design which is used. No analysis, however ingenious, can compensate for bad design. When planning an investigation, therefore, the analysis of the results which will be carried out on completion of the experiment must be kept continually in mind. If a valid and efficient analysis is not possible, then the experimental design is unsatisfactory.

Principles of planning illustrated by a simple experiment

2·2. To fix our ideas we begin with a description of a simple but well-planned experiment. The reason for each step is then discussed in detail.

Description of the experiment: Abrasion resistance of rubber

2·21. The experiment was required to test whether or not treatment with a certain chlorinating agent increased the abrasion resistance of a particular type of rubber. The experimenter took ten test-pieces of the material and divided each piece into two. One half was treated and the other half was left untreated, the choice which half of the specimen should receive the treatment being made by tossing a coin. The abrasion resistances of the ten pairs of specimens were then tested by a machine, the specimens being taken in random order. The ten differences, abrasion resistance of treated specimen minus abrasion resistance of untreated specimen, are shown in Table 2·1.

Table 2·1

DIFFERENCES IN ABRASION RESISTANCE

Test-piece ..	1	2	3	4	5	6	7	8	9	10
Difference: treated minus untreated	2·6	3·1	− 0·2	1·7	0·6	1·2	2·2	1·1	− 0·2	0·6

The mean difference was positive ($\bar{x} = 1\cdot27$), suggesting that the treatment had been favourable, but much variation occurred in the individual results. In order to decide how much confidence could be placed in the apparent improvement a test of significance was made. The appropriate test is the t-test [*S.M.*, § 4·6], which involves a comparison of the mean difference with its standard error. It was found that:

Mean difference $\bar{x} = 1\cdot27$

Estimated standard deviation of differences

$$s = \sqrt{\{\Sigma(x - \bar{x})^2/(n - 1)\}} = 1\cdot127$$

Standard error of the mean $s/\sqrt{n} = 0\cdot356$

$$t = \frac{\text{mean}}{\text{standard error of mean}} = \frac{\bar{x}}{s/\sqrt{n}} = 3\cdot565$$

Entering the t-table (Table C·1) with the degrees of freedom equal to nine (or in general one less than the number of differences), it was found that the appropriate 1% significance point was 2·82. The value of t was therefore significant at the 1% level, and the experimenter concluded that the treatment probably yielded a real increase in abrasion resistance.

It is instructive to study this experiment in detail, and in particular the following aspects:

(i) The reasoning behind the significance test [§ 2·22].

(ii) The need for randomisation [§ 2·23].

(iii) The reason for taking the specimens in pairs [§ 2·24].

(iv) The choice of an appropriate estimate of experimental error [§ 2·25].

(v) The advantages and disadvantages of making the experiment self-contained [§ 2·26].

(vi) The reliability of the mean difference [§ 2·27].

The reasoning behind the significance test

2·22. By means of statistical methods the intuitive type of reasoning which an intelligent person might apply in drawing inferences from data is made objective and precise. This has the important consequence that the logical basis of such reasoning can be examined and the circumstances which justify it more clearly seen. It is then possible to arrange the circumstances of the experiment so that objective and valid conclusions can be drawn at its completion.

Table 2·1 contains ten results, each of which denotes a difference between a test for a treated and an untreated specimen. In attempting to judge the significance of these observations by visual inspection the first difficulty is that the mind does not easily grasp the import of ten separate values. Some way is required therefore of summing up the information they contain. A person with some scientific training but no knowledge of statistics might mentally assess these results in the following way. First he would consider their general level. To give a clear picture of this he might calculate the mean. He would not however be satisfied with this measure alone but would consider the variation of the figures about their mean to see how consistent they were. The fact that the mean difference was positive would not convince him of the efficacy of the treatment unless the smallness of the variation showed that this was unlikely to be a chance result. The statistical test follows precisely the same lines, but the test is made in an exact and objective way. Three steps may be distinguished:

(i) The hypothesis it is desired to test is decided upon. The observer wants to find out whether there is probably a real difference, and to do this he considers whether, in the light of the experimental results, the hypothesis that there is really no difference is tenable. In statistical terminology this hypothesis of no real difference is called the Null Hypothesis. An experiment of the sort described is really a trial in which opportunity is afforded for the Null Hypothesis to be discredited if it is untrue.

(ii) The information of the separate measurements is replaced by a single criterion. The vague intuitive requirements of a criterion which takes account of the mean difference in the light of variation in the data arising due to pure chance are fulfilled by the quantity t, which compares the deviation of the sample mean from the value which would be expected if the Null Hypothesis were true (zero in this case) with the standard error of the mean.

(iii) A decision is made whether the departure from the Null Hypothesis indicated by the criterion is such that this hypothesis must be abandoned. Working intuitively, the observer would have to decide this from common sense and past experience. Except in extreme instances he would find it very difficult to do this. In the precise statistical test this phase corresponds to the reference of the observed value of t to significance tables. From the nature of t it is obvious that the larger its value the less confidence may be placed in the truth of the Null Hypothesis. Under certain reasonable assumptions the exact distribution of t when the Null Hypothesis is true can be calculated. Thus in this particular instance it is seen that the chance is less than 1% of obtaining a value of t as great as or greater than that found if the Null Hypothesis is true. There is therefore a negligible probability that the Null Hypothesis is true, and the Alternative Hypothesis that a real increase has occurred is accepted.

The assumptions mentioned above, in so far as they affect the experimental plan, will now be considered.

If sets of n observations are independently drawn from a Normally distributed universe having mean μ, and the quantity $t = \sqrt{n}(\bar{x} - \mu)/s$ is calculated for each set, then the t's will be distributed symmetrically about zero in a form dependent only upon the number of degrees of freedom involved. This distribution can be determined mathematically, and provides the basis for the t-tables. All the quantities required for the calculation of t, except μ, are obtained from the data; the test is thus strictly relevant for application to actual experimental observations, provided such observations can be regarded as representing independent drawings from a Normally distributed universe in which μ is accurately known. Now it can be shown that even if the universe from which the observations are drawn is not exactly Normal, under the conditions of practical experiment [Appendix 2A] a sufficiently close approximation will usually be supplied by the t-tables. For the moment, therefore, the assumption of Normality will be ignored.

The need for randomisation

2·23. There remain the assumptions that μ should be accurately known and that the observations may be regarded as representing independent drawings from the parent universe. Consider first the value of μ. In the example it is assumed that if the Null Hypothesis were true, that is, if the treatment produced no effect, then μ, the true mean difference, would be zero. If the experiment were badly designed this might not be so. For example, if all the untreated specimens were tested on one day and all the treated specimens were tested on another, then a difference might arise owing to day-to-day fluctuations in the conditions even though no treatment difference occurred. The absence of any systematic difference between the sets other than that deliberately introduced is an obvious requirement for a good experimental design, and few experimenters would wittingly make a mistake of this sort. Unsuspected systematic effects can occur however. Suppose that no coin-tossing or equivalent process of randomisation had been adopted for the allocation of treatments and that at the completion of the experiment it had been discovered that the test-pieces tended to be thicker at one end than at the other and that the difference in thickness influenced the test. If there was also reason to believe that owing to the way in which the experiment was conducted the thick ones were probably those which had received the treatment the experimenter could not rely on his conclusion, for he could not assume that no difference would occur even when the treatment produced no effect. That is to say, he could not assume that when the Null Hypothesis was true μ would be zero, and it is unlikely that he could say accurately what value ought to be taken. In fact the thickness effect and the effect due to the treatment would be hopelessly intermingled (or, in statistical terminology, confounded).

Now it is always possible that mistakes may be made owing to unsuspected sources of disturbance affecting the comparison in some systematic way. The experimenter may carefully examine all the possibilities and attempt to control all known causes of disturbance during the experiment; but even if he can do this there may always be others of which he is unaware which affect the validity of his conclusions. This difficulty can be overcome by randomisation; in the example above, provided the decision which half of the test-piece was to be treated and which was to be left untreated was made by some random process, then the experimenter could be sure that, whatever unsuspected disturbances might occur at this stage of the experiment, they would not influence the value of μ.

The second requirement that the observations should be effectively independent is also met by randomisation. Consider the question of the order of test for the specimens in the above experiment. In operations which must necessarily be carried out in succession it is often found that results obtained at the same time are more alike than results separated by time. Thus the test might be affected by some slight change in the adjustment of the machine or by temperature and humidity, and these could all contribute to cause fluctuations in the results. The experimenter would naturally try to forestall such effects, but he might not always succeed. Where systematic (in contrast to random) disturbances of this sort occurred, the assumption of independence would not be justified. For if one result was unusually high there would be a tendency for the next in the sequence to be high also. Now, by means of the *t*-table, predictions can be made about the quantity *t* calculated from independent observations, but no such predictions could be made about observations which were not independent (unless, as usually would not be the case, the precise nature of the dependence was known). The difficulty is overcome by introducing the random element into the experiment itself, that is to say, by testing the specimens in random order. For fuller discussion of this topic the reader is referred to § **2·61**. The effect of such randomisation is to make it legitimate to analyse the results as if they were independent.

The reason for taking the specimens in pairs

2·24. In order that comparison should be made between specimens as alike as possible, each test-piece was cut into halves, one half being treated and the other half not. The results analysed were the differences in abrasion resistance between the treated and untreated specimens cut from the same test-piece. The comparisons were thus kept entirely within a test-piece and the large variation between test-pieces was eliminated both in the design and in the subsequent analysis. The principle involved is of wide application, and it will be employed many times in later chapters.

The essential plan is to limit comparisons to within aggregates of material which are more homogeneous than the whole; these aggregates are called Blocks. In the example given the blocks are the test-pieces from each of which a treated and an untreated specimen is obtained. The error appropriate for making the test is then that due to the variation between a pair of specimens from the same test-piece if no treatment were applied, the additional variation from one test-piece to another being eliminated. This will be seen more clearly if we consider the individual results given below.

Table 2·2
ABRASION RESISTANCE OF TEST-PIECES

Test-piece	Untreated	Treated	Difference	Test-piece mean
1	12·1	14·7	2·6	13·40
2	10·9	14·0	3·1	12·45
3	13·1	12·9	− 0·2	13·00
4	14·5	16·2	1·7	15·35
5	9·6	10·2	0·6	9·90
6	11·2	12·4	1·2	11·80
7	9·8	12·0	2·2	10·90
8	13·7	14·8	1·1	14·25
9	12·0	11·8	− 0·2	11·90
10	9·1	9·7	0·6	9·40
Mean ..	11·60	12·87	1·27	

C

The right-hand column showing the test-piece means indicates large variation in abrasion resistance from test-piece to test-piece. This has been eliminated by the simple device of confining comparisons to within samples from the same test-piece. A fuller discussion of the increased efficiency to be gained by the use of paired comparisons will be found in *S.M.*, Chapter 4, while a more general consideration of the block principle is given in Chapter 5 of this volume.

The choice of an appropriate estimate of experimental error

2·25. In the experiment we have discussed the estimate of error was based on the variation among the individual differences between test-pieces. Provided the precaution of randomisation to remove possible extraneous disturbances was taken, the estimate was appropriate to assess the significance of the mean difference between treated and untreated specimens. However, mistakes sometimes occur in choosing appropriate error estimates.

Suppose two batches of material are prepared, one by method A and the other by method B, and analyses are made on four representative samples of each batch, with the following results:

Table 2·3

REPEAT ANALYSES ON A BATCH OF MATERIAL MADE BY METHOD A
AND ANOTHER BATCH MADE BY METHOD B

	Method A	Method B
Analysis 1	62·9	65·8
Analysis 2	63·3	64·9
Analysis 3	62·4	65·2
Analysis 4	62·6	65·3
Mean	62·8	65·3

A *t*-test of significance applied to the data shows a significant difference between the two means. All that the experimenter may conclude from this however is that the second batch has a higher mean value than the first. He cannot conclude that method B gives a higher result than method A, because the process of preparation (quite apart from analytical and sampling errors) may itself be subject to variation.

If repeat preparations are made by each method, then the means of replicate analyses may well vary in the way shown in Table 2·4.

The only estimate of error which is appropriate to test an apparent difference between batches prepared by different methods is the estimate

Table 2·4

MEANS OF FOUR ANALYSES

	Method A	Method B
1st preparation (Table 2·3) ..	62·8	65·3
2nd preparation	66·3	64·1
3rd preparation	64·5	63·7

calculated from the variation between batches prepared by the same method. In this instance the error must be calculated from the variation between the values 62·8, 66·3, and 64·5, and between the values 65·3, 64·1, and 63·7.

The advantages and disadvantages of making the experiment self-contained
2·26. In some comparative experiments the mean value for untreated specimens and the standard deviation of repeat observations are known from past experience. The wear test experiment, on the other hand, was arranged so that both these quantities were estimated from the observations themselves; in fact the experiment was completely self-contained and the conclusions were independent of external information.

2·261. Consider first the question whether an internal or an external estimate of the mean of the untreated specimens should be used. An internal estimate is obtained by introducing controls into the design of the experiment, that is to say, parallel observations are made on untreated materials. Controls may be used in two different ways: in some experiments each treated specimen is associated with its own control (this is the pairing or block principle already described); in others the block principle is not utilised but a group of control observations is performed and the mean of the observations on treated specimens is compared with the mean of the control group. The object is to eliminate variation from experiment to experiment (or from block to block in the same experiment) from the comparison of the materials. It is tacitly assumed that such variation will affect treated and control specimens approximately equally and that it will thus be largely eliminated from the differences. The advantage of performing experiments with controls is not only that random variation from experiment to experiment will be eliminated, but also that gross changes due to unwitting alterations of the technique will not be wrongly ascribed to the treatment. Nevertheless it sometimes happens that conditions are so stable that the control observations are unnecessary. This is particularly true when the experiment is a routine one and the factors affecting the test are known and controlled, e.g. tensile tests performed in special laboratories in which humidity and temperature are held constant. In such cases the test results may be compared with standard values known from past experience.

2·262. Consider now whether an internal or external estimate of the standard deviation should be used. The experimenter will often be able to form an advance estimate of the likely magnitude of the experimental error standard deviation σ. The accuracy of such prior estimates will vary greatly in different circumstances. With a routine experiment performed under accurately controlled conditions (for example a routine test on material to check that it conforms to specification) it will often be possible to obtain a precise estimate of σ from the extensive past records available. In these circumstances tests could be based on this prior estimate of σ. (It would, however, be advisable to keep a running check on σ by means of a control chart for range [S.M., Chapter 10] to ensure that unsuspected changes in the test or in the material did not cause a change in σ.) In other experiments knowledge of the magnitude of σ might be much less definite, taking the form of only a rough estimate given by the experimenter from his general experience of similar work. Here it is desirable to employ an estimate calculated from the data of the experiment in making the actual test of significance. The experimenter's rough prior estimate would be valuable however in deciding in advance on a suitable size for the experiment; this point is discussed later.

When the experimental error is large, replication is necessary to obtain adequate precision. From the discrepancies between the replicate observations an adequate internal estimate of error can usually be calculated. It must be remembered, however, that the primary object of the replication is to increase precision and not to obtain an estimate of experimental error. In the situations discussed in Chapters 10 and 11, where the observations are often costly but the experimental error is small, designs are used in which a large number of factors are tested simultaneously. In these experimental arrangements almost all of the possible comparisons among the observations may be utilised to estimate the effects of the factors, and there may be no comparisons or only a few which measure experimental error. In these circumstances no adequate internal estimate of experimental error can be obtained from the data. By replication, of course, such an estimate could be obtained, but if from prior knowledge it seemed likely that the effects of the factors were already determined with adequate precision, replication merely to obtain an estimate of error would usually be unjustifiable. These experiments are however not of the type in which some irrevocable decision is to be made. Rather, they are used to indicate the next set of experiments which should be performed, and it is usually sufficient to use the rough prior estimate of experimental error to give an indication of the confidence to be placed in the results, replication being contemplated only if it appears likely that the precision of the comparisons is insufficient. As further sets of experiments are performed information about the value of σ accumulates, and at the end of the investigation a fairly precise value will usually be available.

The reliability of the mean difference

2·27. In the example of § **2·21** the hypothesis that the true mean difference in abrasion resistance between treated and untreated specimens was zero was rejected by the t-test. The argument was that if μ denoted the true mean difference, then in repeated experiments the statistic

$$\frac{\bar{x} - \mu}{s/\sqrt{n}}$$

would be distributed to a sufficiently close approximation as the tabled quantity t. When μ was put equal to zero, the value required by the Null Hypothesis, this ratio equalled 3·57, a value which would be expected to be equalled or exceeded less than once in a hundred times; the hypothesis that $\mu = 0$ was therefore rejected. This same form of test would be equally appropriate to test the plausibility of any other postulated value for μ. Suppose it was decided to make the test at the 5% level, then since from Table C·2, t has a 5% chance of lying outside the limits $\pm 2\cdot26$, those hypothetical values of μ which made $(1\cdot27 - \mu)/0\cdot356$ fall outside the limits $\pm 2\cdot26$ would be rejected, that is to say, those values of μ falling outside the limits $1\cdot27 \pm 0\cdot80$. It can then be said that at the 5% level of significance the observations are consistent with any value for the true mean difference μ lying between 0·47 and 2·07, but that values for μ outside these limits are contradicted by the data. The above argument is due to R. A. FISHER, who calls these limits the Fiducial Limits [2·2]. In general the fiducial limits for μ would be $\bar{x} \pm ts/\sqrt{n}$. A different justification was used by J. NEYMAN to arrive at these limits, which he calls Confidence Limits [2·3].

NEYMAN showed that if these limits were adopted, that is to say, if on completion of an experiment of this kind it was always said that μ lay within the limits $\bar{x} \pm ts/\sqrt{n}$, where $\pm t$ is the value exceeded with some small probability α, then in the long run this statement would be right in a proportion $1 - \alpha$ of the time. $1 - \alpha$ is called the Confidence Coefficient, and the limits are called the $100(1 - \alpha)\%$ Confidence Limits. For example, if α is taken equal to 0·05, they are the 95% Confidence Limits.

Significance tests and confidence intervals for other simple comparative experiments

2·3. So far, the principles involved in the planning and analysis of simple comparative experiments have been illustrated by a particular example based on the t-distribution. The discussion is now widened to include other comparative experiments. The following types are frequently met:

  (i) Experiments in which mean values are compared, and the standard deviation is assumed to be known in advance and is used in making the test of significance.

 (ii) Experiments in which mean values are compared, but an estimate of the standard deviation is obtained from the observations themselves and is used in the significance test; the wear test experiment is an example of this kind.

(iii) Experiments in which a possible difference in the proportion of times an event happens is the subject of inquiry.

(iv) Experiments in which a possible change in variance is of interest.

The use of randomisation to prevent bias due to unsuspected systematic disturbances is equally important in all such experiments. Before considering the individual tests of significance appropriate to these cases some more general points will be discussed.

Single- and double-sided tests

2·31. A test of significance is a test of a Null Hypothesis. The probability P obtained from significance tables is the probability that a divergence as great as or greater than that which has occurred might happen if the Null Hypothesis were true. The experimenter chooses some small value, for example 0·05, and rejects the Null Hypothesis whenever P is less than this value. That is, he chooses to behave as though P were really zero whenever it is smaller than 0·05. By doing this he ensures that he will assert that a real difference exists when it does not, only once in twenty times. The assertion of a significant difference when none exists is called an Error of the First Kind. The probability of making such an error is thus 0·05 in this case, and is in general denoted by a.

In some experiments the experimenter is testing for a change in one direction only. For example, in the wear test he is seeking a modification which increases the abrasion resistance. The alternative hypothesis to the Null Hypothesis, therefore, is that an increase in the mean value has occurred. In these circumstances the experimenter can make an error of the first kind in only one way, by asserting an increase when none has occurred. The appropriate significance point is therefore that positive value of t which is exceeded with probability a. This value of t will be denoted by t_a. In other experiments the problem is not whether a modification produces a difference in one direction, but whether it produces a difference in either direction. If an experimenter was comparing a new method of chemical analysis A with a standard method B, one question of importance would be, Is method A biased with respect to B? The Null Hypothesis would be that when testing the same sample the true means μ_A and μ_B resulting from the two methods were identical. The Alternative Hypothesis would be that they were not identical, and the experimenter would be equally interested in differences in either direction. Here then an error of the first kind could be made in two different ways. For when there was really no difference between methods A and B one might be led by experimental error to say either that μ_A was greater than μ_B, or that μ_A was less than μ_B. Consequently if the t-test was being used and the test was made at the level of significance a, the experimenter would require two significance points, t_1 and t_2, so that there was a probability $\frac{1}{2}a$ of exceeding t_1 and a probability $\frac{1}{2}a$ of falling short of t_2. If after the experiment had been performed the observed value of t was greater than t_1 he would say a significant increase had occurred, while if the value were less than t_2 he would say a significant decrease had occurred. Since the t-distribution is symmetrical these points would be given by $\pm t_{\frac{1}{2}a}$, where $t_{\frac{1}{2}a}$ is the positive value of t which is exceeded with probability $\frac{1}{2}a$. Clearly the value of t necessary for significance will be larger when a double-sided alternative is considered.

In what follows the notation u_a, t_a, $\chi_a{}^2$, and F_a will mean in each case the value of the statistic which is exceeded with probability a; it is thus the value which cuts off a single-tail area a of the probability distribution.

At the end of this volume single-tail tables are given for the Normal Curve test (Table A·1), t-test (Table C·1), χ^2-test (Table B), and F-test (Table D), and these are appropriate as they stand for tests of a single-sided Alternative Hypothesis. In addition, double-tail tables are given for the Normal Curve test (Table A·2) and the t-test (Table C·2) and are appropriate for testing the double-sided Alternative Hypothesis. Thus Table C·2 gives values of $t_{\frac{1}{2}a}$ for various values of a.

In what follows, the tests are based on single-sided Alternative Hypotheses unless otherwise stated; the only modification required when a double-sided hypothesis is considered will be the doubling of the probability in the single-sided significance tables.

Two types of comparative experiments

2·32. Two types of comparative experiments are considered. In the first type the mean, variance, or proportion, calculated from a sample of observations, is compared with a standard value; in the second, two means, variances, or proportions, each calculated from a sample of observations, are compared. In experiments such as the wear test example, in which the tests are performed in pairs, the differences may be analysed and treated as individual observations. The problem is then to compare the mean of these observations (the mean difference) with the standard value of zero (the universe mean difference when the Null Hypothesis is true). Viewed in this way such experiments are particular examples of the first category and they will not be discussed separately.

Comparisons of means, σ known (Normal Curve test)

2·33. In this and the following section it is assumed that the parent distributions, that is, the distributions of the universes from which the samples are drawn, do not differ too widely from the Normal form. The questions how "too widely" should be interpreted and how non-Normal distributions may be made approximately Normal are discussed in Appendix 2A and § 2·64 respectively.

Comparison with standard value

2·331. The mean $\bar{x}$ of a sample of n observations drawn from a universe with mean μ is distributed approximately Normally about μ with standard deviation $\sigma/\sqrt{n}$, where σ is the universe standard deviation, assumed known [S.M., Chapter 3]. Consequently, to test the Null Hypothesis that μ is equal to some standard value μ_0 against the Alternative Hypothesis that μ is greater than μ_0, the statistic

$$u = \frac{\bar{x} - \mu_0}{\sigma/\sqrt{n}} \quad \dots\dots\dots\dots\dots\dots\dots(2·1)$$

which on the Null Hypothesis denotes a unit Normal deviate, is referred to tables of the Normal Curve. The difference would be judged significant at the level a if u were greater than u_a, which is the deviate of the Normal Curve which cuts off a single-tail area a. By the argument given in § 2·27 the $100(1 - a)\%$ confidence limits for μ are $\bar{x} \pm u_{\frac{1}{2}a}\sigma/\sqrt{n}$.

Confidence limits for single-sided alternative

2·332. When considering a confidence interval, we usually have in mind two limits, one which the population value of the statistic considered is unlikely to exceed, and the other which it is unlikely to fall short of. This is assumed to be the case for instance in the example discussed in § 2·27, where it is appropriate to use the double-sided t-table C·2, the $100(1 - a)\%$ confidence limits being given by $\bar{x} \pm t_{\frac{1}{2}a}s/\sqrt{n}$. Occasionally however we may require a single-sided confidence interval. For example, it might be desired in the example on the abrasion resistance of rubber merely to give from the evidence of the sample a value below which it was unlikely that the true difference fell. In such a case a single limit based on single-tail tables is appropriate and the $100(1 - a)\%$ limit would be given by $\bar{x} - t_a s/\sqrt{n}$. For example, the lower 95% limit is given by $1·27 - (1·83 \times 0·356) = 0·62$. From this calculation we can make the statement that the true value of the difference between abrasion resistance of test and standard materials probably (with confidence coefficient 0·95) exceeds the value 0·62. It will be seen that this limit is higher than the value 0·47 obtained for the lower limit of the 95% confidence interval when two limits were included. This is to be expected since in one case we are saying that there is a 95% chance that the interval 0·47–2·07 includes the true value, in the other case we are saying that there is a 95% chance that the interval 0·62 to infinity includes the true value. A significant difference when the alternative hypothesis is two-sided implies that the two-sided confidence interval does not include the value postulated in the Null Hypothesis; a significant difference when the alternative hypothesis is single-sided implies that the single-sided confidence interval does not include the value postulated in the Null Hypothesis.

Comparison of two sample means

2·333. The difference $\bar{x}_1 - \bar{x}_2$ between two sample means is distributed approximately Normally about $\mu_1 - \mu_2$, the difference between the universe means, with standard deviation $(\sigma_1^2/n_1 + \sigma_2^2/n_2)^{\frac{1}{2}}$, where n_1, n_2 and σ_1, σ_2 are the numbers in the samples and the universe standard deviations respectively. To test the hypothesis that $\mu_1 - \mu_2 = 0$ against the alternative that $\mu_1 \neq \mu_2$ the statistic

$$u = \frac{\bar{x}_1 - \bar{x}_2}{(\sigma_1^2/n_1 + \sigma_2^2/n_2)^{\frac{1}{2}}} \quad \dots\dots\dots\dots\dots\dots(2\cdot2)$$

is referred to tables of the unit Normal Distribution.

The $100(1 - a)$% confidence limits for the difference $\mu_1 - \mu_2$ are

$$\bar{x}_1 - \bar{x}_2 \pm u_{\frac{1}{2}a}(\sigma_1^2/n_1 + \sigma_2^2/n_2)^{\frac{1}{2}} \quad \dots\dots\dots\dots\dots(2\cdot21)$$

In the important case in which σ_1 may be assumed equal to σ_2, Equation (2·2) becomes

$$u = \frac{\bar{x}_1 - \bar{x}_2}{\sigma(1/n_1 + 1/n_2)^{\frac{1}{2}}} \quad \dots\dots\dots\dots\dots\dots(2\cdot22)$$

and the $100(1 - a)$% confidence limits for $\mu_1 - \mu_2$ are

$$\bar{x}_1 - \bar{x}_2 \pm u_{\frac{1}{2}a}\sigma(1/n_1 + 1/n_2)^{\frac{1}{2}} \quad \dots\dots\dots\dots\dots(2\cdot23)$$

Comparison of means, σ estimated from sample (t-test)

2·34. In the more usual circumstances in which no accurate prior value for the standard deviation σ is available, an estimate s obtained from the sample of observations is employed, where $s^2 = \Sigma(x - \bar{x})^2/(n - 1)$.

Comparison with standard value

2·341. When σ is estimated from the sample, the criterion t used in the significance test takes the same form as u in (2·1) except that the estimate s obtained from the sample replaces σ. The test is made entering the t-tables with $\phi = n - 1$ degrees of freedom. The confidence limits are obtained from $(2\cdot11)$, replacing $u_{\frac{1}{2}a}$ by $t_{\frac{1}{2}a}$ and σ by s.

Comparison of two sample means

2·342. Provided it can be assumed that the universe standard deviations σ_1 and σ_2 are equal, the criterion t used in the significance test is the same as u in $(2\cdot22)$ except that s, the estimate based on the sample, replaces σ. The estimate s^2 is supplied by the formula

$$s^2 = \{\Sigma_1(x - \bar{x}_1)^2 + \Sigma_2(x - \bar{x}_2)^2\}/(n_1 + n_2 - 2)$$

As will be seen, s^2 is the weighted mean of the sample variances. The confidence limits are obtained from $(2\cdot23)$, replacing $u_{\frac{1}{2}a}$ by $t_{\frac{1}{2}a}$ and σ by s.

Comparison of proportions or percentages

2·35. A proportion or percentage is sometimes the subject of study. Examples are the percentage kill of insects in experiments on insecticides, the percentage of detonations when charges of explosive are exposed to a given stimulus, and the proportion of batches having unsuitable physical form in experiments designed to improve the quality of a chemical product. Methods for comparing proportions are given in *S.M.*, Chapter 9. A different method which is more convenient for the present purpose is to transform from the observed proportion p to the score x given by

$$x \text{ (radians)} = \text{arc sin } \sqrt{p} \quad \dots\dots\dots\dots\dots(2\cdot3)$$

This artifice converts the proportion p into the quantity x, which is approximately a Normally distributed variable with variance $\sigma^2 = 1/4n$, and x can be treated as the mean of a sample of n Normally distributed observations each having standard deviation $\sigma = 0\cdot5$. (This transformation is discussed in more detail in § 2·62.) This method can be safely applied so long as the proportion is between $0\cdot05$ and $0\cdot95$ (or preferably between $0\cdot10$ and $0\cdot90$) and the number of observations is not less than ten. All the relevant formulae follow at once from those obtained from the Normal Curve tests in § 2·33. This transformation can easily be made by using Table F, which enables x to be found for any desired value of p.

Example. Efficiency of a polymer blender

2·351. In an experiment to assess the efficiency of a blender which was used to thoroughly mix batches of polymer chips, a charge of 50% normal chips and 50% coloured chips was introduced. A sample of very small size compared with the total blend taken from the blender after a given time contained 312 chips, 151 of which were coloured. Assuming the experimenter is prepared to take a risk $a = 0\cdot05$ of asserting a difference when none exists, does this sample proportion of $151/312 = 0.484$ differ significantly from the theoretical value of 0.500 ? From Table F the score corresponding to the theoretical proportion 0.500 is found to be 0.7854. This number corresponds to μ_0 in Formula (*2·1*). The score corresponding to the observed proportion 0.484 is 0.7694, and this value can be treated as though it were the mean of 312 Normally distributed observations, each having standard deviation $\sigma = 0.5$. Applying Formula (*2·1*), we have

$$u = -0.565$$

This is an example of a double-sided Alternative Hypothesis, and on consulting tables of the Normal Curve it is found that if the Null Hypothesis were true, a sample value differing by as much as this would be expected about forty-three times in a hundred. The hypothesis that the true proportion was 0.500 has not been discredited by the experiment and there is no evidence therefore that the polymer chips were not uniformly blended at this time.

The methods of comparing two observed proportions and of obtaining confidence limits follow similar lines, the formulae being obtained at once from those for the Normal Curve test by treating the scores corresponding to proportions observed as if they were means of n Normally distributed observations, each having standard deviation $\sigma = 0.5$.

Comparison of variances

2·36. The experimenter frequently wishes to test, not whether the mean value of some property has changed, but whether the variability as measured by the variance or standard deviation has changed. The tests which follow are used in this situation. The reader is warned that all current statistical tests on variances are rather sensitive to departure from Normality of the distribution [2A·9] and is referred to § **2·63** and § **2A·5**, where this matter is discussed in greater detail.

Comparison with standard value (χ^2-test)

2·361. If from a Normally distributed population having true variance σ^2 a sample of n observations is drawn and from it an estimate $s^2 = \Sigma(x - \bar{x})^2/(n-1)$ of the population variance based on $\phi = n - 1$ degrees of freedom is calculated, then $\phi s^2/\sigma^2$ is distributed as $\chi^2(\phi)$ (chi-squared with ϕ degrees of freedom). The probability points of the distribution of χ^2 are given in Table B. The same distribution is followed by variance estimates based on sums of squares of deviations from regression lines or planes [*S.M.*, Chapters 7, 8] and by those based on sums of squares occurring in the analysis of variance. In each case the parameter ϕ is the number of degrees of freedom upon which the estimate is based. The significance of an apparent departure from some theoretical value σ_0^2 of an estimate s^2 based on ϕ degrees of freedom can be determined by calculating $\chi^2 = \phi s^2/\sigma_0^2$ and referring to tables of the χ^2 distribution with ϕ degrees of freedom.

Example. Strength of yarn

2·362. An accurate value $\sigma_0^2 = 0\cdot110$ for the variance of a certain method of testing was known. Twenty tests were made by a somewhat different technique which it was thought might result in greater variation. The estimate from the sample based on nineteen degrees of freedom was $s^2 = 0\cdot248$. Does this imply a significant increase in variance ? The statistic χ^2 was calculated as follows:

$$\chi^2 = \frac{19 \times 0\cdot248}{0\cdot110} = 42\cdot8$$

Table B shows that the value 38·6 is equalled or exceeded only once in two hundred times. The discrepancy is therefore highly significant.

In some examples the experimenter will want to test for a reduction in variance. Suppose the modification had been expected to reduce the variance and the actual value found for s^2 was 0·062, then:

$$\chi^2 = \frac{19 \times 0\cdot062}{0\cdot110} = 10\cdot7$$

Consulting tables of χ^2 with nineteen degrees of freedom and making a rough interpolation, we see that this value corresponds to a probability of about 0·93. This is the probability that a value of χ^2 greater than 10·7 would be observed. The probability that a value smaller than 10·7 would occur by chance is therefore $1 - 0\cdot93 = 0\cdot07$. The significance of this difference therefore falls a little short of the 5% level.

Confidence intervals

2·363. To find the $100(1 - \alpha)\%$ confidence interval for σ^2 from an estimate s^2 based on ϕ degrees of freedom, values σ_1^2 and σ_2^2 are required which just make the observed value s^2 significant. These are the values $\phi s^2/\chi^2_{1-\frac{1}{2}\alpha}$ and $\phi s^2/\chi^2_{\frac{1}{2}\alpha}$. For example, suppose an estimate of variance $s^2 = 16$ based on ten degrees of freedom was available, what statement could be made about σ^2, the variance of the universe from which the sample was drawn ? To obtain the 95% confidence limits the values $\chi^2_{0\cdot975} = 3\cdot25$ and $\chi^2_{0\cdot025} = 20\cdot5$ are required, for these are the points beyond each of which lies $2\frac{1}{2}\%$ of the χ^2 distribution based on ten degrees of freedom. The 95% confidence limits for σ^2 are therefore $(16 \times 10)/20\cdot5$ and $(16 \times 10)/3\cdot25$, or 7·8 and 49·2. Alternatively, these limits could be given in terms of the standard deviation by taking square roots. The estimate of σ is 4 and the 95% confidence limits for σ are 2·8 and 7·0. It will be noted that these limits are not equally spaced about the value 4, and this is generally true when the distribution curve (in this example, that of χ^2) is not symmetrical.

Equal tail areas have been used for the confidence intervals so far discussed. This has an intuitive appeal, but any two tail areas which together give 5% of the total curve may be said to give 95% confidence intervals. The subject of what constitutes "best" confidence intervals has been investigated by statisticians, but it will not be discussed here. It will be seen however that one reason for employing unequal tail areas would be that it was desired to lay special emphasis on one end of the range. If interest were centred on specifying a value below which σ^2 lay, then the lower tail area only would be used. The value $\chi^2_{0·95}$ is 3·94 for ten degrees of freedom. For this level of probability, therefore, an upper limit for σ^2 would be $(16 \times 10)/3·94$, that is 40·6.

Comparison of two sample variances (F-test)

2·364. If $s_A{}^2$ and $s_B{}^2$ based on ϕ_A and ϕ_B degrees of freedom respectively are independent estimates of the variance σ^2 of a Normally distributed universe, then the ratio $s_A{}^2/s_B{}^2$ is distributed as F with ϕ_A and ϕ_B degrees of freedom.

Possible values of the ratio extend from 0 to infinity, but since the probability that $F = s_A{}^2/s_B{}^2$ is greater than some value F_0 must be the same as the probability that $1/F = s_B{}^2/s_A{}^2$ is less than $1/F_0$, it is only necessary to provide significance tables for values of F greater than unity. These are given in Table D, which is arranged so that the number of degrees of freedom of the larger variance estimate is given as the column heading of the table.

Example

2·365. Six repeat tests using a standard method of analysis yield an estimate of variance $s_A{}^2$ of 0·621, eight repeat tests by a modified method yield an estimate $s_B{}^2$ of 0·497; may we conclude that the modification has effected an improvement in reproducibility? Dividing the larger estimate by the smaller we have $s_A{}^2/s_B{}^2 = F = 1·25$, and entering Table D with $\phi_A = 5$ and $\phi_B = 7$ we see that the 10% significance point for this ratio is 2·88. The difference is therefore not significant, that is to say, we cannot from this evidence alone reject the Null Hypothesis that $\sigma_A{}^2 = \sigma_B{}^2$ in favour of the alternative that $\sigma_A{}^2$ is greater than $\sigma_B{}^2$ (or what is the same thing, that $\sigma_B{}^2$ is less than $\sigma_A{}^2$).

It will be noted that the Alternative Hypothesis here is single-sided; the modification was expected to produce an improvement and we were concerned to test the hypothesis that $\sigma_B{}^2$, the true variance of the modified method, was less than $\sigma_A{}^2$, the true variance of the standard method. Only a large value of the ratio $s_A{}^2/s_B{}^2$ would thus lead us to reject the Null Hypothesis. The F tables given in Table D, which are single-sided tables, are appropriate to test such an hypothesis. Occasionally however the Alternative Hypothesis is double-sided. For example, if the results given above had been obtained from an experiment conducted to determine whether there was any difference in reproducibility between two methods of analysis A and B (either through A being better than B or B being better than A), then the alternative would be double-sided. If the estimates are denoted by s_A^2 and s_B^2, then unduly large values of the ratio s_A^2/s_B^2, or unduly small values, would lead to the rejection of the Null Hypothesis.

The probabilities given in the significance tables must therefore be doubled in making the double-sided test.

2·366. Confidence limits for σ_A^2/σ_B^2 are supplied by the values of this quantity which just make the ratio s_A^2/s_B^2 significant and are given by $(s_A^2/s_B^2)/F_{\frac{1}{2}a}(\phi_A\phi_B)$ and $(s_A^2/s_B^2)/F_{1-\frac{1}{2}a}(\phi_A\phi_B)$ respectively.

The notation $F_{\frac{1}{2}a}(\phi_A\phi_B)$ means the $\frac{1}{2}a$ significance point of F; the numbers in the brackets show the degrees of freedom, which are always written in the order: degrees of freedom in numerator, degrees of freedom in denominator.

To obtain $F_{1-\frac{1}{2}a}(\phi_A\phi_B)$ from Table D we note that $F_{1-\frac{1}{2}a}(\phi_A\phi_B)$ is equal to $1/\{F_{\frac{1}{2}a}(\phi_B\phi_A)\}$.

Thus to find the 90% confidence limits for σ_A^2/σ_B^2 in the example above we have $F_{0.05}(5, 7) = 3·97$, also $F_{0.05}(7, 5) = 4·88$ and therefore $F_{0.95}(5, 7) = 1/4·88 = 0·205$. From the estimate $s_A^2/s_B^2 = 1·25$ we deduce that the 90% confidence limits for σ_A^2/σ_B^2 are $1·25/3·97 = 0·315$ and $1·25/0·205 = 6·10$.

Controlling the risk of errors of the second kind

2·4. When a significant difference is found the experimenter is justified in asserting that the Null Hypothesis is probably false. When no significant difference is found he is not equally justified in asserting that the Null Hypothesis is true. He knows only that the data could easily have occurred if the Null Hypothesis were true. When the data are very variable and few observations have been made, the significance test controls only the error of the first kind at the required level of risk by telling the experimenter to regard as inconclusive all but very large differences. A real, and possibly important, difference may well have occurred, but the experiment may not have been sufficiently sensitive to detect it.

2·41. It will be seen then, that when no particular effort has been made to plan an experiment on a suitable scale, a test of significance is a valuable device which allows the experimenter to decide whether apparent effects, large or small, are probably real. A test of significance is not concerned with the possible importance or lack of importance of effects of a given magnitude, but only with whether they could plausibly be regarded as chance effects or not. To design an experiment which just fulfils the purpose of the experimenter it is necessary to choose the number of observations so that a difference sufficiently large to be of practical importance is nearly always picked out by the test as significant. If an experiment can be so planned, not only will a significant result indicate that a real difference has probably occurred, but a non-significant result will indicate that there was probably no difference sufficiently large to be of practical importance.

Experiments planned in this way are said to control the risk of an Error of the Second Kind, that is the error of failing to detect a real departure from the Null Hypothesis. The probability of making an error of the second kind is denoted by β.

In experiments in which mean values are compared the number of observations which should be made depends, as might be expected, on the quantities σ, δ, a, and β:

σ, the experimental error standard deviation.

δ, the size of difference between the means it is important to detect.

a, the risk of asserting a difference when none exists; that is the level of probability at which the significance test is made.

β, the risk of asserting no difference when a difference of δ exists.

The same number of observations would be required in an experiment in which the difference of importance was δ and the standard deviation was σ as would be needed when the values were respectively $k\delta$ and $k\sigma$. In fact the number of observations is a function of a, β, and $D = \delta/\sigma$. D is the standardised difference, the difference expressed in terms of the standard deviation. In other comparative experiments the number of observations will depend upon a, β, and a quantity analogous to D. Tables have been prepared and are included at the end of this volume by means of which the number of observations required in the various types of comparative experiments may be calculated.

A formula for the number of observations in a simple case

2·42. When the standard deviation is assumed accurately known a simple formula can be derived for the number of observations required in experiments to compare mean values. The case will be considered in which it is desired to compare the mean $\bar{x}$ of a sample of observations with a standard value μ_0. The derivation of this formula is instructive in showing the type of reasoning employed in determining the necessary number of observations. It is required to plan an experiment so that, while maintaining only a small risk a of asserting a significant increase in the population mean when none has occurred, there will only be a small risk β of asserting no difference when a difference of δ exists. Suppose $\bar{x}^*$ is the value which the mean of the sample must exceed for the difference to be significant. Then from Equation (2·1):

$$\bar{x}^* = \mu_0 + u_a \sigma / \sqrt{n} \dots\dots\dots\dots\dots\dots(2·4)$$

If $\bar{x}^*$ is so chosen, there is only a risk α that the sample mean $\bar{x}$ will exceed $\bar{x}^*$ when μ is equal to μ_0. It is also required that when μ is as large as $\mu_0 + \delta$ the risk that a significant increase will not be asserted is only β. This is the risk that the sample mean $\bar{x}$ falls short of $\bar{x}^*$, and consequently

$$\bar{x}^* = \mu_0 + \delta - u_\beta \sigma/\sqrt{n} \dots\dots\dots\dots\dots\dots(2·5)$$

Subtracting the second equation from the first it will be seen that both equations are satisfied when

$$(u_\alpha + u_\beta)\sigma/\sqrt{n} = \delta$$

that is, when $\qquad\qquad n = (u_\alpha + u_\beta)^2 (\sigma/\delta)^2$

or $\qquad\qquad\qquad n = (u_\alpha + u_\beta)^2/D^2 \dots\dots\dots\dots\dots\dots(2·51)$

where $D (= \delta/\sigma)$ is the difference it is important to detect, expressed as a multiple of the standard deviation. The experimenter should therefore perform the number of experiments indicated by (2·51) and make a test of significance at the level α. If the result is significant, he should say that a real difference has occurred; if it is not significant, he should say that no difference as large as δ has occurred. The chances of obtaining a significant result when no difference has occurred and of obtaining a non-significant result when a difference δ has occurred will thus be α and β respectively.

An inspection scheme for primers for explosives

2·43. The simple case discussed above may be used to illustrate a number of important ideas which arise from the concept of the second kind of error. These ideas will be studied by considering the planning of a sampling inspection scheme which may be regarded as a comparative experiment repeated many times over.

Primers of pressed tetryl are used for initiating charges of explosives. A factor affecting their initiating power is their density. For a certain purpose it was desirable that the density of the primers should exceed 1·45 gm./c.c. A scheme was required so that a decision whether to accept the batch as satisfactory or reject it because the average density was too low could be based on the results obtained from testing a fairly small randomly drawn sample of primers from the batch. The standard deviation was known from past experience to be 0·03 and the mean density when the presses were operating normally was 1·54. A rule of the following type was required, therefore:

A random sample of n primers will be drawn from the batch, the density of each primer measured, and the sample mean $\bar{x}$ calculated. If $\bar{x}$ exceeds a value $\bar{x}^*$ the batch will be accepted; if $\bar{x}$ falls short of this value it will be rejected.

To ensure that good batches were nearly always accepted and bad batches nearly always rejected it was decided that the following requirements should be satisfied:

1. If the mean density was as low as 1·50 there should be a 99% chance of rejection (or a 1% chance of acceptance).
2. If the mean density assumed the value 1·54 there should be a 98% chance of acceptance (or a 2% chance of rejection).

The scheme may be regarded as an experiment repeated again and again, the object of which was to determine whether the mean density of primers in a sampled batch was greater than 1·50. A suitable scheme was obtained by accepting the batch only when the sample mean $\bar{x}$ was significantly greater than 1·50. To satisfy the first requirement above, the significance test was made at the level $\alpha = 0·01$, and to satisfy the second, the difference δ was put equal to 0·04 and the chance β of not detecting it to 0·02. Thus

$$\alpha = 0·01, \quad \beta = 0·02, \quad D = \delta/\sigma = 1·33$$

and from Table A·1 $u_\alpha = 2·326$ and $u_\beta = 2·054$. Using Formulae (2·51) and (2·4) it was found that $n = 10·8$ and $\bar{x}^* = 1·521$. A sample of eleven primers was taken therefore and the batch was rejected if the sample mean was less than 1·521. This was of course equivalent to accepting only those batches for which the sample mean was significantly greater at the 1% level than 1·50 (or rejecting only those batches for which the sample mean was significantly less at the 2% level than 1·54).

The problem of finding the number of observations amounts to finding a value of n so that the distribution of $\bar{x}$ when $\mu = \mu_0$ and when $\mu = \mu_0 + \delta$ will overlap a limit $\bar{x}^*$ by amounts α and β respectively. This is illustrated for the present example in Figure 2·1.

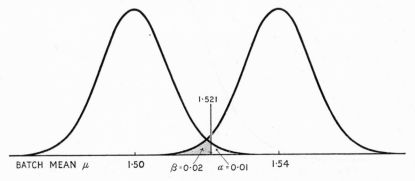

Fig. 2·1. Distribution of means for samples of eleven primers when $\mu = 1·50$ and when $\mu = 1·54$

D

Finding the number of observations required by this test is simple, because the distribution of the criterion $\bar{x}$ is the same both when $\mu = \mu_0$ and $\mu = \mu_0 + \delta$, and is in each case given with sufficient approximation by the Normal Curve, provided the original observations do not depart radically from Normality and n is reasonably large. Other examples are more complicated. With respect to the t-test, when the Null Hypothesis is not true the criterion is no longer distributed in the ordinary t-distribution but in another distribution called the Non-Central t-distribution. The problem of obtaining the required overlap of these two curves is less simple, but the procedure is the same in principle. Tables are provided at the end of the volume for these other tests, and no difficulty arises in practice.

The operating characteristic curve

2·44. The sampling scheme ensures that when the mean density μ of primers in a batch is 1·50 there will be a chance of only 0·01 that the batch will be accepted, but when the mean density is 1·54 this chance will be 0·98. It is natural to inquire what the probability of acceptance or rejection will be (i.e. what the probability of obtaining a significant or a non-significant result will be) when μ takes values other than 1·50 and 1·54. The chance of finding a significant increase for any given values of the batch mean μ is given by the proportion of the distribution of $\bar{x}$ centred on the value μ which exceeds $\bar{x}^* = 1·521$. In Figure 2·2 this chance is plotted against the batch mean μ.

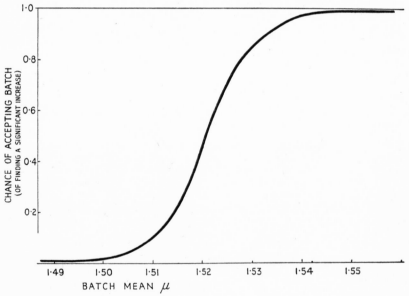

Fig. 2·2. The operating characteristic curve, or power curve, for the test.

The curve which results is called the Operating Characteristic Curve, or Power Curve, for the test.

The curve shows certain important consequences of using the test. The height of the curve above the x-axis indicates the probability that a batch of primers of given mean density will be accepted, while the distance the curve is from the line corresponding to a probability of unity represents the chance that a batch will be rejected. Batches with mean density less than 1·50 will in more than 99% of cases be rejected and in less than 1% of cases be accepted. For greater values of the batch mean density the probability of acceptance will steadily rise and batches of primers having a mean density greater than 1·54 will in more than 98% of cases be accepted. For values of μ between 1·50 and 1·54 the nearer μ is to 1·50 the more likely will it be that the batch will be rejected, while the nearer it is to 1·54 the more likely will it be that the batch will be accepted. These properties correspond to what would normally be required in practice. Batches which were very bad or very good would almost certainly be classified correctly, while batches of intermediate quality might be either accepted or rejected.

The operation of each of the tests discussed could be represented by a curve of this sort. It is usually not necessary to draw these curves, but it is important to realise that a sigmoid curve of this sort passing through the points (α, μ_0) and $(\beta, \mu_0 + D\sigma)$, or their equivalent, will describe the operation of these tests.

The number of observations required in comparative tests of various kinds

2·5. The general principles underlying the choice of the number of observations may now be applied in the various types of comparative experiments given in § 2·3. These are experiments leading to the comparison of means by the Normal Curve and t-tests, the comparison of proportions, and the comparison of variances.

Number of observations, comparison of means: Normal Curve tests

2·51. A test appropriate for the comparison of a sample mean $\bar{x}$ with a standard value μ_0 when σ is assumed known is given in § 2·331. It is shown in § 2·42 that the number of observations required in these circumstances is

$$n = (u_\alpha + u_\beta)^2/D^2 \quad \text{(single-sided alternative)} \quad \ldots\ldots\ldots(2\cdot6)$$

where $D = \delta/\sigma$ is the difference it is important to detect, expressed in terms of the standard deviation, and u_α and u_β are the deviates of the Normal Curve which cut off single-tail areas of α and β respectively. To detect an increase in mean value of one standard deviation with risks α and β both equal to 0·025, sixteen observations would be necessary. For $u_\alpha = u_\beta = 1\cdot96, D = 1$, and consequently

$$n = (1\cdot96 + 1\cdot96)^2/1^2 = 15\cdot4$$

Corresponding to the test of § **2·333**, when two sample means are compared, the number of observations necessary in each group is

$$n = 2(u_\alpha + u_\beta)^2/D^2 \quad \text{(single-sided alternative)} \quad \dots\dots\dots(2\cdot7)$$

where $D = \delta/\sigma$ or $\delta/(\tfrac{1}{2}\sigma_1^2 + \tfrac{1}{2}\sigma_2^2)^{\frac{1}{2}}$ if σ_1 is not equal to σ_2.

When the Alternative Hypothesis is double-sided, the appropriate limits may be found by substituting $\tfrac{1}{2}\alpha$ for α in these formulae, α being the total risk of an error of the first kind.

Number of observations, comparison of means: t-tests

2·52. The number of observations required in an experiment to compare mean values must obviously depend on the precision of the observations. Consequently, if (as is usual) σ is not known accurately when the experiment is planned, it is impossible to predict precisely what the number of observations should be. If nothing at all were known, the experimenter would do best to arrange a small pilot experiment to estimate σ and then plan a larger experiment using this estimate. For a fuller discussion of this procedure, the reader should consult [2·9]. Usually however, some prior knowledge will be available concerning the value of σ (from records of similar experiments* performed in the past), and this knowledge may be used to calculate the approximate number of observations required. In these circumstances the estimate s of σ obtained from the observations themselves is used in making the significance test, that is to say, a t-test is employed.

The number of observations depends, as before, on the quantities α, β, and D, and tables of n for various values of these parameters are given at the end of this volume. The number of observations required when the t-test of significance is to be used is somewhat larger than would be appropriate if an accurately known value of σ were available and the Normal Curve test could be used. Table E is appropriate when the sample mean $\bar{x}$ is compared with a standard value μ_0, and Table E·1 when the means $\bar{x}_1$ and $\bar{x}_2$ from two samples are compared. The latter table has been drawn up for equal numbers of observations in each group, since this is in practice the arrangement which requires the smallest total number of observations.

Comparison of a sample mean with a standard value
Example: Abrasion resistance of rubber

2·521. In the wear test experiment discussed in § **2·21** ten pairs of observations were made. Why was this number chosen ? From past results of similar

---

* The precision of an experimental method is an important property of that method and is as valuable as calibration figures are for thermometers, burettes, etc. Keeping records of standard deviations of past experiments is as important as the preservation of calibration of instruments.

experiments it was thought that σ, the standard deviation of the differences, would be about 1·6. It was decided to arrange the test so that when a significance test was performed at the $\alpha = 0\cdot05$ level an increase in abrasion resistance of $\delta = 2$ units should go undetected with a probability of $\beta = 0\cdot05$. Thus $D = \delta/\sigma$ was 1·25. Table E gives a value of $n = 10$ for $D = 1\cdot25$, $\alpha = \beta = 0\cdot05$, and this was the value adopted.

Comparison of two sample means
Example: Efficiency of the Hydrox device for blasting

2·522. The Hydrox device [2·4] provides an exceptionally safe means of blasting in coal mines. In research aimed at reducing the delay time between the application of the firing current and fracture of a bursting disc it was thought that the substitution of a grade T of blackpowder for the normal grade C might have a favourable effect. The delay period with the normal grade C was $\mu_0 = 0\cdot50$ sec. with approximate standard deviation $\sigma = 0\cdot12$ sec. An experiment was planned in which n shots would be made with the C grade of blackpowder and n shots with the T grade. A reduction in the mean of $\delta = 0\cdot25$ sec. would make the necessary change in manufacture worth while. It was important, however, not to recommend grade T if no improvement really resulted, and α was therefore set at 0·025. The risk β of failing to detect a reduction of 0·25 sec. was set at 0·05.

Entering Table E·1 with $D = (0\cdot25/0\cdot12) \simeq 2$, $\alpha = 0\cdot025$, $\beta = 0\cdot05$, it was found that eight shots in each group were required. The test was single-sided, since the experimenter was interested only in a reduction of delay time. Eight shots were fired with each grade of blackpowder therefore, and the difference in mean delay times was tested by the t-test at the level of significance 0·025. A significant difference was found, and grade T blackpowder was therefore adopted.

The t-test applied in a sampling scheme

2·523. In § **2·43** a sampling scheme for primers was derived based on the Normal Curve test whereby, assuming σ constant and equal to 0·03, there would be only a small risk $\alpha = 0\cdot01$ of accepting a bad batch, that is a batch with mean density as low as 1·50, and only a small risk $\beta = 0\cdot02$ of rejecting a good batch, that is a batch with mean density as high as 1·54. If it had been thought that under certain conditions of manufacture the variability of the product might be temporarily increased, it would have been better to base the scheme on the t-test than on the Normal Curve test. Making a rough interpolation in Table E it will be found that for the values $\alpha = 0\cdot01$, $\beta = 0\cdot02$, and $D = 1\cdot33$, fourteen observations would be necessary. If in these circumstances σ were larger than the value provided for, then the risk of rejecting good batches would be greater than $\beta = 0\cdot02$, but the more important risk of accepting bad batches would be held at the desired level $\alpha = 0·01$. It will be clear from Figure 2·1, on the other hand, that when the Normal Curve test was used an increase in σ would increase both risks.

Exact control of the proportion defective by means of the *t*-test

2·524. The number of observations for the *t*-test depends on α, β, and D only. The prior value of σ is not used in the test of significance as it is in the Normal Curve test, but only to decide the value of D with which the sample number tables should be entered. Thus in the sampling scheme for primers the test is planned to give a risk of $\beta = 0·02$ of finding no significant difference when an increase of 1·33 standard deviations has occurred, and this the test will do, whatever the true value of the standard deviation. If the experimenter is only interested in the actual change in mean value the latter property will not help him very much, for since $\delta = D\sigma$, if σ is in error then so is δ. It frequently happens, however, that in sampling inspection schemes interest is focused on the proportion defective rather than on the change of mean value.

Suppose it could be assumed that the density of individual primers was distributed Normally about the batch mean. Then the distribution of individual primers (not to be confused with the distribution of the sample means shown in Figure 2·1) is shown below when $\mu = \mu_0 = 1·50$ and when $\mu = \mu_0 + D\sigma = 1·50 + 1·33\sigma$.

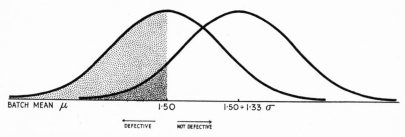

Fig. 2·3. Control of proportion defective by the *t*-test

For convenience of reference a single primer with density less than 1·50 will be called a Defective.* It will be seen from the figure that when the batch mean was 1·50 the proportion defective would be 50%, and when the batch mean was 1·50 + 1·33σ the proportion defective would be 9·2% (this is the

---

* The words "good batch," "bad batch," and "defective" are used only as a convenient terminology. In practice a primer would not be really unsatisfactory unless its density was below about 1·40. The higher limits were taken to ensure a high-quality product.

tail area of the Normal Curve cut off by a deviate of $D = 1·33$ standard deviations). This will be true whatever the value of σ.

It will be seen that although the scheme discussed is not independent of the
value of σ so far as control of the batch mean value is concerned, it is completely independent of σ so far as the control of proportion defective is
concerned. A significance test for comparing proportions is discussed in
§ **2·35** and the number of observations required in connection with these tests
is discussed in § **2·53**. Such tests are usually concerned with qualitative
effects, such as the death of an insect or the occurrence of an explosion,
rather than with the number of quantitative measurements which fall short
of a given value. When the observations are of the latter type a more sensitive
test is obtained by employing the actual numerical values, as is done above,
than by considering only the proportion of the observations in the sample
which fall short of the given level.

Number of observations: comparison of proportions

2·53. It is shown in § **2·35** that tests of significance on proportions may be
made by transforming the proportion p to the score x, given in Table F; x may
then be tested as the mean of n Normally distributed observations each having
a standard deviation 0·5. Using this artifice the number of observations
required can be obtained from the Normal Curve formulae of § **2·51**. The
following example deals with the comparison of two sample proportions.

Example. Detonation of polar blasting gelatine

2·531. Polar blasting gelatine, in $\frac{7}{8}$ in. diameter cartridges, is capable of
detonating with two different velocities, one being about 2500 metres per
second and the other about 7000 metres per second. When a sufficiently
strong detonator is used to initiate the detonation only the high-velocity
results are recorded, but as the strength of the detonator is reduced an
increasing proportion of low-velocity results is recorded. With a certain
detonator and experimental samples of the explosive the proportion of high-
velocity results recorded was about 20%. An investigation was carried out to
determine whether the presence of a small proportion of an additional ingredient would increase the percentage of high-velocity results. The objective
was to obtain high-velocity detonation in every shot, but 90% of such results
would be worth while as a guide to further progress, and a risk $\beta = 0·10$ of
failing to detect such improvement was taken. It was also decided that the
risk of asserting an improvement had occurred when it had not should not be
more than $\alpha = 0·05$. The test was single-sided, as interest lay entirely in the
possibility of increasing the proportion of high-velocity results.

The scores x associated with proportions of 90% and 20% are 1·2490 and
0·4636 respectively; thus with $u_a = 1·645$, $u_\beta = 1·284$, and $D = (0·7854/0·5)$

$= 1\cdot5708$ substituted in Formula $(2\cdot7)$, $n = 6\cdot95$. Hence it was required that seven shots should be fired with each explosive.

Number of observations: comparison of variances

2·54. The significance tests employed in the comparison of variances were discussed in § **2·36.** Two types of test occur, those in which a value s^2 calculated from a sample of observations is compared with a standard value σ_0^2 by means of the χ^2 test, and those in which two sample values s_1^2 and s_2^2 are compared by means of the F-test.

Comparison of a sample variance with a standard value

2·541. In the problem of the comparison of a sample estimate of variance s^2 with a standard value σ_0^2, suppose that a change of variance from σ_0^2 to $R\sigma_0^2$ represents a difference it would be important to detect. Then the number of degrees of freedom ϕ upon which the estimate should be based can be found in terms of α, β, and R, where as usual α is the level of significance at which the test is made, and β is the risk of asserting no significant difference when a change from σ_0^2 to $R\sigma_0^2$ has occurred. Table G, which shows the value of R for a number of values of α, β, and ϕ, is appropriate for testing for an increase in variance (that is to say it is appropriate when R is greater than unity). When it is desired to test for a decrease in variance based on values α, β, and R, with R less than unity, Table G is entered with α', β', and R', where $\alpha' = \beta$, $\beta' = \alpha$, and $R' = 1/R$.

Example. Testing for an increase in variance

2·542. A particular method of analysis had been in use for a certain substance, and a proposal was made to replace it by another method which was considered to have certain advantages. There were two questions to be decided by experiment. One was whether the new method gave essentially the same values as the old one or exhibited a systematic bias, and the other was whether the new method was as precise as the old one. The latter question involved the comparison of variances for the results obtainable by the two methods. From experience it was known that the standard deviation of the old method was $\sigma_0 = 0\cdot04$ unit, and it was decided that the new method would have sufficient advantages in rapidity and economy of materials to justify its adoption, provided that it was not markedly less precise than the old. The test was to be designed so that if the standard deviation of the new method was as great as $0\cdot10$ unit the risk would be not more than $\beta = 0\cdot01$ of failing to discover such a change when the test of significance was made at the $\alpha = 0\cdot05$ level. Duplicate analyses by the new method would be carried out on each of a series of batches of the substance. Thus $\alpha = 0\cdot05, \beta = 0\cdot01$, and $R = (0\cdot10/0\cdot04)^2 = 6\cdot25$. In Table G for $\alpha = 0\cdot05$ and $\beta = 0\cdot01$ it is found that the value $6\cdot25$

occurs between the rows corresponding to $\phi = 10$ and $\phi = 12$, being nearer to the value of $\phi = 12$. Hence the estimate of the variance should be based on twelve degrees of freedom. Each pair of analyses would give one degree of freedom for the estimate of the variance of the new method, so that twelve pairs would be required.

Example. Testing for a decrease in variance

2·543. Had it been desired to discover a new method of greater precision than the old, it might have been decided that the new method should be adopted only if it gave a reduction in standard deviation to 0·02 unit. Suppose the significance test were to be made at the $\alpha = 0.05$ level and a risk were to be taken of only $\beta = 0.01$ of failing to discover a reduction of this magnitude or more, then $R = (0.02/0.04)^2 = 0.25$, $a = 0.05$, and $\beta = 0.01$, and since R is less than unity, Table G is entered with $R' = 4$, $a' = 0.01$, and $\beta' = 0.05$. An estimate of the variance based on seventeen degrees of freedom would evidently be appropriate, and hence seventeen pairs of analyses should be made. Although in using Table G the roles of α and β were interchanged, in the actual significance test α would of course be taken as having its real value of 0·05.

Comparison of two sample variances

2·544. When both variances are to be determined by experiment, the number of observations is obtained from Table H. The level at which significance is to be judged will as usual be a measure of the risk of the error of the first kind which will be involved in reaching a conclusion from the experiment. The discrepancy between the universe variances σ_1^2 and σ_2^2 is measured by $R = \sigma_1^2/\sigma_2^2$, and as before it is necessary to associate with R the risk β that can be taken of failing to detect such a change. Table H shows the values of R for various values of these two risks, a and β, and for different numbers of degrees of freedom ϕ. It is assumed that the number of degrees of freedom ϕ is the same for each of the estimates. In simple comparative experiments there would usually be nothing to gain by departing from this arrangement.

The table is appropriate for the single-sided Alternative Hypothesis when R is greater than unity. By interchanging if necessary the roles of σ_1^2 and σ_2^2 it can always be arranged that this is so.

Example

2·545. Consider again the example discussed in § **2·542** of comparing a proposed new analytical method with another one, but assume it is considered desirable to estimate the variance of each method by experiment. Replicate analyses have to be carried out by both methods on one or more batches of the substance, and the problem is to determine the number of analyses required. It will be assumed as before that the new method will be preferable if it gives a significantly smaller standard deviation than the old, significance being tested at the $\alpha = 0\cdot05$ level, and a risk of $\beta = 0\cdot01$ being taken of failing to assert a significantly lower standard deviation when the standard deviation of the new method is half that of the old. From Table H for $\alpha = 0\cdot05$ and $\beta = 0\cdot01$ a value of ϕ is sought corresponding to $R = 4$. A rough interpolation gives thirty-five as the appropriate value. Two groups each of thirty-six observations would be needed, therefore.

Assumptions made in statistical tests

2·6. The statistical tests discussed in this chapter in which means and variances are compared can be rigorously justified on the assumption that the groups of observations represent random drawings from Normal universes. In comparing the means of two or more sets of observations by the t-test or analysis of variance it is also assumed that the standard deviations of the universes from which the groups are drawn are the same. To put it another way, suppose that when a treatment T is tested the universe generated when repeated observations are made has mean μ_T. Then a particular observation x can be regarded as being made up of the true value μ_T plus an error z:

$$x = \mu_T + z \quad \ldots\ldots\ldots\ldots\ldots\ldots\ldots(2\cdot8)$$

The tests can be derived on the assumptions:
   (i) That the errors are independent (that is to say the value of z in one observation is not influenced by the value of z in another).
  (ii) That, in experiments to compare group means, the variance of the errors is the same in each group.
 (iii) That the errors are Normally distributed.

The assumption of the independence of the errors

2·61. In the mathematical model discussed above the errors are assumed to be distributed independently. Practical situations occur, however, where this would not be so. The most common causes of correlation between errors are time and space trends in the experimental material.

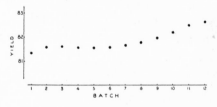

Fig. 2·4. Possible underlying trend with time

Figure 2·4 illustrates a possible underlying trend that might occur in successive yield results from a batch process. Slight variations in quality of starting material, slight changes in techniques by operators in different shifts, weather conditions, etc., could all contribute to a systematic disturbance of this sort. As an example of trends in space, contours of equal abrasion resistance on a sheet of rubber are shown in Figure 2·5.

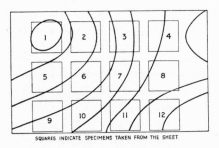

SQUARES INDICATE SPECIMENS TAKEN FROM THE SHEET

Fig. 2·5. Contours of equal abrasion resistance on a rubber-coated sheet, showing possible trends in space

If the mean value for the whole sheet were μ, then it is clear that the errors $z_1 = x_1 - \mu$, $z_2 = x_2 - \mu$, etc., for specimens 1, 2, etc., would not be independent. If z_1 were positive, then it is probable that z_2 and z_5, the errors from specimens closest to specimen 1, would also be positive. It would be inappropriate to compare the mean of a number of such adjacent specimens with a standard value μ_0 assessing the significance of an apparent difference by applying the t-test. In addition to the unsatisfactory design of the experiment, the t-test would be invalidated by the obvious lack of independence of the errors. The practical experimenter would see at once in such a case that control observations were necessary, and if a single treatment were to be compared with the standard treatment this could best be done by making paired comparisons as in the example of § 2·21. The pairs of specimens within which comparisons were to be made would need to be as close together as possible. More generally, when k treatments were to be compared, they would be applied to groups of k specimens of adjacent material, which [§ 2·24] would be called Blocks. However, the existence of trends which makes this type of design valuable will also inevitably lead to correlation between observations in the blocks. The possibility of underlying disturbances of a non-random kind has already been mentioned in § 2·23. The artificial introduction of a chance component by allocating the treatments at random makes it appropriate to analyse the data as though the errors were independent; this principle has wide application.

Trends of the type described represent one possible source of positive correlation. On the other hand, compensating errors sometimes occur, resulting in negative correlation. Evidence of this type of correlation is sometimes found in data for successive batch yields from multi-stage processes. The batches of material do not keep their identity entirely, and rather more than one complete batch may be discharged on one occasion, which will be followed by rather less appearing in the next batch. In all such cases the random allocation of treatments in a suitable statistical design will make it legitimate to analyse the experiment as though the assumption of independence of errors were true.

The assumption of the uniformity of the error variance

2·62. The means of two groups of observations may be compared by the t-test. This test is a particular example of the Analysis of Variance test [*S.M.*, Chapter 6], which may be used for the comparison of the means of any number of groups of observations. In these tests it is assumed that the population variance for each group of observations is the same. Departure from this assumption results in the actual probabilities being different from those given by the significance tables. The discrepancies are most serious when the numbers of observations in the groups are widely different. Sometimes it is found that the standard deviation varies with the size of the mean. In such cases it is often possible to make some simple transformation of the data which renders the standard deviation uniform. When studying the accuracy of methods of chemical analysis for example, it is sometimes found that the standard deviation σ is proportional to the mean μ, that is to say, the percentage error rather than the absolute error is uniform. In such cases, if the logarithms of the observations are analysed instead of the observations themselves, the standard deviation becomes independent of the mean.

Correlation between σ and μ is often accompanied by marked non-Normality, and indicates that the particular form of the original observations is unsuitable. It frequently happens that a transformation which makes the standard deviation independent of the mean also results in the observations being distributed more Normally. An interesting example of this is given in [2·6]. For certain poisons applied to mice and rats it was found that the average survival time was related to the dose, but that the relationship was not linear: the variance increased for those groups of animals which had small doses and so survived a long time, and the distribution was markedly non-Normal. By employing the reciprocal of the survival time, i.e. the rate of dying of the animals, instead of the survival time itself, the relationship was reduced to a linear form, the variance was made uniform and independent of the mean value, and the distribution was made symmetrical and more nearly Normal in form.

Transformations which will make the mean and standard deviation σ of the transformed variate approximately independent when the mean and the standard deviation of the original variate are related in various ways are given below.

Relationship	*Transformation*
σ proportional to μ^2	Take reciprocals of observations
σ proportional to μ	Take logarithms of observations
σ proportional to $\sqrt{\mu}$	Take square roots of observations

In general, if σ is proportional to $f(\mu)$ the appropriate transformation is given by $\int \dfrac{1}{f(\mu)} d\mu$. For example, when considering the number of observations required where two proportions were to be compared [§ **2·35**] the transformation used was

$$x = \text{arc sin } \sqrt{p}$$

This transformation may be derived as follows. If the probability of occurrence of a certain event, such as the firing of a detonator, is p, then the expected proportion of such events in n trials will be p and the variance of the proportion found will be given by [*S.M.*, Chapter 9]

$$\sigma^2 = \frac{p(1-p)}{n}$$

Thus σ is proportional to $\{p(1-p)\}^{\frac{1}{2}}$ and the approximate transformation is obtained by evaluating the indefinite integral

$$\int \{p(1-p)\}^{-\frac{1}{2}} dp \quad \dots\dots\dots\dots\dots\dots\dots(2\cdot9)$$

i.e. the transformation is $x = \text{arc sin } \sqrt{p}$.

Some experiments are concerned with the frequency of occurrence of a particular event, for example the frequency of breaks of a yarn in weaving trials. In such experiments the mean is often roughly proportional to the variance and the square root transformation is therefore appropriate. For further details of the use of transformations and refinements appropriate when the samples are small the reader is referred to [2·7] and [2·8].

The assumption that the errors are Normally distributed

2·63. If the errors are not Normally distributed the true probability of chance occurrence will not be given exactly by the significance tables. A detailed account of the effect of non-Normality is given in Appendix 2A. A summary of the general conclusions is given below.

In practice it is not possible to appreciate small changes in probability. The attitude of the experimenter to an event which had a probability of 1/100 would be little different if the probability had been 1/150. On the other hand, his reaction would be different if these probabilities were 1/10 and 1/100. With this in mind the following conclusions on the effects of non-Normality may be drawn.

1. For experiments which lead to the comparison of means and which contain internal controls (these include the majority of planned experiments) the use of the Normal theory tables of significance will provide an adequate approximation even when fairly large departures from Normality occur.

2. For experiments whose object is to compare variances calculated from independent groups of observations the effect of non-Normality on the methods of test at present available would be more serious. Where possible (for example when past records could be examined) the assumption of Normality should be checked, and if evidence of non-Normality were found the data should be suitably transformed as described below.

Transformation of the data to obtain approximate Normality

2·64. Data are not always recorded in the form most suitable for statistical analysis, and it is always open to the experimenter to seek an improvement by means of some transformation designed to rearrange them on a more workable scale. If an accumulation of past data is available which is non-Normal and it is desired to find an empirical transformation to Normality, the simplest method is to cumulate them and plot the results on arithmetical probability paper. This graph paper has scales arranged so that when with Normally distributed data the proportion of observations less than a given value is plotted against the value, the plotted points lie on a straight line. It is then a question of drawing a smooth curve through or between the points (giving greater weight to those in the middle than to those at the extremes) and finding by trial and error a transformation which straightens the curve. The equation when found provides the required transformation.

Tests based on the randomisation distribution

2·65. It has been pointed out by R. A. FISHER that in experiments in which the means of two or more groups of observations are compared the process of randomisation itself provides a basis for making exact tests of significance but of a rather different kind from those considered above. In such tests the only assumption made is that the process of randomisation has been properly carried out.

Consider once again the wear test example of § **2·21**. To clarify the argument it is supposed that the details of the experiment were as follows. The experimenter labelled the two specimens from the first test-piece 1H and 1T, those from the second test-piece 2H and 2T, and so on for the ten pairs of test-pieces. He then tossed a coin ten times. If the result of the first toss was a head he set aside specimen 1H for treatment, if a tail he set aside specimen 1T. The result of the second toss decided the fate of specimens 2H and 2T, and so on. The treatment was then applied to the selected ten specimens and the abrasion resistances of treated and untreated specimens were assessed by the wear test machine. The ten differences—abrasion resistance of treated specimen minus abrasion resistance of untreated specimen—were 2·6, 3·1, − 0·2, 1·7, 0·6, 1·2, 2·2, 1·1, − 0·2, and 0·6, and the mean difference was $\bar{x} = 1·27$.

To make a test of significance the Null Hypothesis must be assumed true and the probability calculated for a difference as great as or greater than that observed. Now the Null Hypothesis was that the treatment had no effect at all. So far as abrasion resistance was concerned, both specimens in each pair were really untreated, and the coin-tossing merely decided which should be called the treated specimen; that is to say, the sign of each difference had been determined by the fall of the coin. The difference of + 2·6 found between the first pair of specimens, for example, might equally well have been − 2·6 had the coin fallen on its opposite side in the first toss. When this argument is applied to each of the ten differences it is seen that there were 2^{10} possible configurations of positive and negative signs, which would give rise to 2^{10} possible mean differences, one of which $\bar{x} = 1·27$ is that observed. Inspection of the individual values shows that only three results more extreme than that observed were possible, namely those in which either the third observation or the ninth observation or both had positive signs. These configurations would have given mean differences of 1·31, 1·31, and 1·35 respectively. There are therefore four chances out of 1024 that a positive difference as great as or greater than that observed would have occurred if the Null Hypothesis were true, and the result is therefore significant at the level of probability $4/1024 = 0·0039$. The Normal theory value is 0·0030.

The type of argument adopted here can be used in other tests in which randomisation has been applied. Suppose the experiment had been one in which a comparison had been made between ten treated and ten untreated specimens without pairing. Then the random choice of ten specimens to which the treatment should be applied would supply the basis for the randomisation test. On the Null Hypothesis two groups of essentially similar objects have been divided into two groups of ten, and the enumeration of those of the $20!/(10!\ 10!)$ ways in which this could be done which resulted in a difference greater than that observed would enable a test of the Null Hypothesis based on the randomisation distribution to be made. Provided randomisation is introduced as part of the experimental procedure a randomisation test is also possible when there are more than two groups or when the more elaborate designs such as Randomised Blocks and Latin Squares, discussed in later chapters, are used.

In practice the labour involved in enumerating all the possibilities would often rule out the randomisation test as a practical procedure. The ease with which this calculation can be made in the example chosen is deceptive; the number of observations is small and the result is highly significant, so that the enumeration of the few configurations giving a greater mean difference than that observed is simple. This is not generally so: had twenty pairs of specimens been examined and had the result been just significant at the 5% level, then it would have been necessary to evaluate $2^{20} \times 0 \cdot 05$ (about 50,000) configurations more extreme than that observed.

REFERENCES

[2·1] FISHER, R. A. *The Design of Experiments* (6th edition). Oliver and Boyd (London and Edinburgh, 1951).

[2·2] *Idem.* "The Fiducial Argument in Statistical Inference." *Annals of Eugenics*, **6** (1935*b*), 391.

[2·3] NEYMAN, J. "On Two Different Aspects of the Representative Method, etc." *Journal of Royal Statistical Society*, **97** (1934), 558.

[2·4] TAYLOR, J. "Low Temperature Combustion Reactions in the Solid State." *Industrial Chemist*, **24** (1948), 289.

[2·5] SILLITTO, G. P. "Note on Approximations to the Power Function of the 2 × 2 Comparative Trial." *Biometrika*, **36** (1949), 347.

[2·6] BOX, G. E. P., and CULLUMBINE, H. "The Relationship between Survival Time and Dosage with Certain Toxic Agents." *British Journal of Pharmacology and Chemotherapy*, **2** (1947), 27.

[2·7] BARTLETT, M. S. "The Use of Transformations." *Biometrics*, **3** (1947), 39.

[2·8] CURTISS, J. H. "On Transformations used in Analysis of Variance." *Annals of Mathematical Statistics*, **14** (1943), 10.

[2·9] STEIN, C. "A Two-sample Test for a Linear Hypothesis whose Power is independent of the Variance." *Ibid.*, **16** (1945), 243.

APPENDIX 2A

THE ASSUMPTION THAT THE ERRORS ARE NORMALLY DISTRIBUTED

2A·1. It is unlikely that the actual distribution of errors will be exactly Normal. This distribution will, however, provide a fair approximation to many of the error distributions met in practice, and in some cases, where the Normal Distribution would not be expected and a large body of data of similar type was available for study, it would be possible to find a transformed variate which would give approximate Normality. Often however, the data would be too scanty to allow any opinion to be formed whether the errors were approximately Normal, and it is important to know how far the experimenter might be misled by non-Normality. In considering the effect of departures from the Normal assumption it is necessary to have constants which measure the extent of non-Normality of a given parent distribution. Two useful constants measuring particular aspects of non-Normality are γ_1 and γ_2, coefficients of skewness and excess respectively. The coefficient of skewness γ_1 is the standardised third moment of the parent distribution, μ_3/σ^3, where the third moment μ_3 denotes the mean value of the cubes of

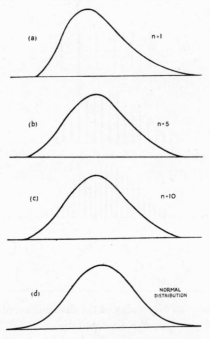

Fig. 2·6. Convergence on Normality of the distribution of means of n observations drawn from a skew population

deviations from the mean. For symmetrical distributions, and in particular for the Normal Distribution, positive and negative cubes cancel and γ_1 is zero. When the long tail of the distribution is in the direction of positive values the positive cubes outweigh the negative ones, γ_1 is positive and the distribution is said to be positively skew. In the contrary case it is said to be negatively skew. Skewness frequently occurs when there is some natural limitation or variation which foreshortens the distribution curve in one direction.

The coefficient of excess (or kurtosis) γ_2 is given by $\mu_4/\sigma^4 - 3$, the fourth moment μ_4 being the mean value of the fourth powers of deviations from the mean. For the Normal Distribution γ_2 is zero. When γ_2 is less than zero the

E

distribution has shorter tails and squarer shoulders than the Normal Distribution, and it is said to be Platykurtic. When γ_2 is greater than zero the distribution has long tails and is more sharply peaked than the Normal Distribution, and it is said to be Leptokurtic. Platykurtosis is often found when artificial limitation of variation in both directions has been imposed. For example, the distribution of outgoing articles from an inspection scheme designed to remove those which differed too greatly from some standard would usually be platykurtic. Marked leptokurtosis is sometimes met in certain tensile

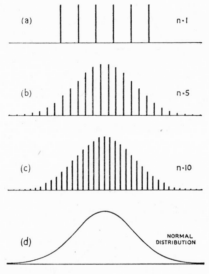

Fig. 2·7. Convergence on Normality of the distribution of means of n throws of a six-sided die

tests where the majority of values appear to be spread over a fairly narrow range, but outliers (apparently wild observations) which cannot be explained by faulty experimental technique occur not infrequently.

Convergence on Normality of a distribution of a mean

2A·11. Figure 2·6 (a) shows a positively skew distribution* for which $\gamma_1 = 0·8165$ and $\gamma_2 = 1$. Figure 2·6 (b) and (c) shows the corresponding distributions of the means of five and ten observations drawn from such a parent population and arranged on equivalent scales. The Normal Distribution is shown for comparison in Figure 2·6 (d). Figure 2·7 (a) shows the

* This is the PEARSON Type III Curve: $p(x) = kx^5e^{-x}$.

distribution of the scores obtained when a single perfect die is thrown repeatedly. The die will be equally likely to show a one, two, three, four, five, or six, so that the probability is $\frac{1}{6}$ that each of these numbers will occur. For this distribution $\gamma_1 = 0$ and $\gamma_2 = -1\cdot269$. The distribution of the means, brought to the same scale, for five and ten throws is plotted in Figures 2·7 (b) and (c), while (d) shows the corresponding Normal Curve. In both cases the means are seen to converge rapidly on the distribution which would be obtained if the assumption of exact Normality for the parent distribution were made. The example illustrates an important theorem in theoretical statistics. For a very wide class of distributions covering all those likely to be met in practice the distribution of the mean of n variables will tend to the Normal form as n is increased. In particular it can be shown that the coefficients γ_1' and γ_2' for the distribution of the mean of n independent observations are given by

$$\gamma_1' = \gamma_1/\sqrt{n} \qquad \gamma_2' = \gamma_2/n$$

Effect of departure from Normality on tests of significance

2A·2. Provided the departure from Normality was not too marked or the sample size too small, the above argument would justify the use of the Normal Curve test discussed in § **2·33**. The t, F, and χ^2 tables are all derived on the assumption of Normality of the parent distribution, but the effect on the tabled probability of non-Normality of the parent distribution is more difficult to study for these tests. A number of investigations have been made, some in which the approximate distribution of the statistic was obtained by actual repeated sampling from a non-Normal population [2A·1, 2A·2], and others in which the theoretical distributions of t, F, etc., have been found for particular non-Normal populations [2A·3 to 2A·9].

A particularly valuable investigation of the latter variety has recently been completed by A. K. GAYEN [2A·6 to 2A·8], who has obtained the theoretical distribution of the statistics t, χ^2, and F when the parent population can be represented by the first few terms of a series due to EDGEWORTH.* The coefficients γ_1 and γ_2 appear as constants in this series, and a wide variety of parent distributions can be produced by varying these quantities.

In the discussion that follows, which will be based upon GAYEN's work, it will be assumed that the skewness and the excess is the same for each of the populations sampled. Further correction terms would be needed if this were not so.

---

* GAYEN considers the distribution of t, F, etc., when the frequency function of the parent distribution is

$$f(x) = \phi(x) - \gamma_1/3! \; \phi^{(3)}(x) + \gamma_2/4! \; \phi^{(4)}(x) + 10\gamma_1^2/6! \; \phi^{(6)}(x)$$

where $\phi(x)$ is the Normal frequency function and $\phi^{(n)}(x)$ is its nth derivative.

Effect of departures from Normality on the t-test

2A·3. Consider first the t-criterion, $t = \dfrac{\bar{x} - \mu_0}{s/\sqrt{n}}$, used for comparing a
sample mean of n observations with a standard value μ_0 and discussed in
§ **2·341**; and as an example suppose $n = 5$ and hence s is based on four degrees
of freedom. The t-tables based on the assumption of a Normal parent
distribution give $t_{0.025} = 2·776$ as the value which is exceeded with 2·5%
probability; since the curve is symmetrical, the probability of a value of less
than $- t_{0.025} = - 2·776$ is also 2·5%. For non-Normal parent distributions
the true probabilities of exceeding $t = \pm 2·776$ for a variety of values of
γ_1^2 and γ_2 are shown in Table 2A·1.

Table 2A·1

t-TEST. COMPARISON OF MEAN OF GROUP OF FIVE OR TEN
OBSERVATIONS WITH A STANDARD VALUE. TRUE PERCENTAGE
PROBABILITIES ASSOCIATED WITH UPPER AND LOWER 2·5% NORMAL
THEORY SIGNIFICANCE POINTS

γ_2 \ γ_1^2		0		1		2	
	$n =$	5	10	5	10	5	10
-2	Upper tail area	3·08	2·80	2·18	1·63	2·56	1·68
	Lower tail area	3·08	2·80	6·56	5·81	8·76	7·60
	Both tails ..	6·16	5·60	8·74	7·44	11·32	9·28
0	Upper tail area	2·50	2·50	1·60	1·33	1·98	1·38
	Lower tail area	2·50	2·50	5·98	5·51	8·18	7·30
	Both tails ..	5·00	5·00	7·58	6·84	10·16	8·68
2	Upper tail area	1·92	2·20	1·02	1·03	1·40	1·08
	Lower tail area	1·92	2·20	5·40	5·21	7·60	7·00
	Both tails ..	3·84	4·40	6·42	6·24	9·00	8·08

It will be seen that the effect of skewness is rather serious, but that kurtosis
does not have a large effect. It is important to remember that the most frequent
application of this test is in experiments where the observations denote
differences between pairs, as in the wear test example discussed in § **2·21**. In
such experiments, if the coefficients γ_1 and γ_2 were the same for treated and
untreated specimens then γ_1' and γ_2', the coefficients for the differences,
would be $\gamma_1' = 0$ and $\gamma_2' = \gamma_2/2$. That is to say, the distribution for the
differences would be symmetrical and have only one half the kurtosis of the

original distributions. In these circumstances the departure from Normality even in worse cases of kurtosis would be unimportant.

When two sample means $\bar{x}$ and $\bar{x}'$ are compared the test of § **2·342** is employed. The true probabilities of exceeding the 2·5% Normal theory significance points for a variety of values of γ_1^2 and γ_2 are shown in Table 2A·2. It is assumed that the degrees of skewness and excess for the two universes sampled are the same.

Table 2A·2

t-TEST. COMPARISON OF MEANS OF TWO GROUPS OF FIVE OBSERVATIONS ($n = 5$) AND TWO GROUPS OF TEN OBSERVATIONS ($n = 10$). TRUE PERCENTAGE PROBABILITIES ASSOCIATED WITH UPPER AND LOWER 2·5% NORMAL THEORY SIGNIFICANCE POINTS

γ_2	γ_1^2	0		1		2	
	n	5	10	5	10	5	10
− 2	Upper tail area / Lower tail area	2·80	2·62	2·87	2·63	2·94	2·64
	Both tails ..	5·60	5·24	5·74	5·26	5·88	5·28
0	Upper tail area / Lower tail area	2·50	2·50	2·57	2·51	2·64	2·52
	Both tails ..	5·00	5·00	5·14	5·02	5·28	5·04
2	Upper tail area / Lower tail area	2·20	2·38	2·27	2·39	2·34	2·40
	Both tails ..	4·40	4·76	4·54	4·78	4·68	4·80

The effect of non-Normality in this test is seen to be not very serious, even when γ_1 and γ_2 depart markedly from zero. Further correction terms producing considerably larger discrepancies would be necessary if the distributions of populations sampled differed widely in skewness. The possibility of large changes in shape occurring as the result of the application of treatments in planned experiments seems unlikely.

Effect of departure from Normality. Comparison of more than two means by analysis of variance test

2A·4. As already noted, the t-test is a particular case of the analysis of variance procedure. This latter procedure enables the means of more than two groups of observations to be compared by the variance ratio or F-test [*S.M.*, Chapter 6].

The effect of non-Normality on the analysis of variance test is illustrated below for the particular example of the comparison of five means each of five observations.

Table 2A·3

ANALYSIS OF VARIANCE TEST. FIVE GROUPS OF FIVE OBSERVATIONS. Variance Ratio of Between and Within Groups Mean Squares based on Four and Twenty Degrees of Freedom Respectively. True Percentage Probabilities associated with 5% Normal Theory Significance Points

$\gamma_1{}^2$ / γ_2	0	1	2
− 1·5	5·36		
0·0	5·00	5·10	5·20
2·0	4·52	4·62	4·72

It will be noted that even extreme non-Normality has little serious effect on the probability levels.

Effect of departure from Normality on the comparison of two variances

2A·5. In § 2·36 tests for the comparison of variances were discussed. The effect of non-Normality on these tests is very much more marked than on the t-tests and analysis of variance tests discussed above. Consider first the comparison of a variance with a standard value by means of the χ^2-test. Suppose a sample variance s^2 having twelve degrees of freedom is compared with a standard value $\sigma_0{}^2$. Then the estimate s^2 would be declared significant at the 5% level when $12s^2/\sigma_0{}^2$ was greater than $\chi_{0\cdot05}{}^2 = 21\cdot0$. The true probability associated with this value for a non-Normal parent population is given for various non-Normal populations in Table 2A·4.

Table 2A·4

χ^2-TEST. COMPARISON OF AN ESTIMATE OF VARIANCE HAVING TWELVE DEGREES OF FREEDOM WITH A STANDARD VALUE. TRUE PERCENTAGE PROBABILITY ASSOCIATED WITH 5% NORMAL THEORY SIGNIFICANCE POINT

$\gamma_1{}^2$ / γ_2	0	1	2
− 1·0	1·46	1·33	1·20
0·0	5·00	4·87	4·74
2·0	12·08	11·95	11·82

For universes showing even a moderate degree of kurtosis conclusions based on the Normal theory universe might be considerably in error. Increasing the sample size does not reduce such error.

Equally serious are the effects of non-Normality when two estimates of variance are compared employing the variance ratio test. Although the criterion F is the same as that employed in the analysis of variance test, the effect of non-Normality is essentially different in the two types of tests. Table 2A·5 shows the effect of departure of the parent distribution from Normality in the comparison of two sample variances calculated from groups of five and twenty-one observations. The comparison leads to an F-test on four and twenty degrees of freedom, and on the Normal theory the significance limits would be the same as for the analysis of variance test discussed in § 2A·4.

Table 2A·5

F-TEST. COMPARISON OF VARIANCES FOR TWO INDEPENDENT SAMPLES HAVING FOUR AND TWENTY DEGREES OF FREEDOM. TRUE PERCENTAGE PROBABILITIES ASSOCIATED WITH 5% NORMAL THEORY SIGNIFICANCE POINTS

$\gamma_1{}^2$ / γ_2	0	1	2
− 1·5	1·12		
0·0	5·00	4·49	3·98
2·0	10·18	9·67	9·16

As will be seen by comparison with Table 2A·3, the effect of non-Normality on this test is very much more serious than in the analysis of variance test. The discrepancy does not decrease if the sample size is increased or if the samples contain an equal number of observations.

Effect of departure from Normality on the comparison of several variances
2A·6. Just as the t-test for comparing two sample means is generalised into a test for comparing several means in the analysis of variance tests, so the F-test for comparing two sample variances is generalised into a test of several variances in the BARTLETT test [2A·10] (for the comparison of two variances the double-sided F-test and the BARTLETT test are equivalent).

It has been shown by Box [2A·9] that the discrepancies produced by non-Normality (already large when there are only two variance estimates to compare) are larger still when more than two variance estimates are compared.

In fact these discrepancies become progressively larger as the number of sample variances to be compared in the BARTLETT test is increased.

The discrepancies from Normal theory values for tests on means become rapidly smaller as the number of observations per sample is increased; for tests on variances however no such effect is found. In fact for some distributions the discrepancies are larger for large samples than for small. As the sample size is increased the true probability associated with any given non-Normal universe tends to a fixed value which depends only on γ_2 for the universe and which, as will be seen from Table 2A·6, may differ markedly from the Normal theory value.

Table 2A·6

BARTLETT TEST. COMPARISON OF k VARIANCES. TRUE PERCEN-
TAGE PROBABILITY IN LARGE SAMPLES ASSOCIATED WITH NORMAL
THEORY 5% POINT

γ_2	Number of variance estimates $= k$			
	2	5	10	20
− 1	0·56	0·08	0·010	0·0004
0	5·0	5·0	5·0	5·0
2	16·6	31·5	48·9	71·8

REFERENCES

[2A·1] PEARSON, E. S. "The Analysis of Variance in Cases of Non-Normal Variation." *Biometrika*, **23** (1931*b*), 114.

[2A·2] HEY, G. B. "A New Method of Experimental Sampling illustrated on Certain Non-Normal Populations." *Ibid.*, **30** (1938), 68.

[2A·3] BARTLETT, M. S. "The Effect of Non-Normality on the *t*-Distribution." *Proceedings of Cambridge Philosophical Society*, **31** (1935*a*), 223.

[2A·4] GEARY, R. C. "The Distribution of Student's Ratio for Non-Normal Samples." *Journal of Royal Statistical Society Supplement*, **3** (1936*b*), 178.

[2A·5] *Idem.* "Testing for Normality," *Biometrika*, **34** (1947), 209.

[2A·6] GAYEN, A. K. "The Distribution of 'Student's' *t* in Random Samples of any Size drawn from Non-normal Universes." *Ibid.*, **36** (1949), 353.

[2A·7] *Idem.* "The Distribution of the Variance Ratio in Random Samples of any Size drawn from Non-Normal Universes." *Ibid.*, **37** (1950), 236.

[2A·8] *Idem.* "Significance of Difference between the Means of Two Non-Normal Samples." *Ibid.*, **37** (1950), 399.

[2A·9] BOX, G. E. P. "Non-Normality and Tests on Variances." *Ibid.*, **40** (1953), 318.

2A·10] BARTLETT, M. S. "Properties of Sufficiency and Statistical Tests." *Proc. Royal Soc. A*, **160** (1937), 268.

CHAPTER 3

SEQUENTIAL TESTS OF SIGNIFICANCE

THE preceding chapter indicated the bases on which the experimenter can decide what number of observations is required to make comparative experiments conclusive, on the assumption that this number must be decided before the experiment is performed. When, as is common in chemical and physical research, the observations are obtained one after another, it is generally possible to adopt an alternative procedure in which, after each observation is made, a simple statistical test is applied to determine whether the results obtained so far indicate a definite conclusion from the experiment, or whether more observations are needed to make the experiment decisive. The experiment thus terminates as soon as a definite conclusion can be drawn, and the average number of observations required in experiments carried out in this manner tends to be definitely less than when the number has to be decided beforehand. Consequently this sequential method of performing comparative experiments has definite advantages, particularly when the observations are expensive or time-consuming. Sequential methods of performing simple comparative experiments of a number of types are described in this chapter.

Introduction

3·1. The experiments discussed in Chapter 2 were designed to answer questions such as whether the average abrasion resistance of rubber specimens was greater when they were prepared by method B instead of by method A. The procedure was to decide in advance how large an experiment would be required so that when the experiment was completed it would be possible to make a decision concerning the merits of methods A and B with only small risks of being wrong. An alternative and more economical procedure may be adopted when the observations are made serially, that is to say, when the result of each separate trial is known before the next is carried out. In this situation special Sequential Tests of Significance may be used. In these tests the number of observations is not fixed in advance, but the test is applied to the accumulating data after each observation, the experiment being terminated as soon as a decision between the alternative hypotheses can be made with the desired degree of certainty.

The principle employed here is of course frequently used in scientific work. If it were suggested that a certain modification in a process might result in higher yields, and the experiments performed to test the suggestion were such that the result of each was known before the next was performed, the investigator would normally carry out one preparation, and if the result was a

57

complete failure or a spectacular success he might feel satisfied with the reality of the effect without further experimentation. If however the effect was less dramatic, he would probably carry out a second preparation before making up his mind. If he felt that the evidence for the two experiments was still indecisive, he would perform a third, and so on until he felt reasonably sure of the result. Whether or not it would be possible or convenient to proceed in such a way would depend on circumstances. If the actual preparation took a comparatively short time but estimating the yield took a number of days, it would usually be better to proceed by the non-sequential method, that is to say, it would be better to plan a sufficient number of preparations so that when the yield estimates became available it would be possible to decide on the value of the modification without further trial.

The intuitive sequential procedure discussed above can be put on an objective basis by a sequential significance test. The quantities required to plan such a test are precisely those needed for a non-sequential test. The test decides as each new observation comes to hand, in the light of all the information available up to that time, whether:

(i) to accept the Null Hypothesis that no change of importance has occurred;

(ii) to accept the Alternative Hypothesis that a real change has occurred; or

(iii) to continue taking observations.

The advantage of testing after each new observation, instead of reserving the decision until the completion of a fixed number, lies, as one might expect, in the smaller number of observations needed on the average to detect a given difference. Frequently this is only one-half of that required by the non-sequential test, and if an unexpectedly large effect occurs, the sequential test may yield a decision after only one or two observations.

The sequential test

3·11. Sequential tests are best explained graphically. As each new observation comes to hand, the value of a function of all the observations recorded up to that time is calculated and plotted against the number of observations on a chart such as that shown in Figure 3·1. On the chart are two boundary lines, the positions of which depend upon the risks α, β, of errors of the first and second kind, the magnitude of the difference it is important to detect, etc. The lines divide the chart into three zones: (1) in which the Null Hypothesis is accepted; (2) in which the Alternative Hypothesis is accepted; and (3) in which there is no decision. The sequential test then consists in plotting the function of the observations $f(x)$ against the number of observations n and continuing to take observations so long as the plotted points fall within zone (3). As soon as a point falls outside this zone, that is, either in zone (1) (acceptance of the Null Hypothesis), or in zone (2) (acceptance of the Alternative

Hypthoesis), the observations are discontinued and the indicated decision is taken. The chosen function $f(x)$ is used because of its powerful properties of discriminating between the hypotheses to be tested. An outline of the theory of these tests is given in Appendix 3A.

In practice the chart is often dispensed with, the boundary values being calculated in advance for each value of n. The test is then made by successive comparisons of the value of $f(x)$ with the appropriate limits. The procedure

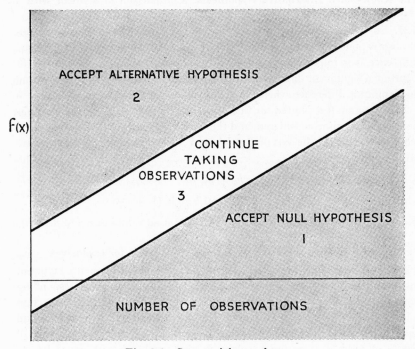

Fig. 3·1. Sequential test chart

will be illustrated in the following cases, for which the parallel non-sequential tests are described in Chapter 2:

   (i) Testing for a difference in mean value when the standard deviation is presumed to be known and is used in the significance test (sequential Normal Curve test) [§**3·2**].

  (ii) Testing for a difference in mean value when an estimate of the standard deviation obtained from the observations themselves is used in the significance test (sequential t-test) [§**3·3**].

 (iii) Testing for a difference in proportions [§**3·4**].

 (iv) Testing for a difference in frequency (sequential POISSON test) [§**3·5**].

  (v) Testing for a difference in variance [§**3·6**].

Testing for a difference in mean value when the standard deviation is known

3·2. The test procedure will depend on whether the experimenter is testing for a change in mean value in a particular direction (single-sided Alternative Hypothesis) or whether he is equally interested in changes in either direction (double-sided Alternative Hypothesis).

The single-sided Alternative Hypothesis. Comparison of a mean with a standard value

3·21. Suppose it is required to test whether the population mean μ of a series of observations is equal to some standard value μ_0. As before, δ denotes the difference it is important to detect, σ the standard deviation, a the risk of asserting a significant difference when none exists, and β the risk of asserting no significant difference when the mean value is really $\mu_1 = \mu_0 + \delta$.

The function $f(x)$ plotted for this test is simply the total T of the observations up to the time considered, and the boundaries are parallel straight lines with slope s, cutting the axis of T at h_1 and h_0. The values* of h_0, h_1, and s are given by the equations

$$h_0 = -b\sigma^2/\delta \qquad h_1 = a\sigma^2/\delta \qquad s = \mu_0 + \tfrac{1}{2}\delta \quad \ldots\ldots\ldots(3\cdot1)$$

where † $a = \ln(1-\beta)/a$ and $b = \ln(1-a)/\beta$

Table K gives values of a and b for commonly used values of a and β.

Example. A sequential inspection scheme for primers for explosives

3·211. It is instructive to compare the sequential and non-sequential types of test upon the same data. An example used to illustrate the corresponding non-sequential test of § **2·43** will therefore be reconsidered. An inspection scheme for primers was required. It was assumed that σ was constant and equal to 0·03, and the scheme was planned so that there would only be a small risk ($a = 0\cdot01$) of accepting a bad batch, that is a batch with mean density as low as $\mu_0 = 1\cdot50$ gm./c.c., and a small risk ($\beta = 0\cdot02$) of rejecting a good batch, that is a batch with mean density $\mu_1 = 1\cdot54$ gm./c.c. Thus $\delta = 0\cdot04$, $\sigma = 0\cdot03$, $a = 0\cdot01$, and $\beta = 0\cdot02$. It was found that for the non-sequential test eleven observations would be required and that the test should be made by calculating the mean of a sample of eleven, rejecting the batch if the mean was less than 1·521 gm./c.c. and accepting it otherwise.

* The test based on these values actually ensures that the risks of error are rather less than a and β, as do all the tests discussed in this chapter. The reason for this is that in practice the boundary lines are crossed before a decision is taken, but in theory a decision would be taken when these lines were reached. The effect is that sequential tests are slightly better than they appear to be.

† ln is used to denote the natural or Napierian logarithm, and log to denote the logarithm to base 10; thus $\ln x = 2\cdot3026 \log x$.

Had it been convenient to use a sequential scheme then as each primer was tested the total T of the observations to date would be calculated and plotted on a chart with suitable boundary lines. It will be found in practice that if μ_0 is large compared with δ these boundary lines will rise very steeply and appear to be very close together, so that the chart will be difficult to use. Since the test is to detect a difference, it will not be affected if a constant amount is subtracted from each observation. For purposes of convenience, therefore, instead of considering the actual density we consider the amount by which the density exceeds 1·40, that is to say, 1·40 is subtracted from each observation.

Then $\mu_0 = 0\cdot10$, $\mu_1 = 0\cdot14$, and from Formula ($3\cdot1$):

$$h_0 = -0\cdot0878 \qquad h_1 = 0\cdot1032 \qquad s = 0\cdot12$$

To construct the chart convenient values are chosen for the two scales, making the vertical axis the axis of T and the horizontal axis the axis of n. Points are marked off 0·1032 unit above zero and 0·0878 unit below zero on the axis of T, and through these points lines are drawn which rise by 0·12 unit of T for each unit increase in n. A chart is then obtained like that in Figure 3·2.

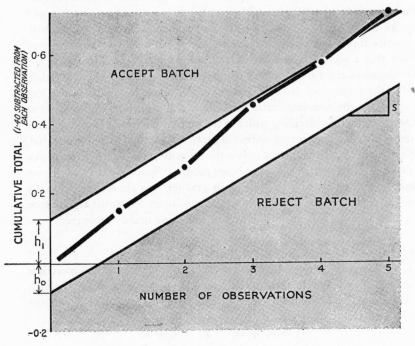

Fig. 3·2. Sequential test applied to inspection scheme

The sequential test consists in plotting, as each new observation is made, the total of the values against the number of observations. Suppose, for example, the first five observations were 1·551, 1·527, 1·581, 1·517, and 1·547. Subtracting 1·400, these would be treated as 0·151, 0·127, 0·181, 0·117, and 0·147, and the cumulative totals, 0·151, 0·278, 0·459, 0·576, and 0·723, would be plotted against the values $n = 1, 2, 3, 4$, and 5 respectively. As will be seen from Figure 3·2, the last point is in the zone of acceptance, and testing would therefore end and the batch would be accepted at this stage.

3·212. Before proceeding it is worth while considering the equations (*3·1*) for h_0, h_1, and s. Those for h_0 and h_1 show that, as might be expected, the larger the standard deviation and the smaller the difference δ it is desired to detect, the farther apart will be the boundary lines and the longer it will take to come to a decision. Also, smaller values of β will make $b (= \ln(1 - \alpha)/\beta)$ larger and will push the line through h_0 farther from the centre, that is to say, they will make us less ready to reject the batch. Similarly, a small value for α will make h_1 larger and make us less ready to accept the batch. The slope s denotes the average rate at which the cumulative total would increase if the true mean value were $\mu_0 + \frac{1}{2}\delta$.

Those newly introduced to sequential tests are often worried by the thought that a sequential test might never terminate, or at least that it might go on for very much longer than the experimenter was willing to contemplate. In practice this is not a serious difficulty, for it can be shown that the probability that a sequential test would require twice or three times as many observations as the corresponding non-sequential test is exceedingly small; usually, the number of observations required for the sequential test is less than that for the non-sequential test. Both non-sequential and sequential methods are used for deciding which is the more proficient of two opponents in games of skill. The scoring system in darts, for example, is non-sequential, while in tennis at a certain stage (when the score 40–all or deuce is reached) a sequential scoring system is used, it being necessary for one of the two players to lead by two points to win. Just as in practice it is almost certain that a game of tennis will end after a few exchanges, so in sequential significance tests there is no serious risk of the experiment being unduly prolonged.

Alternative methods of presenting the results

3·22. Although the graphical method is useful for purpose of exposition, it is not necessarily the best method of setting out the results in practice. In most cases it is quicker to calculate limits T_0 and T_1 for each value of n from the expressions

$$T_0 = h_0 + ns \qquad T_1 = h_1 + ns \dots\dots\dots\dots(3·2)$$

which are the equations of the two boundary lines. This can easily be done on a calculating machine by setting up h_0 or h_1 and successively adding s. The taking of observations is then continued so long as T lies between T_0 and T_1. In the example given here, assuming as before that 1·40 is subtracted from each observation, these limits are as shown in Table 3·1.

Table 3·1

LIMITS FOR AN INSPECTION SCHEME

n	T_0	T_1
1	0·0322	0·2232
2	0·1522	0·3432
3	0·2722	0·4632
4	0·3922	0·5832
5	0·5122	0·7032
6	0·6322	0·8232
7	0·7522	0·9432
8	0·8722	1·0632

In the inspection scheme described the tester would be given these successive values of T_0 and T_1, and he would add up his results after each test and carry on testing primers until the cumulative total for his test results fell outside these limits. For the particular set of observations previously given, the successive cumulative totals T were 0·151, 0·278, 0·459, 0·576, and 0·723. Testing would therefore be discontinued at this stage with acceptance of the batch, since for the first time T falls outside one of the boundaries denoted by T_0 and T_1.

A scoring system

3·221. Alternatively a scoring system may be adopted. It has already been pointed out that since the test is to detect a difference it will not be affected if a constant amount is subtracted from each observation. If $\mu_0 + \frac{1}{2}\delta$ is subtracted from each result, or in other words the observations are measured from the origin $\mu_0 + \frac{1}{2}\delta$, then from Formula (3·1) the values of h_0 and h_1 remain unchanged, but the slope s will now be zero. The boundary lines are now horizontal, and the limits T_0 and T_1 are fixed for all values of n and equal h_0 and h_1 respectively. Then if the amount by which the observed value falls short of or exceeds $\mu_0 + \frac{1}{2}\delta$ is called the Score, the test consists of accumulating the score until it falls below the limit h_0 or above the limit h_1. In the example given the quantity $\mu_0 + \frac{1}{2}\delta = 1·52$ would be subtracted instead of 1·40, and the scores corresponding to the values 1·551, 1·527, 1·581, 1·517, and 1·547 would be 0·031, 0·007, 0·061, − 0·003, and 0·027 respectively. The accumulating scores are 0·031, 0·038, 0·099, 0·096, and 0·123, and since at the fifth observation the total exceeds the limit $h_1 = 0.1032$ the batch would be accepted at this stage. It will be noted that if the first observation had been as large as $1·52 + h_1 = 1·6232$ or as small as $1·52 + h_0 = 1·4122$ the batch would have been accepted or rejected without any further observations being made.

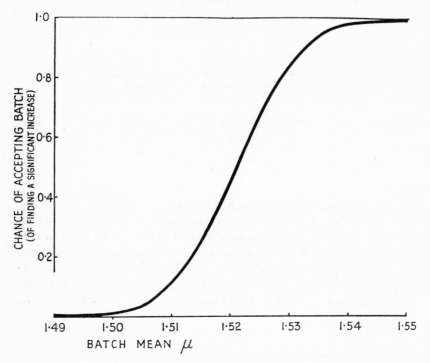

Fig. 3·3. The operating characteristic curve, or power curve, for an inspection scheme

Consequences of applying the test

3·23. The main properties of the test are determined by two curves, the Operating Characteristic Curve (Power Curve) and the Average Sample Number Curve. The first corresponds to the operating characteristic curve for the non-sequential test, which shows the probability that a significant difference will be found (that is that the batch will be accepted) for any prescribed value of the population mean μ. The second shows the average number of tests which will be required to reach a decision for various values of μ.

The operating characteristic curve, or power curve

3·231. Just as in the corresponding non-sequential test of § **2·42**, the sequential test has been designed to ensure certain risks of rejection and acceptance when the true mean of a population is either μ_0 or $\mu_1 = \mu_0 + \delta$. In fact, as is shown in Appendix 3A, the test is derived on the assumption that these two values are the only ones possible. The risks for other values of the population mean μ are given by the operating characteristic curve, or power curve. For the present example this curve is drawn in Figure 3·3.

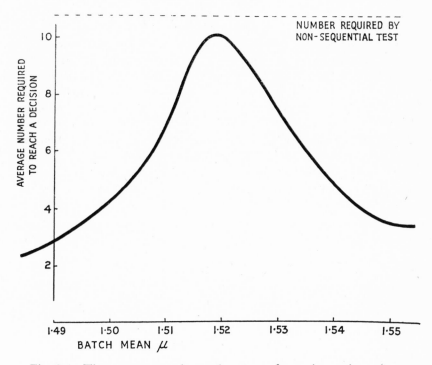

Fig. 3·4. The average sample number curve for an inspection scheme

The derivation of the curve is outlined in Appendix 3B. The operating characteristic curve shows that the test, although derived on the assumption that either $\mu = \mu_0$ or $\mu = \mu_1$, will deal satisfactorily with samples from populations having other values of μ. The sequential scheme is seen to result in probabilities less than $a = 0\cdot01$ of accepting batches having mean values less than 1·50 and probabilities less than $\beta = 0\cdot02$ of rejecting batches having mean values greater than 1·54, while for intermediate values of μ the probability of acceptance steadily rises for higher values of the batch mean density.

F

For the purpose of routine significance testing it is not necessary to draw this curve, but it is important to bear in mind that the operation of the test will be described by a sigmoid curve of this sort.

The number of observations necessary

3·232. The non-sequential test corresponding to the inspection scheme for primers requires eleven observations to reach a decision. It is easy to see that with the sequential procedure a batch of primers having a very low or a very high mean density will be rejected or accepted with fewer tests than this. What is not so clear is how many tests will be required to arrive at a decision when the true value μ is not particularly high nor particularly low but is in the neighbourhood of either of the values 1·50 or 1·54 (i.e. μ_0 or μ_1). Obviously the number of observations required will vary from one test to another, but what can be calculated is the number of observations required on the average to reach a decision for any particular value of μ. If the average sample number required to reach a decision is plotted against the value of μ, the resulting curve is called the Average Sample Number Curve. For the present example this curve is shown in Figure 3·4. The derivation of the curve is outlined in Appendix 3C.

The curve, as might be expected, has its highest point between μ_0 and μ_1, and for most values of μ the average number of observations required is considerably less than the number required by the non-sequential scheme. If the circumstances were such that the sequential scheme could be used, it would be markedly more efficient than the non-sequential scheme described in Chapter 2, in which it was necessary to take eleven observations, irrespective of the true value of μ. The average sample number curve is drawn here for purposes of illustration only, and there usually is no need to plot it. It is advisable, however, before embarking on a sequential scheme to make some calculations for one or two values of μ of the average number of observations likely to be required, as a precaution against choosing impracticable values of α, β, and δ. Experimentation consumes time and money, and it may be found necessary to modify the original scheme in the light of calculations of average numbers of observations required, in order to compromise between what is desirable and what is practicable. For most purposes the calculation of the average sample number required when $\mu = \mu_0$, $\mu = \mu_1$, and $\mu = s$ will suffice. These are of course only average values, and the experimenter must be prepared for greater values to occur; it will rarely be necessary, however, to take three times as many observations as the numbers indicated.

The operating characteristic curve and the average sample number curve, considered together, illustrate the operation of this scheme. When the true mean density is 1·50, 4·3 observations are required on the average to come to a decision, and the decision for a succession of repeat tests will tend to be right ninety-five times out of every hundred. From these curves similar statements can be made for any desired value of μ.

Single-sided Alternative Hypothesis. Testing for a difference in means among paired comparisons

3·24. When it is desired to compare specimens prepared by different methods, A and B, the comparison can often be made by taking the observations in pairs, one based on method A and the other on method B, and applying the sequential test to the differences between the values for A and B. Regarding the difference between the observations for A and B as the new variable, the test reduces to the old form of comparing a mean with a standard value of zero. As before, it is necessary to decide on suitable values for α, β, and δ, the difference it is important to be able to detect with probability $1 - \beta$. The standard deviation of the difference to be measured is assumed known. In an experiment in which A and B vary independently the standard deviation of this difference will be $\sqrt{(\sigma_A^2 + \sigma_B^2)}$, where σ_A and σ_B are the standard deviations of A and B. Sometimes however there are reasons for believing that A and B tend to vary together, owing to a disturbing influence which affects A and B alike in any particular trial, in which case a test based on differences will be particularly desirable because the effect of the common factor causing variation will be removed from the test [§ **2·24**]; the standard deviation of the difference will then be less than $\sqrt{(\sigma_A^2 + \sigma_B^2)}$, and it may sometimes be obtained directly as in the following example.

Example. Modifications in chemical manufacture

3·241. A certain chemical is manufactured by a batch process. Two similar units operate side by side, and each unit produces a batch a day. An examination of the differences in daily yields over a considerable period showed no difference in average between the two plants and gave the standard deviation of the difference in daily yields as a little below 5%. Owing to disturbing factors, such as the quality of the intermediate used, which were shared equally by the two units on a particular day, this direct estimate of standard deviation of the difference was considerably lower than an estimate based on the individual standard deviations on the assumption that the yield variations in the two units were unrelated. As a result of laboratory experimentation it was suggested that a certain modification in the filtration plant would result in an increased yield, and it was decided to test the modification on the plant scale by introducing it into one of the units only and comparing the yields of the modified and unmodified plants. A test was designed so that there was only a small probability $\alpha = 0.05$ of asserting a non-existent difference, and the probability $1 - \beta$ of detecting a difference as great as $\delta = 2\%$ was 0·99.

Then $\mu_0 = 0$, $\mu_1 = 2$, $\delta = \mu_1 - \mu_0 = 2$, $a = 0\cdot05$, $\beta = 0\cdot01$, and $\sigma = 5$. Using Formula (*3·1*):

$$h_0 = -56\cdot9 \qquad h_1 = 37\cdot3 \qquad s = 1$$

The average number of observations required if $\mu = \mu_0 = 0$, $\mu = \mu_1 = 2$, and $\mu = s = 1$ (see Appendix 3C) would be:

$$\bar{n}_0 = 52\cdot2 \qquad \bar{n}_1 = 36\cdot4 \qquad \bar{n}_s = 84\cdot9$$

These average sample numbers were large because of the smallness of the difference which it was desired to detect compared with the standard deviation, but since the plant had to be run in any case they were not regarded as being unreasonably large. The differences were recorded as deviations from s in the manner outlined in § **3·221**, that is to say, the modification was regarded as having scored a point for every 1% that the difference (yield from modified plant minus yield from unmodified plant) exceeded $+1\%$. The test then consisted of the accumulation of the score from day to day until it either reached 37·3, when the modification would be accepted, or fell to

Table 3·2

SCORES FOR A SEQUENTIAL TEST

Batch	Difference	Score (difference − s)	Cumulative score
1	1·5	0·5	0·5
2	0·0	− 1·0	− 0·5
3	3·5	2·5	2·0
4	1·5	0·5	2·5
5	9·5	8·5	11·0
6	− 1·0	− 2·0	9·0
7	3·5	2·5	11·5
8	6·5	5·5	17·0
9	5·0	4·0	21·0
10	7·0	6·0	27·0
11	3·5	2·5	29·5
12	2·0	1·0	30·5
13	− 2·0	− 3·0	27·5
14	4·5	3·5	31·0
15	− 1·5	− 2·5	28·5
16	4·5	3·5	32·0
17	4·0	3·0	35·0
18	2·0	1·0	36·0
19	4·5	3·5	39·5

— 56·9, when it would be rejected. The actual differences recorded in nineteen consecutive observations, together with the scores and cumulative scores, are given in Table 3·2. The cumulative score after nineteen observations was 39·5, which exceeds 37·3, so that the modification was accepted.

Alternatively, the points could have been plotted on a chart or the individual limits worked out for each value of n for the actual differences, using the equations

$$T_0 = -56\cdot9 + n \qquad T_1 = 37\cdot3 + n$$

The cumulative totals T for the actual differences and the limits T_0 and T_1 are shown in Table 3·3.

Table 3·3

LIMITS FOR A SEQUENTIAL TEST

Batch	T_0	T	T_1
1	− 55·9	1·5	38·3
2	− 54·9	1·5	39·3
3	− 53·9	5·0	40·3
4	− 52·9	6·5	41·3
5	− 51·9	16·0	42·3
6	− 50·9	15·0	43·3
7	− 49·9	18·5	44·3
8	− 48·9	25·0	45·3
9	− 47·9	30·0	46·3
10	− 46·9	37·0	47·3
11	− 45·9	40·5	48·3
12	− 44·9	42·5	49·3
13	− 43·9	40·5	50·3
14	− 42·9	45·0	51·3
15	− 41·9	43·5	52·3
16	− 40·9	48·0	53·3
17	− 39·9	52·0	54·3
18	− 38·9	54·0	55·3
19	− 37·9	58·5	56·3

The three methods of presenting the results are of course equivalent, and the experimenter's choice will depend upon circumstances.

Maximum loss owing to adoption of a sequential scheme

3·242. In experiments on chemical processes it is often the case that the more elaborate preliminary experiments are carried out on a laboratory or pilot plant scale. Whatever the conclusions arrived at from the smaller scale experiments, it is only the performance of the full-scale unit which is of ultimate interest, so that, normally, full-scale plant trials of a suggested modification will need to be made, and without interfering too much with production. One advantage of the sequential scheme is that a limit can be set in advance to the amount of production lost by a given experiment. Large losses will only occur of course if a modification expected to give a definite increase in yield gives a marked decrease, and such cases will be rare; but in carrying out experimental work on the plant scale the amount of money involved may be large, and it is important to be able to present the management with an estimate of the maximum loss involved by an unsuccessful experiment.

Suppose a modification had been made to a chemical plant and a sequential test was being carried out to discover whether a real increase above the normal average μ_0 had occurred. If the value μ_0 is taken as origin for the yield observations, then the cumulative total T of these observations represents the accumulated gain or loss in production. If an increase is expected, then the rising lower boundary line T_0 represents the net loss at which action will be taken and at which the experiment will be terminated with rejection of the modification. The potential loss depends upon h_0, which in turn depends very much on the value chosen for β. If a greater risk could be tolerated of not detecting increases if they occurred, less production would be lost if in fact a reduction of yield resulted. The sequential scheme will risk the smallest possible loss consistent with obtaining the required information.

As an example, consider the particular experiment discussed in § 3·241. The difficulty of time trends, which would often arise in an experiment of this sort, was overcome by running a modified and an unmodified unit side by side; the observations were then the differences between the two plant yields for a modified unit and an unmodified unit, and the standard value for the difference was zero. The cumulative total of the differences represented the net loss or gain arising from the modification. Table 3·3, in which the observations are the actual differences (i.e. the origin is at $\mu_0 = 0$), indicates that if the modification was such that it reduced the yield by more than 55·9% of one batch in the first trial, then it would be rejected at once; similarly, if it reduced the yield by 54·9% of one batch in the first two trials, i.e. by 27·5% per batch, the investigation would be terminated, and so on.

The double-sided Alternative Hypothesis

3·25. The technique so far considered is appropriate for testing whether a mean value is significantly greater than some specified value when the standard deviation is accurately known. A precisely similar procedure is used to test whether a mean value is significantly less than the specified value. When, however, the Alternative Hypothesis is that μ may depart from μ_0 in either direction, the test procedure will be different. The value δ will now be the deviation (positive or negative) from the specified value which it is desired to detect. If the Null Hypothesis is true there will be two ways an error of the first kind can be made, for it can be wrongly asserted that an

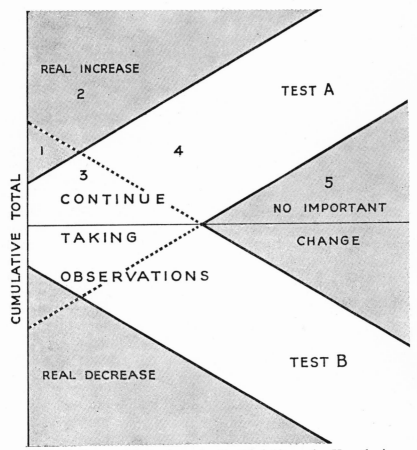

Fig. 3·5. Sequential test chart: double-sided Alternative Hypothesis

increase has occurred or that a decrease has occurred. A suitable* test can be obtained by superimposing two single-sided tests, say A and B, in each of which the error of the first kind is set at ½a, and δ is taken to be positive in one test and negative in the other. The procedure consists of plotting the cumulative sum of the observations, taken with μ_0 as the origin, on a chart such as Figure 3·5 on which both sets of boundary lines are shown.

* This is the two-sided test proposed by BARNARD [3·3]. The test proposed by WALD [3·1] is slightly different.

The lines divide the chart into a number of zones, which may be merged into three shaded zones and the unshaded zone shown. In the upper shaded zone the hypothesis that a real increase has occurred will be accepted, in the centre shaded zone the hypothesis that no important change has occurred will be accepted, and in the lower shaded zone the hypothesis that a real decrease has occurred will be accepted. The logic of this procedure may be seen by considering the nature of the two individual tests A and B. A tests the hypothesis that no increase of importance has occurred against the alternative that a real increase has occurred, and B tests the hypothesis that no decrease of importance has occurred against the alternative that a real decrease has occurred. Referring to Figure 3·5, it will be seen that in zone 1, with regard to test B, sampling would be continued to decide between the possibilities that no decrease of importance had occurred and that a real decrease had occurred, but test A asserts that a real increase has occurred; the hypothesis that an increase has really resulted can therefore be accepted. In zone 2 test A asserts that an increase has occurred and test B that there is no important decrease. The evidence of test A can therefore again be accepted. In zone 3 both tests assert that sampling should be continued, but in zone 4, although in test B we can assert that no decrease has occurred, further observations are necessary, since this hypothesis does not rule out a real increase. Likewise in zone 5 the tests assert that no important increase or decrease has occurred. Similar arguments apply to the corresponding zones in the lower half of Figure 3·5, so that the division of the chart into shaded acceptance and rejection areas is justified.

The boundary lines are given by the formulae

$$\left.\begin{array}{l} T_0 = h_0 + ns \\ T_1 = h_1 + ns \end{array}\right\} A \qquad \left.\begin{array}{l} T_0' = h_0' + ns' \\ T_1' = h_1' + ns' \end{array}\right\} B \ \ldots\ldots\ldots (3·3)$$

where $h_0 = -b'\sigma^2/\delta = -h_0'$, $h_1 = a'\sigma^2/\delta = -h_1'$, $s = \frac{1}{2}\delta = -s'$ ..(3·31) and $a' = \ln(1-\beta)/\frac{1}{2}\alpha$, $b' = \ln(1-\frac{1}{2}\alpha)/\beta$, and δ is taken to be positive.

The calculations are facilitated by the use of Table K, the values of a' and b' being found directly by entering the table with the risk of the error of the first kind equal to $\frac{1}{2}\alpha$ and the risk of the error of the second kind equal to β.

Example. An investigation into synthetic fibre strength
3·251. In an investigation of factors affecting strength of synthetic fibres a modification was made in the preparation of the material and a series of separate preparations of fibre was made in pairs, one of the normal and one of the modified material; and a number of properties of the resulting fibres were determined. The results for each pair of observations were known before the next pair were carried out, so that a sequential test could be employed. The most important property measured was the breaking load, and it was

known from past experience that the standard deviation of the difference
between repeat preparations with respect to this property was approximately
10 units. The experiment was designed so that the risk α of asserting non-
existent changes was 0·05 and so that a difference of ± 10 would normally be

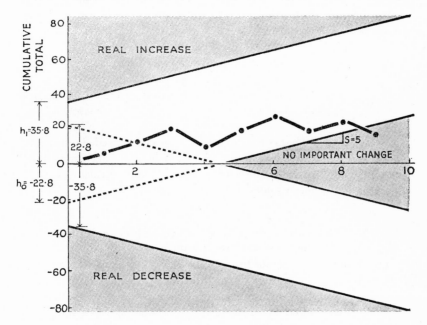

Fig. 3·6. Sequential test for change in breaking load of a synthetic fibre

detected with 90% certainty. Applying the sequential test to the differences
of observed breaking load in repeat pairs of observations, then:

$$\mu_0 = 0 \qquad \mu_1 = \pm 10 \text{ (i.e. } \delta = \pm 10)$$
$$\alpha = 0\cdot05 \qquad \beta = 0\cdot10 \qquad \sigma = 10$$

From Formula (3·31):

$$h_0 = -22\cdot8 \qquad h_1 = 35\cdot8 \qquad s = 5$$

and these values substituted in (3·3) give boundary lines represented by the
two pairs of equations

$$\left. \begin{array}{l} T_0 = -22\cdot8 + 5n \\ T_1 = 35\cdot8 + 5n \end{array} \right\} \qquad \left. \begin{array}{l} T_0' = 22\cdot8 - 5n \\ T_1' = -35\cdot8 - 5n \end{array} \right\}$$

which are shown in Figure 3·6.

In one experiment the following values were recorded for the differences
in breaking load between synthetic fibres prepared in two different ways:

$$7, 5, 8, -11, 10, 8, -9, 6, -7$$

The cumulative sums of the observations are:

$$7, 12, 20, 9, 19, 27, 18, 24, 17$$

and these points are plotted in Figure 3·6. The line crosses the limit T_0 at the ninth observation, so the hypothesis that no important change in breaking load has occurred is accepted.

As before, there is no need to draw the chart; it may be preferable to set out the limits for each value of n calculated from the equations. It will be noticed that in Figure 3·6 no zone appears corresponding to zone 1 in Figure 3·5, the reason being that in this case $\frac{1}{2}\alpha$ is less than β. Figure 3·5 illustrates the more general case when $\frac{1}{2}\alpha$ is greater than β and consequently h_0 is less than h_1'.

In all the sequential tests to be dealt with when a double-sided test situation occurs a satisfactory test procedure will be obtained by superimposing two single-sided tests in the manner illustrated for the particular case of the comparison of two mean values.

Testing for a difference in mean value when an estimate of the standard deviation obtained from the observations themselves is used

3·3. In the sequential tests for the comparison of means discussed in § 3·2 it was assumed that an accurately known value for the standard deviation σ was available in advance and that it was used in making the test. If the true value of σ was different from the value assumed, then both the risks α and β would be different from the values allowed for in the test. In Chapter 2 it was shown that by using the t-test, in which an estimate of the standard deviation calculated from the observations themselves was used in the test of significance, the risk α of error of the first kind would be controlled at the desired level whatever the value of σ. The test could be planned so that if no difference had really occurred, that is if $\mu = \mu_0$, the chance would only be α that a difference would be found, and that if a change of mean to $\mu = \mu_0 + D\sigma$ had occurred, the chance would only be β that no difference would be found. The test could thus be planned precisely to detect a change of D standard deviations. In a test to detect a given change δ in mean value it would be necessary to have some prior knowledge of σ to decide what multiple D of the standard deviation to take. The risk of failing to detect a difference δ would thus be determined only as precisely as the accuracy of the prior value of σ allowed. On the other hand, it is shown in § 2·524 that in an inspection scheme such a test would accurately control the proportion defective whatever the value of σ (assuming the observations were Normally distributed).

A sequential test exactly equivalent to the non-sequential t-test discussed above has been given by BARNARD [3·4] and RUSHTON [3·5].

Barnard's sequential *t*-test

3·31. Suppose it is desired to test for a departure in mean value $\bar{x}$ from a standard value μ_0 and a departure is expected in a definite direction (i.e. the test is single-sided). As explained in § **3·3**, the difference which would be considered important must be defined in terms of the standard deviation σ. Suppose we are testing for an increase of D standard deviations with risks set at α and β respectively.

After each observation is made, the deviation $(x - \mu_0)$ from the standard value is noted and the sum $T = \Sigma(x - \mu_0)$ and the sum of squares $S = \Sigma(x - \mu_0)^2$ of these deviations are calculated. The function of the observations $f(x)$ which is used in the test is

$$U = \frac{T}{\sqrt{S}} \quad \dots\dots\dots\dots\dots\dots\dots\dots\dots(3\cdot4)$$

That is to say, the test is made by calculating U as each new observation appears and referring it to appropriate limits U_0 and U_1. The direct calculation of these limits is complicated, but tables are provided at the end of this volume (Tables L·1 to L·8) which enable the test to be made without difficulty. The signs of the limits U_0 and U_1 in the tables are correct if the test is based on an increase in mean value; in testing for a decrease the signs must be reversed. Alternatively the convention may be adopted that departures in the expected direction (whichever that may be) will always be recorded as positive, and departures in the opposite direction as negative. The limits as given in the tables will then always be appropriate without reversal of sign.

Example. An investigation into the dyeing properties of yarn

3·311. The following example concerns a research investigation carried out on yarn prepared from a synthetic fibre. The object was to discover whether a certain treatment applied to improve the dyeing properties of the yarn produced a decrease in strength. A representative sample of lengths of yarn was taken; each length was then cut into two, one half being treated and the other not. The strength of each of the two pieces was then measured and the difference in strength was recorded. From previous work of a similar character it was expected that the standard deviation σ of the differences would be about one unit. It was judged that a real decrease of half this amount was important, that is, D was set at 0·5 and α and β were each set at 0·05. The test thus ensured that the risk α of asserting the treatment had produced a decrease in strength when no change had really occurred was not more than 0·05, and the risk β of failing to detect a real decrease of half of one standard deviation was not more than 0·05. Since, using the treated yarn, a fall in strength was expected, the observations (x) were taken as the differences (strength of untreated yarn minus strength of treated yarn), so that deviations in the expected direction were positive. Then $\mu_0 = 0$, $D = 0.5$, $a = 0.05$, $\beta = 0.05$. Since in this case $\mu_0 = 0$, the deviations of the observations from μ_0 are equal to the values of the differences themselves; the actual values obtained are given in Table 3·4.

Table 3·4

AN INVESTIGATION INTO THE DYEING PROPERTIES OF YARN

n	Difference $(x - \mu_0)$	$T = \Sigma(x - \mu_0)$	$S = \Sigma(x - \mu_0)^2$	$\sqrt{S}$	U
1	+ 1·2	1·2	1·44	1·20	
2	− 0·1	1·1	1·45	1·20	0·92
3	+ 1·6	2·7	4·01	2·00	1·35
4	+ 1·0	3·7	5·01	2·24	1·65
5	+ 0·6	4·3	5·37	2·32	1·85
6	+ 0·3	4·6	5·46	2·34	1·97
7	− 1·1	3·5	6·67	2·58	1·36
8	+ 0·2	3·7	6·71	2·59	1·43
9	− 0·2	3·5	6·75	2·60	1·35
10	+ 2·4	5·9	12·51	3·54	1·67
11	+ 0·5	6·4	12·76	3·57	1·79
12	+ 1·1	7·5	13·97	3·74	2·01
13	+ 0·7	8·2	14·46	3·80	2·16
14	− 0·5	7·7	14·71	3·84	2·01
15	+ 0·4	8·1	14·87	3·86	2·10
16	+ 1·7	9·8	17·76	4·21	2·33
17	+ 1·0	10·8	18·76	4·33	2·49

Table 3·5

LIMITS FOR THE t-SIGNIFICANCE TEST

n	U_0	U_1
6	− 2·07	—
8	− 1·51	2·56
10	− 1·15	2·46
15	− 0·57	2·34
20	− 0·21	2·31

The *t*-significance test is made by consulting Table L·3. Some of the limits U_0 and U_1 for $\alpha = 0.05, \beta = 0.05$, and $D = 0.5$ are given in Table 3·5.

For intermediate values of n graphical interpolation will normally suffice, and if desired the whole test can be made graphically by plotting the value of U against the number of observations n and drawing smooth curves through the points read off from the table. The appearance of the graphical test is shown in Figure 3·7. In practice it will usually be clear from inspection of the table at what value U crosses one or other of the boundary lines. In the present example it is obvious without actual interpolation that U remains

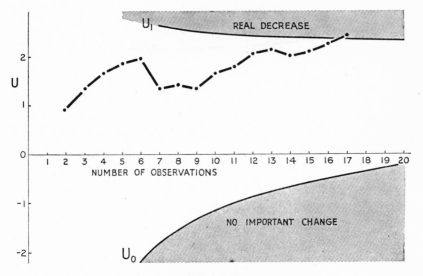

Fig. 3·7. BARNARD's sequential *t*-test

between the limits until the seventeenth observation, when it crosses the limit for U_1. We are therefore led to accept the hypothesis that a real decrease in strength has resulted from the application of the treatment.

The tables L·1 to L·8 give values for the limits U_0 and U_1 for $D = 0.10$, 0·25, 0·50, 0·75, 1·00, 1·50, 2·00, and 3·00 respectively. In each of the tables the limits are given for the nine combinations of α and β for $\alpha, \beta = 0.01, 0.05$, and 0·20, and convenient ranges for n. Intermediate values may be found by graphical or even visual interpolation.

When D is small and α and β are also small, a number will exist which will define the fewest possible tests on which a particular decision can be reached. When such a number exists a bracketed value of U is given for the next lower value of n in the table. The bracketed value is included for purposes of interpolation only; it must not be used for making the actual test. The lowest values of n for which decisions can be taken are shown at the foot of the end column of the table. For larger values of D and larger values of α and β a value of n is reached at which the chance that the test will not have terminated is negligible; for such values of n no values of the limits for U are shown.

Barnard's sequential t-test. The double-sided Alternative Hypothesis

3·32. When the question at issue is not whether a departure from some standard value μ_0 occurs in a stated direction but whether a change occurs in

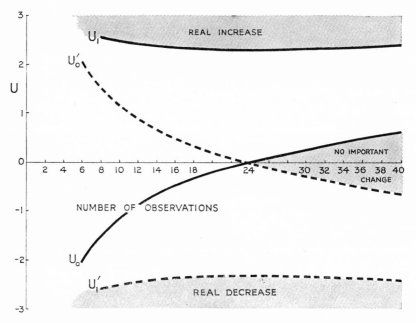

Fig. 3·8. BARNARD'S sequential t-test: double-sided Alternative Hypothesis

either direction, a satisfactory test can be obtained by superimposing two single-sided tests, in each of which the error of the first kind is set equal to $\frac{1}{2}\alpha$ and the error of the second kind equal to β. A test with approximately the right total risks α and β will result.

Suppose it was desired to test the hypothesis that the mean was equal to a standard value μ_0 when a departure from μ_0 of half of one standard deviation in either direction was regarded as important. Suppose also that it was desired to keep the total risk of rejecting the Null Hypothesis when it was true (that is to say, the risk of asserting that a decrease had occurred or that an increase had occurred when there was really no change) at 0·10, and the risk β of asserting no difference when a real increase or decrease of importance had occurred at 0·05. Then a test meeting approximately these requirements would be obtained by superimposing two single-sided tests in each of which a was set at half of 0·10 (i.e. at 0·05), β was set at 0·05, and D was taken as $+0·5$ and $-0·5$ respectively. One set of limits U_0 and U_1, taken with the same signs as are given in the table, is appropriate for testing for an increase, and the other set of limits U_0' and U_1' has opposite signs to those given in the table and is appropriate for testing for a decrease. Only when the limits U_0 and U_0' cross will it be possible to assert that no difference of importance has occurred, and if D is taken to be very small, a large number of observations will usually be required before the assertion can be made.

Testing for a difference in proportions (Binomial test)

3·4. Some observations do not take the form of measurements but rather of events which either do or do not happen. When this is so, a criterion of performance will be the proportion of times the designated event occurs. It is often necessary to compare such a proportion with some standard proportion in order to find whether the event is occurring in a greater or lesser proportion of cases than usual.

Example

3·41. In a certain chemical process a proportion of batches prepared by the normal method was found to be unsatisfactory from the point of view of physical form, and these batches had to be further treated before they reached the quality required. In a case of this sort the proportion of batches requiring re-treatment was a measure of the unsatisfactoriness of the process. Laboratory-scale experiments had suggested that by modifying the filtration plant it might be possible to reduce considerably the proportion of batches requiring re-treatment, and it was desired to test this modified process on the plant scale. Since the observations came to hand one after another, sequential methods were available. Suppose the proportion of unsatisfactory batches normally produced was p_0 and the modification would be justified if the proportion of unsatisfactory batches could be reduced to p_1. The appropriate sequential test consists, as before, of a procedure which is equivalent to plotting a function $f(x)$ of the observations against the number of observations on a chart with suitable boundary lines. The function $f(x)$ plotted in this case is simply the total number of occurrences of the event, i.e. the total number X of unsatisfactory batches. The boundary lines are given by the formulae

$$X_0 = h_0 + ns \qquad X_1 = h_1 + ns \quad \ldots\ldots\ldots\ldots(3\cdot5)$$

where $h_0 = -b/(P+Q)$, $h_1 = a/(P+Q)$, and $s = Q/(P+Q)$ ....$(3\cdot51)$

$P = \ln p_1/p_0$, $\quad Q = \ln (1-p_0)/(1-p_1)$, $\quad a = \ln (1-\beta)/a$, $\quad$ and $\quad b = \ln (1-a)/\beta$.

The average sample numbers required when $p = p_0$, $p = p_1$, and $p = s$ are given by

$$\bar{n}_0 = \frac{(1 - a)h_0 + ah_1}{p_0 - s} \qquad \bar{n}_1 = \frac{\beta h_0 + (1 - \beta)h_1}{p_1 - s} \qquad \bar{n}_s = \frac{- h_0 h_1}{s(1 - s)} \qquad (3·52)$$

In the actual experiment, calculations on past performance of the process showed that the proportion of batches which it had been necessary to re-treat over a considerable period was 31%. Although this was the average value, it seemed likely that the underlying proportion of bad batches might vary with time, so that for a given month 31% might not be a good estimate of p_0. By comparing the actual variance of the proportion in successive months with the theoretical binomial variance pq/n [S.M., Chapter 9] the extent of this variation could be estimated and limits within which the true proportion p would be expected to lie for any given month could be worked out. It was found to be unlikely that this proportion p would be less than 24% in any one month. The laboratory trials had indicated that a marked improvement could be expected as a result of the modification, and consequently a sequential trial was designed with $p_0 = 0·24$ and $p_1 = 0·10$.

It was decided to set the risk a of asserting that a reduction in the proportion of unsatisfactory batches had occurred, when in fact it had not, at 0·05, and the risk β of failing to detect a true reduction in the proportion of bad batches at 0·10.

We have then:

$$p_0 = 0·24 \qquad p_1 = 0·10 \qquad a = 0·05 \qquad \beta = 0·10$$

From Formula (3·51):

$$h_0 = 2·155 \qquad h_1 = - 2·767 \qquad s = 0·162$$

and from Formula (3·52):

$$\bar{n}_0 = 24·5 \qquad \bar{n}_1 = 36·7 \qquad \bar{n}_s = 43·9$$

Normally ten batches were made per week, so that it was expected that using these values of a and β a decision could be made after about three or four weeks' experimentation, and the trial was almost certain to be completed in less than three months. In the circumstances in which these experiments were performed this was regarded as satisfactory. It is interesting to note that if the non-sequential test were used with the same risks of error it would have been necessary to make sixty observations (§ 2·53).

A chart showing the boundary lines for this example is plotted in Figure 3·9.

In the actual trial a decision was reached after thirty batches. It was in fact only necessary to re-treat two batches, the fifth and the seventeenth. The line (plotted in Figure 3·9) crossed the limit X_1 at the thirtieth observation, and the hypothesis that a real reduction had resulted in the proportion of batches needing re-treatment was therefore accepted.

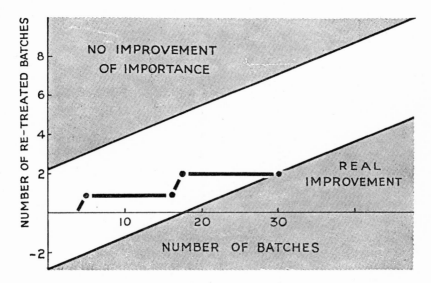

Fig. 3·9. Sequential test for a proportion of unsatisfactory batches

Alternative methods of presenting the results

3·411. The exact limits can be calculated for each value of n from Formula *(3·5)*.

In the present example limits obtained from this formula, together with X, the total number of occurrences of the event (in this case the occurrence of an unsatisfactory batch), are shown in Table 3·6.

The Alternative Hypothesis, that a reduction in the proportion of batches which need to be re-treated has occurred, is accepted after the thirtieth observation, since 2 is less than the limit 2·09.

Now the values of X_0 for n less than 3 and of X_1 for n less than 17 are meaningless; for even if the value p for the proportion of unsatisfactory batches had increased to 1·00 so that it was certain that every batch would have to be re-treated, it is seen from the table that the modification could not be rejected after less than three batches. This is because it is not until the third batch that the value for the limit X_0 is less than n, the total number of batches. Similarly, even if p had been reduced to zero, so that no batches had to be re-treated, the modification could not be accepted in less than eighteen batches, since it is not until the eighteenth batch that the limit X_1 is greater

G

Table 3·6

LIMITS FOR A SEQUENTIAL EXPERIMENT

n	X_0	X	X_1
1	2·32	0	− 2·61
2	2·48	0	− 2·44
3	2·64	0	− 2·28
4	2·80	0	− 2·12
5	2·97	1	− 1·96
6	3·13	1	− 1·80
7	3·29	1	− 1·63
8	3·45	1	− 1·47
9	3·61	1	− 1·31
10	3·78	1	− 1·15
11	3·94	1	− 0·99
12	4·10	1	− 0·82
13	4·26	1	− 0·66
14	4·42	1	− 0·50
15	4·59	1	− 0·34
16	4·75	1	− 0·18
17	4·91	2	− 0·01
18	5·07	2	0·15
19	5·23	2	0·31
20	5·40	2	0·47
21	5·56	2	0·64
22	5·72	2	0·80
23	5·88	2	0·96
24	6·04	2	1·12
25	6·20	2	1·28
26	6·37	2	1·45
27	6·53	2	1·61
28	6·69	2	1·77
29	6·85	2	1·93
30	7·02	2	2·09

than zero. Further, since X must be a whole number, the inclusion of decimals in the values of X_0 and X_1 is pointless, and the limits can be rounded up or down to the appropriate whole number. These limits X_0 and X_1 are rounded outward. Thus when $n = 26$ the limit for X_0, which is 6·37, is rounded up to 7; and the limit for X_1, which is 1·45, is rounded down to 1. The table can be most conveniently given therefore in the revised form,

Table 3·7, where X_1 and X_0 can now be called the acceptance numbers for the two hypotheses.

Table 3·7

ACCEPTANCE NUMBERS FOR A SEQUENTIAL EXPERIMENT

n	X_0	X	X_1
1	—	0	—
2	—	0	—
3	3	0	—
4	3	0	—
5	3	1	—
6	4	1	—
7	4	1	—
8	4	1	—
9	4	1	—
10	4	1	—
11	4	1	—
12	5	1	—
13	5	1	—
14	5	1	—
15	5	1	—
16	5	1	—
17	5	2	—
18	6	2	0
19	6	2	0
20	6	2	0
21	6	2	0
22	6	2	0
23	6	2	0
24	7	2	1
25	7	2	1
26	7	2	1
27	7	2	1
28	7	2	1
29	7	2	1
30	8	2	2

Alternatively, a scoring system may be adopted. If the origin of the measurements is changed to s and the occurrence and non-occurrence of the event are scored as $1 - s$ and $- s$ respectively instead of 1 and 0, the limits will then be h_1 and h_0, and the same for all values of n. In the present example each bad batch would be scored as 0·838 and each good batch as − 0·162. The procedure would be terminated as soon as the cumulative score had reached $h_0 = 2·155$, when the modification would be rejected, or $h_1 = − 2·767$, when the modification would be accepted. It is sometimes possible to simplify these schemes further by multiplying the scores by a suitable constant which will give approximately whole-number scores. Thus, in the present case, if the scores are multiplied by 6, the test is approximately represented by the following rule, starting with a score of zero.

For every bad batch add 5 units to the score, for every good batch subtract 1 unit; as soon as the score reaches or exceeds 13 reject the modification, or as soon as the score reaches or falls below − 17 accept the modification.

An approximation of this sort will make little difference to the characteristics of the test.

Testing for a difference in frequency

3·5. When an event has only a very small constant probability of occurring but many trials are made, so that the event does in fact happen with measurable frequency, the number of occurrences is given by the Poisson distribution [*S.M.*, § 9·2]. In the spinning of certain types of yarn the threads are examined for faults by winding a considerable length of yarn on to a frame which is illuminated obliquely so that faults in the yarn can be seen. The probability of a fault in any particular short length of yarn will be very small, but such a length of yarn can be viewed at the same time on the frame that faults will appear with measurable frequency, and if the faults are distributed at random this frequency will be given by the Poisson distribution.

There is clearly an upper limit to the average number of faults that can be tolerated per frame. Suppose it is decided to introduce a sequential inspection scheme which will consist in examining consecutive frames of yarn, recording the number of faults, and deciding after each frame is examined whether:

1. To accept the yarn.
2. To reject the yarn.
3. To reserve judgment and to inspect at least one further frame.

Four quantities must be decided upon: m_0, m_1, α, and β. When the value of m, the average number of breaks per frame, is really m_0 there is a risk α of saying that an increase in the number of breaks has occurred, and when the value is m_1 the risk is β of saying that no important increase has occurred.

The function plotted in this case is Y, the total number of breaks recorded, and the boundary lines are given by the formulae:

$$Y_0 = h_0 + ns \qquad Y_1 = h_1 + ns \quad \dots\dots\dots\dots\dots(3·6)$$

where $h_0 = -b/\ln(m_1/m_0)$, $h_1 = a/\ln(m_1/m_0)$, $s = (m_1 - m_0)/\ln(m_1/m_0)$ and $a = \ln(1-\beta)/a$, $b = \ln(1-a)/\beta$.

The average sample numbers required when $m = m_0$, $m = m_1$, and $m = s$ are given by

$$\bar{n}_0 = \frac{(1-a)h_0 + ah_1}{m_0 - s} \qquad \bar{n}_1 = \frac{\beta h_0 + (1-\beta)h_1}{m_1 - s} \qquad \bar{n}_s = \frac{-h_0 h_1}{s} \quad ..(3 \cdot 61)$$

As before, the actual test may be carried out in any one of the following ways:

(i) By plotting the observations on a chart with the above boundary lines.

(ii) By calculating acceptance numbers for each value of n (the limits may be rounded to whole numbers, since Y must be a whole number).

(iii) By employing a scoring system.

Example. Synthetic yarn experiment

3·51. For a certain synthetic yarn it was decided that an average frequency not exceeding two faults per frame could be regarded as normal, but that an average frequency of six or more faults per frame could not be tolerated. The risk a of asserting a significant increase in frequency of faults when there was really only an average number of two per frame was set at 0·05, and the risk β of failing to detect an increase to six faults per frame was set at 0·01, that is to say:

$$m_0 = 2 \qquad m_1 = 6 \qquad a = 0 \cdot 05 \qquad \beta = 0 \cdot 01$$

which on substitution in Formulae (3·6) and (3·61) yield the values

$$h_0 = -4 \cdot 15 \qquad h_1 = 2 \cdot 72 \qquad s = 3 \cdot 64$$
$$\bar{n}_0 = 2 \cdot 32 \qquad \bar{n}_1 = 1 \cdot 12 \qquad \bar{n}_s = 3 \cdot 09$$

From the size of the average sample numbers it is clear that the inspection of only two or three frames will usually be sufficient to reach a decision. For the first six observations the acceptance values (i.e. the calculated limits rounded outwards to the nearest integer) are given in Table 3·8.

Table 3·8

ACCEPTANCE VALUES FOR A SYNTHETIC YARN EXPERIMENT

n	Y_0	Y_1
1	—	7
2	3	10
3	6	14
4	10	18
5	14	21
6	17	25

From Table 3·8 it will be seen that if there were as many as seven faults on the first frame it could be concluded at once that a real increase above two faults per frame had occurred. On the other hand, even if no faults occurred on the first frame no decision could be taken until a further frame had been seen. After the inspection of two frames, if the total number of faults were less than three, the hypothesis that no important increase had occurred could be accepted at once.

Problems in which the POISSON distribution is appropriate are often met in connection with counting; for example in the counting of yeast and blood cells, dust particles, etc. It is well to bear in mind that the distribution to be expected will only conform exactly to the POISSON distribution when the small probability of the occurrence of the event is essentially constant.

Testing for a difference in variance

3·6. The application of sequential methods to the testing of hypotheses concerning mean values has been considered when the parent distribution is of Normal, Binomial, or POISSON type. Sometimes the question at issue does not concern the mean value of a set of data but rather the extent of variation which it exhibits. The reproducibility of a chemical test is sometimes more important than the mean value it gives, since a constant bias can always be allowed for but variation which is an inherent property of a method can only be reduced by making a large number of repeat tests. In the testing of yarn the extent to which the strength of the yarn varies along its length may be more important than the mean value of the strength, for the strength of the specimen of yarn will be the strength of the weakest part.

Consider the problem of testing for an increase or a decrease in the value of the variance from some standard value σ_0^2. To obtain a suitable sequential test some value σ_1^2 is chosen such that if the true variance were σ_1^2 and not σ_0^2 then the risk of failing to detect this difference would be β, while if the true variance were σ_0^2 the risk of accepting that such a difference had occurred would be α. The function of the observations upon which the test is based is the cumulative sum of squares of deviations from the mean (Z). If an observation is denoted by x and the mean value of the observations recorded up to a given time by $\bar{x}$, this sum of squares $Z = \Sigma(x - \bar{x})^2$. Since the mean $\bar{x}$ will alter after each observation, Z can most easily be calculated by using the identity

$$Z = \Sigma(x - \bar{x})^2 = \Sigma x^2 - T\bar{x} = \Sigma x^2 - T^2/n \quad \ldots\ldots\ldots(3\cdot7)$$

where T is the sum of the observations, i.e. $T = \Sigma x = n\bar{x}$.

In carrying out the test the value of Z is calculated after each observation from the cumulative sum of squares Σx^2, the cumulative sum T of the observations, and the value of the mean $\bar{x}$, and Z is compared with the limits given by the formulae

$$Z_0 = h_0 + (n - 1)s \qquad Z_1 = h_1 + (n - 1)s \quad \ldots\ldots\ldots(3\cdot8)$$

The factor $(n - 1)$ and not n is appropriate because the n deviations $x - \bar{x}$ represent only $n - 1$ independent comparisons. No decision could be made on a single observation, since no information about variation could be obtained from a single observation unless some prior estimate of the mean was available, so that it is only after the second observation (at the earliest) that a decision could be reached.

The values of h_0, h_1, and s are given by

$$h_0 = \frac{-2b}{\dfrac{1}{\sigma_0^2} - \dfrac{1}{\sigma_1^2}} \qquad h_1 = \frac{2a}{\dfrac{1}{\sigma_0^2} - \dfrac{1}{\sigma_1^2}} \qquad s = \frac{\ln(\sigma_1^2/\sigma_0^2)}{\dfrac{1}{\sigma_0^2} - \dfrac{1}{\sigma_1^2}} \quad \ldots(3\cdot81)$$

where $a = \ln(1 - \beta)/a$ and $b = \ln(1 - a)/\beta$.

The average sample numbers when $\sigma^2 = \sigma_0^2$, $\sigma^2 = \sigma_1^2$, and $\sigma^2 = s$ are given by

$$\left.\begin{array}{c} \bar{n}_0 = 1 + \dfrac{(1 - a)h_0 + ah_1}{\sigma_0^2 - s} \qquad \bar{n}_1 = 1 + \dfrac{\beta h_0 + (1 - \beta)h_1}{\sigma_1^2 - s} \\[2mm] \bar{n}_s = 1 - \dfrac{h_0 h_1}{2s^2} \end{array}\right\} \ (3\cdot82)$$

Example. An investigation into the strength of resin films

3·61. The following is an example taken from some experimental work on a method for determining the strength of resin films. Metal panels of standard thickness were coated with a known thickness of film. The coated panels were then stoved and the strength of the resin film was assessed by a machine which screwed a steel ball into the panel, thereby stretching the film on the reverse side until the film ruptured. When rupture occurred, electric contact was completed through the panel and a relay operated to stop the machine. The depth of penetration of the ball was a measure of the film strength.

The reproducibility of the original method, as measured by the variance, was known accurately from a large number of trials but was not considered satisfactory, and various experiments were conducted with a view to improvement. For these experiments panels were prepared under standard conditions, and sequential methods were adopted to reduce testing to a minimum. A good deal of information was available about the operation of the original unmodified method: in testing resin films of the strength concerned the standard deviation was a little over 4 units; the standard value for the variance was therefore taken as 16. In one typical experiment an attempt was made to improve reproducibility by specially preparing the surface of the panels prior to coating them with the resin. It was decided that a suitable test would be one which would give fairly high probability of detecting a reduction in variance to half its normal value. Keeping in mind the concept of the operating characteristic curve, it was decided that a should be set at 0·05 and β at 0·10, and the test was then based on the values

$$\sigma_0{}^2 = 16 \qquad \sigma_1{}^2 = 8 \qquad a = 0{\cdot}05 \qquad \beta = 0{\cdot}10$$

and from Formulae (3·81), (3·82) and Table K:

$$h_0 = 72{\cdot}032 \qquad h_1 = -92{\cdot}480 \qquad s = 11{\cdot}090$$
$$\bar{n}_0 = 14{\cdot}0 \qquad \bar{n}_1 = 25{\cdot}6 \qquad \bar{n}_s = 28{\cdot}1$$

The first eleven values recorded were 75·1, 71·9, 77·3, 70·1, 68·1, 78·6, 73·0, 71·8, 65·2, 75·8, and 67·1. To save arithmetic, 60 was subtracted from each of these values; the work was then set out in the form of Table 3·9.

Table 3·9

AN INVESTIGATION INTO THE STRENGTH OF RESIN FILMS

n	x	Σx^2	T	$\bar{x}$	$Z = \Sigma x^2 - T\bar{x}$	Z_0	Z_1
1	15·1	228·01	15·1	15·1000	—	—	—
2	11·9	369·62	27·0	13·5000	5·12	83·12	—
3	17·3	668·91	44·3	14·7667	14·75	94·21	—
4	10·1	770·92	54·4	13·6000	31·08	105·30	—
5	8·1	836·53	62·5	12·5000	55·28	116·39	—
6	18·6	1,182·49	81·1	13·5167	86·29	127·48	—
7	13·0	1,351·49	94·1	13·4429	86·51	138·57	—
8	11·8	1,490·73	105·9	13·2375	88·88	149·66	—
9	5·2	1,517·77	111·1	12·3444	146·31	160·75	—
10	15·8	1,767·41	126·9	12·6900	157·05	171·84	7·33
11	7·1	1,817·82	134·0	12·1818	185·46	182·93	18·42

Since Z must clearly be positive no zero values for the limits need be recorded, for such numbers merely imply that no decision could be made at this stage however small the value for Z. Nor need values be recorded for Z_0 and Z_1 when $n = 1$, since, as has already been explained, at least two observations will be needed before a decision can be reached. In the trial it will be seen that Z_0 was exceeded after the eleventh observation, so that the modified test was rejected.

SUMMARY OF SEQUENTIAL TESTS DISCUSSED IN CHAPTER 3

3·7. To help the reader in applying the various sequential tests introduced in this chapter the procedure in each case is now summarised.

Testing for a change in mean value. The standard deviation known

3·71. To test for a change in a given direction (single-sided Alternative Hypothesis) the quantities required are:

μ_0, the standard value.

$\delta = \mu_1 - \mu_0$, the difference which it is important to be able to detect.

a, the risk of asserting a difference when none exists.

β, the risk of asserting no difference when a difference of δ exists.

σ, the standard deviation of the observations.

The procedure is as follows:

1. Calculate:
$$h_0 = - b\sigma^2/\delta, \; h_1 = a\sigma^2/\delta, \; \text{and} \; s = (\mu_0 + \mu_1)/2$$
where $a = \ln(1 - \beta)/a$ and $b = \ln(1 - a)/\beta$.

2. Calculate the average sample numbers required when $\mu = \mu_0$, $\mu = \mu_1$. and $\mu = s$:

$$\bar{n}_0 = \frac{(1 - a)h_0 + ah_1}{\mu_0 - s} \qquad \bar{n}_1 = \frac{\beta h_0 + (1 - \beta)h_1}{\mu_1 - s} \qquad \bar{n}_s = \frac{- h_0 h_1}{\sigma^2}$$

If these values are too large, modify the scheme.

3. Take observations, and arrive at a decision in any one of the following (equivalent) ways:

(a) Plot the cumulative total T of the observations against the number of observations on a chart with boundary lines

$$T_0 = h_0 + ns \qquad T_1 = h_1 + ns$$

The indicated decision is made when one of these boundaries is crossed,

(b) Calculate the limits T_0 and T_1 for successive values of n and compare the cumulative total T with the appropriate limits as each new observation comes to hand. Take the indicated decision as soon as a limit is reached.

(c) Measure all the observations from the origin s and compare the cumulative total T with the limits $T_0 = h_0$ and $T_1 = h_1$, and take the indicated decision when a limit is reached.

To test for a difference between pairs of observations treat the differences between pairs of values as the observations. Test the Null Hypothesis that the standard value of this difference is zero.

When there is equal interest in a change in either direction (double-sided Alternative Hypothesis), superimpose two single-sided tests with the values $\frac{1}{2}a, \beta, + \delta$, and σ for one, and $\frac{1}{2}a, \beta, - \delta$, and σ for the other.

Barnard's sequential *t*-test for a change in mean value

3·72. To test for a change in a given direction (single-sided Alternative Hypothesis) the quantities required are:

μ_0, the standard value.

D,* the difference stated in terms of the standard deviation which it is important to be able to detect.

α, the risk of asserting a difference when none exists.

β, the risk of asserting no difference when a difference of D standard deviations exists.

To make the test for a departure from a standard value μ_0 in a stated direction, record differences departing from μ_0 in the expected direction as positive and differences departing from μ_0 in the opposite direction as negative; calculate T, the total of these departures, S, the sum of their squares, and $U = T/\sqrt{S}$ as each observation is made. Refer to Tables L·1 to L·8, which give values of the appropriate limits U_0 and U_1. Accept the hypothesis that no significant difference has occurred in the stated direction as soon as U falls short of U_0, and the hypothesis that there is a significant difference in the stated direction as soon as U exceeds U_1.

To test for a difference between pairs of observations, treat the differences between the pairs as the original observations. Test the Null Hypothesis that the standard value of this difference is zero.

When there is equal interest in a change in either direction (double-sided Alternative Hypothesis), superimpose two single-sided tests with values $\frac{1}{2}\alpha$, β, $+\delta$, and σ for one, and $\frac{1}{2}\alpha, \beta$, $-\delta$, and σ for the other.

Testing for a change in proportion from some standard value in a given direction (Binomial test)

3·73. The quantities required are:

p_0, the standard proportion.

p_1, the proportion which constitutes a difference from p_0 which it is important to be able to detect.

α, the risk of asserting a difference when none exists.

β, the risk of asserting no difference when a difference $p_1 - p_0$ exists.

The procedure is then as follows:

1. Calculate:

$$h_0 = -b/(P + Q), \; h_1 = a/(P + Q), \text{ and } s = Q/(P + Q)$$

where $P = \ln p_1/p_0$, $Q = \ln (1 - p_0)/(1 - p_1)$, $a = \ln (1 - \beta)/\alpha$, and $b = \ln (1 - \alpha)/\beta$.

---

* As explained in § 3·3, the test is designed to detect a change of D standard deviations. To detect a given change $\delta = D\sigma$ in mean value some prior estimate of the standard deviation σ is required.

2. Calculate the average sample number required when $p = p_0$, $p = p_1$, and $p = s$:

$$\bar{n}_0 = \frac{(1-a)h_0 + ah_1}{p_0 - s} \qquad \bar{n}_1 = \frac{\beta h_0 + (1-\beta)h_1}{p_1 - s} \qquad \bar{n}_s = \frac{-h_0 h_1}{s(1-s)}$$

If these values are too large, modify the scheme.

3. Take observations, and arrive at a decision in any one of the following (equivalent) ways:

(a) Plot the total number X of occurrences of the event against the number of observations on a chart with boundary lines:

$$X_0 = h_0 + ns \qquad X_1 = h_1 + ns$$

The indicated decision is made when one of these boundaries is crossed.

(b) Calculate the limits X_0 and X_1 for successive values of n and compare the total number of occurrences of the event with the appropriate limits as each new observation comes to hand. The limits can be rounded outwards to integral values (since X is an integer) which are called the acceptance numbers. Take the indicated decision when a limit is reached.

(c) Measure all the observations from the origin s (i.e. score $1 - s$ when the event occurs and $- s$ when it does not), and take the indicated decision when the cumulative score reaches h_0 or h_1. A simplified approximate scheme can often be obtained by multiplying $1 - s$ and s by a scale factor such that the new scores are approximately whole numbers, the limits being scaled up correspondingly.

Testing for a change in frequency (Poisson variate) from some standard value in a given direction

3·74. The quantities required are:

m_0, the standard frequency.

m_1, the frequency which constitutes a difference from m_0 which it is important to be able to detect.

a, the risk of asserting a difference when none exists.

β, the risk of asserting no difference when a difference $m_1 - m_0$ exists.

The procedure is then as follows:

1. Calculate:

$$h_0 = - b/\ln (m_1/m_0), \quad h_1 = a/\ln (m_1/m_0), \quad s = (m_1 - m_0)/\ln (m_1/m_0),$$
where $a = \ln (1 - \beta)/a$, $b = \ln (1 - a)/\beta$.

2. Calculate the average sample numbers required when $m = m_0$, $m = m_1$, and $m = s$:

$$\bar{n}_0 = \frac{(1-a)h_0 + ah_1}{m_0 - s} \qquad \bar{n}_1 = \frac{\beta h_0 + (1-\beta)h_1}{m_1 - s} \qquad \bar{n}_s = \frac{-h_0 h_1}{s}$$

If these values are too large, modify the scheme.

3. Take observations and arrive at a decision in any one of the following (equivalent) ways:

(a) Plot the values for the cumulative frequency Y against the number of observations on a chart with boundary lines

$$Y_0 = h_0 + ns \qquad Y_1 = h_1 + ns$$

The indicated decision is made when one of these boundaries is crossed.

(b) Calculate the limits Y_0 and Y_1 for successive values of n and compare the cumulative frequency with the appropriate limits as each new observation comes to hand. The limits can be rounded outwards to integral values (since Y is an integer) which are called the acceptance numbers. Take the indicated decision when a limit is reached.

(c) Measure all the observations from the origin s, call this the score, and take the indicated decision when the cumulative score reaches h_0 or h_1.

Testing for a change in variance from a standard value in a given direction

3·75. The quantities required are:

σ_0^2, the standard value of the variance.

σ_1^2, the value of the variance which constitutes a departure from σ_0^2 which it is important to be able to detect.

a, the risk of asserting a difference when $\sigma^2 = \sigma_0^2$.

β, the risk of asserting no difference when $\sigma^2 = \sigma_1^2$.

The procedure is then as follows:

1. Calculate:

$$h_0 = \frac{-2b}{\dfrac{1}{\sigma_0^2} - \dfrac{1}{\sigma_1^2}} \qquad h_1 = \frac{2a}{\dfrac{1}{\sigma_0^2} - \dfrac{1}{\sigma_1^2}} \qquad s = \frac{\ln(\sigma_1^2/\sigma_0^2)}{\dfrac{1}{\sigma_0^2} - \dfrac{1}{\sigma_1^2}}$$

where $a = \ln(1 - \beta)/a$ and $b = \ln(1 - a)/\beta$.

2. Calculate the average sample numbers required when $\sigma^2 = \sigma_0^2$, $\sigma^2 = \sigma_1^2$, and $\sigma^2 = s$:

$$\bar{n}_0 = 1 + \frac{(1 - a)h_0 + ah_1}{\sigma_0^2 - s}$$

$$\bar{n}_1 = 1 + \frac{\beta h_0 + (1 - \beta)h_1}{\sigma_1^2 - s}$$

$$\bar{n}_s = 1 - \frac{h_0 h_1}{2s^2}$$

If these values are too large, modify the scheme.

3. Take observations and arrive at a decision in either of the following (equivalent) ways:

(a) Plot the values for the cumulative sum of squares $Z = \Sigma(x - \bar{x})^2$ against the number of observations on a chart with boundary lines

$$Z_0 = h_0 + (n - 1)s \qquad Z_1 = h_1 + (n - 1)s$$

The indicated decision is made when one of these boundaries is crossed.

(b) Calculate the limits Z_0 and Z_1 for successive values of n and compare the cumulative sum of squares with the appropriate limits as each new observation comes to hand. Take the indicated decision when a limit is reached.

The cumulative sum of squares is most easily computed from the identity

$$Z = \Sigma(x - \bar{x})^2 = \Sigma x^2 - T\bar{x}$$

where T is the sum of the observations.

REFERENCES

[3·1] WALD, A. *Sequential Analysis.* John Wiley (New York, 1947).
[3·2] BARNARD, G. A. "Sequential Tests in Industrial Statistics." *J. R. Statist. Soc. Suppl.*, **8** (1946), 1.
[3·3] *Idem.* "Review." *J. Amer. Statist. Assoc.*, **42** (1947), 658.
[3·4] *Idem.* "Statistical Inference." *J. R. Statist. Soc. Suppl.*, **11** (1949).
[3·5] RUSHTON, S. "Sequential *t*-Test." *Biometrika*, **37** (1950), 326.

APPENDIX 3A

SEQUENTIAL TESTS OF SIMPLE HYPOTHESES

IN this book the theory of sequential significance tests is not discussed in detail. The following brief outline is designed to illustrate the type of argument employed rather than to provide a rigorous derivation of the tests. For this purpose sequential tests of what are called simple hypotheses are considered. Such hypotheses concern the value of a particular parameter θ, such as the mean μ, the remaining parameters being assumed known. The Normal Curve test, Binomial test and POISSON test described in this chapter are of this type.

Suppose the parameter θ can take only two values $\theta = \theta_0$ or $\theta = \theta_1$ and the object of an experiment is to decide which of these alternatives is true. A useful principle is provided by the likelihood ratio, which was first suggested as a method of obtaining a test criterion by NEYMAN and PEARSON [3A·1]. The likelihood ratio with respect to the quantities θ_0 and θ_1 is given by

$$\lambda = \frac{\text{Probability* of sample arising when } \theta = \theta_0}{\text{Probability of sample arising when } \theta = \theta_1}$$

* Probability should read as probability density in the case of continuous distributions throughout this appendix.

The hypothesis H_0 that $\theta = \theta_0$ will be preferred when λ is large, and the hypothesis H_1 that $\theta = \theta_1$ will be preferred when λ is small. WALD [3·1] applied this criterion to the problem of sequential tests. In this application λ is calculated after each observation, and two limits λ_0 and λ_1 are adopted such that, if H_0 is accepted as soon as λ is greater than or equal to λ_0 and H_1 is accepted as soon as λ is less than or equal to λ_1, and sampling is continued when λ falls between these limits, then the risk of saying H_1 is true when H_0 is true will not exceed some value a, and the risk of saying that H_0 is true when H_1 is true will not exceed some value β.

The test is then represented as follows:

$$\text{Accept } H_1 \text{ when } \lambda \leqslant \lambda_1$$
$$\text{Continue taking observations while } \lambda_1 < \lambda < \lambda_0$$
$$\text{Accept } H_0 \text{ when } \lambda \geqslant \lambda_0$$

Now imagine a large number of sequential tests to have been made. There are two sets of final samples, the first having a likelihood ratio equal to or slightly greater* than λ_0 (when sampling will have been terminated with H_0 being accepted), and the second having a likelihood ratio equal to or slightly less than λ_1 (when sampling will have terminated with H_1 being accepted). Now consider the entire population of possible samples of the first set. For each of these samples the probability that the sample has really originated from the population with parameter θ_0 is about λ_0 times as great as the probability that it has originated from a population with parameter θ_1, and this is true of every one of the samples; so that the total chance of obtaining a sample of this sort is about λ_0 times as large when H_0 is true as when H_1 is true. But the chance of getting such a sample from a population in which $\theta = \theta_0$ is to be $1 - a$ and the chance of getting such a sample from a population in which $\theta = \theta_1$ is to be β. Consequently in order to satisfy both conditions λ_0 must be approximately equal to $(1 - a)/\beta$. A similar argument shows that λ_1 must be approximately equal to $a/(1 - \beta)$. In practice it is usually found that some simple function of λ is more convenient to use than λ itself.

The results of the application of this principle in a number of important cases have been given in this chapter. For illustration, the derivation of the sequential test when the observations are Normally distributed and the test is for the hypothesis that the mean is μ_0 against the hypothesis that it is μ_1, the standard deviation being known, is now given. The derivations of the sequential Binomial, POISSON, etc., tests follow similar lines.

---

* A finite number of observations will not normally result in a likelihood ratio exactly equal to λ_0, and in practice λ_0 will usually be slightly exceeded; similarly the likelihood ratio will usually be less than λ_1 when H_1 is accepted. The practical consequence is that sequential tests are conservative, the actual risks of making wrong decisions being less than those allowed for in the scheme.

If μ_0, μ_1, a, β, and σ are given and n observations have been taken, and it is assumed that the observations are distributed Normally, then since the probability for a single observation x_i originating from a Normal distribution having mean μ_0 and standard deviation σ is

$$\frac{1}{\sigma(2\pi)^{\frac{1}{2}}} \exp \left\{ - \frac{(x_i - \mu_0)^2}{2\sigma^2} \right\}$$

the probability $p(H_0)$ of a sample of n independent observations $(x_1, \ldots x_i, \ldots, x_n)$ originating from this distribution is the product of n such expressions:

$$p(H_0) = \frac{1}{\sigma^n (2\pi)^{n/2}} \exp \left\{ - \frac{\Sigma_i(x_i - \mu_0)^2}{2\sigma^2} \right\}$$

Similarly the probability that the sample has arisen from a population in which $\mu = \mu_1$ is

$$p(H_1) = \frac{1}{\sigma^n (2\pi)^{n/2}} \exp \left\{ - \frac{\Sigma_i(x_i - \mu_1)^2}{2\sigma^2} \right\}$$

Thus the likelihood ratio is given by

$$\lambda = \frac{\exp \left\{ - \Sigma_i(x_i - \mu_0)^2 / 2\sigma^2 \right\}}{\exp \left\{ - \Sigma_i(x_i - \mu_1)^2 / 2\sigma^2 \right\}} \dots \dots \dots \dots (3A \cdot 1)$$

Taking logarithms and rearranging:

$$\Sigma x_i = T = \frac{- \sigma^2 \ln \lambda}{\mu_1 - \mu_0} + \frac{n}{2} (\mu_1 + \mu_0) \dots \dots \dots (3A \cdot 2)$$

Therefore, since T is a single-valued function of λ, instead of calculating λ after each observation and using the limits λ_0 and λ_1, the sum of observations $\Sigma_i x_i = T$ may be calculated using the limits T_0 and T_1 obtained by substituting the values for λ_0 and λ_1 in equation $(3A \cdot 2)$, i.e.:

$$T_0 = h_0 + ns \qquad T_1 = h_1 + ns \dots \dots \dots \dots (3A \cdot 3)$$

where $h_0 = - b\sigma^2/\delta$, $h_1 = a\sigma^2/\delta$, and $s = (\mu_1 + \mu_0)/2$ and $\delta = \mu_1 - \mu_0$, $a = \ln(1 - \beta)/a$, and $b = \ln(1 - a)/\beta$.

So far it has been assumed that μ_0 and μ_1 are the only possible values for the parameter μ, and the hypothesis H_0 is that $\mu = \mu_0$, and H_1 is that $\mu = \mu_1$. From the operating characteristic curve showing for various values of μ the probabilities that H_1 will be accepted it is seen that for values of μ less than μ_0 H_1 will almost certainly be rejected, but that when the value of μ is greater than μ_0 the probability of acceptance of H_1 increases and is large in the neighbourhood of μ_1, approaching the value unity as μ is further increased. Thus in the general case when μ_0 and μ_1 are not the only values possible but merely convenient values to define the test, the sequential scheme serves to distinguish a pair of more general hypotheses. The hypothesis H_0 has the wider interpretation that no important increase above μ_0 has occurred, important being interpreted to mean a difference as great as $\mu_1 - \mu_0 = \delta$, while the hypothesis H_1 implies that there is a real increase from μ_0. This argument, although it is illustrated in the particular case of the test for mean values, applies generally.

REFERENCE

[3A·1] NEYMAN, J., and PEARSON, E. S. "On the Use and Interpretation of Certain Test Criteria for Purposes of Statistical Inference." *Biometrika*, 20A (1928), 175 and 263.

APPENDIX 3B

THE OPERATING CHARACTERISTIC CURVE, OR POWER CURVE

THE derivation of the operating characteristic curve will be illustrated in the case of the Normal Curve sequential test. This form of the argument, which is due to BAKER [3B·1], may be used for the derivation of the corresponding curves for all the tests of simple hypotheses discussed in this chapter. Suppose the test is based on the quantities μ_0, μ_1, α, β, and σ, where $\mu_1 > \mu_0$ as in Appendix 3A. We require to know the probability α' of accepting the Alternative Hypothesis H_1 when the true population mean is μ. Suppose a large number of sequential tests are made on observations drawn from a population in which the mean is μ and the variance σ^2, then the proportion α' of tests that conclude with the acceptance of H_1 depends only on the quantities h_0, h_1, and s. The operating characteristic curve for any test based on μ_0', μ_1', α', β', and σ which happened to give the same values of h_0, h_1, and s would therefore be the same. Suppose $\mu_0' = \mu$, then μ_1' must equal $\mu_0 + \mu_1 - \mu$, since only if this is so will $s = \{\mu + (\mu_0 + \mu_1 - \mu)\}/2 = (\mu_0 + \mu_1)/2$ remain unchanged. Also (see Equation $(3A·3)$), in order that h_0 and h_1 should remain unchanged:

$$h_0 = \frac{-\sigma^2}{\mu_1 + \mu_0 - 2\mu} \ln\left(\frac{1 - \alpha'}{\beta'}\right) = \frac{-\sigma^2}{\mu_1 - \mu_0} \ln\left(\frac{1 - \alpha}{\beta}\right) \quad \ldots (3B·1)$$

$$h_1 = \frac{\sigma^2}{\mu_1 + \mu_0 - 2\mu} \ln\left(\frac{1 - \beta'}{\alpha'}\right) = \frac{\sigma^2}{\mu_1 - \mu_0} \ln\left(\frac{1 - \beta}{\alpha}\right) \quad \ldots (3B·2)$$

Write $\quad A = \dfrac{1 - \beta}{\alpha} \quad\quad B = \dfrac{1 - \alpha}{\beta} \quad\quad t = \dfrac{\mu_1 + \mu_0 - 2\mu}{\mu_1 - \mu_0} \quad \ldots\ldots(3B·3)$

Equations $(3B·1)$ and $(3B·2)$ may be written

$$\frac{1 - \alpha'}{\beta'} = B^t$$

$$\frac{1 - \beta'}{\alpha'} = A^t$$

Solving for a':

$$a' = \frac{B^t - 1}{A^t B^t - 1} \quad \dots\dots\dots\dots\dots\dots(3B\cdot4)$$

Values of $t = (\mu_1 + \mu_0 - 2\mu)/(\mu_1 - \mu_0)$ are calculated for suitable values of μ and the ordinate a' of the operating characteristic curve is then given by Equation ($3B\cdot4$).

REFERENCE

[3B·1] BAKER, A. G. "Properties of some Tests in Sequential Analysis." *Biometrika*, **37** (1950), 334.

APPENDIX 3C

THE AVERAGE SAMPLE NUMBER

WITH the exception of BARNARD's sequential t-test all the tests considered have been linear tests: that is to say, they have involved the plotting of some function $f(x)$ of the observations on a chart with limits given by the two straight lines:

$$\left.\begin{array}{l} f_0(x) = h_0 + ns \\ f_1(x) = h_1 + ns \end{array}\right\} \quad \dots\dots\dots\dots\dots\dots(3C\cdot1)$$

In these cases formulae for the average sample numbers can be found very simply. It has been shown how the tests can be reduced to a simple scoring system. The procedure consisted of taking s as the origin for all the observations and calling the resultant numbers the score, the test being terminated as soon as the cumulative total of the score had reached either of the limits h_0, h_1. Suppose the test is for the hypothesis H_0 that $\theta = \theta_0$ against the hypothesis H_1 that $\theta = \theta_1$, and suppose a very large number (k) of sequential tests using the same testing scheme to have been made in which $\theta = \theta'$ was true in every case. Suppose finally that the total number of observations made was N. If a' was the probability of accepting the Alternative Hypothesis H_1 when $\theta = \theta'$, on the average $k(1 - a')$ of the tests would terminate with a score of about h_0 (H_0 being accepted) and ka' of the tests would terminate with a score of about h_1 (H_1 being accepted). Now if the tests always terminated with the score exactly equal either to h_0 or to h_1 the total of the scores for all the N observations would be exactly equal to $k(1 - a')h_0 + ka'h_1$.

In practice the test usually terminates when the score is slightly greater than h_1 or slightly less than h_0, so that the above equality still holds approximately. The total of the scores for the N observations is N times the average score per observation; consequently

$N \times$ (average score per observation when $\theta = \theta'$ true)

$$\simeq k\{(1 - a')h_0 + a'h_1\} \quad \dots.(3C\cdot2)$$

H

Hence the average sample number $\bar{n}'$ when $\theta = \theta'$ is given by

$$\bar{n}' = \frac{N}{k} \simeq \frac{(1-a')h_0 + a'h_1}{\text{Average score per observation when } \theta = \theta'} = \frac{(1-a')h_0 + a'h_1}{\theta' - s} \quad \dots (3C\cdot3)$$

and a' is the appropriate ordinate of the power curve. In particular when $\theta = \theta_0$ and $\theta = \theta_1$:

$$\bar{n}_0 \simeq \frac{(1-a)h_0 + ah_1}{\theta_0 - s} \quad \text{and} \quad \bar{n}_1 \simeq \frac{\beta h_0 + (1-\beta)h_1}{\theta_1 - s} \quad \dots \dots (3C\cdot4)$$

When $\theta = s$ both numerator and denominator are zero and the above expressions are indeterminate. The average sample number $\bar{n}_s$ may still be determined however (see for example [3·71]) and the appropriate expressions are given in the chapter.

CHAPTER 4

INVESTIGATION OF SAMPLING AND TESTING METHODS

SAMPLING and testing methods are fundamental in a great deal of chemical research and it is necessary to know their precision before one can effectively carry out experiments on factors affecting yield, quality, etc. It may also be necessary to investigate the relative precision of the various stages involved in sampling and testing with the object of attaining greater overall precision, of deciding between the suitability of alternative methods, or of framing a specification. Experiments on this subject should be so arranged that the overall variation can be analysed to show the variation arising from different sources, such as the various stages of sampling and testing, the differences between the batches sampled, and the different operators, methods of analysis, etc., which may be involved. The general principles are discussed and illustrated by full descriptions of typical experiments.

Introduction

4·1. In this chapter we shall discuss, and illustrate by examples, the design analysis, and interpretation of experiments for the study of sampling and testing errors before proceeding to the wider field of chemical experimentation. The first essential in carrying out an investigation into testing errors is to understand clearly what sources of error exist and how they can be measured and controlled; these matters are discussed in §§ **4·12** and **4·13**. Example **4·1** deals with a straightforward investigation into errors of sampling and analysis; it is used to illustrate the general principles underlying the design and analysis of experiments of this type. Examples 4·2, 4·3, and 4·4 introduce additional features: in Example 4·2 a number of laboratories are compared; in Example 4·3 two laboratories are compared in greater detail, using several tests on several batches; Example 4·4 is more complex, involving different analytical methods as well as sampling errors. Examples 4·2–4·4 are discussed in detail, but are not interspersed with general matter as in Example 4·1.

4·11. The first step in planning any experiment is to form a clear picture of the objects of the experiment, the factors which may affect the results, and the errors which will inevitably arise. The chief objects of the experimental design are:

(i) To arrange the experiment so that the effect of changing each condition can be readily measured and separated from the effects of changing the other conditions, and from experimental error.

(ii) To obtain a valid estimate of error appropriate for assessing the statistical significance of the effects of the factors.

(iii) To enable the effects to be measured with the required accuracy.

In general, one or more of the experimental conditions will be varied deliberately, others will be held constant, while others again will vary without being controlled. In a well-designed experiment the variations due to the causes being studied can be estimated individually; variation due to other relatively unimportant and perhaps unidentifiable causes is classed as experimental error. To take a simple and rather obvious example, if two analysts carry out tests on two methods of analysing a given material and one analyst uses only the first method while the other uses only the second, then any difference in the average results, assuming it to be statistically significant, may be due either to a difference between the methods, to a difference between the analysts, or to a combination of both. But if each analyst does half his tests by each method, the differences between the two methods and between the two analysts can be estimated separately.

This is clear from the following table:

Analyst	Method of analysis		Average
	I	2	
A	x_{1a}	x_{2a}	$\bar{x}_a$
B	x_{1b}	x_{2b}	$\bar{x}_b$
Average ..	$\bar{x}_1$	$\bar{x}_2$	—

x_{1a} = observed value for method I, analyst A, etc.

The difference between the results obtained by methods 1 and 2 is $(\bar{x}_1 - \bar{x}_2)$; this is averaged over both analysts and would be regarded as the true measure of the difference between the methods if it were the same, apart from experimental errors, for both analysts. Similarly the difference between the results obtained by analysts A and B is measured by $(\bar{x}_a - \bar{x}_b)$, which is averaged over both methods. If the two methods do not agree but are biased with respect to each other (if, for example, method 2 consistently gives higher results than method 1), the comparison of the two analysts is still valid, since the measure of the difference between analysts is independent of any constant difference between methods, and similarly the measure of the difference between methods is independent of any constant difference between analysts.

It is possible that a differential effect may exist if for example analyst B gets higher results than analyst A using method 2 but equivalent results using method 1. It is important to be able to determine the differential effect, and this can be done with the above design by comparing $(x_{1a} - x_{1b})$ with $(x_{2a} - x_{2b})$. If these two differences agree within experimental error the conclusion is that no differential effect exists; if they do not agree, then a differential effect exists measured by the difference $(x_{1a} - x_{1b}) - (x_{2a} - x_{2b})$. There are thus three functions of the data which measure respectively the average difference between methods, the average difference between analysts, and the differential effect. The average differences are termed the Main Effects of methods and analysts, and the differential effect is termed the Interaction between methods and analysts. These are treated in greater detail in Chapter 7. An important feature is that all three functions use all the data; each is in fact an algebraic sum of the four observations, with two positive and two negative terms. This, as will be shown in later chapters, is a feature of well-designed experiments; all the data should contribute to every conclusion drawn from the experiment.

This is a simple illustration. The bad design quoted earlier in which one analyst uses only the first method and the other only the second is not likely to be used; but it is easy, especially in more complex experiments, to make similar but less obvious mistakes which throw away large amounts of information. In most situations encountered by the chemist there is a considerable advantage in making the numbers of tests for each analyst and each method the same—a less obvious but important point. The formal treatment which is necessary in more complex experiments is an extension of the common-sense principles illustrated above.

Replicate analyses

4·12. It is usual to carry out chemical analyses or other tests two or more times with the object of reducing the effect of experimental error, but on close examination it is often found that the replication reduces only some of the errors involved leaving important errors unaffected. An example which arose in the testing of a synthetic fibre will illustrate this point. In the experimental production of the fibre a cone of yarn was made under certain conditions and was tested by cutting off a length from one end, on which ten tensile tests were performed. On the basis of these results the process was modified in an endeavour to find the best spinning conditions. In order to reduce the effect of testing errors the number of tests was increased, but this brought about no improvement. Statistical investigation showed that there was a considerable systematic variation in strength throughout the cone; ten tests on adjacent pieces of yarn gave fairly concordant results, ten from a different section of the cone gave results concordant among themselves but not with the first set. To get a true measure of the average strength of the cone it was necessary to spread the replicate tests over the whole cone. Replication on adjacent pieces of yarn reduced the effect of testing errors but not the effect of yarn variation, which was equally important.

The same principles apply in chemical analysis; the analysis may involve several steps, yielding a solution of the material to be estimated by the final step of titration, or colorimetric estimation, or precipitation and weighing, etc. If the last step only is repeated, errors due to inaccuracies in weighing, or titrating, etc., will be reduced, but not those due to the previous steps, and if these involve considerable sources of error the replication of the final stage may not be effective. It may guard against gross mistakes, but the concordance of the replicate tests must not be taken as a measure of the precision of the analysis. It is thus essential to know how complete the replication is; it may be anything between a repetition of the last stage in the analysis and a repetition of the whole process of sampling the chemical and all stages of analysis carried out independently by a different analyst. The extent to which the process is replicated will vary with the object of the experiment: if an absolute measure of the composition of the material is required, then the replicate tests should be as independent as possible; if the object is to compare two methods of carrying out the final stage, say titration or precipitation, only the final stage need be replicated, so that all the tests by both methods would be performed on identical material.

The term replication is used not only for sampling and analytical tests, but also in later chapters for repetition of an entire experiment. It should be noted that the expressions "replicated once" and "a single replicate" refer to a process or experiment carried out once only; "replicated twice" means twice only, and so on.

The errors of chemical analysis
4·13. A brief description of the various forms of error which together constitute the analytical error is necessary to avoid ambiguities. It is first necessary to consider the object of an analysis. The object is to measure, in an absolute sense, the composition of a chemical, say the percentage of one ingredient. Any one analysis is subject to several distinct sources of error.

Variations in repeat tests performed under equivalent conditions at the same time
   (i) Some variation will exist even among repeated tests carried out at the same time with all conditions seemingly constant—same analyst, same apparatus, same standard solutions, etc. The results of such tests will vary round a mean value with variance V_0, say.

Variations due to operator bias

  (ii) If an exactly similar set of tests is carried out by another analyst, the mean value of his results will in general differ slightly because of some personal factor which causes a slight bias between the analysts. The means for a number of analysts will vary round some overall mean with variance V_a, say. This is, of course, additional to the variance V_0.

Variations between analyses made at different times

  (iii) If the set of tests carried out in (i) is repeated by the same analyst on different occasions, perhaps with different apparatus and different standard solutions, the results will vary round an overall mean with variance V_t additional to V_0.

Thus any one set of tests carried out under apparently uniform conditions will exhibit a variance V_0, but the mean of the test results will not in general tend to the true composition μ, because of the variations due to different analysts, etc. If we imagine the experiment extended over a large number of analysts and occasions, then unless the method is biased the grand mean averaged over all the tests tends to the true mean, or more precisely is the best possible estimate of the true mean obtainable from the data above. Consequently the error variance of any one analysis is

$$V_1 = V_t + V_a + V_0$$

Other terms could be included to correspond to any other assignable causes of variation.

To obtain a closer estimate, i.e. one with a smaller error, a number of analyses can be averaged. If these are carried out at one time by the same analyst the process of averaging does not reduce the bias associated with the analyst or the time. The variance of the average of two such analyses is in fact

$$V_2 = V_t + V_a + \tfrac{1}{2}V_0$$

To go to the other extreme, if the two tests are carried out in different laboratories the tests will be completely independent and the process of averaging reduces the errors due to all sources, giving a variance

$$V_3 = \tfrac{1}{2}(V_t + V_a + V_0)$$

This is clearly less than V_2; consequently if we require an estimate of the true composition the best procedure is to make the separate analyses completely independent.

Suppose on the other hand that the object of the analysis is to measure the difference between the percentages of the ingredient contained in two samples then the best procedure is to carry out the two analyses together, aiming at the same experimental conditions for both analyses. If the particular standard solution used is not exactly right, it is immaterial: both tests are biased to the same extent, and the difference is unaffected. The same argument applies if the particular analyst exhibits a bias. The variance of the difference is

$$V_1(d) = 2V_0$$

If the two analyses are carried out completely independently the variance will be

$$V_2(d) = 2(V_t + V_a + V_0)$$

which is clearly greater than $V_1(d)$.

These simple illustrations show that the design of the testing scheme and the appropriate measure of analytical error vary widely according to the objects of the test.

4·131. Definitions which are useful in discussion of analytical errors are:

Accuracy. Correctness or truth, i.e. closeness of agreement between the experimental value and the true value. (It is usually impossible to ascertain the true value.)

Reproducibility. A method of high reproducibility is one capable of yielding closely concordant results in replicate analyses. These results, while showing a small variation among themselves, do not necessarily vary about the true value, so that a method may be reproducible without being accurate.

Error. A divergence from the truth which arises from causes inherent in the analytical method, e.g. from the fact that a burette can be read, at best, correct to one-fifth of a division.

Mistake. A divergence arising from an unintentional departure from the usual procedure, e.g. a misreading of a burette, a copying mistake, etc.

Random error. An error which individually is unpredictable but whose average tends to zero in the long run. If a length is measured to the nearest scale division on a ruler graduated in millimetres, the error on one occasion may be anything between $+ 0·5$ and $- 0·5$ mm., but the average of a long series of such measurements will be virtually correct.

Bias, or systematic error. An error which persists during a series of the same or similar measurements or analytical determinations and which is therefore not eliminated by any process of averaging. The total error of any measurement may contain both a bias and a random component; averaging several measurements reduces the random component, but does not affect the bias.

4·14. The assessment of the various sources of error in chemical sampling and analysis is a simple and fruitful field for planned experiments. Since most chemical experiments, on whatever scale, involve taking samples of material and the subsequent analysis of these samples, it is frequently required to design the experiment so that an estimate of the errors of sampling and analysis or, as is often sufficient, of the combined error of sampling and analysis, can be obtained from the experiment itself. This may be considered unnecessary if an adequate estimate of the errors is available from past data. Such data should be collected and should be freely used, but it may be thought advisable to carry out a rough check, say by duplicating a few of the trials in the experiment.

It is natural, therefore, to consider as the first examples of designed experiments those involving sampling and testing errors only. Later examples will include the effects of varying physical and chemical factors as well as estimating the sampling and testing errors which are used as yardsticks in assessing the significance of the effects of the deliberately varied factors. An investigation into errors of testing should, if possible, provide answers to the following questions or such of them as are appropriate.

(i) What is the reproducibility of the method ?

(ii) Is the method biased, i.e. does it, on the average, yield a result different from the true result ? The existence of bias can be tested only if the true result is known with high accuracy, but some indication may be obtained by comparing two or more methods.

(iii) Does the test operate equally well over the whole range of composition for which it is to be used ?

(iv) Is the reproducibility the same for all operators concerned ?

(v) Are the operators biased relative to one another, i.e. do they differ in their average results ?

(vi) If two or more methods are being examined, do they differ in reproducibility or in accuracy, and are these affected by operator bias ? Personal factors may vary considerably: in some tests, especially where the readings are made from instruments, personal factors are unimportant, and any conclusions about the test should apply to any operator. In others, especially if the routine cannot be precisely laid down (e.g. in cement testing), there is a large personal factor.

Example 4·1. Sampling and testing an organic chemical

4·2. This example represents an investigation carried out to determine the errors involved in sampling and testing an organic chemical used in the manufacture of certain dyestuffs. The chemical is produced as a paste containing 35–50% solids; the yield of a batch is estimated by weighing the batch and analysing a sample. Considerable variations were found in the yields so calculated from batch to batch, and before investigating the reasons for the variation it was necessary to investigate the errors of sampling and analysis.

To do this nine consecutive batches from normal production were sampled in the normal manner and the sampling was repeated three times on different occasions. Each batch was contained in several casks, and in order to obtain a representative sample the casks were sampled by means of an auger; the material was then compounded and reduced to a suitable size from which two identical half-pound samples for analysis were taken. This gave $9 \times 3 \times 2 = 54$ samples, which were coded and sent for analysis in a random order over a period of several weeks. The samples were indistinguishable from normal routine analyses and the testers were unaware of the correspondence between the samples. A sufficiently long period of time was covered in order to include all the factors contributing to normal routine analytical error.

4·21. Table 4·1 gives the complete results: A, B, and C represent the three samples.

It is required to determine:

(i) The magnitude of the analytical error. This is estimated from the difference between the two tests on each sample.

(ii) Whether there is an appreciable sampling error, and if so its magnitude. The sampling error is estimated from the variation between the A, B, and C averages (or totals) for each batch after due allowance for the variation attributable to testing error.

(iii) The most economical scheme of sampling and analysis which will give a specified degree of accuracy in the estimate of the batch composition.

Analysis of variance: general remarks

4·22. In this and in nearly all the examples in this book extensive use is made of the Analysis of Variance. It is assumed that at least the elements of this technique are known [*S.M.*, Chapter 6], but a résumé will be given at this stage. It is, as the name implies, a technique for estimating how much of the total variation in a set of data can be attributed to one or more assignable causes of variation [*S.M.*, § 10·3], the remainder, not attributable to any assignable cause, being classed as the residual or error variation. It also provides for tests of significance (including the F-test), by which we can decide whether the assignable causes have probably resulted in real variation or whether the apparent variation ascribed to them is the result only of the chance causes which produce the error variation.

Consider the general situation in which there are b batches, k samples being taken from each batch, and n repeat analytical tests being carried out on each sample. Denote the variance of the analytical error by σ_0^2, the variance of the sampling error by σ_1^2, and the variance between batches by σ_2^2 (assuming the batches to be a random sample from a universe of batches). The object of the experiment is to estimate these three variances.

Table 4·1

PER CENT STRENGTH OF SAMPLES OF PASTE

Batch No.	Sample A		Sample B		Sample C		Batch total	Mean batch strength	Estimated batch yield
	Observations	Sum	Observations	Sum	Observations	Sum			
1	50·3 49·8	100·1	50·1 49·5	99·6	51·1 49·4	100·5	300·2	50·03	756
2	45·8 45·4	91·2	44·4 44·7	89·1	44·7 44·4	89·1	269·4	44·90	804
3	41·0 41·4	82·4	42·7 41·6	84·3	43·1 43·3	86·4	253·1	42·18	764
4	48·7 50·0	98·7	48·0 50·4	98·4	47·9 48·5	96·4	293·5	48·92	800
5	48·9 49·4	98·3	48·4 46·8	95·2	46·5 45·4	91·9	285·4	47·57	787
6	47·0 46·1	93·1	47·4 47·2	94·6	45·1 47·5	92·6	280·3	46·72	768
7	46·3 45·0	91·3	44·6 44·0	88·6	45·6 44·2	89·8	269·7	44·95	782
8	44·9 42·3	87·2	45·1 43·4	88·5	43·3 41·6	84·9	260·6	43·43	803
9	55·7 55·4	111·1	56·3 56·3	112·6	55·1 55·0	110·1	333·8	55·63	768
Total ..		853·4		850·9		841·7	2,546·0		7,032
Mean ..		47·4		47·3		46·8	47·1		781

The repeat analyses on each sample differ because of testing error only, and the variance within samples gives an estimate of σ_0^2. (The variance within samples is calculated by taking the sum of squares of the deviations of each observation from its own sample mean and dividing by the number of degrees of freedom, viz. $bk(n-1)$, there being $(n-1)$ for each of the bk samples.) The variance of the mean of the n repeat tests on each sample due to analytical error is σ_0^2/n. The k sample means from each batch will differ also because of the sampling error σ_1^2, and since sampling and testing errors are independent, their variances are additive, and the variance of each sample mean is $\sigma_1^2 + \sigma_0^2/n$. This quantity is estimated from the observations by the variance between sample means within batches. Extending the argument, the mean of the k samples per batch will have a variance of $(\sigma_1^2 + \sigma_0^2/n)/k$ due to sampling and testing errors. These means are subject also to the variance σ_2^2 between true batch means, giving $\sigma_2^2 + \sigma_1^2/k + \sigma_0^2/nk$ for the variance between the observed batch means.

Denoting an observation by y, the means of the sample and the batch to which it belongs by $\bar{y}_s$ and $\bar{y}_b$ respectively, and the mean of all the observations by $\bar{y}$, then the above results may be summed up as follows:

Source of variation	Observed variance	Quantity estimated	
Between means of batches	$\dfrac{\Sigma(\bar{y}_b - \bar{y})^2}{(b-1)}$	$\sigma_2^2 + \sigma_1^2/k + \sigma_0^2/kn$	(i)
Between means of samples about means of batches	$\dfrac{\Sigma(\bar{y}_s - \bar{y}_b)^2}{b(k-1)}$	$\sigma_1^2 + \sigma_0^2/n$	(ii)
Between repeat tests about sample means	$\dfrac{\Sigma(y - \bar{y}_s)^2}{bk(n-1)}$	σ_0^2	(iii)

In the computations of the analysis of variance, (i) is multiplied by kn and (ii) by n in order to make all the coefficients of σ_0^2 equal to unity, the reason being that each variance (called Mean Square when multiplied in this way) will then give an independent estimate of σ_0^2 when σ_2^2 and σ_1^2 are zero.

The quantities are conveniently set out in Table 4·101.

The quantities estimated by the mean square are usually referred to as the Expectations of the mean squares. The expectations when the number of tests per sample are not necessarily the same for all samples and the number of samples per batch are not necessarily the same for all batches are given in Appendix 4A.

Table 4·101

ANALYSIS OF VARIANCE

Source of variation	Degrees of freedom	Sum of squares*	Mean square and quantity estimated
Between batches	$(b-1)$	$kn\Sigma(\bar{y}_b - \bar{y})^2$	$(MS)_2 \rightarrow \sigma_0^2 + n\sigma_1^2 + kn\sigma_2^2$
Between samples within batches	$b(k-1)$	$n\Sigma(\bar{y}_s - \bar{y}_b)^2$	$(MS)_1 \rightarrow \sigma_0^2 + n\sigma_1^2$
Analytical error	$bk(n-1)$	$\Sigma(y - \bar{y}_s)^2$	$(MS)_0 \rightarrow \sigma_0^2$
Total	$bkn-1$	$\Sigma(y - \bar{y})^2$	

* In practice the sums of squares are more conveniently derived from the sample and batch totals, e.g. sum of squares between batches = $\Sigma(T_b - T)^2/kn$, and between samples = $\Sigma(T_s - T_b)^2/n$ [*S.M.*, Chapter 6].

If all samples and all batches are identical, $(MS)_0$, $(MS)_1$, and $(MS)_2$ are all estimates of σ_0^2 and will not differ significantly. If all batches are identical but the three samples from a batch differ because of sampling error, $(MS)_1$ and $(MS)_2$ will both tend to be greater than $(MS)_0$, since they are estimates of σ_0^2 plus a term due to sampling error; this term is $n\sigma_1^2$, where σ_1^2 is the variance associated with the sampling error. $(MS)_1$ and $(MS)_2$ are then both estimates of $\sigma_0^2 + n\sigma_1^2$ and will not differ significantly. If in addition there is real variation from batch to batch, $(MS)_2$ will tend to be greater than $(MS)_1$ since it is an estimate of $\sigma_0^2 + n\sigma_1^2$ plus a term attributable to the batch-to-batch variation. This term is $kn\sigma_2^2$, where σ_2^2 is the variance of the true batch averages.

In the tests of significance we calculate $F_1 = (MS)_1/(MS)_0$. If F_1 is greater than the tabulated value we conclude that there is a sampling error; if not, we may assume that σ_1^2 is negligible. If $F_2 = (MS)_2/(MS)_1$ is greater than the tabulated value we conclude that there is real batch-to-batch variation; if not, we may assume that σ_2^2 is negligible.

Analysis of Example 4·1

4·23. The calculations of the analysis of variance are given in Appendix 4C. The formal presentation of the analysis is given in Table 4·11.

Sampling and testing errors

4·24. The main purpose of the investigation was to obtain estimates of the variances, associated with testing error, sampling error, and batch-to-batch

Table 4·11

ANALYSIS OF VARIANCE OF TABLE 4·1

Source of variation	Degrees of freedom	Sum of squares	Mean square	Quantity estimated by the mean square
Between batches ..	8	792·88	99·11	$\sigma_0^2 + 2\sigma_1^2 + 6\sigma_2^2$
Between samples within batches	18	25·32	1·41	$\sigma_0^2 + 2\sigma_1^2$
Analytical error ..	27	20·17	0·75	σ_0^2
Total	53	838·37		

variation. The mean square 0·75 gives directly an estimate of σ_0^2 based on 27 degrees of freedom. 1·41 is an estimate of $\sigma_0^2 + 2\sigma_1^2$, whence $(1·41 - 0·75)/2 = 0·33$ is an estimate of σ_1^2. Finally, 99·11 is an estimate of $(\sigma_0^2 + 2\sigma_1^2 + 6\sigma_2^2)$, whence $(99·11 - 1·41)/6 = 16·28$ is an estimate of σ_2^2. The corresponding standard deviations are as follows:

$$0·866 \to \sigma_0 \qquad 0·574 \to \sigma_1 \qquad 4·03 \to \sigma_2$$

From a knowledge of the standard errors of analytical testing and of sampling we can devise suitable sampling and testing schemes to give any required degree of precision to the estimate of the composition of the batch. If a batch is sampled k times and n independent tests are made on each sample, the variance of the average for the batch will be, using the variances found in Example 4·1:

$$\frac{\sigma_1^2}{k} + \frac{\sigma_0^2}{kn} = \frac{0·33}{k} + \frac{0·75}{kn}$$

This formula also applies when the k samples are blended together, and a total of kn tests carried out on the blended sample. This assumes that the blending can be carried out without error.

The variance and standard error of the batch mean for various combinations of k and n, up to eight tests per batch, are given in Table 4·12.

A given value for the standard error can be achieved by different combinations of k and n; for example $(k = 2, n = 4)$ and $(k = 4, n = 1)$ give approximately the same standard error, although the latter involves only half the total number of tests. If, as in the present example, testing is much more expensive than sampling, the second arrangement is the more economical.

Table 4·12

VARIANCE OF THE BATCH MEAN

No. of samples k	No. of tests per sample n	Total No. of tests $N = kn$	Variance of batch mean	Standard error of batch mean
I	I	I	1·077	1·04
	2	2	0·704	0·84
	4	4	0·517	0·72
	8	8	0·423	0·65
2	I	2	0·538	0·73
	2	4	0·352	0·59
	4	8	0·258	0·51
4	I	4	0·269	0·52
	2	8	0·176	0·42

Economics of sampling and testing

4·241. In general, the costs of both sampling and testing must be taken into account in devising sampling schemes: the best scheme is that which gives the required accuracy with the minimum cost. We may take k samples and analyse each n times, or bulk the samples two or more at a time and carry out a total of $N = kn$ analyses. If mixing is perfect, the methods are equivalent for given values of k and N. When the samples are bulked $n = N/k$ is not necessarily integral.

The variance of the mean of k samples and n tests per sample is

$$V = (\sigma_1{}^2 + \sigma_0{}^2/n)/k \quad\dots\dots\dots\dots\dots\dots\dots(4\cdot1)$$

Let S be the cost of taking one sample and A the cost of carrying out one test. Then the total cost for k samples and kn tests is

$$C = k(S + nA) \quad\dots\dots\dots\dots\dots\dots(4\cdot2)$$

Substituting for k from Equation $(4\cdot1)$:

$$C = (\sigma_1{}^2 + \sigma_0{}^2/n)(S + nA)/V$$

$$= \frac{1}{V}(S\sigma_1{}^2 + A\sigma_0{}^2 + S\sigma_0{}^2/n + nA\sigma_1{}^2) \quad\dots\dots\dots\dots(4\cdot3)$$

This gives the total cost of sampling and testing for any stipulated variance V. The only unknown quantity is n, and to find the scheme for which C is a minimum we differentiate C with respect to n, equate the expression to zero, and solve for n:

$$\frac{dC}{dn} = -\frac{S\sigma_0{}^2}{Vn^2} + \frac{A\sigma_1{}^2}{V} = 0$$

giving
$$n = \frac{\sigma_0}{\sigma_1} \sqrt{\frac{S}{A}} \quad \dots\dots\dots\dots\dots\dots\dots(4\cdot4)$$

The quantity n, representing the number of repeat tests to be carried out on each sample, is thus independent of V and k. Given the estimates of the standard errors σ_0 and σ_1 and the ratio of the costs of sampling and testing S/A, the most economical sampling scheme is that for which the number of tests per sample is given by $(4\cdot4)$. The calculated value will not in general be integral; if the samples are not bulked it must be made integral, the nearest integral value being chosen.

Having found the optimum value for n, we substitute it in $(4\cdot1)$ and hence find the value of k which will give the required value of V. As an illustration, we derive the most economical schemes for the process of Example 4·1, using the values 0·866 and 0·574 found for σ_0 and σ_1. The required standard error of the batch mean is taken to be 0·5, corresponding to a variance of 0·25, and two cases are considered, one in which the ratio S/A is 0·1, and the other in which the ratio is 4·0.

(i) $S/A = 0\cdot1$
$$n = (0\cdot866/0\cdot574)\sqrt{0\cdot1} = 0\cdot477$$

On an average we require approximately one test on two samples. If the samples cannot be bulked then we must take $n = 1$, whence from Equation $(4\cdot1)$, $k = 4\cdot3$. Taking the next larger integer, $k = 5$, we conclude that the sampling scheme should provide for five samples per batch, each tested once. If the samples can be bulked, then we would bulk eight samples and test four times, since for $n = 0\cdot477$, $k \sim 8$. Another approximate solution is to take eight samples, bulk two at a time, and test each once.

(ii) $S/A = 4\cdot0$
$$n = (0\cdot866/0\cdot574)\sqrt{4} = 3\cdot02$$

This means that every sample should be tested three times. For $n = 3$, $k = 3$, and we require three samples. If the samples can be bulked we take three samples and test the bulk nine times.

In the sampling and analysis of chemicals, analysis will usually be much more expensive than sampling. But in the testing of rubber or synthetic fibres the expensive process is the preparation of the sample by compounding or spinning; subsequent physical testing is relatively easy.

Precision of estimates of variance

4·3. We have estimated the three variances σ_0^2, σ_1^2, and σ_2^2, associated with testing errors, sampling error, and batch variation. Being estimates they are subject to some uncertainty, and before using them as a basis for future action we must calculate this uncertainty. Conversely, in designing an experiment the ideal is to arrange its scale so that the experiment gives sufficient precision. These considerations are important because the estimates of σ_1^2 and σ_2^2 in a rather small experiment have a surprisingly large range of uncertainty or, in other words, widely spaced confidence limits [§ 2·363].

4·31. A convenient method of expressing the uncertainty of an estimate of any statistic is to calculate its confidence limits. The testing error σ_0^2 is estimated directly from the variance within samples, and as shown in § 2·363; the confidence limits for σ_0^2 can readily be found using tables of the χ^2 distribution. The confidence limits for σ^2 are $\phi s^2/\chi^2_{1-\frac{1}{2}a}$ and $\phi s^2/\chi^2_{\frac{1}{2}a}$; for 90% confidence ($a = 0\cdot10$) we use the 95% and 5% points of χ^2. The estimate s_0^2 of σ_0^2 is 0·75, based on 27 degrees of freedom, and from Table B the 5% and 95% points of χ^2, with 27 degrees of freedom, are 40·1 and 16·2 respectively. We then obtain:

Upper confidence limit $= 27 \times 0\cdot75/16\cdot2 = 1\cdot250$
Lower confidence limit $= 27 \times 0\cdot75/40\cdot1 = 0\cdot505$

We may therefore say, with 90% confidence, that the true value σ_0^2 lies within the range 0·505–1·250, or that σ_0 lies within the range 0·711–1·118.

4·32. The estimate of the sampling error variance σ_1^2 is not found directly but from the difference between two mean squares. It does not therefore follow the χ^2 distribution, and exact confidence limits are not available. Approximations have been derived, but they are not very accurate except for large numbers of degrees of freedom. Confidence limits are, however, readily calculable for the ratio σ_1^2/σ_0^2 as shown in Chapter 2 [§ 2·366].

If an accurate estimate of σ_0^2 is available it leads to confidence limits for σ_1^2, but otherwise we must be content with limits for the ratio $R = \sigma_1^2/\sigma_0^2$, and usually this will be sufficient. We may note that the ratio R enters into the formula giving the most economic arrangement for the number of tests per sample. The method of calculating the limits for a ratio of two variances was given in § 2·366. This method is applied in Appendix 4B to the ratio of two mean squares, from which the upper and lower confidence limits for R are derived. These limits are

$$\frac{1}{n}\left\{\frac{M_1}{M_0 F_{\frac{1}{2}a}} - 1\right\} \qquad \text{and} \qquad \frac{1}{n}\left\{\frac{M_1}{M_0 F_{1-\frac{1}{2}a}} - 1\right\}$$

where M_1 is the mean square between samples and M_0 the mean square of analytical error. To obtain the 90% limits we put $a = 0\cdot10$. $F_{1-\frac{1}{2}a}$ for ϕ_1 and

I

ϕ_2 degrees of freedom is equal to $1/F_{\frac{1}{2}a}$ for ϕ_2 and ϕ_1 degrees of freedom, that is, with the degrees of freedom reversed [§ **2·366** and Appendix 4B].

For Example 4·1, $n = 2$, $\phi_1 = 18$, $\phi_2 = 27$, $F_{\frac{1}{2}a} = 2·01$, and $F_{1-\frac{1}{2}a} = 1/2·13$, and the limits are:

$$\text{Lower limit for } R = R_1 = (0·94 - 1)/2 = -0·03$$
$$\text{Upper limit for } R = R_2 = (4·00 - 1)/2 = 1·50$$

The 90% confidence interval is thus $-0·03$ to $1·50$. Negative values of R cannot be real but may appear because of sampling fluctuations. We conclude that with slightly less than 90% confidence* the sampling error variance lies between zero and 1·5 times the testing error variance, the best estimate being $(1·41 - 0·75)/2(0·75) = 0·44$. In terms of the standard deviations:

$$\text{Lower limit of } \sigma_1/\sigma_0 = 0$$
$$\text{Upper limit of } \sigma_1/\sigma_0 = 1·22$$
$$\text{Best estimate of } \sigma_1/\sigma_0 = 0·66$$

These limits are quite wide: to establish closer limits for R it is necessary to have more degrees of freedom for both mean squares. If both degrees of freedom were increased to 120, the 90% confidence limits for $\sigma_1{}^2/\sigma_0{}^2$ would then be 0·47 to 0·88.

Note that since the lower limit is zero the data are consistent at the 5% probability level with the hypothesis that $\sigma_1{}^2$ is zero. This result agrees with the F-test carried out in the usual way, which gives a probability of between 5% and 10% on the Null Hypothesis.

The confidence limits may indicate that $\sigma_0{}^2$ and/or the ratio of $\sigma_1{}^2$ to $\sigma_0{}^2$ have not been estimated with sufficient precision. The remedy is to carry out further experimental work. A good indication of the additional samples and tests required can be obtained by increasing n and k in the above formulae until the required precision is obtained. Similar considerations may be used at the outset in order to have some guide as to the amount of work necessary, using some plausible values for $\sigma_0{}^2$ and $\sigma_1{}^2$ based on prior knowledge.

To sum up, the conclusions are as follows.

Analytical error. The standard deviation σ_0 probably (i.e. with 90% confidence) lies between 0·711 and 1·118, the best estimate being 0·866.

Sampling error. The ratio of the sampling error standard deviation to the analytical error standard deviation probably (i.e. with 90% confidence) lies between 0 and 1·22, the best estimate being 0·66.

Test of significance

4·33. A test of significance is applied when the object is to decide between two alternative hypotheses, the Null Hypothesis that the variation in experimental

*If we narrow the interval by using 0 instead of $-0·03$ for the lower limit we slightly reduce the probability that R lies in the interval.

conditions has no effect on the result of the trial, and the Alternative Hypothesis that the variation does affect the results. In Example 4 1 the experimenter might have set out to test the hypothesis that no appreciable sampling error exists (the Null Hypothesis) against the alternative that a sampling error does exist. He would then have applied the F-test to the mean squares for sampling error and analytical error. If the value of F were not significant he would have accepted the Null Hypothesis.

In Example 4·1 it is known from the nature of the product that some variation must exist, and there would be no point in testing the hypothesis that it did not exist. The object rather is to estimate the magnitude of the sampling error; the problem is one of estimation, not a test of a hypothesis. This is an important distinction, and before designing and analysing an experiment the experimenter should make sure what he wants to know. If the problem is one of estimation there is no point in carrying out a test of significance and, having found a non-significant value of F, concluding that no real effect exists. The results would be consistent with a hypothesis that this was so, but would equally be consistent with other hypotheses. A better procedure is to calculate the confidence limits for the quantity in question (e.g. a variance) and conclude that, with a given probability, the true value lies somewhere between these limits. The confidence interval may include zero, as in Example 4·1, and this means that with the appropriate probability the data are consistent with a true value of zero. To state the confidence limits is more informative than merely to give the results of a significance test. If the confidence limits are too wide the statistic is not estimated with sufficient precision and further experimental work will be required.

For some sampling problems the test of significance may be appropriate. A blending machine may be capable of mixing so perfectly that any variations are too small to be detected by the analytical method used. If an alteration in the method of running is made or a different raw material is used we may want to test whether the blender still functions as before or whether the change has affected its performance. The Null Hypothesis would be that its performance is as good as before, i.e. the sampling error may be taken as zero; the Alternative Hypothesis would be that the change has introduced a sampling error. It will often be found, however, that even when it is reasonable to test a Null Hypothesis it may be better to calculate confidence intervals and draw conclusions from these.

Example 4·2. Testing the bulk density of chalk
4·4. An instrument was being developed for the measurement of the bulk density of precipitated chalk, and it was proposed to use the machine in testing chalk for conformity with a specification. The development trials in

the maker's works suggested that the results obtained were sufficiently reproducible. It was decided to send a machine to each of a number of laboratories and to send samples taken from chalks covering a range of bulk densities to each laboratory for test. The main problem was to test whether different laboratories agreed in their average results. It could be assumed that the reproducibility of results would be about the same in all laboratories, and it was not necessary for each laboratory to carry out a large number of tests to give a reliable estimate of the reproducibility within laboratories because the information on all laboratories could be combined. It was also necessary to find whether the reproducibility within and between laboratories varied with the bulk density of the chalk and for this reason chalks of different densities were tested. The data used in this example represent only part of the investigation and relate to two chalks only.

There are four sources of variation: the variation between repeat tests in one laboratory, the variation between the average results obtained in the different laboratories, a possible sampling error, and the variation between the two chalks. The last is of a different nature from the other three; the two chalks were deliberately chosen to have different densities in order to investigate the testing error at different densities. Because of the nature of the test it was expected that the error would be proportional to the bulk density so that the coefficient of variation rather than the standard deviation was expected to be constant for chalks of different bulk densities. The appropriate transformation to equalise the variances for the different chalks is then logarithmic [§ 2·62].

4·41. Table 4·2 gives the logarithms of the bulk densities observed on two chalks in eleven laboratories, each of which carried out three tests on each chalk.

The first step is to test whether the standard deviation of the logarithm is the same for both chalks. This can be done for two sources of error: between repeat tests within laboratories, and between laboratory means. We therefore carry out the analysis of variance for these sources of variation for each chalk separately. The details are given in Appendix 4D; the analysis of variance table is shown in Table 4·21.

Since each laboratory mean is based on three tests the expectations of the mean squares are as shown. The estimates of σ_0^2 based on 22 degrees of freedom for the two chalks are:

$$\text{A:} \quad 0 \cdot 000010 \qquad \text{B:} \quad 0 \cdot 000007$$

These do not differ significantly.

The estimates of σ_1^2 are:

$$\text{A:} \quad (0 \cdot 000315 - 0 \cdot 000010)/3 = 0 \cdot 000102$$
$$\text{B:} \quad (0 \cdot 000255 - 0 \cdot 000007)/3 = 0 \cdot 000083$$

Table 4·2

INVESTIGATION OF BULK DENSITY OF CHALK

Log (Bulk density/10)

Labora-tory	Chalk A				Chalk B				Mean of chalks A and B
	Observations			Mean	Observations			Mean	
1	0·851	0·851	0·851	0·851	0·681	0·686	0·681	0·683	0·767
2	0·863	0·866	0·860	0·863	0·690	0·690	0·695	0·692	0·777
3	0·854	0·854	0·854	0·854	0·686	0·686	0·690	0·687	0·771
4	0·863	0·869	0·869	0·867	0·690	0·690	0·690	0·690	0·779
5	0·869	0·872	0·872	0·871	0·699	0·703	0·699	0·700	0·786
6	0·875	0·869	0·872	0·872	0·686	0·690	0·686	0·687	0·780
7	0·845	0·857	0·851	0·851	0·672	0·672	0·681	0·675	0·763
8	0·869	0·869	0·872	0·870	0·699	0·695	0·695	0·696	0·783
9	0·857	0·857	0·857	0·857	0·681	0·681	0·681	0·681	0·769
10	0·869	0·881	0·875	0·875	0·695	0·690	0·690	0·692	0·783
11	0·881	0·881	0·881	0·881	0·708	0·708	0·708	0·708	0·795
Mean				0·865				0·690	0·777

Table 4·21

ANALYSIS OF VARIANCE: CHALKS A AND B SEPARATELY

Source of variation	Degrees of freedom	Chalk A		Chalk B		Expectation of mean square
		Sum of squares	Mean square	Sum of squares	Mean square	
Between laboratories	10	0·003151	0·000315	0·002551	0·000255	$\sigma_0{}^2 + 3\sigma_1{}^2$
Within laboratories	22	0·000216	0·000010	0·000147	0·000007	$\sigma_0{}^2$
Total ..	32	0·003367		0·002698		

These obviously do not differ significantly. We cannot however apply the F-test to compare these estimates of σ_1^2; in doubtful cases it would be necessary to calculate the confidence limits of σ_1/σ_0.

The data are consistent with the hypothesis that the coefficient of variation is the same for both chalks. We may therefore analyse the data as a whole, the derived variances being applicable to both chalks. Combining the information on the two chalks we obtain from Table 4·21 an estimate of 0·0000082 based on 44 degrees of freedom for the reproducibility within laboratories. This corresponds to a standard deviation of 0·0029. To convert to ordinary units we take the antilogarithm, which is 1·0067. Applying the limits $\pm0·0029$ to the logarithm of a bulk density is equivalent to multiplying and dividing the actual bulk density by 1·0067. It is seen, therefore, that a standard deviation of 0·0029 on a log scale corresponds to a standard deviation (or coefficient of variation) of approximately 0·67% on the natural scale. This indicates that the reproducibility within laboratories is exceedingly good.

This reproducibility within laboratories, however, does not represent the whole error of the test; we recognise two other sources of error.

(i) Bias between laboratories. All laboratories may not interpret the test procedure or apply the method in exactly the same way; consequently some laboratories will tend to produce higher results on the average than other laboratories. We denote the variance between laboratories by σ_1^2.

(ii) All laboratories test the two chalks A and B. If σ_0^2, the reproducibility within laboratories, represents the only variation within laboratories, then, however large the bias between them, the laboratories will agree, within the limits expected from the error σ_0^2 in reporting the difference between the bulk densities of the two chalks. It is possible, however, that the difference* between chalks A and B will not so agree between laboratories, in other words, that there will be an interaction between samples and laboratories. Firstly, samples of each chalk when tested by the various laboratories might differ either because of errors in sampling the original bulk or because of changes in the sample on keeping. Secondly, since the total of six tests in one laboratory on the two samples were not carried out in a random order and all repeats on one sample were completed before the second sample, differences may have arisen between the two samples due to the effects of time trends. The repeat tests would not then be subject to the whole of the testing error, whereas comparisons of two laboratories would include the additional source of error.

* A constant difference between logarithms implies a constant ratio of bulk densities, and vice versa.

We now form Table 4·22.

Table 4·22

DIFFERENCE AND SUM OF LOG DENSITY OF CHALKS A AND B

Laboratory	Mean of log (density) = x		Difference A − B	Sum A + B
	A	B		
1	0·851	0·683	0·168	1·534
2	0·863	0·692	0·171	1·555
3	0·854	0·687	0·167	1·541
4	0·867	0·690	0·177	1·557
5	0·871	0·700	0·171	1·571
6	0·872	0·687	0·185	1·559
7	0·851	0·675	0·176	1·526
8	0·870	0·696	0·174	1·566
9	0·857	0·681	0·176	1·538
10	0·875	0·692	0·183	1·567
11	0·881	0·708	0·173	1·589
Total ..	9·512	7·591	1·921	17·103
Mean ..	0·865	0·690	0·175	

We may consider the interaction as measuring an additional error, e.g. sampling error, between the samples A and B which may vary from one laboratory to another, and we assume this error has a variance of $\sigma_2{}^2$. The sum or difference between two means of three repeat results on the samples A and B will then have a variance of $2\sigma_2{}^2 + \frac{2}{3}\sigma_0{}^2$ due to these sources of error. The difference is not affected by the bias between laboratories, but the sum is; the variance of the sums of A and B between laboratories is therefore $4\sigma_1{}^2 + 2\sigma_2{}^2 + \frac{2}{3}\sigma_0{}^2$. The reason for the multiplier 4 is that the bias applies equally to the two samples, so that in the sum the bias will be multiplied by two and the variance of $2x$ is four times the variance of x.

On calculation we find:

(i) Variance within repeat tests .. $= 0.000008$ (estimates $\sigma_0{}^2$)

(ii) Variance of the difference between means of A and B between laboratories $\Big\}$ $= 0.000032$ (estimates $\frac{2}{3}\sigma_0{}^2 + 2\sigma_2{}^2$)

(iii) Variance of the sums of the means of A and B between laboratories $\Big\}$ $= 0.000348$ (estimates $\frac{2}{3}\sigma_0{}^2 + 4\sigma_1{}^2 + 2\sigma_2{}^2$)

Multiplying (ii) and (iii) by $\frac{3}{2}$ in order to make all variances estimates of σ_0^2 when σ_1^2 and σ_2^2 are zero, we obtain the following analysis of variance.

Table 4·23

ANALYSIS OF VARIANCE: BOTH CHALKS

Source of variation	Degrees of freedom	Sum of squares	Mean square	Expectation of mean square
Between chalks ..	1	0·503040	0·503040	—
Between labora- tories	10	0·005223	0·000522	$\sigma_0^2 + 3\sigma_2^2 + 6\sigma_1^2$
Interaction: labora- tories and chalks	10	0·000478	0·000048	$\sigma_0^2 + 3\sigma_2^2$
Within repeats ..	44	0·000363	0·000008	σ_0^2
Total	65	0·509104	—	—

It is usually better from the standpoint of arithmetical computation to derive this analysis of variance by the equivalent method of Appendix 4D, where we deal with totals and not means. The details of the calculations are given in this appendix. In any case, where there are more than two samples the difference method given above is cumbersome and lengthy.

The estimates of σ_0^2, σ_1^2, and σ_2^2 are:

$$\sigma_0^2 = 0·000008 \qquad \sigma_0 = 0·0029 \qquad v \text{ (coefficient of variation)} = 0·67\%$$
$$\sigma_1^2 = 0·000079 \qquad \sigma_1 = 0·0089 \qquad v \text{ (coefficient of variation)} = 2·1\%$$
$$\sigma_2^2 = 0·000013 \qquad \sigma_2 = 0·0036 \qquad v \text{ (coefficient of variation)} = 0·83\%$$

The main error is clearly due to the bias between laboratories. The error called interaction is only slightly larger than that of the reproducibility, and both are small compared with the variation between laboratories. If it is required to test the existence of σ_1^2 we use the F-test to compare the mean square between laboratories with the interaction mean square; to test the existence of σ_2^2 we compare the mean square of the interaction with the mean square within repeats. Both values of F are highly significant.

The conclusion from the investigation is that, while the laboratories vary among themselves by more than is accounted for by the variation between replicate tests, this variation is not excessive, and the test is precise enough for practical use.

The above experiment was carried out by the Committee of the British Standards Institution engaged in drafting B.S. 1460, *Determination of Bulk Density of Precipitated Chalk*. The results are quoted by permission of the Director, British Standards Institution.

Example 4·3. Testing dyestuffs

4·5. In Example 4·2 the main objective was to compare the results obtained by a number of laboratories upon the assumption that the reproducibility among repeat tests in one laboratory was the same for all. It was sufficient for each laboratory to carry out three tests on each of two samples; since there were eleven laboratories, the experiment provides an adequate number of degrees of freedom for the testing error, or "within laboratories" variance. In Example 4·3 only two laboratories are concerned, but they are studied in greater detail because we want to compare them for both relative bias and reproducibility. For this reason more samples were used and more repeat tests were carried out on each.

4·51. The investigation relates to the assessment of the "strength" of different batches of a dyestuff, strength being a measure of colouring power. This is assessed by a dye test, in which a piece of cloth is dyed with a standard concentration of the dyestuff under carefully controlled conditions, the depth of colour achieved being assessed by visual comparison with a standard. The test clearly requires the services of a highly trained operator; even so it contains a subjective element. The experimental arrangement was as follows:

A large sample was taken from each of six batches of a dyestuff, covering the range of variation normally encountered in manufacture. Each sample was well mixed and twelve identical sub-samples were taken, six of these being sent to each laboratory. The 36 samples (6 per batch) were submitted to each laboratory in random order over a period of several weeks in the normal manner for routine testing so that the laboratory was not aware that they were special samples. Points to be noted in these arrangements are:

(i) The two laboratories were widely separated and they were therefore completely independent.

(ii) The samples were tested over a period of several weeks, and the experimental error included all sources normally encountered.

(iii) The materials tested covered the normal range of variation encountered in routine production.

(iv) Enough replicates of each batch by each method were tested to give an adequate estimate of experimental error for each laboratory separately.

(v) The number of repeat tests was the same in every case, and each batch was tested by both laboratories. This gives a balanced design, resulting in maximum efficiency, and leads to ease in interpretation.

(vi) The samples for testing were coded, so that their identity was not known to the laboratories, and they were submitted as routine samples.

4·52. There are six independent measurements on each of the six batches by each laboratory, so that we can estimate:

(i) The error of dye trial for each of the two laboratories, with 30 degrees of freedom for each.

(ii) The difference (bias) between the two laboratories, and the variation of this difference from batch to batch.

The design is similar to the one used in the previous example: batches in Example 4·3 correspond to laboratories in Example 4·2, and laboratories in Example 4·3 correspond to samples of chalk in Example 4·2.

4·53. The complete computations are given in Appendix 4E. The following is a summary of the essential points.

Table 4·3 gives the complete set of results, the units being strength as a percentage of a standard.

Experimental errors

4·54. From the variation within batches for each laboratory we find the standard deviation corresponding to the testing errors.

Laboratories	Variance	Standard deviation
A	7·164	2·68
B	4·469	2·11

These are of the expected order of magnitude.

We test the hypothesis that the two laboratories have the same experimental error. The F-test (double-sided, § **2·364**) shows that the variances A and B do not differ significantly, and the two are combined to give an overall estimate of 5·816 for the variance, or 2·41 for the standard deviation.

Comparison of laboratories

4·55. The differences (A − B) in Table 4·3 are used to determine whether the two laboratories get results which differ by more than can be accounted for by the experimental errors. The results may differ in two ways:

(i) There may be a consistent bias, so that one laboratory always tends to get higher results than the other; such bias may sometimes be masked by the random errors, but it may exist on the average.

Table 4·3

PERCENTAGE STRENGTH OF DYESTUFFS SAMPLES

Batch	Result		Average (less 90)			Difference
	A	B	A	B	A + B	A − B
I	92·0	94·5				
	93·0	93·0				
	90·0	91·0				
	88·5	89·0				
	90·0	96·5				
	90·0	88·0	0·583	2·000	2·583	− 1·417
II	95·0	89·0				
	90·5	90·0				
	96·0	92·5				
	96·0	88·5				
	87·0	91·5				
	90·0	91·5	2·417	0·500	2·917	1·917
III	96·0	88·5				
	90·0	93·5				
	90·0	93·5				
	90·0	88·0				
	90·0	92·5				
	90·0	91·5	1·000	1·250	2·250	− 0·250
IV	97·0	100·0				
	100·0	99·0				
	100·0	100·0				
	95·0	98·0				
	98·0	95·0				
	100·0	97·5	8·333	8·250	16·583	0·083
V	92·5	91·5				
	93·0	93·0				
	90·0	90·0				
	88·5	92·5				
	90·0	89·0				
	87·0	91·0	0·167	1·167	1·334	− 1·000
VI	100·0	98·5				
	97·0	100·0				
	100·0	98·0				
	92·0	100·0				
	100·0	96·5				
	100·0	98·0	8·167	8·500	16·667	− 0·333
Average overall			3·445	3·611		− 0·166

(ii) On some batches A may give higher results than B, and on other batches B higher results than A, these differences being too great to be accounted for by random errors. This may be called a "variable bias" as opposed to the consistent bias, and will appear as an interaction between laboratories and batches. Both types may operate simultaneously.

It is possible for a variable bias to arise because all six batches have varying degrees of purity, different impurities affecting the two laboratories in different ways. A variable bias of this type may arise when two analytical methods are compared. An example of this is considered later [see § 4·62].

The data can be treated by analysis of variance methods; the calculations are given in Appendix 4E, leading to the following analysis of variance table.

Table 4·31

ANALYSIS OF VARIANCE OF TABLE 4·3

Source of variation	Degrees of freedom	Sum of squares	Mean square
Between batches .. B	5	828·36	165·67
Between laboratories L	1	0·50	0·50
Interaction .. BL	5	20·08	4·02
Residual = Experimental error	60	348·98	5·82
Total	71	1,197·92	—

The mean square between batches is of no interest in the present investigation. The mean squares for L and BL are less than the error variance and are thus not significant, i.e. there is no evidence for the existence of either a constant or a variable bias, and the two laboratories appear to be equivalent.

The mean squares corresponding to B, L, and BL can be obtained from the sums and differences given in Table 4·3 in the same way as in Example 4·2. The reader is recommended to do this, because it assists in a greater understanding of the analysis of variance.

Example 4·4. Sampling and analysis of a fertiliser

4·6. The following experiment (actually part of a much larger experiment) is designed to investigate the errors of sampling and analysing a compound fertiliser for the percentage of potash (expressed as K_2O). Two methods of analysis are involved: one (A), the method prescribed in the specification, is lengthy but accurate; the other (R) is a rapid method used for plant control and may not have the same accuracy as A. Eight batches each contained in a number of bags were sampled by inserting an auger into a bag chosen at random from each batch, the sampling being repeated next day; it could be safely assumed that no systematic difference existed between the two samples, i.e. there is no tendency for the first sample to be consistently higher or lower than the second. Each sample was carefully subdivided into two sub-samples which were analysed in separate laboratories, one using method A and the other method R.

The results are given in Table 4·4.

Table 4·4

DATA OF EXAMPLE 4·4

Sample	S_1		S_2		Total	
Method	A	R	A	R	A	R
Batch						
1	15·6	15·5	15·5	15·4	31·1	30·9
2	15·4	14·9	15·2	15·0	30·6	29·9
3	15·3	15·4	14·6	14·6	29·9	30·0
4	15·0	15·5	15·0	15·5	30·0	31·0
5	15·5	15·0	15·4	15·1	30·9	30·1
6	14·8	14·8	15·0	14·8	29·8	29·6
7	14·9	15·0	14·9	15·3	29·8	30·3
8	15·0	15·8	15·2	15·8	30·2	31·6
Total ..					242·3	243·4
Average					15·14	15·21

4·61. The sources of variation are shown in the following analysis:

Source of variation	Degrees of freedom
Between batch means B	7
Bias between analytical methods M ..	1
Interaction BM	7
Sampling error S..	8
Analytical error	8
Total	31

If for each batch the two tests for A were carried out on one sample and the two tests for R were carried out on the other, the design and analysis would be similar to the previous two examples with sampling and analytical error combined to give an error variance based on 16 degrees of freedom.

The additional feature in this example is that, for each batch, one test under A and one under R are made on one sample, and the other tests on another sample, thus enabling a direct estimate to be made of the sampling error. This is explained in detail in § **4·62**.

The physical interpretation is that the main effect represents a bias between the results obtained by methods A and R. It is possible however that this bias may not be the same for every batch; there may for example be another constituent, present in variable amount, which affects one method but not the other, or affects the two to different extents. It can be assumed that the standard method is not so affected (elaborate and accurate methods usually involve the elimination of all elements likely to interfere with the final determination), but it may be that the rapid method is affected. Such a state of affairs would result in a variable bias between methods, which appears as an interaction between batches and methods. It is essentially an additional source of analytical error in method R.

4·62. Let us now consider how the different factors affect the various sub-totals or averages. The four results for each batch may be set out in a 2×2 table as in Table 4·41.

Table 4·41

ARRANGEMENT OF TEST ON EACH BATCH

Method	Sample		Mean
	1	2	
A	A_1	A_2	$\bar{A}$
R	R_1	R_2	$\bar{R}$
Mean ..	S_1	S_2	M

Assume for the moment that the reproducibility is the same for both methods, and denote the variance by σ_0^2; denote the sampling error variance by σ_1^2.

The mean values S_1 and S_2 differ because of sampling error; if this were the only reason for the difference each would be subject to a variance σ_1^2, and the difference, $S_1 - S_2$, would have a variance $2\sigma_1^2$. But both S_1 and S_2.

being averages of two analyses, have analytical error variance $\sigma_0^2/2$, so that $S_1 - S_2$ has a variance from this source of σ_0^2. Since S_1 and S_2 are averaged over both methods they are not affected by any bias between methods. Sampling and analytical errors act independently, so that the total variance of $S_1 - S_2$ is $\sigma_0^2 + 2\sigma_1^2$, and this is the expected value of the mean square between samples in the analysis of variance.

The difference $\bar{A} - \bar{R}$ is similarly affected by analytical error but not by sampling error. It is equal to the bias appropriate to the batch plus a random component due to analytical error. If the bias is not the same for all batches it may be split into a constant component (the average bias) and one which varies from batch to batch; let the true variance of the latter be σ_2^2; this applies to method R only, since method A is known to be free from bias. The difference $\bar{A} - \bar{R}$ thus varies from batch to batch round a mean value (the average bias) with variance $\sigma_0^2 + \sigma_2^2$,* and this is the expected value of the mean square for the interaction between batches and methods.

The average value of $\bar{A} - \bar{R}$ over all batches is equal to the constant bias D plus random components due to variable bias and analytical error. Sampling errors do not arise in the comparison of methods, and D has a variance of $\frac{1}{8}\sigma_0^2 + \frac{1}{8}\sigma_2^2$ due to σ_0^2 and σ_2^2. The expectation of the mean square is $\sigma_0^2 + \sigma_2^2 + Q$, Q being a quantity corresponding to the true difference between methods, analogous in form to a variance, but since D is not a random quantity it is not an estimate of any true variance. Q is in fact equal to $8D^2$, as will be seen in Chapter 7, but its exact composition does not matter here.

The interaction between samples and methods for each batch must be due to testing error only, and its mean square with eight degrees of freedom is $(\Sigma d_i^2/4)/8$, where $d_i = (A_1 - A_2) - (R_1 - R_2)$ for the ith batch. The variance of d is $4\sigma_0^2$, so that the mean square has expectation σ_0^2.

There remains only the variation between batches; this is seen to be affected by analytical and sampling errors, by variable bias, and by the real variation between batches. The mean square has the expectation $\sigma_0^2 + 2\sigma_1^2 + \sigma_2^2 + B$, where B is a quantity dependent on the true batch-to-batch variation.

4·63. Details of the calculations are given in Appendix 4F, leading to the analysis of variance of Table 4·42.

The experiment does not provide for the separate estimation of the reproducibility of methods A and R. If σ_A^2 and σ_R^2 are the reproducibility variances for methods A and R, the variance σ_0^2 is $\frac{1}{2}(\sigma_A^2 + \sigma_R^2)$. If it were known that σ_A^2 and σ_R^2 were the same or differed only very slightly it would

---

* If it is not known that one method is free from bias the assumption has to be made that the σ_2^2 operates independently on both methods; the difference $\bar{A} - \bar{R}$ will then vary from batch to batch with a variance of $\sigma_0^2 + 2\sigma_2^2$.

Table 4·42

(Derived from Table 4·4)

ANALYSIS OF VARIANCE

Source of variation	Degrees of freedom	Sum of squares	Mean square	Expectation of mean square
Between batches B	7	1·4522	0·2075	$\sigma_0{}^2 + 2\sigma_1{}^2 + \sigma_2{}^2 + B$
Between methods				
A and R .. M	1	0·0378	0·0378	$\sigma_0{}^2 + \sigma_2{}^2 + Q$
Variable bias .. BM	7	1·0697	0·1528	$\sigma_0{}^2 + \sigma_2{}^2$
Sampling error S	8	0·6175	0·0772	$\sigma_0{}^2 + 2\sigma_1{}^2$
Analytical error A	8	0·0775	0·0097	$\sigma_0{}^2$
Total	31	3·2547		

be legitimate to write $\sigma_0{}^2$ for the common value, as is done in Table 4·42; otherwise it is not strictly valid to carry out the significance tests using this error variance. But it is known that if the experiment is symmetrical, as in Example 4·4, and if the two variances are not widely different, the procedure is approximately correct, i.e. the conclusions from the significance tests will be only slightly in error. It was known from past experience that the error variances for methods A and R did not differ widely, and no great error is committed by using a common value $\sigma_0{}^2$.

From Table 4·42 we obtain the following estimates:

$$\sigma_0{}^2 = 0·0097 \qquad \sigma_0 = 0·098$$
$$\sigma_1{}^2 = 0·0338 \qquad \sigma_1 = 0·184$$
$$\sigma_2{}^2 = 0·1431 \qquad \sigma_2 = 0·378$$

There is thus an appreciable sampling error and there is also an appreciable source of error represented by $\sigma_2{}^2$ affecting method R. Since it is known that method A is unbiased, it can be used in testing material for conformity with the specification. Method R is unsatisfactory even for plant control; however many times the analysis is repeated on one batch there is still a considerable uncertainty due to the unknown value of the bias appropriate to that batch, this uncertainty being represented by the variance $\sigma_2{}^2$, regardless of the number of analyses carried out.

We can thus estimate the uncertainty in the observed value for the composition of a batch. If k samples are taken and each is analysed n times we have:

Variance of average:

Analytical method A   .. $\dfrac{\sigma_0^2}{kn} + \dfrac{\sigma_1^2}{k}$

Analytical method R   .. $\dfrac{\sigma_0^2}{kn} + \dfrac{\sigma_1^2}{k} + \sigma_2^2$

These are compared for various values of n and k in Table 4·43.

Table 4·43

STANDARD ERRORS OF AVERAGE BATCH COMPOSITION

k	n	kn	σ_0^2/kn	σ_1^2/k	Variance		Standard error	
					A	R	A	R
1	1	1	0·0097	0·0338	0·0435	0·1866	0·208	0·432
1	2	2	0·0048	0·0338	0·0386	0·1817	0·196	0·426
2	1	2	0·0048	0·0169	0·0217	0·1648	0·147	0·406
2	2	4	0·0024	0·0169	0·0193	0·1624	0·139	0·403
4	1	4	0·0024	0·0084	0·0108	0·1539	0·104	0·392

It is most economical, assuming sampling to be much less expensive than testing, to take a number of samples and analyse each once only; this is because the sampling error is large. With method R there is a large uncertainty, due to the error of the method, whose magnitude in any particular batch cannot be determined by method R alone. The result is that repeating the sampling and analysis has little effect on the standard error, which cannot be less than $\sqrt{0·1431} = 0·378$, however many samples and analyses are used. Note that one analysis on one sample by method A is better than the average of any number by method R so far as accuracy is concerned.

4·64. Before going on to consider the significance of the variation between batches, we note that the interaction BM is significantly large compared with the residual (analytical) error A. While this implies significant variations from batch to batch in the observed results by one or both methods, these may not, for the reasons discussed above, represent variations in K_2O content, but in some other constituent which affects method R. If we are interested only in the variation in K_2O between batches it is necessary (in the present instance) to analyse the results for method A only. This may be left to the reader.

K

The expectations indicate the appropriate error mean square to assess the significance of any given mean square. In Table 4·42 no single mean square exists against which the mean square between batches can be tested. Although in this particular example, for the reasons given above, we would use the information on the analytical results by method A to assess the variation between batches, there may be other examples where we would require to assess a mean square, such as that between batches, directly. An appropriate error mean square may be obtained by a combination of mean squares. For example (BM + S − A) has the expectation $\sigma_0{}^2 + 2\sigma_1{}^2 + \sigma_2{}^2$, which is appropriate for testing B. An approximate method exists for assigning degrees of freedom to this combined mean square in order to use the F-test to assess B. This method is given in detail in [4·1], to which the reader is referred.

Conclusions

4·7. In this chapter we have considered only simple experiments, introducing the essential features of good design. The requirements are partly technical— for example adequate sampling and control of sources of variation other than those being studied—and partly statistical. The latter class includes as very important features:

(i) The use of balanced designs; by this means maximum efficiency is assured, the conclusions are more easily drawn, and the separate factors and their interactions are capable of independent assessment with the minimum of subsidiary assumptions. The calculations are also simplified.

(ii) A clear preliminary statement of what the experiment is required to do.

(iii) Careful consideration of the physical meaning of effects and especially of interactions, and interpretation of these in terms which have a meaning to the experimenter.

(iv) Study of the conclusions from the statistical analysis and their interpretation in physical terms, followed by a suggested breakdown or rearrangement of the original data so as to make the conclusions clear.

(v) Assessment of the uncertainties of the quantities estimated, in particular, calculation of confidence limits for these quantities. This shows at once how accurate or otherwise the estimates are, and thus whether the experiment was large enough for the purpose in mind.

REFERENCE

[4·1] JOHNSON, L. P. V., and KEEPING, E. S. "Composite Mean Squares and their Degrees of Freedom." *Applied Statistics*, 1, 202–5, 1952.

Appendix 4A

EXPECTATION OF MEAN SQUARES WITH UNEQUAL NUMBERS OF OBSERVATIONS IN THE GROUPS

Sampling and testing error

For k samples and n_j tests in the jth sample, the expectations of the mean squares [given also in *S.M.*, Appendix 6B] are as follows:

Table 4A·1

EXPECTATIONS OF MEAN SQUARES

Source of variation	Degrees of freedom	Expectation of mean square
Between samples.. ..	$k - 1$	$\sigma_0^2 + \bar{n}_1\sigma_1^2$
Analytical error	$\Sigma(n_j - 1)$	σ_0^2

where $\sigma_0^2 =$ variance of analytical error

$\sigma_1^2 =$ variance of sampling error

$\bar{n}_1 = (N - \Sigma n_j^2/N)/(k - 1)$ ....(4A·1)

$N =$ total number of tests $= \Sigma n_j$ ....(4A·2)

When there are b batches, let k_i be the number of samples for the ith batch, N_i the total number of tests on the ith batch, and n_{ij} the number of tests on the jth sample in the ith batch. Then the expectations of the mean squares are:

Table 4A·2

EXPECTATIONS OF MEAN SQUARES

Source of variation	Degrees of freedom	Expectation of mean square
Between batches.. ..	$b - 1$	$\sigma_0^2 + \bar{n}_2\sigma_1^2 + \bar{N}\sigma_2^2$
Between samples.. ..	$\Sigma(k_i - 1)$	$\sigma_0^2 + \bar{n}_1\sigma_1^2$
Analytical error	$\Sigma\Sigma(n_{ji} - 1)$	σ_0^2

where:

(i) $\sigma_2^2 =$ variance between batches.

(ii) The degrees of freedom for analytical error are summed over *all* samples.

(iii) $\bar{n}_1 = \sum_{i=1}^{b} \left(N_i - \sum_{j=1}^{k_i} n_{ij}^2/N_i \right) \bigg/ \sum_{i=1}^{b} (k_i - 1)$. (This is derived by summing the numerator of $\bar{n}_1$ of Equation (4A·1) for all batches and dividing by the total number of degrees of freedom.)

(iv) $\bar{N} = \left(N - \sum\limits_{i=1}^{b} N_i{}^2/N \right)\Big/(b-1)$, where $N = \Sigma N_i$, i.e. the grand total
of the observations.

(v) $\bar{n}_2 = \sum\limits_{i=1}^{b} \left[\left(\sum\limits_{j=1}^{k_i} n_{ij}{}^2 \right)\left(\frac{1}{N_i} - \frac{1}{N} \right) \right]\Big/(b-1)$

Methods for calculating the confidence limits for σ_0, σ_1 and σ_2 are given
in *S.M.* (Third Edition), Chapter 6.

Appendix 4B

CONFIDENCE LIMITS FOR THE RATIO OF TWO VARIANCES
ESTIMATED FROM AN ANALYSIS OF VARIANCE

IF V_s and V_0 are estimates of two variances $\sigma_s{}^2$ and $\sigma_0{}^2$ based on ϕ_1 and ϕ_2
degrees of freedom, then it was shown in § **2·366** that the $100(1-a)\%$
confidence limits for the estimate of the ratio $\sigma_s{}^2/\sigma_0{}^2$ are

Lower limit: $\qquad\qquad \dfrac{V_s}{V_0}\Big/F\tfrac{1}{2}a(\phi_1, \phi_2)$ ....(4B·1)

Upper limit: $\qquad\qquad \dfrac{V_s}{V_0}F\tfrac{1}{2}a(\phi_2, \phi_1)$ ....(4B·11)

These considerations may be applied directly to the ratio of two mean
squares in an analysis of variance. For a sampling experiment like Example
4·1, if V_s denotes the mean square between samples and V_0 the mean square
due to testing error, the confidence limits for the ratio are as above. For
Example 4·1 V_s is a function of two variances and estimates $\sigma_0{}^2 + n\sigma_1{}^2$
$= \sigma_0{}^2(1 + nR)$, where $R = \sigma_1{}^2/\sigma_0{}^2$ and $\sigma_1{}^2$ denotes the variance due to
sampling errors only, and $\sigma_0{}^2$ the variance due to testing error only. The ratio
of the mean squares is then $(1 + nR)$. Denote this by M. Then

$$R = (M-1)/n \quad ....(4B\cdot2)$$

The confidence limits for M are as (4B·1), with M in place of V_s/V_0.

Substituting these limits for M in (4B·2), we obtain the confidence limits
for R, which are

Lower limit: $\qquad\qquad \dfrac{1}{n}\left\{\dfrac{M}{F\tfrac{1}{2}a(\phi_1, \phi_2)} - 1\right\}$ ....(4B·3)

Upper limit: $\qquad\qquad \dfrac{1}{n}\left\{MF\tfrac{1}{2}a(\phi_2, \phi_1) - 1\right\}$ ....(4B·31)

Multiplying (4B·3) and (4B·31) by the estimate of $\sigma_0{}^2$ gives approximate
confidence limits for $\sigma_1{}^2$ (see *S.M.*, Third Edition, Chapter 6).

Appendix 4C
COMPUTATION FOR EXAMPLE 4·1

4C·1. Table 4C·1 gives the data of Table 4·1, transformed for ease of working into $x = (\% \text{ strength} - 40)$.

Table 4C·1
(Based on Table 4·1)
PER CENT STRENGTH OF SAMPLES OF PASTE

Batch No.	Sample A			Sample B			Sample C			Batch total	Batch mean strength
			Sum			Sum			Sum		
1	10·3	9·8	20·1	10·1	9·5	19·6	11·1	9·4	20·5	60·2	10·03
2	5·8	5·4	11·2	4·4	4·7	9·1	4·7	4·4	9·1	29·4	4·90
3	1·0	1·4	2·4	2·7	1·6	4·3	3·1	3·3	6·4	13·1	2·18
4	8·7	10·0	18·7	8·0	10·4	18·4	7·9	8·5	16·4	53·5	8·92
5	8·9	9·4	18·3	8·4	6·8	15·2	6·5	5·4	11·9	45·4	7·57
6	7·0	6·1	13·1	7·4	7·2	14·6	5·1	7·5	12·6	40·3	6·72
7	6·3	5·0	11·3	4·6	4·0	8·6	5·6	4·2	9·8	29·7	4·95
8	4·9	2·3	7·2	5·1	3·4	8·5	3·3	1·6	4·9	20·6	3·43
9	15·7	15·4	31·1	16·3	16·3	32·6	15·1	15·0	30·1	93·8	15·63
Total	68·6	64·8	133·4	67·0	63·9	130·9	62·4	59·3	121·7	386·0	

The calculations for the analysis of variance are as follows:

(1) Correction for mean $= 386·0^2/54$ $= 2759·19$

Crude sums of squares

(2) Total sum of squares of all 54 observations $= 3597·54$

(3) Sum of squares between batches =
$(60·2^2 + 29·4^2 + \ldots + 93·8^2)/6$ $= 3552·07$

Corrected sums of squares

(4) Total $= (2) - (1)$ $= 838·35$

(5) Between batches $= (3) - (1)$ $= 792·88$

Testing error

4C·2. This may be estimated from the difference between the two results in each sample. The variance is found by squaring these differences, adding, and dividing by 2×27 (27 = number of pairs of tests, see *S.M.*, § 3·341). The working detail is shown in Table 4C·2, where w denotes the difference between duplicates.

Table 4C·2

CALCULATIONS FOR SUM OF SQUARES OF ANALYTICAL ERROR

Batch No.	Sample A		Sample B		Sample C		Batch total w^2
	w	w^2	w	w^2	w	w^2	
1	0·5	0·25	0·6	0·36	1·7	2·89	3·50
2	0·4	0·16	− 0·3	0·09	0·3	0·09	0·34
3	− 0·4	0·16	1·1	1·21	− 0·2	0·04	1·41
4	− 1·3	1·69	− 2·4	5·76	− 0·6	0·36	7·81
5	− 0·5	0·25	1·6	2·56	1·1	1·21	4·02
6	0·9	0·81	0·2	0·04	− 2·4	5·76	6·61
7	1·3	1·69	0·6	0·36	1·4	1·96	4·01
8	2·6	6·76	1·7	2·89	1·7	2·89	12·54
9	0·3	0·09	0	0	0·1	0·01	0·10

Total .. 40·34

Sum of squares $= \Sigma w^2/2 = 40\cdot34/2 = 20\cdot17$
Mean square for error $= s_0^2 = 20\cdot17/27 = 0\cdot75$

Sampling error

4C·3. Calculate the sum of squares from the three sample totals for each of the 9 batches.

For Batch 1 crude sum of squares $= (20\cdot1^2 + 19\cdot6^2 + 20\cdot5^2)/2 = 604\cdot21$
Correction $= 60\cdot2^2/(3 \times 2) = 604\cdot01$

Sum of squares .. .. $= \quad 0\cdot20$

The divisor 2 is introduced because the sample totals each contain two observations.

The arithmetical detail in tabular form is shown in Table 4C·3.

When a machine is used for the computation it is not necessary to detail the calculations because the totals of the columns are all that is required, the final column total (3) being obtained by subtracting the total of (2) from the total of (1).

Corrected sum of squares $= 25\cdot32$. This is based on 18 degrees of freedom (2 per batch).

Sampling error mean square $= 25\cdot32/18 = 1\cdot41$

Table 4C·3

CALCULATIONS FOR SUM OF SQUARES BETWEEN SAMPLES WITHIN
BATCHES

Batch No.	Crude sum of squares $\Sigma x^2/2$	Correction $(\Sigma x)^2/(3 \times 2)$	Corrected sum of squares
1	604·21	604·01	0·20
2	145·53	144·06	1·47
3	32·61	28·60	4·01
4	478·61	477·04	1·57
5	353·77	343·53	10·24
6	271·76	270·68	1·08
7	148·84	147·01	1·83
8	74·05	70·72	3·33
9	1,467·99	1,466·40	1·59
Total ..	3,577·37	3,552·05	25·32
	(1)	(2)	(3)

Batch-to-batch variation

4C·4. The mean square among batches is found as follows:

Sum of squares $= (60·2^2 + 29·4^2 + \ldots + 93·8^2)/6 - 386·0^2/54$
$$= 21{,}312·40/6 - 2759·19$$
$$= 792·88$$

Mean square $= 792·88/8 = 99·11$

The complete analysis of variance is shown in Table 4C·4.

Table 4C·4

COMPLETE ANALYSIS OF VARIANCE

Source of variation	Degrees of freedom	Sum of squares	Mean square
Between batches	8	792·88	99·11
Between samples within batches	18	25·32	1·41
Testing error	27	20·17	0·75
Total	53	838·37	

CHECK. Sum of squares of all the individual results = 3597·54. Subtracting the correction for the mean, 2759·19, gives 838·35, which agrees within rounding-off errors with the total of Table 4C·4.

APPENDIX 4D

COMPUTATION FOR EXAMPLE 4·2

TABLE 4D·1 gives the data of Table 4·2, adjusted to simplify the computations by subtracting 0·600 from each entry.

Table 4D·1

INVESTIGATION OF BULK DENSITY OF CHALK

Labora-tory	Chalk A			Chalk B			Total of chalks A and B
	Observations		Total	Observations		Total	
1	0·251 0·251 0·251		0·753	0·081 0·086 0·081		0·248	1·001
2	0·263 0·266 0·260		0·789	0·090 0·090 0·095		0·275	1·064
3	0·254 0·254 0·254		0·762	0·086 0·086 0·090		0·262	1·024
4	0·263 0·269 0·269		0·801	0·090 0·090 0·090		0·270	1·071
5	0·269 0·272 0·272		0·813	0·099 0·103 0·099		0·301	1·114
6	0·275 0·269 0·272		0·816	0·086 0·090 0·086		0·262	1·078
7	0·245 0·257 0·251		0·753	0·072 0·072 0.081		0·225	0·978
8	0·269 0·269 0·272		0·810	0·099 0·095 0·095		0·289	1·099
9	0·257 0·257 0·257		0·771	0·081 0·081 0·081		0·243	1·014
10	0·269 0·281 0·275		0·825	0·095 0·090 0·090		0·275	1·100
11	0·281 0·281 0·281		0·843	0·108 0·108 0·108		0·324	1·167
Total ..			8·736			2·974	11·710
(1)	(2)		(3)	(4)		(5)	(6)

We must first test whether the standard deviation of log (bulk density) can be assumed the same for both chalks. There are two sources of error, between repeat tests within laboratories, and between laboratories. We therefore carry out analyses of variance within and between laboratories for the two chalks separately. The computations are as follows.

	Chalk A	Chalk B
(1) Correction for the mean	2·312657	0·268020

Crude sums of squares

	Chalk A	Chalk B
(2) Total	2·316024	0·270718
(3) Between laboratories	2·315808	0·270571

Corrected sums of squares

	Chalk A	Chalk B
(4) Total = (2) − (1)	0·003367	0·002698
(5) Between laboratories = (3) − (1)	0·003151	0·002551
(6) Remainder = Within laboratories = (4) − (5)	0·000216	0·000147

The analysis of variance is shown in Table 4D·2.

Table 4D·2

ANALYSIS OF VARIANCE: CHALKS A AND B SEPARATELY

Source of variation	Degrees of freedom	Chalk A		Chalk B		Expectation of mean square
		Sum of squares	Mean square	Sum of squares	Mean square	
Between laboratories	10	0·003151	0·000315	0·002551	0·000255	$\sigma_0^2 + 3\sigma_1^2$
Within laboratories	22	0·000216	0·000010	0·000147	0·000007	σ_0^2
Total ..	32	0·003367		0·002698		

$$\sigma_0^2 = \text{true variance within laboratories}$$

$$\sigma_1^2 = \text{true variance between laboratories}$$

The estimates of σ_0^2 and σ_1^2 for the two chalks are thus:

	Chalk A	Chalk B
σ_0^2	0·000010	0·000007
σ_1^2	0·000102	0·000083
σ_0	0·0032	0·0026
σ_1	0·0101	0·0091

The estimates for the two chalks are sufficiently close to justify the assumption that for both sources of variation the standard error of the logarithms is the same for both chalks, i.e. the coefficient of variation is substantially independent of the bulk density within the range considered.

Applying the F-test, we see that for both chalks the mean square between laboratories is significantly greater than that within laboratories.

The complete analysis of variance can now be carried out on the assumption that the errors for both chalks are the same. The sources of variation are:

Between chalks	C
Between laboratories	L
Interaction of chalks and laboratories ..	CL
Testing error within laboratories	E

To calculate C, L, and CL we form a two-way table, the entries being the totals for each laboratory and each chalk. This table is simply based on columns (3), (5), and (6) of Table 4D·1. The sums of squares are found as follows.

(1) Correction for the mean $11·710^2/66$ $= 2·077638$

Crude sums of squares

(2) Total* $= 2·586742$
(3) Between chalks: $(8·736^2 + 2·974^2)/33$ $= 2·580678$
(4) Between laboratories: $(1·001^2 + \ldots + 1·167^2)/6$ $= 2·082861$
(5) Sample totals: $(0·753^2 + 0·789^2 + \ldots + 0·843^2 + 0·248^2 + \ldots + 0·324^2)/3*$ $= 2·586379$

Corrected sums of squares

(6) Total $= (2) - (1)$ $= 0·509104$
(7) Between chalks $= (3) - (1)$ $= 0·503040$
(8) Between laboratories $= (4) - (1)$ $= 0·005223$
(9) Between sample totals $= (5) - (1)$ $= 0·508741$
(10) Interaction $= (9) - (7) - (8)$ $= 0·000478$
(11) Error within laboratories $= (6) - (9)$ $= 0·000363$

The analysis of variance is shown in Table 4D·3.

* Sum of the crude sum of squares for A and B already calculated on p. 137 and denoted by (2) and (3).

Table 4D·3

COMPLETE ANALYSIS OF VARIANCE

Source of variation	Degrees of freedom	Sum of squares	Mean square	Expectation of mean square
Between chalks ..	1	0·503040	0·503040	—
Between laboratories	10	0·005223	0·000522	$\sigma_0{}^2 + 3\sigma_2{}^2 + 6\sigma_1{}^2$
Interaction	10	0·000478	0·000048	$\sigma_0{}^2 + 3\sigma_2{}^2$
Within laboratories ..	44	0·000363	0·000008	$\sigma_0{}^2$
Total..	65	0·509104		

Note that the sum of squares within laboratories is the sum of the two values in Table 4D·2; the sum of that between laboratories and the interaction is the sum of the two sums of squares between laboratories in Table 4D·2.

$\sigma_2{}^2$ is the variance due to the presence of the interaction between chalks and laboratories.

The estimates of the individual variances and standard deviations are:

Variance	Standard deviation
$\sigma_0{}^2 = 0\cdot000008$	$\sigma_0 = 0\cdot0029$
$\sigma_2{}^2 = 0\cdot000013$	$\sigma_2 = 0\cdot0036$
$\sigma_1{}^2 = 0\cdot000079$	$\sigma_1 = 0\cdot0089$

The mean squares for the variation between laboratories and for interaction are both highly significant, as is seen from the following ratios:

Between laboratories .. $F_1 = 10\cdot9$ $\phi_1 = 10$ $\phi_2 = 10$
Interaction   ..   .. $F_2 = 6\cdot0$ $\phi_1 = 10$ $\phi_2 = 44$

APPENDIX 4E

CALCULATIONS FOR EXAMPLE 4·3

THE data, from which 90 has been subtracted in order to simplify the arithmetic, are given in Table 4E·1.

Table 4E·1

PERCENTAGE OF STRENGTH OF DYESTUFFS SAMPLES (minus 90)

Batch	A	B	Sum A	Sum B	(Sum A + Sum B)	(Sum A − Sum B)
1	2·0	4·5	3·5	12·0	15·5	− 8·5
	3·0	3·0				
	0·0	1·0				
	− 1·5	− 1·0				
	0	6·5				
	0	− 2·0				
2	5·0	− 1·0	14·5	3·0	17·5	11·5
	0·5	0				
	6·0	2·5				
	6·0	− 1·5				
	− 3·0	1·5				
	0	1·5				
3	6·0	− 1·5	6·0	7·5	13·5	− 1·5
	0	3·5				
	0	3·5				
	0	− 2·0				
	0	2·5				
	0	1·5				
4	7·0	10·0	50·0	49·5	99·5	0·5
	10·0	9·0				
	10·0	10·0				
	5·0	8·0				
	8·0	5·0				
	10·0	7·5				
5	2·5	1·5	1·0	7·0	8·0	− 6·0
	3·0	3·0				
	0	0				
	− 1·5	2·5				
	0	− 1·0				
	− 3·0	1·0				
6	10·0	8·5	49·0	51·0	100·0	− 2·0
	7·0	10·0				
	10·0	8·0				
	2·0	10·0				
	10·0	6·5				
	10·0	8·0				
Total			124·0	130·0	254·0	− 6·0

Calculate testing error for each tester separately as in Table 4E·2.

Table 4E·2

Batch	Crude sum of squares		Correction		Sum of squares about mean of batch	
	A	B	A	B	A	B
1	15·25	77·50	2·04	24·00	13·21	53·50
2	106·25	14·00	35·04	1·50	71·21	12·50
3	36·00	39·25	6·00	9·38	30·00	29·87
4	438·00	426·25	416·67	408·38	21·33	17·87
5	26·50	19·50	0·17	8·17	26·33	11·33
6	453·00	442·50	400·17	433·50	52·83	9·00
Total ..	1,075·00	1,019·00	860·09	884·93	214·91	134·07

Testing error variance of A $= 214·91/30 = 7·164$
Testing error variance of B $= 134·07/30 = 4·469$

These clearly do not differ significantly using the double-tailed F-test [$S.M.$, § 4·8].

Combining the variance of A and B we obtain
$$(214·91 + 134·07)/60 = 5·816$$

Sum of squares between batches

Crude sum of squares $= (15·5^2 + 17·5^2 + \ldots + 100·0^2)/12 = 1724·42$
Correction due to mean $= 254^2/72$ $= 896·06$

Corrected sum of squares $= 828·36$

Sum of squares of bias of tester

Since there are only two testers, this reduces to
$$(124·0 - 130·0)^2/72 = (-6·0)^2/72 = 0·50$$

Interaction of testers and batches

The calculation can again be simplified, since there are only two testers. This is the corrected sum of squares of the differences (sum A − sum B) for the six batches.

Crude sum of squares $= \{(-8·5)^2 + 11·5^2 + \ldots + (-2·0)^2\}/12 = 20·58$
Correction $= (-6·0)^2/72$ $= 0·50$

Corrected sum of squares $= 20·08$

This leads to the analysis of variance of Table 4E·3.

Table 4E·3

ANALYSIS OF VARIANCE

Source of variation	Sum of squares	Degrees of freedom	Mean square
Between batches ..	828·36	5	165·67
Bias between testers	0·50	1	0·50
Interaction of testers and batches	20·08	5	4·02
Testing error ..	348·98	60	5·82
Total	1,197·92	71	

As a check we calculate the total sum of squares directly. This is:

Crude sum of squares of all 72 observations $= 2094 \cdot 00$

Correction due to mean $\qquad\qquad = \ \ 896 \cdot 06$

Corrected sum of squares $\qquad\qquad = 1197 \cdot 94$

This agrees within rounding-off errors with the total of Table 4E·3.

APPENDIX 4F

COMPUTATIONS FOR EXAMPLE 4·4

IN order to simplify the arithmetic we subtract 15·0 from the data of Table 4·4, giving the results of Table 4F·1.

Table 4F·1

SAMPLING AND ANALYSIS OF A FERTILISER

Batch	Sample 1		Sample 2		Total of sample 1	Total of sample 2	Total of method A	Total of method R	Total per batch
	A	R	A	R					
1	0·6	0·5	0·5	0·4	1·1	0·9	1·1	0·9	2·0
2	0·4	− 0·1	0·2	0·0	0·3	0·2	0·6	− 0·1	0·5
3	0·3	0·4	− 0·4	− 0·4	0·7	− 0·8	− 0·1	0·0	− 0·1
4	0·0	0·5	0·0	0·5	0·5	0·5	0·0	1·0	1·0
5	0·5	0·0	0·4	0·1	0·5	0·5	0·9	0·1	1·0
6	− 0·2	− 0·2	0·0	− 0·2	− 0·4	− 0·2	− 0·2	− 0·4	− 0·6
7	− 0·1	0·0	− 0·1	0·3	− 0·1	0·2	− 0·2	0·3	0·1
8	0·0	0·8	0·2	0·8	0·8	1·0	0·2	1·6	1·8
Total	1·5	1·9	0·8	1·5	3·4	2·3	2·3	3·4	5·7

The steps in the computations are as follows.

Total sum of squares

Crude sum of squares of all 32 observations $= 4 \cdot 27$
Correction due to mean $= 1 \cdot 0153$

Corrected sum of squares $= 3 \cdot 2547$

Sum of squares between batches

Crude sum of squares $= (2 \cdot 0^2 + 0 \cdot 5^2 + \ldots + 1 \cdot 8^2)/4 = 2 \cdot 4675$
Corrected sum of squares $= 2 \cdot 4675 - 1 \cdot 0153$ $= 1 \cdot 4522$

Sum of squares between methods (overall bias)

Since there are only two methods, this is simply

$$(3 \cdot 4 - 2 \cdot 3)^2/32 = 0 \cdot 0378$$

Sum of squares due to sampling error

Sampling error is represented by the difference between samples 1 and 2 within each batch. Since there are only two samples per batch, the sampling sum of squares is simply the sum of squares of the differences between the two sample totals per batch divided by 4, thus:

Sampling error sum of squares $= \{(1 \cdot 1 - 0 \cdot 9)^2 + (0 \cdot 3 - 0 \cdot 2)^2 + \ldots$
    $+ (0 \cdot 8 - 1 \cdot 0)^2\}/4 = 0 \cdot 6175$

Interaction of methods and batches (variable bias)

Since there are only two methods, this reduces to corrected sum of squares of the differences between sum A and sum R per batch, divided by 4:

Crude sum of squares $= \{(1 \cdot 1 - 0 \cdot 9)^2 + (0 \cdot 6 + 0 \cdot 1)^2 + (- 0 \cdot 1 - 0)^2$

                                $+ \ldots + (0 \cdot 2 - 1 \cdot 6)^2\}/4 = 1 \cdot 1075$
Correction $=$ (sum of differences)$^2/32$
                    $= (2 \cdot 3 - 3 \cdot 4)^2/32$ $= 0 \cdot 0378$

Corrected sum of squares $= 1 \cdot 0697$

Remainder sum of squares (analytical error)

This may be obtained by subtraction from the total. It may also be obtained directly, since it represents the sum of squares of the interaction of samples and methods for each batch. If for any one batch we denote the tests on one sample by A_1, R_1 and on the other by A_2, R_2, the interaction is $(A_1 - R_1) - (A_2 - R_2)$. For the eight batches these quantities are respectively $0 \cdot 0$, $0 \cdot 3$, $- 0 \cdot 1$, $0 \cdot 0$, $0 \cdot 2$, $- 0 \cdot 2$, $0 \cdot 3$, and $- 0 \cdot 2$. Their sum of squares is $\{0 \cdot 0^2 + 0 \cdot 3^2 + \ldots + (- 0 \cdot 2)^2\}/4 = 0 \cdot 0775$. When calculated directly the result may be used as a check. The analysis of variance table then reads as Table 4F·2.

Table 4F·2

ANALYSIS OF VARIANCE

Source of variation	Sum of squares	Degrees of freedom	Mean square
Between batches ..	1·4522	7	0·2075
Bias between methods	0·0378	1	0·0378
Interaction of batches and methods	1·0697	7	0·1528
Between samples ..	0·6175	8	0·0772
Analytical error (= remainder)	0·0775	8	0·0097
Total	3·2547	31	

After reading Chapter 7, the reader will note that the data may be analysed by considering them as eight 2 × 2 designs.

CHAPTER 5

RANDOMISED BLOCKS AND LATIN SQUARES

WHEN several experimental treatments are to be compared it is clearly desirable that all other conditions shall be kept as nearly constant as is practicable. Random variations will occur and appear as experimental error, and some replication under similar conditions will be required to compare the treatments with sufficient reliability; such replication also supplies the information to estimate the experimental error, and this is required to assess the reliability. The number of repeat tests required may be too great for all to be carried out under similar conditions, but it is frequently possible to carry out one complete set of tests at a time under uniform conditions, these conditions being different from set to set. It is shown that by using the appropriate design, Randomised Blocks, the differences between the conditions under which each set of treatments is carried out can be separated from the differences between the treatments and from experimental error. The design amounts to a subdivision of the experimental conditions into blocks of relatively uniform conditions. Sometimes this subdivision can be effected in more than one way; for instance, in a multiple plant the various units may differ in performance, and in addition there may exist a trend in time, as in certain electrolytic and catalytic processes. The most efficient design for the comparison of different experimental treatments is then the Latin Square.

RANDOMISED BLOCKS

Introduction

5·1. Suppose it is required to compare the effects of five treatments, say five lots of material prepared in different ways, or five temperatures of reaction, and in order to reduce the uncertainties caused by experimental error it is decided to test each treatment three times, making fifteen trials in all, then the ideal design will provide for all fifteen trials to be carried out under uniform conditions, apart from deliberate variation of the treatments. In practice it may be impossible to do this because, for example, sufficient raw material of uniform quality for fifteen trials cannot be made. But it may be that a homogeneous batch of raw material sufficient for five trials can be made, and if so the experiment may be arranged so that all five treatments are tested on each of three batches which are homogeneous but not necessarily identical, with the consequence that any variation from batch to batch does not affect comparisons between the treatments. A typical example arises in the testing of rubber or other material in sheet form. Suppose five methods of treating the rubber are to be tested and large sheets are available. Adjacent samples cut from a rubber sheet are usually more alike than non-adjacent samples, and this property suggests that comparisons between treatments should be made between adjacent samples of rubber. To compare five treatments, replicating the experiment three times, three pieces should be cut from different parts of the sheet and each piece cut into five, for in this way the variation from one set of five to another does not affect comparisons between the five treatments, which are made entirely within the sets. Had fifteen pieces of rubber been cut from the sheet and the five treatments applied at random the experiment would have been less sensitive, because the heterogeneity of the material would have inflated the experimental error.

In this context the set of five pieces taken from the same part of the sheet is called a Block. In statistics a block means, in general, a set of observations in which the error variation (i.e. the variation not associated with any deliberate variation in the experimental conditions) is expected to be less than in the whole series of observations. As a precaution against systematic variation from one trial to another within a block, here exemplified by cuttings from a sheet of rubber, it is desirable to arrange the treatments within each block in random order, and when this has been done the result is a Randomised Block design. The terminology originated with agricultural field trials. In order to minimise the effects of differential fertility the experimental area is divided into compact blocks, each supposed more homogeneous than the whole, and the blocks are subdivided into plots, one treatment being assigned to each plot. If the plots were arranged systematically within blocks the experiment would be vitiated by any fertility gradient occurring in the same direction; consequently the treatments must be allotted to the plots in random order.

5·11. In the above example the size of the block is not restricted, except by the consideration that the larger the block the greater is the variation within it likely to be, and therefore the less the gain from dividing the material into blocks. Elsewhere the block size may be necessarily restricted; for example in some machines designed to test the resistance to wear of rubberised fabric the number of samples that can be tested simultaneously is limited. In the MARTINDALE wear tester four samples can be tested in one run. If four materials are to be tested three times each, the effect of run-to-run variation, which is known to be large, can be eliminated by testing all four materials in each of three runs, i.e. each run represents a block. To yield a randomised block experiment the materials would be allotted at random to the four test positions.

Restriction in block size may occur when, in order to produce homogeneous material for an experiment on the plant, a number of batches are blended and the capacity of the blender is limited. If sufficient blended material is available for four trials and four or fewer treatments are to be tested, a randomised block design may be used. Comparisons between treatments will then be based entirely on samples taken from one homogeneous blend and will therefore be more precise than if they had been made on samples from different blends. If the number of treatments exceeds the block size a straightforward randomised block design cannot be used, but advantage can be taken of the smaller variation within a block by the methods described in Chapter 6.

Effect of interactions

5·12. When using a randomised block design it is generally assumed that while the general level of the results may be different in the different blocks the relative effects of the treatments are the same in all blocks apart from experimental error, in other words that there is no interaction between treatments and blocks. In practice we interpret this as meaning that the interactions, if they exist, are not appreciable compared with the treatment effects. Interactions will be inseparable from experimental error, and if the interactions are large the experiment may yield misleading results.

Effect of time trends

5·13. An important objective of randomised block experiments, particularly on the plant scale, is to reduce the effect of time trends. When a chemical plant is producing a given material regularly, either by a continuous process or in a series of batches, systematic variations in yield are apt to occur. Sometimes these variations may be ascribed to seasonal influences such as changes in the temperature of cooling water or to changes in quality of raw materials, but more often there remain trends or fluctuations of unknown origin and incapable of control in any event. It is not a question of short-term random variations, which may be called normal process variations, but of slow changes in the average level. The yields of two successive batches or of two successive shifts in a continuous process will be nearly identical except for normal process variations if conditions are not deliberately varied; but two yields at an interval of a month may differ more widely because of a change in the mean yield of the plant. In designing experiments to be carried out on the plant scale it is important to take account of possible trends and to ensure that the conclusions drawn from the experiment are not seriously affected. The randomised block design provides a method of eliminating or reducing the effects of trends. The design is not limited to experiments on the plant but applies whenever the trials are spread over a period of time or space and the possibility of systematic variations or trends exists.

Figure 5·1 shows data for the percentage yield in the manufacture of an organic chemical taken over a period of a year. Results for single batches and

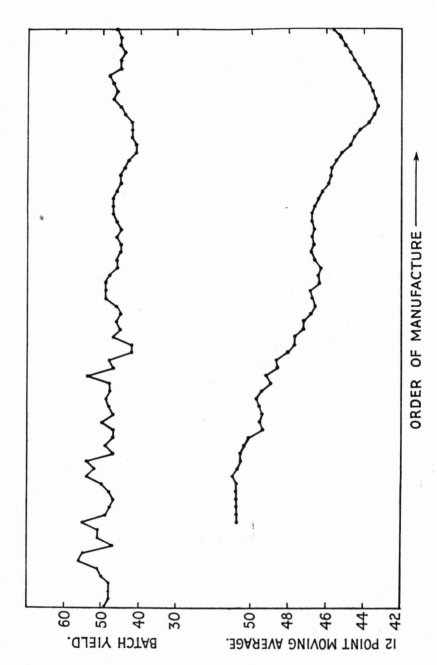

Fig. 5·1. Yield of organic chemical, showing trend

for the moving average of twelve batches are shown, and the trends are clearly seen, especially from the moving average chart.

5·131. A time trend is a particular case of correlation between observations. In the absence of correlation any particular observation is in no way affected by previous observations, and vice versa. If a process yield exhibits a steady increase, any particular yield is likely to be higher than the previous one and the results exhibit positive correlation, i.e. successive observations are more alike than pairs of observations taken at random. When successive observations are less alike than pairs taken at random the results exhibit negative correlation. Negative correlation is less common. It may be exhibited by the yields of a batch process if a reaction vessel cannot be completely emptied; if an unusually large residue is left on emptying one batch, the yield from that batch will be low; if the residue from the next batch is normal or low, the yield will be high. Under these conditions there is a danger that the correlation between successive batches will cause a bias in the comparisons between the treatments. The method of overcoming this difficulty is to randomise the order of testing the treatments. Randomisation is entirely effective in preventing bias whatever the nature of the correlation between the observations.

Example of randomised blocks in plant scale experiment

5·14. Suppose it is decided to examine how the yield of a manufacturing process is affected by the preparation of a catalyst by four different methods, one week being sufficient to give a reasonable trial and a period of six months being available for the whole experiment. If each catalyst is tested over a month, differences between monthly yields may occur because of variations in plant efficiency arising from other causes, such as variations in raw materials. If each catalyst is tested over a week and the four are tested in consecutive weeks, the effects of variations are likely to be less serious, but the experiment loses in precision because the average for each catalyst is taken over one week instead of four. In order to utilise the whole available period and yet confine the comparison between catalysts to results obtained within a short space of time the period is split into six intervals of one month, and all four catalysts are tested in each month. Each interval of one month is a block. Even this arrangement is not entirely satisfactory, for if it happened that the efficiency tended to rise throughout the six months, and if the four catalysts were tested in the same order in each block, say A, B, C, D, catalyst D may appear to be the best, even though there were no real differences. The remedy is to change the order of testing from block to block, the order being chosen at random each time; any systematic changes in plant efficiency will not then bias the relative averages for the four catalysts. The experimental material is thus subdivided into blocks, each of which is likely to be more homogeneous than the whole, and the order of the treatments is randomised within each block giving a randomised block experiment. If it is known beforehand that the efficiency is likely to rise or fall approximately linearly throughout the experiment a more efficient method exists for eliminating the effect of the trend; this is dealt with in §§ 5·4 *et seq.* (Latin Squares). Usually, however, the nature of the trend is unknown, and a randomised block design is used.

It is assumed that the efficiencies of the four catalysts remain substantially the same relative to one another in every month, i.e. that there is no appreciable interaction between blocks (months) and treatments (catalysts). If an interaction exists it will form part of the experimental error, which is thereby inflated, and if the interaction is large the experiment may be inconclusive or misleading. If the interaction is not large relative to the effect of varying the treatments the experiment will be satisfactory, although its sensitivity is reduced because of the inflation of the experimental error.

Analysis of randomised block experiments

5·15. The results of a randomised block experiment can be exhibited in a two-way table such as Table 5·1.

Table 5·1

RANDOMISED BLOCK EXPERIMENTS: PRESENTATION OF RESULTS

Treatment	Block			Mean
	I	II	III	
1				
2				
3				
4				
5				
Mean ..				

Data classified in this way have already been encountered in §§ 4·4 *et seq.* and *S.M.*, Chapter 6. There are two assignable sources of variation: between the five treatments and between the three blocks, with four and two degrees of freedom respectively. Any additional variation in the data is ascribed to experimental error, and since there are fourteen degrees of freedom altogether, eight are available for the estimate of error. In general, with k blocks and m treatments the analysis of variance takes the following form:

ANALYSIS OF VARIANCE: RANDOMISED BLOCK DESIGN

Source of variation	Degrees of freedom	Mean square
Between blocks	$k - 1$	$(MS)_B$
Between treatments ..	$m - 1$	$(MS)_T$
Residual (error)	$(k - 1)(m - 1)$	$s_0{}^2$
Total	$km - 1$	

Though the variation between blocks may be of no direct interest, a large value of $(MS)_B$ would mean that the subdivision into blocks had been effective in separating from the other comparisons a considerable amount of variation which, if included in the residual, would have made the experiment less sensitive. Knowledge that this variation exists may be used to improve the process; it may be possible to bring the overall performance of the process under investigation up to that of the best blocks if a reason for the variation can be found.

Conditions for using randomised blocks

5·16. The following discussion defines more precisely the assumption made in randomised block experiments, that the relative effects of the treatments are the same in all blocks. It follows from this assumption that the result of any trial, say that on the jth treatment in the ith block, may be expressed as

$$y_{ij} = \mu + B_i + T_j + e_{ij} \dots\dots\dots\dots\dots(5\cdot1)$$

where y_{ij} is the result (response) of the trial.

μ is a constant—the grand mean of all the responses which would be obtained if there were no error.

B_i is a term peculiar to the ith block and is independent of the treatment. It is the amount by which a response in the ith block would differ from the corresponding average over all blocks if there were no error, this amount being by hypothesis the same whatever the treatment.

T_j is a term peculiar to the jth treatment and is independent of the block. It is the amount by which the response under the jth treatment would differ from the corresponding average over all treatments if there were no error, this amount being by hypothesis the same in all blocks.

e_{ij} denotes the experimental error in the i, jth trial. It is assumed to be a random variable with standard deviation σ_0.

The quantities μ, B, and T are true values, the values estimated from the experiment being denoted by $\bar{y}$, b, and t. On changing from treatment 1 to treatment 2 in any block the response changes by $(T_2 - T_1)$—apart from experimental error—whichever the block. Similarly if any treatment is tested in blocks 1 and 2 the response changes by $(B_2 - B_1)$—apart from experimental error—whichever treatment is used. If Equation $(5·1)$ is fulfilled, therefore, the conditions required for using a randomised block design are fulfilled.

The analysis of the results may be regarded as involving the estimation from the data of the best values for μ, B, T, and σ_0, i.e. fitting Equation $(5·1)$ to the observations. Let the number of treatments be m and the number of blocks k.

The best estimate of B_i is found by summing all the observations in the ith block, dividing by the number of trials in a block, and subtracting the grand mean $\bar{y}$. Similarly the best estimate of T_j is found by summing all the observations on the jth treatment, dividing by the number of trials of the treatment, and subtracting $\bar{y}$. Using these estimates we can calculate the most probable values of the observations in the absence of experimental error, i.e.

$$\bar{y} + b_i + t_j \dots\dots\dots\dots\dots\dots\dots\dots(5·2)$$

The difference between this and the observed value y_{ij} is an estimate of the experimental error e_{ij} in this trial. If all the values of e are calculated in this way, Σe_{ij}^2 divided by the number of degrees of freedom, $(k-1)(m-1)$, gives an estimate of σ_0^2, the error variance. From the values of b we calculate the mean square between blocks, $m\Sigma b^2/(k-1)$, and from those of t the mean square between treatments, $k\Sigma t^2/(m-1)$. These quantities are more easily found by the methods of calculation normally used in the analysis of variance, which are short-cut methods, but it is informative to calculate at least one example by the above method, which shows the physical meaning more clearly. The longer method is self-checking, since each sum of squares is calculated independently, but for routine use the method of analysis whereby the error sum of squares is found by difference would be preferred. In Appendix 5B the data of Example 5·1 are analysed by both methods.

5·17. By subdividing the trials into k blocks we use up $(k-1)$ degrees of freedom which would have been available for estimating the error if no subdivision had been made. If there are no real differences between the blocks the error is not reduced by the subdivision and it is estimated with fewer degrees of freedom, i.e. with less precision. There will usually be some prior knowledge from which to judge whether differences between blocks are to be expected, and if there is any risk of such differences existing it is advisable to subdivide the trials into blocks.

5·18. If the block is large enough to allow each treatment to be tested more than once we can check the assumption that the relative effects of the treatments are the same in all blocks, since we can estimate the error variance directly from the differences between the results for each treatment within each block. We can then assess the interaction mean square between blocks and treatments against the error variance. If the interaction is statistically significant the relative performances of the treatments are not the same in each block.

Example 5·1. Manufacture of an organic chemical

5·2. This investigation concerned the chlorsulphonation of acetanilide. The yield is somewhat below the theoretical, mainly because of loss of product in the mother liquor (i.e. the liquor removed when the product is filtered). It was required to test whether different blends of acetanilide gave different losses, and to do this five different blends were made and three batches of products were prepared from each blend. If the blends had been tested one at a time, i.e. three batches from blend 1, then three batches from blend 2, and so on, any variation from blend to blend might have been due to a time trend in the process and not to any real differences between the blends. To eliminate this effect the experiment was designed in randomised blocks. There were fifteen batches in all, divided into three blocks of five, the five in one block being prepared from the five blends of acetanilide in random order. The following table gives the order of preparation, the blend used, and the percentage loss.

Table 5·2

LOSS OF PRODUCT IN MANUFACTURE OF AN ORGANIC CHEMICAL

Block	Batch	Blend of acetanilide	Per cent loss
I	1	B	18·2
	2	A	16·9
	3	C	17·0
	4	E	18·3
	5	D	15·1
II	6	A	16·5
	7	E	18·3
	8	B	19·2
	9	C	18·1
	10	D	16·0
III	11	B	17·1
	12	D	17·8
	13	C	17·3
	14	E	19·8
	15	A	17·5

Averages:	Block	I	..	..	17·10
		II	..	..	17·62
		III	..	..	17·90
	Blend	A	..	..	16·97
		B	..	..	18·17
		C	..	..	17·47
		D	..	..	16·30
		E	..	..	18·80

The significance of the variations between blends and between blocks must be assessed against the experimental error.

5·21. The statistical analysis is straightforward and is given in full in Appendix 5B. The following is an outline.

Correction for the mean (CM)

Square the grand total and divide by 15.

Total sum of squares

Square all results and add. Subtract CM.

Sum of squares between blocks

Square the three block totals, add, and divide by 5. Subtract CM.

Sum of squares between blends

Square the five blend totals, add, and divide by 3. Subtract CM.

Sum of squares due to error

From the total sum of squares subtract the sums of squares for blocks and blends.

Divide the sums of squares by their degrees of freedom: 2 for blocks, 4 for blends and $(15 - 1 - 2 - 4) = 8$ for error, to give the mean squares. These calculations lead to Table 5·21.

Table 5·21

ANALYSIS OF VARIANCE: DATA FROM TABLE 5·2

Source of variation		Degrees of freedom	Sum of squares	Mean square	Expectation of mean square*
Between blocks	..	2	1·65	0·82	$\sigma_0^2 + 5S_B^2$
Between blends	..	4	11·56	2·89	$\sigma_0^2 + 3S_A^2$
Error	..	8	6·99	0·87	σ_0^2
Total	..	14	20·20		

* The quantities S_B and S_A are measures of the variation due to blocks and blends respectively, analogous in form to standard deviations. If the blends can be regarded as a random sample from a population of blends, S_A will then be an estimate of the standard deviation between blends. S_B can be interpreted similarly (see Appendix 5D).

The variation among blends is significant at the 10% level:

$$F = 3{\cdot}32 \qquad 10\% \text{ value} = 2{\cdot}81 \qquad 5\% \text{ value} = 3{\cdot}84$$

The test of significance is appropriate in this example because we were interested in testing the existence of blend-to-blend variation which, on chemical grounds, did not seem likely. Since the mean square between blends is only significant at the 10% level, we conclude that there is some evidence of blend-to-blend variation. If the existence of this variation was not in question but only its magnitude, the problem would be one of estimation and the result would require to be interpreted in terms either of errors of the first and second kinds or of confidence limits.

Although the apparent variation among blocks is not confirmed (i.e. it might well be ascribed to experimental error), future experiments should still be carried out in the same way. There is no clear evidence of a trend in this set of trials, but it might well appear in another set, and no complication in experimental arrangement is involved.

Errors of the second kind

5·22. The meaning of errors of the first and second kinds has been explained in Chapter 2. If in Example 5·1 there is no real variation between blends but because of experimental errors the conclusion is reached that there is real variation, an error of the first kind is committed. If on the other hand the blends differ appreciably from one another but the differences are concealed by experimental errors and the conclusion reached is that there is no real variation, an error of the second kind is committed. In Chapter 2 it was shown how to adjust the scale of a simple comparative trial so as to control both kinds of error. Although it is possible to extend the reasoning to the comparison of more than two treatments the method loses much of its simplicity, and its practical interpretation is not so clear. However, it is readily possible to calculate the confidence limits to the means of each treatment and, presupposing an approximate knowledge of the experimental error, to decide on the number of replicates required to give sufficient precision in the estimate of the mean of each treatment.

Confidence limits

5·23. In Example 5·1, testing by means of the F-test the hypothesis that all blends give the same result shows that the variation between blends is significantly greater at the 10% level than the error variance, i.e. there is weak evidence that the blends differ in their effect on yield. If it is expected that the blends will vary it is more informative to calculate the confidence limits for the five blends; this gives some indication of the extent of variation.

The variance of the average for one blend is $\sigma_0^2/3$, i.e. 0·29, giving a standard error of 0·54. The 95% confidence limits are therefore obtained by adding and subtracting $0·54t$, the observed average, t being the tabulated value for a probability of 5%, with eight degrees of freedom; therefore the limits for the five blends are as follows: $t = 2·31$, $0·54t = 1·25$.

Blend	Average	95% Confidence limits	
		Lower	Upper
A	16·97	15·72	18·22
B	18·17	16·92	19·42
C	17·47	16·22	18·72
D	16·30	15·05	17·55
E	18·80	17·55	20·05

There is no clear indication that any one blend is better or worse than the others, the confidence limits overlap considerably, but there is a suggestion that blends B and E give higher yields than blend D. This agrees with the conclusion drawn from the F-test, i.e. that there is only weak evidence of blend-to-blend variation.

If the five blends can be regarded as random samples of plant production we may regard $S_A{}^2$ of Table 5·21 as an estimate of $\sigma_A{}^2$, the variance of the true yields of the blends. We then have

$$2·89 - 0·87 \rightarrow 3\sigma_A{}^2$$
$$\therefore \quad 0·67 \rightarrow \sigma_A{}^2$$
$$0·82 \rightarrow \sigma_A$$

We may now deduce the range of variation to be expected, but since only five blends were tested the estimate is rather uncertain. Further experimental work on these lines is necessary to establish with confidence that variation between blends exists, and considerably more work is necessary to obtain a reliable estimate of the extent of this variation, assuming it to exist.

Summary: Randomised blocks

5·3. There is no need to multiply examples of randomised blocks since design and analysis are straightforward. The illustrations used have been mainly confined to the reduction of the effect of trends or other correlations between observations, but the block design is useful whenever it is thought that a small set of trials may give more uniform results than a large set. In quality control charts small samples are used to estimate the error standard deviation because in general a small sample is more uniform than a day's make, and it thus gives a measure of the inherent variability of the product, not inflated by changes in the average level. In many types of analysis it is found that tests done on the same day or by the same operator tend to be more alike than tests done on different days or by different operators. If two or more materials are to be tested several times, and the number of tests that can be done on one day is limited, it is better to test each material once on the same day using the same operator, and repeat the tests on several days or using several operators. Each day or operator corresponds to one block, and all comparisons of the materials are made within blocks, so that the variation between blocks does not contribute to the estimate of experimental error.

Missing values

5·31. It has been assumed hitherto that every treatment is equally represented in every block, so that the effects of block and treatment variation can be assessed by simple averaging. It may happen that in one of the blocks one treatment is not tested, or more generally the results of one or more treatments in one or more blocks are not available. We cannot then use the simple analysis given above; we might abandon those blocks in which the complete set of treatments was not tested, but this would be wasteful unless there were so many blocks that the loss of one would not be serious. The general analysis for such data is given in detail in Appendix 6B, but a short explanation, applied to randomised block design when a limited number of results are missing, may be given here. For simplicity consider Example 5·1 and suppose that for some reason the results of two trials, say batch 1 (block I, blend B) and batch 15 (block III, blend A), are not available. The procedure is to calculate from the remaining trials the most probable value for batch 1, using the estimates of the effects of block I and of blend B, and similarly for batch 15.

To do this we insert symbols in place of the two missing values, carry out the analysis of variance including these symbols, and then calculate values for them such that the residual or error variance is a minimum. These are the best estimates of the missing values in the sense that they minimise the error variance. Table 5·22 gives the results, with x for batch 1 and y for batch 15.

We now calculate the error sum of squares, differentiate partially with respect to x and y, and equate the derivatives to zero to give the values of x and y which minimise the sum of squares.

Carrying out the step-by-step calculations for the sums of squares under the headings Total, Between blocks, and Between blends [§ **5·21**], we obtain the following expression for the remainder sum of squares:

$$E = (8x^2 + 8y^2 + 38x + 30y + 2xy)/15 + \text{terms not involving } x \text{ or } y$$

Table 5·22

DATA FROM TABLE 5·2, BATCHES 1 AND 15 MISSING
UNIT = 10(% loss − 17·5)

Blend	Block I	Block II	Block III	Total
A	− 6	− 10	x	$x − 16$
B	y	17	− 4	$y + 13$
C	− 5	6	− 2	− 1
D	− 24	− 15	3	− 36
E	8	8	23	39
Total	$y − 27$	6	$x + 20$	$x + y − 1$

Dropping the divisor 15, differentiating with respect to the unknowns x and y, and equating the partial derivatives to zero, we have:

$$\frac{\partial E}{\partial x} = 16x + 38 + 2y = 0$$

$$\frac{\partial E}{\partial y} = 16y + 30 + 2x = 0$$

Hence
$$x = − 2·2$$
$$y = − 1·6$$

The estimates of the missing values are thus (in the original units):

Batch 1 .. .. 17·5 − 0·16 = 17·34 (observed 18·2)
Batch 15 .. .. 17·5 − 0·22 = 17·28 (observed 17·5)

In general let there be m rows and n columns and let

R_1 = total of known observations of row containing x
R_2 = total of known observations of row containing y

C_1 = total of known observations of column containing x
C_2 = total of known observations of column containing y

S = total of all known results

omitting x and y from these totals.

Then the equations to solve for the missing values are

$$(m − 1)(n − 1)x = mR_1 + nC_1 − S − y$$
$$(m − 1)(n − 1)y = mR_2 + nC_2 − S − x$$

From Table 5·22:

$$R_1 = -16 \qquad S = -1$$
$$R_2 = +13 \qquad m = 5$$
$$C_1 = +20 \qquad n = 3$$
$$C_2 = -27$$

Therefore substituting these values will yield the same equation in x and y as above.

When only one value (x) requires to be estimated the formula reduces to

$$(m-1)(n-1)x = mR_1 + nC_1 - S$$

The same process can be applied to more than two missing values. With more than four missing values it may be easier to solve the equations by successive approximation, as described in Appendix 6B.

An approximate analysis of variance can now be carried out in the usual way, using the estimates for batches 1 and 15, with the difference that the error variance has only six degrees of freedom instead of eight, because two of the results are estimated. The resulting analysis is shown in Table 5·23. The rigorous analysis is given in Appendix 6B; the approximate method fails when many values are missing.

Table 5·23

ANALYSIS OF VARIANCE OF EXAMPLE 5·1 WITH TWO VALUES MISSING

Source of variation	Degrees of freedom	Sum of squares	Mean square
Between blocks ..	2	2·28	1·14
Between blends ..	4	10·94	2·74
Error	6	6·55	1·09
Total	12	19·77	

In this analysis the error mean square is greater than before and the mean square between blends is not significant. The F-test is less sensitive than before because of the reduction in the degrees of freedom for error.

LATIN SQUARES

Introduction

5·4. In an experiment which is not divided into blocks the replicated treatments are distributed at random over the whole of the experimental material, the heterogeneity of the material together with the testing errors giving the residual (or error) variation. In a randomised block experiment the hetero-geneity is controlled by applying the treatments over compact blocks of relatively homogeneous material, thus reducing the residual variation and making the comparisons more sensitive. Under suitable conditions the experiment may be subdivided in more than one way, giving in each case greater homogeneity. In a wear-testing machine with four positions the results obtained in the four positions may vary apart from testing error, and comparisons between different materials will be more precise if all are tested in the same position. This means, however, that they cannot be tested in the same run of the machine. There may also be variation from run to run, and comparisons between different materials will be more precise if all are tested in the same run, in which case they cannot all be tested in the same position. If the variation between runs or between positions did not exist or could be ignored a randomised block design could be used, but in order to eliminate both sources of variation from the comparison of treatments a more elaborate design would be required. It is impossible to make every comparison, say treatment 1 with treatment 2, in both the same run and the same position, but it is possible to ensure that each treatment is tested the same number of times in every position and also in every run, provided the number of runs is equal to the number of positions. The average response for each treatment is then an average over all runs and over all positions, and provided the position effect is independent of the run effect all the treatment averages are equally affected by the run and position variations. The relative values of these averages are thus unaffected and they are estimated as precisely as if the run and position variations did not exist.

5·41. The arrangement of the trials to ensure that each treatment is tested once in every run and once in every position makes use of the Latin Square. This is a square containing m rows and m columns, and consequently m^2 cells. Each cell contains one of m letters, corresponding to m treatments, and each letter occurs once and once only in each row and each column. An example of such a square is given in Table 5·3 for $m = 4$.

Table 5·3

4 × 4 LATIN SQUARE

Run	Position number			
	1	2	3	4
1	A	B	C	D
2	B	C	D	A
3	C	D	A	B
4	D	A	B	C

Each treatment is tested four times.

The total variation among the results is made up of four separate contributions:

(a) Between rows   (runs)
(b) Between columns (positions)
(c) Between letters   (treatments)
(d) Residual   (error)

Just as with randomised blocks, and as explained in § 5·42, it must be assumed that the factors act independently. The analysis of variance takes the form of Table 5·31.

Table 5·31

FORM OF ANALYSIS OF VARIANCE FOR LATIN SQUARE EXPERIMENT

Source of variation		Degrees of freedom
Between rows (runs)	R	$(m - 1) = 3$
Between columns (positions)	C	$(m - 1) = 3$
Between letters (treatments)	T	$(m - 1) = 3$
Residual (error) ..	..	$(m^2 - 1) - 3(m - 1) = (m - 1)(m - 2) = 6$
Total	..	$m^2 - 1 = 15$

Conditions for using Latin Square designs

5·42. The assumptions made in using a Latin Square design should be carefully noted; they represent an extension of those for a randomised block design. It is assumed that, apart from experimental error:

(a) The true effect of changing from one treatment to another is the same in every row (run) and in every column (position).

(b) The true effect of changing from one position to another is the same in every run and for every treatment.

(c) The true difference between one run and another is the same for every position and every treatment.

In other words, the runs, positions, and treatments affect the result independently of one another. In practice this is taken to mean that the interactions are not large compared with the effects required to be estimated. When interactions are large, in addition to inflating the experimental error they confuse the effects required to be estimated and may give misleading results. Because of experimental error the observed results will not strictly fulfil conditions (a), (b), and (c), but it is assumed that the divergence is caused

M

by experimental error only; thus any interaction is assumed to be part of the experimental error. The error is assumed to be random and Normally distributed with standard deviation σ_0. This applies to all runs, positions, and treatments.

The effects then combine according to an additive law expressed by

$$y_{ijk} = \mu + R_i + C_j + T_k + e_{ijk} \dots\dots\dots\dots\dots(5\cdot3)$$

where y_{ijk} denotes the observed result.

μ denotes the grand mean of all results if there were no experimental error.

R_i is the difference between the average of the ith row and the average over all rows if the column and treatment were the same and if there were no experimental error. It is the same for all columns and treatments.

C_j is the difference between a result in the jth column and the average over all columns if the row and treatment were the same and if there were no experimental error. It is the same for all rows and treatments.

T_k is the difference between the result on the kth treatment and the average over all treatments if the row and column were the same and if there were no experimental error. It is the same for all rows and columns.

e_{ijk} is the experimental error in the trial in the ith row, the jth column, and with the kth treatment.

It is important, before a Latin Square design is used, to verify that the factors corresponding to rows, columns, and letters are of such a nature that they are likely to act independently of one another. In the above example of the testing machine this is a reasonable assumption; one run may be more severe than another, but it is likely to be equally severe with respect to all positions and all treatments; and the same applies *mutatis mutandis* to positions and treatments. Because of experimental errors these statements may not be true of individual trials, but they may generally be assumed true on the average. It may be advisable to confirm the assumptions if a long series of experiments based on Latin Square designs is contemplated.

The factors usually studied in chemical processes—temperature, rate of throughput, concentration, etc.—are not likely to act independently, and Latin Square designs are unsuitable except perhaps in preliminary trials to pick out any large effects, or in experiments in which the ranges of the variables studied are very small so that departures from the additive law of Equation (5·3) may be neglected. Latin Squares are most valuable when applied to testing methods, where it can usually be safely assumed that the various sources of error act independently of one another.

Randomisation

5·43. As with randomised blocks, the trials must be arranged in random order so far as this is consistent with the Latin Square design. A strip of extruded rubber varies in physical properties over its width and over its length, the variation over the width being about the same throughout the length. If this were strictly true, a piece of the sheet could be split up into m^2 pieces, and m treatments could be applied in the form of a Latin Square as in Table 5·3. Now suppose that, contrary to expectation, there exists a more complex trend in the physical properties of the untreated rubber resulting in a ridge of high values running in a diagonal direction, and suppose that all the D trials of Table 5·3 which fall on a diagonal coincide with this ridge. This would give an apparently high result for treatment D. If the square is randomised, the observations may be analysed as though no trend (correlation) existed, that is, the occurrence of a particular arrangement which corresponds to the trend will happen only by chance. If a result attains significance at a given level, say 5%, the chance that it is due to a fortuitous arrangement is also 5%; as in any other application of a test of significance, randomisation ensures that this is so.

Any linear trend in any direction, diagonal or otherwise, is eliminated by the Latin Square. Trends which appear as an interaction between rows and columns are not eliminated; they appear as part of the error and if large will tend to mask the effects of the factors and may render the experiment valueless.

From a given square such as Table 5·3 many different squares can be generated by permuting the rows, columns, and letters. Other squares exist which cannot be so generated. As is shown later, there are four basic sets of 4×4 Latin Squares, and $4! \times 3! \times 4 = 576$ different squares in all. The randomisation procedure selects, in effect, one of these squares at random. It is not practicable to enumerate all the squares and select one by a random process: the method adopted is to enumerate all the squares which are essentially different, i.e. not convertible into one another by permuting rows, columns, and letters, to choose one of these by a random process, and then to arrange the order of rows, columns, and letters also by a random process. This process of selecting a Latin Square is fully described in [5·1].

Example 5·2. Wear testing of textile fabrics

5·5. The following is an example of an experiment relating to the testing of rubber-covered fabric in the MARTINDALE wear tester carried out as a 4×4 Latin Square. The machine consists of four rectangular brass plates on each of which is fastened an abrading surface consisting of special-quality emery paper. Four weighted bushes, into which test samples of fabric are fixed, rest on the emery surfaces, and a mechanical device moves the bushes over the surface of the emery, thus abrading the test specimens. The loss in weight after a given number of cycles is used as a criterion of resistance to abrasion. There are slight differences between the four positions on the machine, and it is known from past experience that if a run is repeated under apparently identical conditions and using apparently identical samples, slightly different results are obtained, ascribable partly to variations in the emery paper and partly to variations in temperature, humidity, etc.

If samples of fabric are to be compared it is clearly desirable to eliminate the effect of variation from one position to another, and from one run to another, as far as possible. It could be assumed that the three factors, positions, runs, and materials acted independently, so that if one position gave a higher rate of wear than another it would do so in every run and on any material, and so on.

5·51. The experiment described involved four materials tested together in each of four runs on the machine. These numbers were chosen because the machine has four positions, so that a Latin Square design could be used [Table 5·4]. The entries denote the loss in weight (units of 0·1 mgm.) in a run of standard length, and the letters A to D refer to the four materials.

Table 5·4

RESULTS OF WEAR-TESTING EXPERIMENT: LATIN SQUARE

Run	Position in machine				Average
	4	2	1	3	
2	A(251)	B(241)	D(227)	C(229)	237
3	D(234)	C(273)	A(274)	B(226)	252
1	C(235)	D(236)	B(218)	A(268)	239
4	B(195)	A(270)	C(230)	D(225)	230
Average ..	229	255	237	237	240

Total for A = 1063   Average for A = 266
Total for B = 880   Average for B = 220
Total for C = 967   Average for C = 242
Total for D = 922   Average for D = 231

From a simple inspection of the averages it appears that:

(i) Material B is best (lowest loss).

(ii) Run 3 gives higher losses on the average than the others.

(iii) Position 2 is more severe than the others.

However, a statistical analysis is required to test the significance of these apparent differences.

5·52. The calculations are briefly as follows. (The analysis of all Latin Square experiments is similar.)

Correction for the mean (CM)

Square the total and divide by 16 (the number of observations).

Total sum of squares

Square all entries and add. Subtract CM.

Sum of squares between positions

Square the totals for each of the four positions and add. Divide by 4 (the number of observations in each total) and subtract CM.

Sum of squares between runs

Square the totals for each of the four runs and add. Divide by 4 and subtract CM.

Sum of squares between materials

Square the totals for each of the four materials and add. Divide by 4 and subtract CM.

Error sum of squares (residual)

From the total sum of squares subtract the sums of squares for runs, positions, and materials.

The complete calculations are given in Appendix 5C and lead to the analysis of variance shown in Table 5·41.

Table 5·41

ANALYSIS OF VARIANCE: DATA FROM TABLE 5·4

Source of variation	Degrees of freedom	Sum of squares	Mean square	Expectation of mean square*
Between runs	3	986·5	328·8	$\sigma_0^2 + 4S_R^2$
Between positions ..	3	1,468·5	489·5	$\sigma_0^2 + 4S_C^2$
Between materials ..	3	4,621·5	1,540·5	$\sigma_0^2 + 4S_T^2$
Residual	6	367·5	61·25	σ_0^2
Total	15	7,444·0		

* See Appendix 5A.

All three effects are significant: for $\phi_1 = 3$, $\phi_2 = 6$ the 5% level of F is 4·76. The value of F corresponding to materials greatly exceeds the 1% level, 9·78. The design has been successful in eliminating a considerable amount of variation associated with runs and positions which would otherwise have decreased markedly the sensitivity of the comparisons between materials.

The residual variance is 61·25. The variance, due to experimental error, of the average for one material (4 tests) is thus $61·25/4 = 15·3$. The standard error is $\sqrt{15·3} = 3·9$, based on 6 degrees of freedom. The value of t for 6 degrees of freedom and a significance level of 5% is 2·45, so that the 95% confidence limits are $\pm 2·45 \times 3·9 = \pm 9·6$ from the observed mean. For the four materials the confidence limits are:

A	..	256 to 276	C	..	232 to 252
B	..	210 to 230	D	..	221 to 241

There is little doubt that A is the worst, and that B is better than C. The confidence interval for D overlaps considerably those for B and C, so that D clearly cannot be distinguished with confidence from either B or C. In doubtful cases it would be necessary to calculate the confidence limits of the *differences* B — D and C — D directly.

Example 5·3. Preparation of an insecticide dust

5·53. Before a powerful insecticide can be used economically some means must be found for distributing it sparingly over the area to be treated, and this is usually done either by spraying a dilute solution of the insecticide in a suitable solvent or by mixing the insecticide with an inert powder and spreading the mixture over the area. When using the second method it is essential that the insecticide be uniformly distributed throughout the mixture, for otherwise there will be areas which receive too little or too much insecticide.

The object of the investigation described below was to find the best method of preparing a dust from a certain insecticide. Three factors were involved: (*a*) the inert powder used, (*b*) the method of mixing the ingredients, and (*c*) the form of the active ingredient itself, since several different forms, which might well vary in the effectiveness of dispersion, were available. It was required to study about six to eight variants of all three factors, and since this would lead to a lengthy experiment if all possible combinations were studied it was decided to use seven variants of each factor in a Latin Square design. It was reasonable to suppose that the three factors would act independently, to a first approximation at least, and even if this assumption were not strictly true the experiment would certainly pick out any important differences in time for the results to be used.

The Latin Square used is shown in Table 5·5. The letters A–G represent the seven diluents (inert powders) used, and the numbers in the cells are measures of the persistence of the insecticide, i.e. its ability to remain effective after spreading.

Table 5·5

PERSISTENCE OF INSECTICIDE POWDERS

Method of mixing	Form of active ingredient							Total	Mean
	1	2	3	4	5	6	7		
1	A 98	B 117	C 89	D 64	E 63	F 132	G 244	807	115
2	B 69	E 67	A 70	G 70	F 111	D 60	C 218	665	95
3	C 37	F 83	G 83	B 74	D 70	A 75	E 169	591	84
4	D 65	G 60	E 91	F 56	C 61	B 59	A 150	542	77
5	E 56	D 44	B 70	C 68	A 88	G 111	F 220	657	94
6	F 113	C 105	D 65	A 51	G 83	E 57	B 233	707	101
7	G 64	A 62	F 65	E 86	B 45	C 108	D 187	617	88
Total ..	502	538	533	469	521	602	1,421	4,586	
Mean ..	72	77	76	67	74	86	203		93·6

Diluent	A	B	C	D	E	F	G
Total ..	594	667	686	555	589	780	715
Mean ..	85	95	98	79	84	111	102

It is clear from inspection that active ingredient 7 is by far the most effective, with all methods and all diluents. Any differences between methods and diluents are less clear. The analysis of variance carried out in the usual way (details are given in Appendix 5D) gives Table 5·51.

Table 5·51

ANALYSIS OF VARIANCE OF DATA IN TABLE 5·5

Source of variation	Degrees of freedom	Sum of squares	Mean square	Expectation of mean square
Between methods.. ..	6	6,317	1,053	$\sigma_0^2 + 7S_R^2$
Between active ingredients	6	99,157	16,526	$\sigma_0^2 + 7S_C^2$
Between diluents	6	5,487	915	$\sigma_0^2 + 7S_T^2$
Error	30	13,541	451	σ_0^2
Total	48	124,502		

For the ingredients the value of F is obviously highly significant, mainly because ingredient 7, as already noted, is outstandingly good. The other two mean squares are possibly significant, i.e. at the 10% level of significance.

The error variance of one trial is 451; that of the mean of seven trials is 64·4 corresponding to a standard error of 8·0. The 95% confidence limits for the means are $\pm 2\cdot04 \times 8\cdot0 = \pm 16\cdot3$. Similarly, the 95% confidence limits of a difference between two means are $\pm 2\cdot04 \times 8\cdot0 \times \sqrt{2} = \pm 23\cdot0$. An observed difference greater than 23·0 indicates that a true difference exists.

Of the active ingredients, 7 exceeds all the others by 117 or more. The 95% confidence limits for the remainder are:

No.	Mean	95% Confidence limits	
		Lower	Upper
1	72	56	88
2	77	61	93
3	76	60	92
4	67	51	83
5	74	58	90
6	86	70	102

No difference between these means exceeds 23·0, and the conclusion is that all ingredients except 7 may be considered equally effective.*

The confidence limits for the seven methods and diluents are as follows:

Method	Mean	95% Confidence limits		Diluent	Mean	95% Confidence limits	
		Lower	Upper			Lower	Upper
1	115	99	131	A	85	69	101
2	95	79	111	B	95	79	111
3	84	68	100	C	98	82	114
4	77	61	93	D	79	63	95
5	94	78	110	E	84	68	100
6	101	85	117	F	111	95	127
7	88	72	104	G	102	86	118

* There is a likelihood of interaction when one ingredient is so much better than the rest. If it is required to differentiate further between ingredients 1 to 6, omit results of 7 and analyse as a Latin Square with one treatment missing. The design is then a YOUDEN Square (Chapter 6).

There are no clear differences between the methods and the diluents. If it is required to select with confidence the best diluent or method to use with ingredient 7, further trials should be carried out with ingredient 7 and the methods and diluents of interest. If it is required to recommend a formula without further experiments, ingredient 7, diluent F, method 1 would be suggested.

Form 7 is that in which the insecticide is now used for a number of important applications, but it is a crude form, and for some applications form 1 is used. The dust is prepared by the most economical of the methods (none of which gave outstandingly better performances than the others). The diluent used in practice is a mixture of G and C, this mixture being used to give a product of the desired bulk density.

Notes on design

5·531. The great advantage of the Latin Square design is that seven variants of each of the three factors can be tested with only 49 preparations. To carry out the full number of $7^3 = 343$ tests would have taken too long. It was realised that the three factors might not act completely independently, but previous experience suggested that any lack of independence would not be serious and any important differences would be shown up. It is clear, for example, that ingredient 7 is much better than any of the others, and knowledge on this point reduces the amount of testing necessary in any future investigation.

Estimate of missing values

5·54. The method of § **5·31** may be used to estimate missing values. For one missing value x and with the notation

R = total of known values in row containing x

C = total of known values in column containing x

T = total of known values in treatment values containing x

S = total of all available values

m = number of treatments, columns, or rows

then $$(m - 1)(m - 2)x = m(R + C + T) - 2S$$

Orthogonal squares

5·6. In many cases it is possible to find two squares of the same size which possess a property known as Orthogonality. Consider, for example, the following 4 × 4 squares based on two sets of four letters, denoted by their initial letters for brevity:

Set A	Set P
A B C D	P Q R S
B A D C	R S P Q
C D A B	S R Q P
D C B A	Q P S R

If these squares are superimposed we have the resultant square

AP BQ CR DS
BR AS DP CQ
CS DR AQ BP
DQ CP BS AR

Because both the original squares are Latin, each letter of set A occurs exactly once in each row and column, and so does each letter of set P. In addition each letter of set A occurs exactly once in the same cell as each letter of set P; and if the sets A and P represent two distinct sets of treatments then in the sixteen trials each member of the A set is tested exactly once with each member of the P set. The two sets of treatments are then said to be Orthogonal to each other and the two squares are said to be an orthogonal pair, or if there happen to be more than two distinct squares possessing the property, they form an orthogonal set. There are in fact three orthogonal 4 × 4 squares. The third, using the letters W X Y Z is

Set W

W X Y Z
Z Y X W
X W Z Y
Y Z W X

Superimposing this on the combination of squares A and P we have

APW BQX CRY DSZ
BRZ ASY DPX CQW
CSX DRW AQZ BPY
DQY CPZ BSW ARX

Every A now occurs once in each column, once in each row, once in conjunction with every P, and once in conjunction with every W, and so on. This orthogonality is not affected by any interchange of rows, columns, or treatments, within any set. There are therefore many orthogonal sets derivable from the basic set given above.

For the 5×5 square there are four orthogonal squares, 6×6 none, 7×7 six, and so on [5·1, p. 62]. When two sets of letters are used it is common to use Latin letters for one set and Greek letters for the second, and such squares are called Graeco-Latin Squares.

With these designs it is possible to test several sets of treatments in a compact experiment, provided the effects of the treatments are independent of one another and of the variations between rows and columns. But since the total number of degrees of freedom is $(m^2 - 1)$ the number of sets of letters is limited; each row, each column, and each set of m letters requires $(m - 1)$ degrees of freedom. With only one set this leaves $(m^2 - 1) - 3(m - 1)$ $= (m - 1)(m - 2)$ degrees of freedom for error. With two sets the factors require $4(m - 1)$ degrees of freedom, leaving only $(m^2 - 1) - 4(m - 1)$ $= (m - 1)(m - 3)$ for the residual, i.e. none for a 3×3 square. With three sets the factors take $5(m - 1)$, leaving $(m^2 - 1) - 5(m - 1) = (m - 1)(m - 4)$ for the residual, i.e. none for a 4×4 square. In general an $m \times m$ square can be used for not more than $(m - 2)$ sets of letters if an estimate of error variance is required; for an $m \times m$ square, with p sets ($p = 1$ for a Latin Square, $p = 2$ for a Graeco-Latin Square, and so on) and p not greater than $(m - 3)$, we have the following partition of the degrees of freedom:

Rows	$m - 1$
Columns	$m - 1$
Letters, i.e. factors other than those in rows and columns	$p(m - 1)$
Residual	$(m - p - 1)(m - 1)$
Total	$m^2 - 1$

The following example uses an 8×8 Graeco-Latin Square.

Example 5·4. Annealing copper tubes

5·61. The object of this experiment was to ascertain whether a modified annealing procedure could be introduced into the production of light gauge domestic copper tube. Essential conditions were that the tensile strength of the product should be uniform, with a minimum of 17 tons/sq. in., which had been achieved hitherto by annealing the tubes fully and then applying a light final draft. A possible alternative procedure was to anneal the material at a lower temperature than that required for full annealing, thereby eliminating the final drawing operation, and the experiments were designed to investigate this alternative.

In deciding the form of the tests it was necessary to consider possible causes of variation in the results, including variation in the material itself and variations in temperature over the annealing furnace. Material variations were studied by taking samples of eight tubes at random on each of eight days spread over a period of three weeks, thus allowing normal process variations to be covered adequately. In order to minimise temperature effects the furnace used was chosen to give as uniform a temperature as possible. The 64 tubes were held in the furnace in a jig having eight horizontal rows and eight vertical columns of holes, i.e. an 8 × 8 square. Tests were made at various nominal temperatures to determine that most likely to lead to favourable results. The construction of the furnace indicated that temperature variations, if present, would be mainly horizontal or vertical, and no appreciable interaction was expected between rows and columns.*

The absence of appreciable interaction enabled factors to be examined by means of a Latin or Graeco-Latin Square. A Graeco-Latin arrangement was, in fact, employed in the experiment, so that two factors each of eight treatments could be allotted to the 64 cells in such a way that the two factors and the row and column effects could be determined independently. The two factors were:

1. Day of manufacture.
2. Number allotted to an individual tube within the sample of eight.

From the point of view of this example the second is a dummy factor, since the numbering of the tubes did not correspond to any physical reality. It was included to ensure that the results from each tube at the various temperatures could be identified, and it has been left in the calculations for illustrative purposes. The numbers 1 to 8 could, if required, represent order of manufacture during the day, different pre-treatments, or different after-treatments of the tubes.

A separate square selected at random was used for each temperature, and the rows, columns, and letters were themselves randomised. The results for the nominal temperature of 300° C. are shown in Table 5·6, in which the rows and columns represent positions in the furnace, the letters A to H the day of manufacture, and the numbers 1 to 8 the designation within the sample. The figures in brackets are the tensile strengths in tons per square inch.

---

* This assumption cannot always be made, because the variation in temperature of some furnaces is radial. This could give rise to an appreciable interaction which would inflate the experimental error and render the experiment based on Latin or Graeco-Latin Squares insensitive. More complicated designs would then be necessary, on the lines of those given in Chapter 11.

Table 5·6

TESTS ON ANNEALING LIGHT GAUGE DOMESTIC COPPER TUBES

Column	1	2	3	4	5	6	7	8	Average
Row									
1	D3 (16·6)	H4 (16·9)	C5 (17·4)	B6 (17·4)	E8 (15·8)	A1 (18·2)	G2 (15·7)	F7 (15·8)	16·72
2	F6 (15·9)	E5 (16·4)	G4 (15·8)	A3 (19·0)	H2 (17·6)	B7 (17·8)	C8 (18·9)	D1 (17·1)	17·31
3	B5 (17·1)	C6 (16·8)	H3 (19·2)	D4 (16·6)	G1 (15·8)	F8 (17·8)	E7 (18·4)	A2 (18·3)	17·55
4	A4 (17·7)	G3 (15·9)	E6 (16·3)	F5 (16·0)	C7 (17·6)	D2 (17·8)	H1 (18·1)	B8 (16·5)	16·99
5	C1 (17·4)	B2 (17·0)	D8 (16·8)	H7 (19·2)	A5 (20·3)	E3 (18·4)	F4 (15·9)	G6 (15·7)	17·59
6	E2 (16·5)	F1 (16·0)	A7 (16·9)	G8 (15·9)	D6 (17·1)	C4 (17·5)	B3 (17·4)	H5 (19·6)	17·11
7	G7 (15·8)	A8 (16·9)	F2 (15·9)	E1 (16·5)	B4 (17·6)	H6 (19·4)	D5 (17·1)	C3 (18·3)	17·19
8	H8 (18·6)	D7 (17·4)	B1 (17·4)	C2 (19·2)	F3 (16·8)	G5 (15·7)	A6 (17·4)	E4 (18·4)	17·61
Average ..	16·95	16·66	16·96	17·48	17·33	17·82	17·36	17·46	17·25

Lot ..	A	B	C	D	E	F	G	H	Overall
Average..	18·09	17·28	17·89	17·06	17·09	16·26	15·79	18·58	17·25
Number	1	2	3	4	5	6	7	8	—
Average..	17·06	17·25	17·70	17·05	17·45	17·00	17·36	17·15	—

5·62. Carrying out the analysis of variance [Appendix 5E] we obtain Table 5·61.

Table 5·61

ANALYSIS OF VARIANCE OF DATA FROM TABLE 5·6

(Working units of 0·1 ton/sq. in.)

Source of variation	Degrees of freedom	Sum of squares	Mean square
Between rows of jig ..	7	543·2	77·6
Between columns of jig	7	769·9	110·0 (?)
Between positions ..	14	1,313·1	93·8 (?)
Between lots (letters) ..	7	4,831·7	690·3*
Between numbers ..	7 ⎫ 42	322·2 ⎫ 2,175·1	46·0 ⎫ 51·8
Residual	35 ⎭	1,852·9 ⎭	52·9 ⎭
Total	63	8,319·9	

(?) = Possibly significant (10% level)   * = Highly significant (1% level)

As expected, the mean square of the factor represented by numbers does not differ significantly from the mean square of the residual. The sum of squares for the number factor was therefore combined with that for the residual to provide a new estimate of error with 42 degrees of freedom.

Variation between columns (i.e. across the furnace) and total variation among positions (variation over all positions in the furnace) were judged possibly significant. There was no evidence of variation in a vertical direction in the furnace, but there was highly significant variation among the lots of tubes. Clearly the major factor causing variation in the strength was variation in the lots of tubes; position in the furnace was of little or no importance. Of the eight lots, six were supposedly identical, but F and G were of a slightly different composition. Further analysis showed that even if F and G are omitted there is still considerable variation between the lots, that is in daily manufacture.

Variation over the furnace had little or no effect on the total variation, confirming that the furnace was behaving well. Annealing at 300° C. did not keep the tensile strength of all tubes above 17 tons/sq. in., and the total variation was of the order of 4 tons. Tests at lower temperatures led to higher mean values but similar variability, which was unacceptable. Only by full annealing could reasonable uniformity be obtained, and then the tensile strength had to be raised to the required value by a further draft. The conclusion, therefore, was that the process could not be modified with current qualities of tube.

The 3 × 3 Latin Square

5·7. As will appear in Chapters 8 and 9, the properties of the 3 × 3 Latin Square are very useful in the design of factorial experiments with factors at three levels, and it is appropriate to consider this square in some detail at this stage.

An example in standard form is given in Table 5·7.

Table 5·7

3 × 3 LATIN SQUARE IN STANDARD FORM

Row	Column 1	Column 2	Column 3
1	L (1)	M (4)	N (7)
2	M (2)	N (5)	L (8)
3	N (3)	L (6)	M (9)

The cells are numbered 1–9 in the order shown. To measure the variation between the rows the three row totals are used:

$$R_1 = 1 + 4 + 7$$
$$R_2 = 2 + 5 + 8$$
$$R_3 = 3 + 6 + 9$$

Similarly for columns:

$$C_1 = 1 + 2 + 3$$
$$C_2 = 4 + 5 + 6$$
$$C_3 = 7 + 8 + 9$$

For the letters (treatments):

$$L = 1 + 6 + 8$$
$$M = 2 + 4 + 9$$
$$N = 3 + 5 + 7$$

The mean squares for rows, columns, and treatments are measures of the variation among these totals. They absorb six of the eight degrees of freedom, leaving two for the residual, which are ascribed to error.

Now form the Graeco-Latin Square, keeping the same numbering for the cells.

Table 5·71

3 × 3 GRAECO-LATIN SQUARES

Row	Column		
	1	2	3
1	LU (1)	MW (4)	NV (7)
2	MV (2)	NU (5)	LW (8)
3	NW (3)	LV (6)	MU (9)

The totals for rows, columns, and treatments (L, M, N) are as before. In addition we have the three treatments (U, V, W):

$$U = 1 + 5 + 9$$
$$V = 2 + 6 + 7$$
$$W = 3 + 4 + 8$$

The totals for (L, M, and N) are seen to be the sums of the three upward diagonals of the square, and those for (U, V, and W) the sums of the downward diagonals. The variation among the U, V, W totals leads to the mean square for the (U, V, W) treatments, with two degrees of freedom.

All the variation among the nine observations is accounted for by the four sources—rows, columns, (L, M, N) treatments, and (U, V, W) treatments— and it can be confirmed that the total sum of squares for the nine trials is identically equal to the total of the four sums of squares for rows, columns, and diagonals (L, M, N) and (U, V, W), each with two degrees of freedom. The total sum of squares is thus split into four independent components. Every total used in calculating the sum of squares for R represents a summation over all three columns, all three L-treatments, and all three U-treatments. For example:

$$R_1 = LUC_1 + MWC_2 + NVC_3$$
$$R_2 = MVC_1 + NUC_2 + LWC_3$$
$$R_3 = NWC_1 + LVC_2 + MUC_3$$

Thus any change in the relative effects of, say, C_1, C_2, and C_3 does not alter the relative values of R_1, R_2, and R_3; it will change them all by the same amount, and the sum of squares for rows is unaltered. The same argument applies to the other three sets of totals. The four sums of squares are thus independent of one another.

Suppose now that the treatments (L, M, N) and (U, V, W) are dummy treatments, i.e. the nine trials are simply the nine combinations of R and C. The total sum of squares can still be split into four independent components, two corresponding to rows and columns as before; the other two do not correspond to any treatments, but measure the extent by which the observations are not accounted for by simple row and column effects. If rows and columns are known to act independently of each other the remaining variation can only be error; otherwise it is a combination of interaction and error—the two cannot be separately estimated. The sum of the two diagonal sums of squares is therefore the interaction sum of squares, identical with that obtained in the usual way, i.e. by subtracting from the total sum of squares those due to rows and columns. It has, however, been split into two independent and easily calculated components. An immediate advantage is that the interaction sum of squares can be calculated independently, giving a check on the whole calculation. More important uses are made of the independent components of the interaction in Chapters 9 and 10.

The two components of the interaction are conventionally known as the I (downward diagonal) and J (upward diagonal) components. The separate diagonal totals are denoted by i_0, i_1, i_2, and j_0, j_1, j_2, and they are used in calculating the interaction sums of squares in exactly the same way as the row and column totals are used in calculating the row and column sums of squares.

The I and J components of the interaction do not usually correspond to any physically important effects. They are mathematically convenient, but there is in general no point in assessing them separately for significance. If the combined mean square is significant the factors interact, but there is nothing to be gained by testing the I and J components separately.

Example 5·5 consists of a number of 3×3 Graeco-Latin Squares, and the calculations for it serve to illustrate the above methods.

Example 5·5. Variation in the physical properties of synthetic yarn

5·71. Latin Squares, as has been pointed out, are appropriate when the sources of variation act independently, i.e. when they do not interact with one another. They can frequently be used to advantage in investigations like those of Chapter 4 or Example 5·2, in which the aim is to separate the effects of several assignable causes of variation and to estimate the magnitude of the resulting variations. If more than three causes are to be investigated, Graeco-Latin or higher squares must be used. In any $m \times m$ square the number of values that can be assigned to each variable is m. This may be a limitation, but it can be overcome to some extent by testing m of the treatments of one set in one square, m in another square, and so on. The same process can be used with more than one factor, and at the sacrifice of some information on the factors which are spread over several squares the utility of the Latin Square design may be greatly increased. The method of constructing and analysing such a design is best illustrated by an example.

N

The example used arose in an investigation into the causes of variation in physical properties of a synthetic yarn produced on an experimental unit. The yarn is produced in three stages:

(a) Molten polymer is extruded through fine orifices, producing a number of continuous filaments. This process is known as spinning.

(b) The filaments from stage (a) are collected on bobbins and run through a machine which imparts a twist to them, giving them greater cohesion. This process is known as pre-twisting.

(c) The twisted filaments are run through a machine—the drawframe— which stretches them to several times their original length. This process is known as drawing.

The object of the experiment was to isolate, and estimate the magnitude of, the variations in yarn properties associated with each stage of manufacture.

(i) It was thought possible that the spinning process might not be stable (variations in viscosity or rate of extrusion), and it was decided to take samples of the yarn from stage (a) at twelve equally spaced intervals of time during a run.

(ii) The positions on the pre-twist machine may differ systematically in some way which affects the properties of the yarn. Three sub-samples from each of the twelve from the spinning stage were twisted in three different positions on the pre-twister.

(iii) Variations associated with the drawing process may arise in two ways. First, there may be systematic differences between the positions on the frame; second, the drawing process may be unstable, so that there may be variations between one time of drawing and another. It was decided to examine yarn drawn in three positions on the frame and to draw on twelve successive days.

The variable conditions are thus:

Time of spinning   ..   .. $1, 2, 3, \ldots, 12$
Position in pre-twister ..   ..   A, B, C
Position in drawframe ..   ..   X, Y, Z
Day of drawing ..   ..   .. $1, 2, 3, \ldots, 12$

The variances of yarn strength—the property under investigation— associated with each of these factors are denoted by σ_S^2, σ_T^2, σ_D^2, and σ_{DD}^2 respectively. We are justified in assigning a variance to each of these factors because the values chosen can be regarded as a sample from a larger universe, e.g. the three positions in the drawframe can be regarded as a sample from the whole universe of drawframes of this kind. The object of the experiment is to test for the existence of these four variances and to determine the nature of the variations which have been shown to exist.

If each combination of the four factors were tested once, 1296 trials would be required. But if we assume that the four factors affect the yarn strength independently—in the present example this was a reasonable assumption— a much smaller experiment can be used, and the design used below involves 36 trials consisting of four 3×3 Graeco-Latin Squares. If there were only three times of spinning and three days of drawing, one Graeco-Latin Square could be used as follows:

Table 5·72

ARRANGEMENT OF THE NINE TRIALS IN A GRAECO-LATIN SQUARE

Day of drawing	Time of spin		
	1	2	3
1	AX	BY	CZ
2	CY	AZ	BX
3	BZ	CX	AY

The analysis of variance for this square would be:

Table 5·73

ANALYSIS OF VARIANCE OF TABLE 5·72

Source of variation	Degrees of freedom	Expectation of mean square
Time of spin	2	$\sigma_0^2 + 3\sigma_S^2$
Day of drawing	2	$\sigma_0^2 + 3\sigma_{DD}^2$
Position in pre-twister ..	2	$\sigma_0^2 + 3\sigma_T^2$
Position in drawframe ..	2	$\sigma_0^2 + 3\sigma_D^2$
Total	8	

The four factors use all the degrees of freedom, but if the error variance were known we could estimate the values of the four variances separately; otherwise the experiment must be enlarged. Twelve times of spin and twelve days of drawing can be examined in four 3×3 Graeco-Latin Squares, three times of spin and three days of drawing being allotted to each square. In order to avoid bias it is important to allot these factors to each square in a random order, e.g. by drawing lots.

Table 5·8

ARRANGEMENT OF EXPERIMENT IN FOUR SQUARES

Square No.		I				II		
Time of spinning		1	9	12		2	6	8
Day of drawing	Day 4 9 12	AY CX BZ	BX AZ CY	CZ BY AX	Day 1 3 6	CZ AX BY	BX CY AZ	AY BZ CX

Square No.		III				IV		
Time of spinning		3	7	10		4	5	11
Day of drawing	Day 5 8 10	BX CY AZ	AY BZ CX	CZ AX BY	Day 2 7 11	AZ CY BX	BY AX CZ	CX BZ AY

Four separate mean squares of time of spinning are provided—one from each square—and these may be combined to give an estimate of $\sigma_0^2 + 3\sigma_s^2$, based on eight degrees of freedom. Similarly we obtain an estimate of $\sigma_0^2 + 3\sigma_{DD}^2$ by combining the four sums of squares for day of draw. The four sums of squares are in each case based on four different sets of times or days, but since these were picked at random, each sum of squares provides an independent estimate of the same mean square, and the four can be combined to give an estimate based on eight degrees of freedom.

The same three positions on the pre-twister were tested in each square; we thus have four separate estimates of the mean strength of yarn twisted in each position, and from these we obtain:

(a) A more precise estimate of the effect of varying the twist position by averaging over the four squares.

(b) An estimate of error based on the discrepancies between the four estimates.

The analysis of variance for the pre-twist position would be as follows:

Source of variation	Degrees of freedom	Expectation of mean square
Between squares	3	—
Between pre-twist positions	2	$\sigma_0^2 + 12\sigma_T^2$
Error	6	σ_0^2
Total	11	

The mean for each position is the mean of twelve results, and the multiplier of σ_T^2 is therefore 12.

The same argument applies to drawframe positions, and the final analysis of variance takes the form of Table 5·81.

Table 5·81

ANALYSIS OF VARIANCE OF EXPERIMENT

Source of variation	Degrees of freedom	Expectation of mean square
Between squares	3	—
Between times of spin ..	8	$\sigma_0^2 + 3\sigma_S^2$
Between days of draw ..	8	$\sigma_0^2 + 3\sigma_{DD}^2$
Between positions in pre-twister	2	$\sigma_0^2 + 12\sigma_T^2$
Between positions on draw-frame	2	$\sigma_0^2 + 12\sigma_D^2$
Error	12	σ_0^2
Total	35	

At the end of the experiment 36 cones of yarn were obtained, corresponding to the 36 treatment combinations. Each of these was sampled by taking three lengths at random, and two tests were carried out on each. The means of these six tests were used in the analysis. One of the properties measured was tensile strength, the results for which are set out in Table 5·82.

Table 5·82

RESULTS FOR EXAMPLE 5·5

BLOCK I

Time	1 9 12				Total	Twist position totals			
Day 4	AY BX CZ	4·53	4·25	3·97	12·75	A	B	C	Total
9	CX AZ BY	4·05	3·05	3·61	10·71	10·90	12·26	10·80	33·96
12	BZ CY AX	4·40	2·78	3·32	10·50	Draw position totals			
Total		12·98	10·08	10·90	33·96	X	Y	Z	Total
						11·62	10·92	11·42	33·96

BLOCK II

Time	2 6 8				Total	Twist position totals			
Day 1	CZ BX AY	3·58	4·48	4·29	12·35	A	B	C	Total
3	AX CY BZ	4·68	3·85	3·23	11·76	13·04	12·21	11·14	36·39
6	BY AZ CX	4·50	4·07	3·71	12·28	Draw position totals			
Total		12·76	12·40	11·23	36·39	X	Y	Z	Total
						12·87	12·64	10·88	36·39

BLOCK III

Time	3 7 10				Total	Twist position totals			
Day 5	BX AY CZ	4·76	3·22	4·01	11·99	A	B	C	Total
8	CY BZ AX	4·54	2·97	4·10	11·61	11·62	11·70	11·64	34·96
10	AZ CX BY	4·30	3·09	3·97	11·36	Draw position totals			
Total		13·60	9·28	12·08	34·96	X	Y	Z	Total
						11·95	11·73	11·28	34·96

BLOCK IV

Time	4	5	11				Total	Twist position totals			
Day 2	AZ	BY	CX	4·10	4·18	3·46	11·74	A	B	C	Total
7	CY	AX	BZ	4·35	4·60	3·76	12·71	11·20	12·20	11·16	34·56
11	BX	CZ	AY	4·26	3·35	2·50	10·11	Draw position totals			
Total	..	..		12·71	12·13	9·72	34·56	X	Y	Z	Total
								12·32	11·03	11·21	34·56

		A	B	C	Total
Overall totals for twist position	.. .. ..	46·76	48·37	44·74	139·87

		X	Y	Z	Total
Overall totals for draw position	.. .. ..	48·76	46·32	44·79	139·87

The complete calculations are given in Appendix 5F; the following is a summary.

Correction terms

Overall $= CM_0 =$ (grand total)^2/36

Block I $= CM_1 =$ (Block I total)^2/9

Similarly for Blocks II–IV.

Sum of squares

Total　　　Square all 36 entries; add; subtract CM_0. Degrees of freedom $= 35$.

Twist position　Square the three overall totals A, B, and C; add; divide by 12; subtract CM_0. Degrees of freedom $= 2$.

Draw position　Square the three overall totals X, Y, and Z; add; divide by 12; subtract CM_0. Degrees of freedom $= 2$.

Days　　　Square the day totals in Block I; add; divide by 3; subtract CM_1.

　　　　　Repeat for Blocks II, III, and IV; add the four sums of squares. Degrees of freedom $= 4 \times 2 = 8$.

Times　　　As for Days.

Blocks　　Square the four block totals; add; divide by 9; subtract CM_0. Degrees of freedom $= 3$.

Error   From the total sum of squares subtract the other five. Degrees of freedom $= 35 - 2 - 2 - 8 - 8 - 3 = 12$.

The analysis of variance is shown in Table 5·83.

Table 5·83

ANALYSIS OF VARIANCE

Source of variation	Degrees of freedom	Sum of squares	Mean square
Between blocks	3	0·3561	0·1187
Between times	8	6·7939	0·8492*
Between days	8	2·3170	0·2896 (?)
Between twist positions	2	0·5514	0·2757
Between draw positions	2	0·6682	0·3341 (?)
Remainder (error)	12	1·3413	0·1118
Total	35	12·0279	

* = Highly significant   (?) = Possibly significant.

There is thus clear evidence of variation between times of spinning, and weak evidence of variation between days and between draw positions. In order to identify the nature of the variation the relevant averages are calculated. On technical grounds it can be assumed that, in spite of the weak evidence, there is little or no real variation from day to day; this means that all the averages for different times of spinning can be compared with one another; if this had not been the case we could have compared, for instance, times (1, 9, 12) with one another but not with the remainder, which correspond to different days of drawing. The overall averages for the three drawframe positions can be compared directly, since each is an average over all times, all days, and all pre-twister positions, and these are assumed to operate independently. The averages for the three drawframe positions are as follows:

MEANS OF DRAWFRAME POSITIONS

X	Y	Z	Grand mean
4·06	3·86	3·73	3·89

Draw position X appears to give better results than Y or Z, but the evidence for a draw position variation is weak. The nature of the variation between the times of spinning is indicated by the following averages for the twelve times:

MEANS OF TIMES OF SPINNING

1	2	3	4	5	6	7	8	9	10	11	12	Overall
4·33	4·25	4·53	4·24	4·04	4·13	3·09	3·74	3·36	4·03	3·24	3·63	3·89

It is clear that the strength fell suddenly after the sixth time and remained low for the remainder of the run. The reason for this should clearly be sought, but it may be noted that if the times had not been allocated at random to the four squares most of the variation between times would have appeared in the mean square "between squares" and could not have been attributed to either times of spinning or days of drawing.

LATIN CUBES

5·8. The principle of the Latin Square can be extended to more than two dimensions. Suppose, for example, a cube is divided into 27 cells consisting of three layers, each being a 3 × 3 square. The three layers can be made into three Latin Squares, two being derived from the first by cyclic permutation of rows, columns, or letters. One such set is the following.

LATIN CUBE

Column	Layer 1			Layer 2			Layer 3		
	1	2	3	1	2	3	1	2	3
Row									
1	A	B	C	B	C	A	C	A	B
2	B	C	A	C	A	B	A	B	C
3	C	A	B	A	B	C	B	C	A

Every combination of rows, columns, and letters occurs exactly once in each layer, and if the three layers are placed on top of one another to form a cube we see that each letter occurs three times in each layer, but these three are in three different rows and three different columns. Each combination of row and letter occurs three times, once in each layer and once in each column, and similarly for each combination of row and column, column and letter, layer and letter, etc.

Thus the average of the nine results for one letter is an average over three results in each row, three in each column, and three in each layer, and similarly for the average of the nine results in one row, column, or layer. The cube thus has properties similar to those of a Latin Square, and on the same assumptions of independence of factors as are made with the square, it provides estimates of the effect of rows, columns, layers, and letters. These require two degrees of freedom each, leaving $26 - 4 \times 2 = 18$ degrees of freedom for error.

The concept of orthogonal squares can be applied to cubes, giving Graeco-Latin cubes, etc. Hypercubes in more than three dimensions can also be constructed. For ease of illustration a $3 \times 3 \times 3$ cube has been used in the above discussion, but the same considerations apply to cubes of any size.

REFERENCE

[5·1] FISHER, R. A., and YATES, F. *Statistical Tables for Biological, Agricultural and Medical Research* (third edition). Oliver and Boyd (London, 1948).

APPENDIX 5A

EXPECTATIONS OF MEAN SQUARES

5A·1. The meaning of an expectation or expected value was explained in Chapter 4, and the expectations of the mean squares in the analysis of variance of simple sampling and testing experiments were obtained. The method of arriving at expressions for the expectations is given in this appendix and is applied to randomised blocks and Latin Squares.

5A·2. Two general equations are used. The first expresses the fact, which may be accepted as self-evident, that the expectation of the sum of a number of quantities is equal to the sum of the separate expectations, e.g. if a, b, and c are constants:

$$W = ax + by + cz$$
$$E(W) = aE(x) + bE(y) + cE(z) \quad \dots\dots\dots\dots(5A\cdot1)$$

This is true whatever the quantities x, y, and z, whether they are independent of one another or not.

The second equation follows from Equation $(5A\cdot1)$ and from the definition of the variance. The expectation of y is the true, or universe, mean, i.e.:

$$E(y) = \mu$$

The variance of y is by definition

$$\sigma^2 = V(y) = E(y - \mu)^2 = E\{y - E(y)\}^2$$
$$= E(y^2) - \{E(y)\}^2$$
$$\therefore \quad E(y^2) = \{E(y)\}^2 + V(y) \quad \dots\dots\dots\dots\dots(5A\cdot2)$$

Application of Equations $(5A \cdot 1)$ and $(5A \cdot 2)$ enables the expectation of the mean squares to be derived quite simply.

Randomised Blocks

5A·3. As stated in § **5·16**, the assumption made in using a randomised block design is that the effects of blocks and treatments are independent and additive, i.e.

$$y_{ij} = \mu + B_i + T_j + e_{ij}$$

Since $E(e) = 0$:

$$E(y_{ij}) = \mu + B_i + T_j$$

Table 5A·1 gives the analysis of variance.

Table 5A·1

ANALYSIS OF VARIANCE OF RANDOMISED BLOCKS

Source of variation	Sum of squares	Degrees of freedom	Mean square
Between blocks ..	$m\Sigma_i(\bar{y}_i - \bar{y})^2$	$k - 1$	
Between treatments	$k\Sigma_j(\bar{y}_j - \bar{y})^2$	$m - 1$	
Remainder.. ..	$\Sigma_{ij}(y_{ij} - \bar{y}_i - \bar{y}_j + \bar{y})^2$	$(k - 1)(m - 1)$	
Total	$\Sigma_{ij}(y_{ij} - \bar{y})^2$	$mk - 1$	

In the table $\bar{y}_i$ denotes the mean of a block, $\bar{y}_j$ the mean of a treatment, and $\bar{y}$ the grand mean. Σ_i denotes summation over blocks, Σ_j summation over treatments, and Σ_{ij} summation over all observations.

In computations we normally use expressions containing the sums and not the means, but both forms are seen to be equivalent.

The following relations may easily be verified.

$$E(\bar{y}_i) = \mu + B_i$$
$$E(\bar{y}_j) = \mu + T_j$$
$$E(\bar{y}) = \mu$$
$$\Sigma B_i = \Sigma T_j = 0$$
$$E(\bar{y}_i - \bar{y}) = B_i$$
$$E(\bar{y}_j - \bar{y}) = T_j$$
$$E(y_{ij} - \bar{y}) = B_i + T_j$$

In a randomised block experiment with k blocks and m treatments the expression for the sum of squares between blocks is

$$(\text{SS})_B = m\Sigma_i(\bar{y}_i - \bar{y})^2$$
$$\therefore \quad E(\text{SS})_B = mE[\Sigma_i(\bar{y}_i - \bar{y})^2] = m\Sigma_i[E(\bar{y}_i - \bar{y})^2]$$
$$= m\Sigma_i[E(\bar{y}_i - \bar{y})]^2 + m\Sigma_i[V(\bar{y}_i - \bar{y})]$$
$$= m\Sigma_i B_i^2 + kmV(\bar{y}_i - \bar{y})$$

$V(\bar{y}_i - \bar{y})$ is obtained as follows:

$$\bar{y}_i - \bar{y} = \bar{y}_i - \frac{1}{k}(\bar{y}_1 + \bar{y}_2 + \ldots + \bar{y}_k)$$

$$= -\frac{\bar{y}_1}{k} - \frac{\bar{y}_2}{k} + \ldots + \frac{k-1}{k}\bar{y}_i - \ldots - \frac{\bar{y}_k}{k}$$

Now for any set of independent variables $x_1, x_2, \ldots$ [S.M., § 3·63]:

$$V(ax_1 + bx_2 + \ldots) = a^2V(x_1) + b^2V(x_2) + \ldots$$

Now
$$V(\bar{y}_1) = V(\bar{y}_2) = \ldots = \sigma_0^2/m$$

$$\therefore \quad V(\bar{y}_i - \bar{y}) = \frac{\sigma_0^2}{m}\left\{\frac{k-1}{k^2} + \frac{(k-1)^2}{k^2}\right\} = \frac{k-1}{k}\frac{\sigma_0^2}{m}$$

$$\therefore \quad E(\text{SS})_B = m\Sigma_i B_i^2 + (k-1)\sigma_0^2$$

$$\therefore \quad E(\text{MS})_B = \frac{m\Sigma_i B_i^2}{k-1} + \sigma_0^2$$

where $(\text{MS})_B$ denotes the mean square between blocks.

$\Sigma_i B_i^2/(k-1)$ is analogous to a variance, i.e. it is a sum of squared deviations from the mean, divided by the number of degrees of freedom. If the blocks represented a random selection it would be an estimate of the variance of the universe of blocks, and may sometimes be so regarded.

An exactly similar argument leads to the expectation of the mean square between treatments:

$$E(\text{MS})_T = \frac{k\Sigma_j T_j^2}{m-1} + \sigma_0^2$$

For the total sum of squares the argument is again similar:

$$E(\text{TSS}) = E\{\Sigma_i\Sigma_j(y_{ij} - \bar{y})^2\} = \Sigma_i\Sigma_j E(y_{ij} - \bar{y})^2$$
$$= \Sigma_i\Sigma_j\{E(y_{ij} - \bar{y})\}^2 + \Sigma_i\Sigma_j V(y_{ij} - \bar{y})$$
$$= \Sigma_i\Sigma_j(B_i + T_j)^2 + (km-1)\sigma_0^2$$
$$= m\Sigma_i B_i^2 + k\Sigma_j T_j^2 + (km-1)\sigma_0^2$$

since $\Sigma_i B_i = \Sigma_j T_j = 0$.

The error sum of squares is found by subtracting from the total the sums of squares "between blocks" and "between treatments." This gives

$$E(\text{SS})_0 = \sigma_0{}^2(km - 1 - k + 1 - m + 1)$$
$$= \sigma_0{}^2(k - 1)(m - 1)$$
$$E(\text{MS})_0 = \sigma_0{}^2$$

The expectations of all mean squares are therefore as shown in Table 5A·2.

Table 5A·2

EXPECTATIONS OF MEAN SQUARES IN RANDOMISED
BLOCK DESIGNS

Source of variation	Degrees of freedom	Expectation of mean square
Between blocks ..	$k - 1$	$\sigma_0{}^2 + m\Sigma_i B_i{}^2/(k - 1)$
Between treatments ..	$m - 1$	$\sigma_0{}^2 + k\Sigma_j T_j{}^2/(m - 1)$
Residual error.. ..	$(k - 1)(m - 1)$	$\sigma_0{}^2$
Total	$km - 1$	

Latin Squares

5A·4. For a Latin Square the set-up is

$$y_{ijk} = \mu + R_i + C_j + T_k + e_{ijk}$$

i, j, k run from 1 to m for an $m \times m$ square

and as before $\Sigma R_i = \Sigma C_j = \Sigma T_k = 0$

To illustrate how the particular properties of the Latin Square affect the reasoning, consider the two squares in Table 5A·3; I is Latin; II is not.

Table 5A·3

I

Row	Column 1	Column 2	Column 3	Expectation of total
1	X	Y	Z	$3\mu + 3R_1$ $+ \Sigma C + \Sigma T$
2	Y	Z	X	$3\mu + 3R_2$ $+ \Sigma C + \Sigma T$
3	Z	X	Y	$3\mu + 3R_3$ $+ \Sigma C + \Sigma T$
Expectation of total	$3\mu + 3C_1$ $+ \Sigma R + \Sigma T$	$3\mu + 3C_2$ $+ \Sigma R + \Sigma T$	$3\mu + 3C_3$ $+ \Sigma R + \Sigma T$	$9\mu + 3\Sigma R$ $+ 3\Sigma C + 3\Sigma T$

II

Row	Column			Expectation of total
	1	2	3	
1	X	Y	Z	$3\mu + 3R_1$ $+ \Sigma C + \Sigma T$
2	X	Z	Y	$3\mu + 3R_2$ $+ \Sigma C + \Sigma T$
3	Y	Z	X	$3\mu + 3R_3$ $+ \Sigma C + \Sigma T$
Expectation of total	$3\mu + 3C_1$ $+ \Sigma R + 2T_1$ $+ T_2$	$3\mu + 3C_2$ $+ \Sigma R + T_2$ $+ 2T_3$	$3\mu + 3C_3$ $+ \Sigma R + \Sigma T$	$9\mu + 3\Sigma R$ $+ 3\Sigma C + 3\Sigma T$

The expectations of the treatment totals are

Treatment	Square I	Square II
X	$3\mu + \Sigma R + \Sigma C + 3T_1$	$3\mu + \Sigma R + 2C_1 + C_3 + 3T_1$
Y	$3\mu + \Sigma R + \Sigma C + 3T_2$	$3\mu + \Sigma R + \Sigma C + 3T_2$
Z	$3\mu + \Sigma R + \Sigma C + 3T_3$	$3\mu + \Sigma R + 2C_2 + C_3 + 3T_3$

Since $\Sigma R = \Sigma C = \Sigma T = 0$, we see that the three totals for the treatments are, in the Latin Square, affected only by the treatment terms (and the mean), whereas in the other square they also contain contributions from the columns (in the general case also from rows). The following relations are therefore true for Latin Squares but not for any other squares.

$$E(y_{ijk}) = \mu + R_i + C_j + T_k$$
$$E(\bar{y}_i) = \mu + R_i$$
$$E(\bar{y}_j) = \mu + C_j$$
$$E(\bar{y}_k) = \mu + T_k$$
$$E(\bar{y}) = \mu$$

The expectations of the mean squares are found in exactly the same way as for randomised blocks. For example, the sum of squares for rows is

$$(SS)_R = m\Sigma(\bar{y}_i - \bar{y})^2$$
$$E(SS)_R = m\Sigma_i\{E(\bar{y}_i - \bar{y})\}^2 + m\Sigma_iV(\bar{y}_i - \bar{y})$$
$$= m\Sigma_iR_i^2 + (m - 1)\sigma_0^2$$

Similarly for columns and treatments:

$$E(\text{SS})_C = m\Sigma_j C_j^2 + (m-1)\sigma_0^2$$
$$E(\text{SS})_T = m\Sigma_k T_k^2 + (m-1)\sigma_0^2$$

Total sum of squares $= \text{TSS} = \Sigma_{ij}(y_{ijk} - \bar{y})^2.$

$$E(\text{TSS}) = \Sigma_{ij}\{E(y_{ijk} - \bar{y})\}^2 + \Sigma_{ij}V(y_{ijk} - \bar{y})$$
$$= m\Sigma_i R_i^2 + m\Sigma_j C_j^2 + m\Sigma_k T_k^2 + (m^2 - 1)\sigma_0^2$$

Because of the properties of the Latin Square, summation of y_{ijk} over all values of i and j (all rows and columns) is a summation over all treatments, m times each. Hence, if T_k^2 is summed over all rows and columns the result is $m\Sigma_k T_k^2$.

By subtraction we find the error sum of squares:

$$E(\text{SS})_0 = \sigma_0^2\{(m^2 - 1) - 3(m - 1)\}$$
$$= \sigma_0^2(m - 1)(m - 2)$$

The mean squares are found by dividing by the degrees of freedom $(m-1)$ or R, C, and T, and $(m-1)(m-2)$ for the residual, giving Table 5A·4.

Table 5A·4

EXPECTATIONS IN LATIN SQUARE DESIGNS

Source of variation	Degrees of freedom	Expectation of mean square
Between rows	$m-1$	$\sigma_0^2 + m\Sigma R^2/(m-1)$
Between columns ..	$m-1$	$\sigma_0^2 + m\Sigma C^2/(m-1)$
Between treatments ..	$m-1$	$\sigma_0^2 + m\Sigma T^2/(m-1)$
Residual error	$(m-1)(m-2)$	σ_0^2
Total	m^2-1	

APPENDIX 5B

COMPUTATION FOR EXAMPLE 5·1

5B·1. Table 5B·1 gives the data of Table 5·2, after subtracting 17·5 and multiplying by 10, and rearranging according to blends.

Table 5B·1

Blend of acetanilide	$y = 10(\%\ \text{loss} - 17\cdot5)$							
	Block I		Block II		Block III		$T\ (= \Sigma y)$	T^2
	y	y^2	y	y^2	y	y^2		
A	− 6	36	− 10	100	0	0	− 16	256
B	7	49	17	289	− 4	16	20	400
C	− 5	25	6	36	− 2	4	− 1	1
D	− 24	576	− 15	225	3	9	− 36	1,296
E	8	64	8	64	23	529	39	1,521
Total ..	− 20	750	6	714	20	558	6	3,474

Grand Total $\Sigma y = 6$ $\Sigma y^2 = 2022$

Correction for mean $= \text{CM} = 6^2/15$ $= 2\cdot40$

Total sum of squares $= 2022 - 2\cdot4$ $= 2019\cdot6$

Blocks sum of squares $= \frac{1}{5}\{(-20)^2 + 6^2 + 20^2\} - 2\cdot4$

                      $= 167\cdot2 - 2\cdot4$ $= 164\cdot8$

Blends sum of squares $= 3474/3 - 2\cdot4$

                      $= 1158\cdot0 - 2\cdot4$ $= 1155\cdot6$

Error sum of squares $= 2019\cdot6 - 164\cdot8 - 1155\cdot6$

                      $= 2019\cdot6 - 1320\cdot4$ $= 699\cdot2$

These sums of squares, divided by 100 and rounded off to the second decimal place, which is adequate for these small numbers of degrees of freedom, are inserted in Table 5·21.

5B·2. The following is an alternative method of calculation, described briefly in § **5·16.** It is longer than the method used above and is introduced to make the physical implications clear. We start from the equation

$$y_{ij} - \bar{y} = B_i + T_j + e_{ij} \quad \dots\dots\dots\dots\dots(5B\cdot1)$$

and estimate the B_i's and the T_j's. The estimated values of B_i and T_j are denoted by b_i, t_j.

$\bar{y}$ = grand mean = + 6/15 $= +\ 0\cdot4$

Deviation of $\begin{cases} b_1 = -\ 20/5 - 0\cdot4 \\ b_2 = +\ 6/5 - 0\cdot4 \\ b_3 = +\ 20/5 - 0\cdot4 \end{cases}$ $\begin{matrix} = -\ 4\cdot4 \\ = +\ 0\cdot8 \\ = +\ 3\cdot6 \end{matrix}$

block means from

grand mean

                   Sum b 0·0

Deviation of
treatment means
from grand
mean

$$\begin{cases} t_1 = -16/3 - 0.4 & = -5.7 \\ t_2 = +20/3 - 0.4 & = +6.3 \\ t_3 = -1/3 - 0.4 & = -0.7 \\ t_4 = -36/3 - 0.4 & = -12.4 \\ t_5 = +39/3 - 0.4 & = +12.6 \end{cases}$$

Sum t $+0.1$

The sum is 0·1 instead of 0 because of rounding errors.

We can now calculate the expected values of the results from

$$E(y_{ij}) = \bar{y} + b_i + t_j \dots\dots\dots\dots\dots(5B \cdot 2)$$

Table 5B·2 gives the calculated and observed yields and the differences, which are attributed to errors.

Table 5B·2

Block	Treatment	Yield		(Obs. − Exp.) = e	e^2
		y (expected) (1)	y (observed) (2)	(3)	(4)
1	A	− 9·7	− 6	+ 3·7	13·69
	B	+ 2·3	+ 7	+ 4·7	22·09
	C	− 4·7	− 5	− 0·3	0·09
	D	− 16·4	− 24	− 7·6	57·76
	E	+ 8·6	+ 8	− 0·6	0·36
2	A	− 4·5	− 10	− 5·5	30·25
	B	+ 7·5	+ 17	+ 9·5	90·25
	C	+ 0·5	+ 6	+ 5·5	30·25
	D	− 11·2	− 15	− 3·8	14·44
	E	+ 13·8	+ 8	− 5·8	33·64
3	A	− 1·7	0	+ 1·7	2·89
	B	+ 10·3	− 4	− 14·3	204·49
	C	+ 3·3	− 2	− 5·3	28·09
	D	− 8·4	+ 3	+ 11·4	129·96
	E	+ 16·6	+ 23	+ 6·4	40·96
Total		+ 6·3	+ 6	− 0·3	699·21

The sum of column (1) should be equal to the sum of column (2), and the sum of column (3) should be zero, as they are, apart from rounding-off errors. The sum of e^2 agrees exactly with that already found above:

$$s_0^2 = 699 \cdot 21/8 = 87 \cdot 40 \to \sigma_0^2$$

O

To find the sums of squares between blocks we square the deviations of the block means from the grand mean, sum the squares, and multiply by 5, the number of tests in each block. This multiplication is necessary because each of the squared quantities is the average of five responses. For the sum of squares between blends the procedure is the same, multiplying by 3 instead of 5.

Sum of squares
between blocks $= 5(4\cdot4^2 + 0\cdot8^2 + 3\cdot6^2) = 164\cdot80$

Sum of squares
between blends $= 3(5\cdot7^2 + 6\cdot3^2 + 0\cdot7^2 + 12\cdot4^2 + 12\cdot6^2) = 1155\cdot57$

To test the significance of the variation between blends we compare 288·9 ($= 1155\cdot57/4$) with 87·4 by the F-test with four and eight degrees of freedom. This establishes the significance of the variation. These sums of squares and mean squares have to be divided by 100 to express them in terms of the original units (see Table 5·21).

5B·3. The above method of presenting the analysis shows that the procedure is to assume that the results can be expressed by Equation (*5B·1*) and estimate the constants of the equation. We then calculate the results that would be expected with these values of the constants in the absence of experimental error and ascribe the differences between the calculated and observed results to error.

APPENDIX 5C

COMPUTATIONS FOR EXAMPLE 5·2

TABLE 5C·1 gives the data of Table 5·4 with 240 subtracted.

Table 5C·1

Run	Position in machine				Total
	4	2	1	3	
2	(A) + 11	(B) + 1	(D) − 13	(C) − 11	− 12
3	(D) − 6	(C) + 33	(A) + 34	(B) − 14	+ 47
1	(C) − 5	(D) − 4	(B) − 22	(A) + 28	− 3
4	(B) − 45	(A) + 30	(C) − 10	(D) − 15	− 40
Total ..	− 45	+ 60	− 11	− 12	− 8

Total material A ..   .. $+ 103$
Total material B ..   .. $- 80$
Total material C ..   .. $+ 7$
Total material D ..   .. $- 38$

(1) Correction for the mean $= (- 8)^2/16$ $= 4\cdot0$

Crude sums of squares

(2) Total $= 7448$

(3) Between runs $\dfrac{(- 12)^2 + 47^2 + (- 3)^2 + (- 40)^2}{4}$ $= 990\cdot5$

(4) Between positions $\dfrac{(- 45)^2 + 60^2 + (- 11)^2 + (- 12)^2}{4} = 1472\cdot5$

(5) Between materials $\dfrac{103^2 + (- 80)^2 + 7^2 + (- 38)^2}{4}$ $= 4625\cdot5$

Corrected sums of squares

(6) Total $= (2) - (1)$ $= 7444\cdot0$
(7) Between runs $= (3) - (1)$ $= 986\cdot5$
(8) Between positions $= (4) - (1) = 1468\cdot5$
(9) Between materials $= (5) - (1) = 4621\cdot5$
(10) Error $= (6) - (7) - (8) - (9) = 367\cdot5$

The analysis of variance is shown in Table 5C·2.

Table 5C·2

Source of variation	Degrees of freedom	Sum of squares	Mean square	Expectation of mean square
Between runs ..	3	986·5	328·8	$\sigma_0^2 + 4S_R^2$
Between positions ..	3	1,468·5	489·5	$\sigma_0^2 + 4S_C^2$
Between materials ..	3	4,621·5	1,540·5	$\sigma_0^2 + 4S_T^2$
Error..	6	367·5	61·25	σ_0^2
Total..	15	7,444·0		

The alternative method of analysis given for randomised blocks in Appendix 5B can also be applied, using Equation (*5·3*). This may be left as an exercise for the reader.

APPENDIX 5D

COMPUTATIONS FOR EXAMPLE 5·3

THE data are given in Table 5·5.

    (1) Correction for mean $= 4586^2/49$ $= 429{,}212$

        Crude sums of squares

    (2) Total $= 553{,}714$

    (3) Between methods (rows) $=$
$$(807^2 + 665^2 + 591^2 + 542^2 + 657^2 + 707^2 + 617^2)/7 = 435{,}529$$

    (4) Between active ingredients (columns) $=$
$$(502^2 + 538^2 + 533^2 + 469^2 + 521^2 + 602^2 + 1421^2)/7 = 528{,}369$$

    (5) Between diluents (letters) $=$
$$(594^2 + 667^2 + 686^2 + 555^2 + 589^2 + 780^2 + 715^2)/7 = 434{,}699$$

        Corrected sums of squares

          (6) Total $= (2) - (1)$ $= 124{,}502$

          (7) Methods $= (3) - (1)$ $= 6{,}317$

          (8) Ingredients $= (4) - (1)$ $= 99{,}157$

          (9) Diluents $= (5) - (1)$ $= 5{,}487$

         (10) Error $= (6) - (7) - (8) - (9) = 13{,}541$

These sums of squares are entered in Table 5·51.

APPENDIX 5E

COMPUTATIONS FOR EXAMPLE 5·4

TABLE 5E·1 reproduces the data of Table 5·6 with 15 subtracted and multiplied by 10, i.e. $y = 10(\text{strength} - 15)$.

Table 5E·1

Column	1	2	3	4	5	6	7	8	Total	Average
Row										
1	D3(16)	H4(19)	C5(24)	B6(24)	E8(8)	A1(32)	G2(7)	F7(8)	138	17·2
2	F6(9)	E5(14)	G4(8)	A3(40)	H2(26)	B7(28)	C8(39)	D1(21)	185	23·1
3	B5(21)	C6(18)	H3(42)	D4(16)	G1(8)	F8(28)	E7(34)	A2(33)	200	25·0
4	A4(27)	G3(9)	E6(13)	F5(10)	C7(26)	D2(28)	H1(31)	B8(15)	159	19·9
5	C1(24)	B2(20)	D8(18)	H7(42)	A5(53)	E3(34)	F4(9)	G5(7)	207	25·9
6	E2(15)	F1(10)	A7(19)	G8(9)	D6(21)	C4(25)	B3(24)	H5(46)	169	21·1
7	G7(8)	A8(19)	F2(9)	E1(15)	B4(26)	H6(44)	D5(21)	C3(33)	175	21·9
8	H8(36)	D7(24)	B1(24)	C2(42)	F3(18)	G5(7)	A6(24)	E4(34)	209	26·1
Total	156	133	157	198	186	226	189	197	1,442	—
Average	19·5	16·6	19·6	24·8	23·3	28·3	23·6	24·6	—	22·53

Table 5E·1 (*continued*)

Lot	A	B	C	D	E	F	G	H	Overall
Total ..	247	182	231	165	167	101	63	286	1,442
Average ..	30·9	22·8	28·9	20·6	20·9	12·6	7·9	35·8	—
Number ..	1	2	3	4	5	6	7	8	—
Total ..	165	180	216	164	196	160	189	172	1,442
Average ..	20·6	22·5	27·0	20·5	24·5	20·0	23·6	21·5	—

The analysis of variance computations follow the usual lines, the steps being as follows:

(1) Correction for the mean = 32,490·1

Crude sums of squares

(2) Total (square all entries and add) = 40,810·0
(3) Between rows (square row totals, add, and divide by 8) = 33,033·3
(4) Between columns (square column totals, add, and divide by 8) = 33,260·0
(5) Between lots (square lot totals, add, and divide by 8) = 37,321·8
(6) Between numbers (square number totals, add, and divide by 8) = 32,812·3

Corrected sums of squares

(7) Total = (2) − (1) = 8319·9
(8) Between rows = (3) − (1) = 543·2
(9) Between columns = (4) − (1) = 769·9
(10) Between lots = (5) − (1) = 4831·7
(11) Between numbers = (6) − (1) = 322·2
(12) Error = (7) − (8) − (9) − (10) − (11) = 1852·9

These sums of squares and the corresponding mean squares (based on seven degrees of freedom for rows, columns, lots, and numbers; 35 for error) are entered in Table 5·61.

APPENDIX 5F

COMPUTATION FOR EXAMPLE 5·5

THE data of Table 5·82 and the various totals lead to the following computations for the analysis of variance:

Correction terms

(1) Overall $CM_0 = 139.87^2/36$ $= 543.4338$

(2) Square I $CM_1 = 33.96^2/9$ $= 128.1424$

(3) Square II $CM_2 = 36.39^2/9$ $= 147.1369$

(4) Square III $CM_3 = 34.96^2/9$ $= 135.8002$

(5) Square IV $CM_4 = 34.56^2/9$ $= 132.7104$

(6) Sum of CM_1 to CM_4 $= 543.7899$

Crude sums of squares

(7) *Total* = Sum of squares of all 36 entries $= 555.4617$

(8) *Pretwister positions*

$\{46.76^2 + 48.37^2 + 44.74^2\}/12$ $= 543.9852$

(9) *Drawframe positions*

$\{48.76^2 + 46.32^2 + 44.79^2\}/12$ $= 544.1020$

(10) *Times of spinning.* Square the 12 totals for spinning
times, add, and divide by 3 $= 550.5838$

(11) *Day of draw.* Square the 12 totals for day of draw,
add, and divide by 3 $= 546.1069$

(12) *Blocks.* Square the 4 block totals, add, and divide by 9 $= 543.7899$

(Note that (12) is identical with (6).)

Corrected sum of squares

(13) Total $= (7) - (1)$ $=$ 12.0279

(14) Between pre-twister positions $= (8) - (1)$ $=$ 0.5514

(15) Between drawframe positions $= (9) - (1)$ $=$ 0.6682

(16) Between times of spinning $= (10) - (6)$ $=$ 6.7939

(17) Between days of drawing $= (11) - (6)$ $=$ 2.3170

(18) Between blocks $= (12) - (1)$ $=$ 0.3561

(19) Error $= (13) - (14) - (15) - (16) - (17) - (18)$ $=$ 1.3413

These sums of squares are entered in Table 5.83.

CHAPTER 6

INCOMPLETE RANDOMISED BLOCK DESIGNS

The principles of designing experiments for comparing a number of treatments when uniform conditions can be maintained within blocks of observations, each accommodating one replicate (or the same number of replicates) of each treatment, were discussed in Chapter 5. Sometimes experimental conditions will not permit blocks large enough to include every treatment, so that all treatments cannot be tested under uniform conditions; nevertheless, by suitably designed experiments, valid and efficient comparisons between the treatments can be made without being disturbed by the differences between the blocks. The appropriate designs, which must be rigorously followed, may be regarded as elaborations of the idea of a control treatment, which is familiar to experimenters. A list of these designs is given, and the method of analysing the results is described, with examples. An appendix gives the appropriate method of dealing with the results of a designed experiment in which some of the results are missing.

Introduction

6·1. Chapter 5 dealt with the straightforward comparison of a number of treatments,* such as different processes or different solvents. In agronomic work such comparisons are known as varietal trials. A trial in which each treatment is applied only once rarely gives adequate precision; it must usually be replicated in order to reduce the experimental error. To keep the error variance as small as possible the experiment is arranged in blocks, one replicate per block if the block is large enough; the comparisons of the treatments may then be made within blocks. The randomised block design of Table 5·2 involved five treatments (A, B, C, D, E) with three replications each, the fifteen observations being arranged in three blocks of five in such a way that every block contained one replicate of each treatment. The Latin Square design of Table 5·3 developed the block principle and coupled it with the restriction that the material must be classifiable into four blocks in two ways instead of one, with the consequence that the design must take the form of a square. The two ways referred to corresponded to the rows and columns of the table, the observations being assigned to the cells in the manner explained. As in the first example, every treatment was equally represented in every block, counting in either direction, and every block contained exactly one replicate of each treatment.

* The term "treatment" is used generically to denote any controlled variation in conditions. In this sense different processes, different varieties of plants, different solvents in a chemical process, and so on, are effectively different treatments.

In practice, owing to shortage of apparatus or experimental facilities, it may not be possible to examine all the treatments together under comparable conditions; further, the materials may not be classifiable in precisely the number of categories required. In such cases the straightforward designs dealt with in Chapter 5 cannot be applied. It is possible, at the price of some complication, to use designs in which every treatment is not equally represented in every block; such designs are known as Incomplete Block Designs. They occur in using the MARTINDALE wear tester [§ 5·4], in which only four treatments can be compared in one run; in rubber testing, in which the number of samples that can be cured together is limited and curing conditions are not exactly reproducible; in testing rubber for fatigue and flex-cracking, in which the number of samples that can be examined simultaneously is limited.

In chemical work the available batches of raw material of uniform quality may not suffice for more than a limited number of trials; if the experiment requires a greater number, each replicate must be spread over two or more batches. In the comparison of the effects of different conditions on the yield of penicillin by the stirred culture technique only a limited amount of specially designed laboratory apparatus was available; the test occupied a week, and there were rather large week-to-week variations. Consequently the important comparisons had to be kept within sets carried out at the same time.

When there are more treatments than can be compared at one time and all comparisons are equally important, the treatments should be selected in a balanced manner, so that any two occur together the same number of times as any other two. For eight treatments compared six at a time, balance may obviously be secured by taking the treatments in all possible combinations six at a time, the number of sets required being $8!/(6!\,2!) = 28$. Frequently complete balance may be preserved with fewer sets; thus, with 11 treatments examined six at a time, balance may be secured with 11 sets instead of 462 (§ 6A·63). Designs of this sort are called Balanced Incomplete Block Designs and belong to the wider class of incomplete block designs. An incomplete block design is balanced when every pair of treatments occurs together in a block the same number of times.

Only basic principles and methods of analysis, illustrated by simple examples, will be considered in this chapter; these will be found sufficient for most practical purposes. A full treatment of incomplete block designs is beyond the scope of this book, and any reader wishing to pursue the subject should consult [6·1] and [6·7].

Example 6·1. Road tests on tyres

6·11. The only satisfactory way yet known of assessing the life of a motor tyre is to run the tyre on a test car under normal road conditions. If it is required to compare different treatments, e.g. rubber treads prepared in different ways using different compounding ingredients or different amounts of compounding ingredients, then the tyres must be run on the same car in order to eliminate the large variations which usually exist between one car and another, and they must be interchanged frequently in order to eliminate variations due to position. With four tyres per car the design is limited to the comparison of four treatments at a time, or at least to four treatments per car. Usually the experimenter can arrange his work so that at any given time he is interested in the comparison of two or four treatments and there is no difficulty. But if there are five treatments and all comparisons are equally important, then five runs will be needed for a balanced arrangement, which consists of all combinations taken four at a time, as shown in Table 6·1.

Table 6·1

BALANCED DESIGN FOR COMPARING FIVE TREATMENTS IN

SETS OF FOUR

Run	Treatment			
1	A	B	C	D
2	A	B	C	E
3	A	B	D	E
4	A	C	D	E
5	B	C	D	E

where A to E denote the five treatments.

If it is impracticable to make five runs, then some comparisons must be given more weight than others. With two runs (Nos. 1 and 2 only) treatments A, B, and C will be compared among themselves with greater precision than with D or E; and since D and E do not appear together in the same run, any comparison between them must be made via A, B, and C. Denoting the standard deviation of the life or rate of wear of each tyre by s, then in the unbalanced arrangement represented by the first two runs only, the standard error of the mean difference within the two runs between any pair taken from A, B, and C will also be s. Either D or E may be compared with A, B, or C in the same run with a standard error of $s\sqrt{2}$. To compare D with E it is necessary to compare $D - (A + B + C)/3$ in run 1 with $E - (A + B + C)/3$ in run 2, the difference yielding an estimate of $D - E$ with a standard error of $s\sqrt{(8/3)}$.* Evidently any design consisting of only two runs is unbalanced; in certain circumstances, however, two runs may well be adequate.

An unbalanced design usually complicates the analysis and interpretation of the data, since the method of Least Squares, which provides the basis of the analysis of all experimental designs, fails to simplify, and the experimenter must start from first principles, either estimating the missing values or estimating the effects by fitting constants. These matters are considered later.

Road tests of this kind are usually subject to large experimental error, which may be reduced by building up a tyre in two or more parts corresponding to the different treatments to be tested (Figure 6·1). Two-part and three-part treads are not uncommon. Comparisons between different parts of the same tyre are evidently more reliable than comparisons between different tyres.

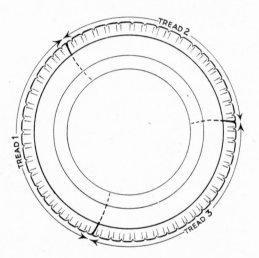

Fig. 6·1. Building up tyre in parts
Three-part tread

* The difference between the totals of runs 1 and 2, being $(A + B + C + D) - (A + B + C + E)$, supplies an additional estimate of the difference between D and E. This is affected by variations between runs, which are usually so large that any such comparison turns out unreliable. In other words, while it is possible to recover information on inter-block comparisons, that information is not usually worth the labour of compiling.

In costly experiments, or in experiments where the variation between blocks is small, it may be worth while recovering information based on inter-block comparisons. The reader should then consult [6·1].

A design permitting the comparison of four compounds A, B, C, and D, by means of three-part treads using one test car is:

Tyre 1	..	..	Compounds A, B, C
Tyre 2	..	..	Compounds A, B, D
Tyre 3	..	..	Compounds A, C, D
Tyre 4	..	..	Compounds B, C, D

This is a balanced incomplete block design in which the compounds are compared in all combinations three at a time. In an actual road test the relative wear values shown in Table 6·11 were obtained after a suitable length of run.

Table 6·11

ROAD TESTS ON TYRES: RELATIVE WEAR
(arbitrary units)

Compound (= treatment)	Tyre (= block) 1	2	3	4
A	238	196	254	—
B	238	213	—	312
C	279	—	334	421
D	—	308	367	412

The chief interest is the comparison of the amounts of wear between the four compounds; a secondary interest is the comparison of the wear on the four tyres. Treatments A and B are common to tyres 1 and 2 but not to the other two, so that the difference between the means of treatments A and B will be affected by the difference between tyres 3 and 4; a similar argument holds for any two treatments or any two tyres. The problem is how to calculate the treatment effects eliminating the tyre effects, and then the tyre effects eliminating the treatment effects. The main steps in calculating the effects for the general case, and for Table 6·11 in particular, are described in §§ **6·2** *et seq.*

Table 6·11 may be regarded as an incomplete two-way table in which certain treatment combinations, referred to as missing values, are not applied. The problem of missing values is discussed in Appendix 6B. The method described is applicable to any type of design, e.g. randomised blocks, Latin Squares, factorial experiments, and so on. When the design is balanced the analysis is simplified and may then be systematised; when the design becomes unbalanced by accident, e.g. a burst or cut tyre, or by intention, e.g. further limitations on the conditions of the experiment, then it is necessary to use the method given in Appendix 6B.

Analysis of balanced incomplete block designs

6·2. In a balanced incomplete block design every pair of treatments occurs together the same number of times. The following notation is used:

$$N = \text{number of observations}$$
$$t = \text{number of treatments}$$
$$r = \text{number of replications of each treatment}$$
$$b = \text{number of blocks}$$
$$k = \text{number of experimental units per block}$$

Clearly $N = tr = bk$.

Now any particular treatment occurs in r blocks, each of which contains another $k - 1$ treatments out of $t - 1$ possible ones. The number of blocks containing two specified treatments is therefore

$$\frac{r(k-1)}{t-1} = \frac{N(k-1)}{t(t-1)} = \lambda \text{ (say)}$$

The observations are presented in the form of Table 6·2.

Table 6·2

INCOMPLETE BLOCK DESIGN: PRESENTATION AND ANALYSIS

Treatment	Block					Total	Q	P	Corrected treatment mean
	1	2	3	...	b				
1	X	$-$	X	...	X	T_1	Q_1	P_1	
2	X	X	$-$	...	$-$	T_2	Q_2	P_2	
3	$-$	X	X	...	X	T_3	Q_3	P_3	
.						.	.	.	.
.						.	.	.	.
.						.	.	.	.
t	X	X	$-$	...	X	T_t	Q_t	P_t	
Total ..	B_1	B_2	B_3	...	B_b	G	o	o	

NOTE. The last three columns are explained later.

Calculation of treatment effects

6·21. Any treatment is represented in r of the b blocks, but each treatment corresponds to a different set of r blocks. Thus differences between the treatment totals $T_1, T_2, \ldots, T_t$, or the corresponding means $T_1/r, T_2/r, \ldots, T_t/r$, are affected by differences between blocks, and are not directly indicative of any true differences which may exist between the effects of different treatments. An analysis must therefore be devised which will separate the treatment and the block effects. YATES [6·2] has shown that, since the design is balanced, the treatment effects, free of block effects, may readily be estimated as follows*:

(i) For each treatment, i.e. for each row of Table 6·2, calculate $Q_i = kT_i$ — (Sum of the totals for all blocks containing the ith treatment).† The sum of the Q_i's should be zero.

(ii) Obtain P_i by dividing Q_i by $N(k - 1)/(t - 1) = t\lambda$. The sum of the P_i's should similarly be zero.

The P_i's are the estimated treatment effects, or more strictly the estimated deviations of particular treatment effects from the average effect of all treatments used in the experiment. This average treatment effect is incorporated with the average block effect in the grand mean G/N and is conventionally equated to zero, since comparisons of the effects of different treatments are unaffected thereby. Corrected treatment means may be obtained by adding the P_i's to the grand mean; they are estimates of the treatment means which would have been obtained if all treatments had been used in every block. Since however they relate only to the blocks used in the experiment, their general applicability depends upon the extent to which these blocks can be considered as a random sample of all possible blocks.

Calculation of error variance and significance of treatment effects

6·22. In a complete design, in which all treatments are equally represented in every block, the error or remainder sum of squares is obtained by subtracting from the total sum of squares the sums of squares due to blocks and to treatments [§ **5·21**]. An analogous procedure applies to balanced incomplete blocks. The successive steps in the calculation and reasoning are as follows.

(i) Calculate the total sum of squares of all N observations about the grand mean, that is, $\Sigma x_{ij}^2 - G^2/N$.

(ii) Calculate the sum of squares between block totals. This is simply the sum of squares of the actual block totals divided by k, the number in each block, minus the correction due to the mean, i.e.

$$(B_1^2 + B_2^2 + \ldots + B_b^2)/k - G^2/N$$

(iii) Calculate the sum of squares due to treatments. This is given [6·2] by the sum of squares of the quantities Q_i of Table 6·2 divided by $Nk(k - 1)/(t - 1) = kt\lambda$.

(iv) The analysis of variance table may then be constructed as in Table 6·21.

* The results quoted may be obtained by the method of Least Squares, given in Appendix 6B.

† It may be quicker to subtract the quantity G — (Sum of the totals for all blocks not containing the ith treatment).

Table 6·21

ANALYSIS OF VARIANCE OF INCOMPLETE BLOCK DESIGN
(Derived from Table 6·2)

Source of variation	Sum of squares	Degrees of freedom	Mean square
Between corrected treatment totals	$\dfrac{(t-1)}{Nk(k-1)}\Sigma Q_i{}^2$	$t-1$	
Between actual block totals	$\Sigma B_j{}^2/k - (G^2/N)$	$b-1$	(Discard)
Remainder = interaction = error ..		$N-t-b+1$	
Total..	$\Sigma x_{ij}{}^2 - G^2/N$	$N-1$	

The interaction, or error, sum of squares and number of degrees of freedom are obtained by subtraction from the totals. Some comment is required on the sum of squares between blocks: the differences between block totals are affected by differences between the treatments; consequently the sum of squares between block totals is a complex function of the variation between blocks and the variation between treatments, and in general it will have little meaning. However, the Null Hypothesis to be tested is that all treatments have the same effect, and according to this hypothesis the variation between block totals is unaffected by treatments. If the Null Hypothesis is disproved, the mean square between blocks becomes meaningless. Thus Table 6·21 may be used to assess the significance of the differences between treatments by comparing the mean square between treatments with the error mean square using the F-test, but cannot be used to assess the mean square between blocks in general, for this particular mean square, derived on the assumption that there are no treatment differences, has been introduced only as a means of arriving at the error variance. Having served this purpose it must be discarded. If it is desired to assess the significance of the difference between block means allowing for variation between treatment means, other methods must be used [Appendices 6B and 6C]. A rigorous justification of this procedure is provided by the method of Least Squares of Appendix 6B.

Comparison between two particular treatments

6·23. Denote the remainder, or error, variance by s^2. We may wish to compare two particular treatment means, say P_i and P_j. Now the P's of Table 6·2 have been derived from the data as a whole. Each P represents a different linear function of the observations, but for any two there will in general be a proportion of observations common to both. The quantities P_i and P_j are therefore not independent, and the variance of the difference between them will not be the sum of their separate variances. The difference will also be a linear function of the observations, and its variance will be s^2 times the sum of squares of the coefficients of the observations in the linear function [S.M., § 3·71]. For the balanced incomplete block design the standard error of a difference between two treatment means reduces to [6·2]:

$$s\sqrt{\left\{\frac{2k(t-1)}{N(k-1)}\right\}} = s\sqrt{\frac{2k}{\lambda t}}$$

which may be used to assess the significance of the difference between two treatments.

Analysis of Example 6·1
6·24.

Table 6·22

ANALYSIS OF RELATIVE WEAR ON THREE-PART TREADS
(Derived from Table 6·11)

Compound (= treatment)	Tyre (= block)				Sum	Q	P	Corrected treatment mean
	1	2	3	4				
A	238	196	254	—	688	− 363	− 45·4	252·3
B	238	213	—	312	763	− 328	− 41·0	256·7
C	279	—	334	421	1,034	+ 247	+ 30·9	328·6
D	—	308	367	412	1,087	+ 444	+ 55·5	353·2
Sum	755	717	955	1,145	3,572	0	0	

In this example:

Number of compounds $= t = 4$
Number per block $= k = 3$
Number of replications $= r = 3$
Number of blocks $= b = 4$
Number of observations $= N = 12$
Number of blocks in which any two compounds
   occur together $= \lambda = 2$

The steps in the calculations are:

(i) Calculate the quantities Q_i, i.e. k times treatment total minus sum of the totals for all blocks containing the treatment. Treatment A occurs in blocks 1, 2, and 3; therefore:

$$Q_1 = 3 \times 688 - 755 - 717 - 955 = -363, \text{ and similarly}$$
$$Q_2 = 3 \times 763 - 755 - 717 - 1145 = -328$$
$$Q_3 = 3 \times 1034 - 755 - 955 - 1145 = +247$$
$$Q_4 = 3 \times 1087 - 717 - 955 - 1145 = +444$$
$$\Sigma Q = 0$$

(ii) The P's are formed by dividing the corresponding Q's by

$$N(k-1)/(t-1) = 8 \qquad \Sigma P = 0$$

(iii) The grand mean $= M = 3572/12 = 297\cdot7$. The corrected treatment means are obtained by adding the grand mean to the corresponding P's.

Calculation of error variance and significance of treatment differences

6·25. Follow the steps given for the general case:

(i) Calculate total sum of squares of the 12 observations about the grand mean:

$$= 1,124,868 - 3572^2/12 = 1,124,868 - 1,063,265 = 61,603$$

(ii) Calculate the sum of squares of the actual block totals:

$$= (755^2 + 717^2 + 955^2 + 1145^2)/3 - 3572^2/12$$
$$= 1,102,388 - 1,063,265 = 39,123$$

(iii) Calculate the sum of squares due to treatments, corrected for block differences:

$$= \Sigma Q_i^2 \text{ divided by } Nk(k-1)/(t-1)$$
$$= \{(-363)^2 + (-328)^2 + 247^2 + 444^2\}/24$$
$$= 20,729$$

(iv) Construct analysis of variance table as shown in Table 6·23.

Table 6·23

ANALYSIS OF VARIANCE OF TABLE 6·22 WITH RESPECT TO TREATMENTS

Source of variation	Sum of squares	Degrees of freedom	Mean square
Between corrected treatment totals	20,729	3	6,910
Between actual block totals	39,123	3	(Discard)
Remainder = interaction = error	1,751	5	350
Total	61,603	11	

The ratio of the treatment mean square to error mean square $= 19\cdot7$. Based on three and five degrees of freedom, this value is highly significant (1% value of $F = 12\cdot1$).

The standard deviation of the difference between the corrected means of any two compounds is

$$s\sqrt{\left\{\frac{2k(t-1)}{N(k-1)}\right\}} = \sqrt{\left\{\frac{350\times3}{4}\right\}} = \sqrt{262\cdot5} = 16\cdot2$$

The difference required for significance at the 5% level is $2\cdot57\times16\cdot2 = 41\cdot6$, where $2\cdot57$ is the 5% value of t for five degrees of freedom. It is thus seen that compounds A and B are significantly better than C and D and that we cannot discriminate between A and B or between C and D. If the only evidence for grouping the treatments into (A, B) and (C, D) were that supplied by the data, then this test of significance would be questionable on strictly logical grounds; for comparisons suggested by the data without there being prior reasons for making them must be regarded with caution. However, in this case there was prior resemblance between A and B and also between C and D, which justified comparing the former group with the latter and also comparing A with B, and C with D.

Comparison of the efficiency of balanced incomplete blocks with designs using controls in each block

6·26. The classical method when the number of treatments exceeds the number that can be examined in one block is to use a control in every block. Consider the comparison of (say) eleven samples of penicillin (one a standard) by the cylinder plate method when the number that can be compared on a plate is limited to six. In this type of test a bulk-inoculated nutrient agar medium is poured (while warm) into a Petri dish of approximately 9 cm. diameter, known as a plate. When the medium has set, six small hollow cylinders or pots (about 0·4 cm. in diameter) are cemented on to the surface at equally spaced intervals. A few drops of the penicillin solutions to be compared are placed in the respective cylinders and the whole plate is placed in an incubator for a given time. Penicillin diffuses from the pots into the agar, and this produces a clear circular zone of inhibition of growth of the organisms, which can be readily measured. The diameter of the zone is related in a known way to the concentration of penicillin in the solutions.

Denoting ten of the samples by the letters A, B, C, ..., J, and the eleventh (the standard) by S, one arrangement using S as control is:

Plate 1 ..   ..   S   A   B   C   D   E ⎫ Replicate 6 times.
Plate 2 ..   ..   S   F   G   H   I   J ⎭ Total of 12 plates

If V is the variance of each observation, the variance of the comparison of any sample with the standard on one plate is $2V$, and the variance over the average

P

of six replicate plates is $V/3 = 0·33V$. This also gives the variance of the comparison of any two samples appearing together. The variance of the difference between samples appearing on different plates, e.g. A — F, is $2V/3 = 0·67V$, since to compare A with F we must compare A — S on one set of plates with F — S on the other set of plates.

As an alternative to the classical method, 11 samples could be compared by means of a balanced incomplete block design using 11 plates. The design is No. 6A·63, taken from Appendix 6A, in which the treatments (= samples) and blocks (= plates) have been arranged in random order.

Table 6·24

DESIGN FOR THE COMPARISON OF 11 SAMPLES OF PENICILLIN BY METHOD OF BALANCED INCOMPLETE BLOCKS

Sample	\ Plate (= block)										
	5	3	11	7	2	8	1	10	9	4	6
E		X	X		X				X	X	X
D	X	X		X	X					X	X
B	X	X		X	X		X				X
S	X	X	X		X	X		X			
H		X	X	X	X	X		X			
A		X	X	X		X	X		X		
G		X	X	X		X	X				X
J	X				X	X	X		X	X	
C		X			X	X	X			X	X
I	X		X			X	X	X			X
F	X	X		X				X	X	X	

In this balanced block arrangement the variance of the difference between any two samples will be $V \times 2k(t - 1)/\{N(k - 1)\}$. Here t = number of samples = 11, k = number per plate = 6, N = number of observations $= 11 \times 6 = 66$, and on substitution the variance equals $4V/11 = 0·36V$. Since the balanced arrangement uses one plate fewer than the arrangement using controls, the variance should be multiplied by 11/12, giving $0·33V$, for strict comparison of the two methods. For the comparison of any two samples within the two sets and for the comparison of any sample with the standard, both methods give the same degree of efficiency; but when it is a question of comparing any of A–E with any of F–J the variance by the balanced method is one-half of the variance by the classical method. The increase in precision of this design must be weighed against its complexity, involving closer supervision.

Symmetrical balanced incomplete blocks

6·3. In the balanced incomplete block design of Table 6·11 each pair of treatments occurs together twice, for A and B occur together in blocks (tyres) 1 and 2, A and C in blocks 1 and 3, C and D in blocks 3 and 4, and so on. Here, but not always, the converse is true, for the design also represents a balanced incomplete block when treatments and blocks are interchanged; that is, the design is balanced with respect to both treatments and blocks. The same remark applies to the design of Table 6·24. Such designs are called Symmetrical Balanced Incomplete Blocks. In view of this property it is possible to use similar procedures to calculate both:

(i) the effects of the compounds, corrected for differences between tyres;

(ii) the effects of the tyres corrected for differences between compounds;

and this represents a considerable practical advantage.

Balanced incomplete blocks are not necessarily symmetrical, but for many industrial applications the useful designs belong to the symmetrical type. The term symmetrical is applied in general to balanced incomplete block designs in which every pair of blocks has the same number of treatments in common. The necessary and sufficient condition for a symmetrical design is $b = t$, i.e. the number of blocks equals the number of treatments; consequently $k = r$. In some experiments the block effects may be important, e.g. in Example 6·1 the differences in rates of wear between the four tyres are also interesting.

The calculation of the block effects follows the same lines as that used in the calculation of the treatment effects, viz:

(i) $Q_i' = r \times$ block total — (Sum of totals for all treatments appearing in the given block). The quantity r is the number of replications of each treatment, but this could be replaced by k, the number of experimental units per block, because $r = k$.

(ii) The divisor for each Q_i' in order to derive P_i', the block effect, is $N(r - 1)/(b - 1)$.*

(iii) The sum of squares due to corrected block effects is $\Sigma Q_i'^2$ divided by $Nr(r - 1)/(b - 1)$.*

No. (iii) is based on $(b - 1)$ degrees of freedom and the variance may be assessed for significance against the remainder variance as calculated previously. If in addition the corrected sum of squares for the actual treatment totals $(\Sigma T_j^2/r - G^2/N)$ is calculated, subtraction from the total will again

---

* Since $r = k$ in a symmetrical balanced incomplete block design, the divisors are the same as those used for calculating the corrected treatment means and their sums of squares.

supply the interaction sum of squares, and this may be used as a check. A convenient form for the final table is shown in Table 6·3.

Table 6·3

ANALYSIS OF VARIANCE FOR SYMMETRICAL BALANCED INCOMPLETE BLOCK DESIGNS

Source of variation	Sum of squares	Degrees of freedom	Mean square
Test for treatments:			
(1) Between treatments, adjusting for blocks	$\dfrac{(t-1)}{Nk(k-1)} \Sigma Q_i{}^2$	$t-1$	$\mathrm{MS}_{(T)}$
(2) Between blocks, ignoring treatments	$(\Sigma B_j{}^2/k - G^2/N)$	$b-1$	(Discard)
Test for blocks:			
(3) Between blocks, adjusting for treatments	$\dfrac{(b-1)}{Nr(r-1)} \Sigma Q_j{}'^2$	$b-1$	$\mathrm{MS}_{(B)}$
(4) Between treatments, ignoring blocks	$(\Sigma T_i{}^2/r - G^2/N)$	$t-1$	(Discard)
(5) Remainder = interaction between treatments and blocks = error variance	By subtraction Total — (1) — (2) or Total — (3) — (4)	$N-t-b+1$	$\mathrm{MS}_{(E)}$
Total	$\Sigma x_{ij}{}^2 - G^2/N$	$N-1$	

Application to Example 6·1

6·31. The block totals for Table 6·11 and the calculations required to derive the corrected tyre means are shown in Table 6·31.

Table 6·31

ANALYSIS OF TABLE 6·11 WITH RESPECT TO TYRES

	Tyre (= block)				Sum
	1	2	3	4	
Block total ..	755	717	955	1,145	3,572
Q'	− 220	− 387	56	+ 551	0
P'	− 27·5	− 48·4	7·0	+ 68·9	0
Corrected tyre means	270·2	249·3	304·7	366·6	

$$Q_1' = 3 \times 755 - 688 - 763 - 1034 = -220$$
$$Q_2' = 3 \times 717 - 688 - 763 - 1087 = -387$$
$$Q_3' = 3 \times 955 - 688 - 1034 - 1087 = +56$$
$$Q_4' = 3 \times 1145 - 763 - 1034 - 1087 = +551$$
$$N(r-1)/(b-1) = 8, \text{ therefore } P_j' = Q_j'/8$$

Sum of squares due to tyre effects $= (220^2 + 387^2 + 56^2 + 551^2)/24 = 21{,}038$

The corrected sum of squares due to treatments assuming no block differences is

$$(688^2 + 763^2 + 1034^2 + 1087^2)/3 - 3572^2/12 = 1{,}102{,}079 - 1{,}063{,}265$$
$$= 38{,}814$$

The complete analysis of variance table is then as Table 6·32.

Table 6·32

COMPLETE ANALYSIS OF VARIANCE OF TABLE 6·11 WITH RESPECT
TO BOTH TREATMENTS AND TYRES

Source of variation	Sum of squares	Degrees of freedom	Mean square
(1) Between treatments ..	20,729	3	6,910
(2) (Actual treatment totals)	(38,814)	(3)	(Discard)
(3) Between blocks (tyres) ..	21,038	3	7,013
(4) (Actual block totals) ..	(39,123)	(3)	(Discard)
(5) Remainder = interaction = error	1,751	5	350
Total	61,603	11	

$(1) + (4) = 59{,}852 = (2) + (3)$, which provides a check.

The variance between tyre effects is highly significant. As before, a difference of 41·6 is required between the corrected means for two tyres for significance at the 5% level, and this makes tyre No. 4 significantly worse than any of the others. Note that the sum of squares of $(1) + (3) + (5)$ does not equal the total sum of squares, for the additive property only applies to effects which are all orthogonal to one another and to the mean, and these effects are not orthogonal.

Tables of balanced incomplete block designs

6·32. A list of balanced incomplete block designs is given in Appendix 6A. This list is not by any means exhaustive, but it represents the designs most likely to be required in industrial work. More extensive lists involving larger numbers of treatments are given in [6·1] and [6·7], which should be consulted if required.

The complement of a design is the design formed from the blanks of the table. In design 6A·34 the X's give the design for 7 treatments in 7 blocks of 3, while the blanks give a design for 7 treatments in 7 blocks of 4, that is, design 6A·43; generally the complement of a balanced incomplete block is also a balanced incomplete block. It is interesting to note that whereas 6 treatments require 10 blocks of 3, 7 treatments may be examined in 7 blocks of 3, that is in fewer blocks. If therefore it is required to examine six treatments in blocks of three, and if three replications are adequate, it is advantageous either to introduce a further treatment or to repeat one of the six. Note also that 8 treatments require 14 blocks of 4 but 7 treatments only require 7 blocks of 4. If the amount of replication given in the first one is not required, then consideration should be given to reducing the number of treatments to seven.

Youden Squares

6·4. The simple randomised incomplete block design covering four treatments in four blocks (design 6A·31) may be written in the alternative form of Table 6·4.

Table 6·4

INCOMPLETE BLOCK DESIGNS: ALTERNATIVE FORM

Block	Treatment		
1	A	B	C
2	D	C	A
3	B	A	D
4	C	D	B

Table 6·4 represents a balanced incomplete block design, because it satisfies the requirement that every pair of treatments occurs together in the same block the same number of times, in this case twice, e.g. A and B occur in blocks 1 and 3, A and D in blocks 2 and 3, and so on. Letting each column represent a position in the block, the averages of the columns are seen to be independent of the variations between treatments and between blocks. If therefore there existed a constant difference between the positions in the block it should be possible to eliminate that difference in addition to the variation between blocks, thus reducing the experimental error and increasing the precision. The conditions are similar to those for the Latin Square discussed in Chapter 5. The design is known as a YOUDEN Square, and it has the same advantages over a randomised incomplete block experiment as a Latin Square has over a complete block experiment. A YOUDEN Square is in fact an incomplete Latin Square, because if a final column were added containing treatment D in the first block, B in the second, C in the third, and A in the fourth, the result would be a Latin Square. Table 6·4 is then a Latin Square from which one column is missing; the design may in fact be presented in the form of a square as shown in Table 6·41, in which a, β, and γ represent the positions in the block.

Table 6·41
YOUDEN SQUARE DESIGN

| Block | Treatment | | | |
	A	B	C	D
1	a	β	γ	—
2	γ	—	β	a
3	β	a	—	γ
4	—	γ	a	β

Written in this form the design resembles a Latin Square from which one of the diagonals is missing. In general, a YOUDEN Square is defined as a symmetrical balanced incomplete block design in which each treatment occurs once and once only in each position in the block. Although a YOUDEN Square is always a Latin Square from which one or more rows (or columns or diagonals) are missing, the converse is not always true; a Latin Square from which more than one row (or column or diagonal) is missing is not necessarily a YOUDEN Square, since removing rows from a Latin Square may destroy the balance. It is, however, possible to construct YOUDEN Squares from all symmetrical balanced incomplete block designs [6·3].

6·41. The analysis of a YOUDEN Square is carried out in the first place as for a symmetrical balanced incomplete block experiment, ignoring the position in the block (Table 6·3). Now every position occurs once and once only in each block and once with each treatment. The variation between the totals for each position is therefore independent of block and treatment effects (i.e. the positions are orthogonal to blocks and treatments), and the sum of squares between the totals for each position may then be deducted from the remainder sum of squares of Table 6·3. An example is worked out in the next section.

Example 6·2. Abrasion resistance of samples of rubber

6·42. Example 5·2 of the previous chapter described the use of a MARTINDALE wear tester to compare the abrasion resistance of samples of rubber. Four treatments were compared in four runs and the treatments were arranged in the form of a Latin Square with the position in the machine as the third factor. An experiment with this machine need not be restricted to the comparison of four treatments in four runs: the main restriction relates to a maximum of four treatments per run. By the use of a YOUDEN Square it is possible to compare 5 treatments in 5 runs, 7 treatments in 7 runs, and 13 treatments in 13 runs, and at the same time to eliminate the variation between runs and between positions of the machine so as to achieve maximum precision.

YOUDEN Squares do not exist for six treatments, or for intermediate numbers between 7 and 13 when the number of treatments per block is restricted to four.

For five treatments in five runs the appropriate YOUDEN Square is shown in Table 6·42, where A, B, C, D, and E represent the treatments.

Table 6·42

YOUDEN SQUARE TO TEST FIVE MATERIALS IN FIVE RUNS

Run	Position in the machine			
	α	β	γ	δ
1	A	B	C	D
2	E	A	B	C
3	D	E	A	B
4	C	D	E	A
5	B	C	D	E

This is equivalent to a Latin Square from which one column (E, D, C, B, A) is missing. For the purpose of analysis it is more convenient to rearrange the observations as in Table 6·43. The figures quoted represent actual weight losses in milligrams in an experiment to compare the resistance to wear of five different Vulcaprene plasticised leathers.

Table 6·43

COMPARISON OF RATES OF WEAR BY MARTINDALE MACHINE
(Weight losses in mg.)

Material (= treatment)	Run (= block)				
	1	2	3	4	5
A	α 268	β 233	γ 254	δ 281	—
B	β 249	γ 231	δ 314	—	α 240
C	γ 280	δ 291	—	α 256	β 250
D	δ 271	—	α 265	β 250	γ 248
E	—	α 251	β 249	γ 270	δ 289

α, β, γ, and δ denote positions in machine

In the notation of § 6·2, $N = 20$, $t = b = 5$, $r = k = 4$, and $\lambda = 3$.

Analysis of Example 6·2

6·43. A figure of 200 is subtracted from each of the observations of Table 6·43 in order to simplify the arithmetic, and the transformed observations together with the derived values of the converted treatment and run means are given in Table 6·44.

Table 6·44

ESTIMATION OF EFFECTS IN A YOUDEN SQUARE

(Derived from Table 6·43)

Material (= treatment)	Run 1	2	3	4	5	Total	Q	P	Corrected treatment mean
A	α 68	β 33	γ 54	δ 81	—	236	− 69	− 4·6	57·4
B	β 49	γ 31	δ 114	—	α 40	234	− 47	− 3·1	58·9
C	γ 80	δ 91	—	α 56	β 50	277	150	10·0	72·0
D	δ 71	—	α 65	β 50	γ 48	234	− 98	− 6·5	55·5
E	—	α 51	β 49	γ 70	δ 89	259	64	4·3	66·3
Totals ..	268	206	282	257	227	1240	0		
Q' ..	91	−182	165	22	−96	0			
P' ..	6·1	−12·1	11·0	1·5	−6·4				
Corrected run mean	68·1	49·9	73·0	63·5	55·6				

Position totals: $\alpha = 280, \beta = 231, \gamma = 283, \delta = 446$
Position means: $\alpha = 56\cdot0, \beta = 46\cdot2, \gamma = 56\cdot6, \delta = 89\cdot2$

The quantities Q and Q' are calculated as before, that is, 4 times the total for a given treatment (run) less the sum of the runs (treatments) containing (contained in) the given treatment (run). The divisor to derive P from Q is $N(k-1)/(t-1) = 15$. The divisor to derive P' from Q' is $N(r-1)/(t-1)$, which owing to the symmetry of the design is also equal to 15. The divisor for the ΣQ^2 and $\Sigma Q'^2$ is $Nk(k-1)/(t-1) = 60 = Nr(r-1)/(t-1)$.

The following are the quantities required for the derivation of the analysis of variance:

(i) Correction due to mean
  $= 1240^2/20 = 76,880$

(ii) Total sum of squares of all 20 observations
  $= 85,358 - 76,880 = 8478$

(iii) Sum of squares due to actual treatment totals
$$= (236^2 + \ldots + 259^2)/4 - \text{correction}$$
$$= 77,254\cdot5 - 76,880\cdot0 = 374\cdot5$$

(iv) Sum of squares due to corrected treatment totals
$$= \Sigma Q^2/60 = 43,170/60 = 719\cdot5$$

(v) Sum of squares due to actual run totals
$$= (268^2 + \ldots + 227^2)/4 - \text{correction}$$
$$= 77,840\cdot5 - 76,880\cdot0 = 960\cdot5$$

(vi) Sum of squares due to corrected run totals
$$= \Sigma Q'^2/60 = 78,330/60 = 1305\cdot5$$

(vii) Sum of squares due to position totals
$$= (280^2 + \ldots + 446^2)/5 - \text{correction}$$
$$= 82,153\cdot2 - 76,880\cdot0 = 5273\cdot2$$

These lead to the analysis of variance shown in Table 6·45.

Table 6·45

ANALYSIS OF VARIANCE OF TABLE 6·44

Source of variation	Sum of squares	Degrees of freedom	Mean square
Test for treatments:			
(1) Between treatments, adjusting for runs	719·5	4	179·9 ⎫
(2) Between runs, ignoring treatments	960·5	4	(Discard) ⎬
	1,680·0	8	⎭
Test for runs:			⎫
(3) Between runs, adjusting for treatments	1,305·5	4	326·4
(4) Between treatments, ignoring runs	374·5	4	(Discard) ⎬
	1,680·0	8	⎭
(5) Between positions on the machine	5,273·2	3	1,757·7
(6) Remainder	1,524·8	8	190·6
Total	8,478·0	19	

If the corrected run means are not required, then the calculations for Q' and P' may be omitted, together with the sums of squares of (3) and (4).

There are clearly no significant differences between the treatments. Note the large variance due to the position in the machine: had this experiment been carried out as an incomplete block experiment, randomising the treatments on the machine for each run, a considerably larger error variance would have resulted. The method of calculating this error variance is given in § 4·37 of Ref. [6·7]; application to Table 6·45 shows that the use of the YOUDEN Square design in place of a balanced incomplete block design has reduced the error variance from 476·8 to 190·6. In order to obtain the same degree of precision from a balanced incomplete block design as that obtained from the above YOUDEN Square, between two and three replications of the former would be required.

The highly significant variation between positions is seen to be due to the δ position, which gives a considerably higher rate of wear than the other positions, possibly signifying some faulty adjustment in this particular experiment.

6·44. A YOUDEN Square may be constructed for any symmetrical randomised block design in which the number of blocks is equal to the number of treatments, and a systematic method of doing this is given in [6·3]. In the balanced incomplete design for 11 treatments in 11 blocks of five, a third factor, denoting position in blocks, can be introduced as in Table 6·46.

Table 6·46
YOUDEN SQUARE FOR ELEVEN TREATMENTS IN ELEVEN RUNS
OF FIVE

Treatment	Run (= blocks)										
	1	2	3	4	5	6	7	8	9	10	11
A	α			θ		δ	γ	β			
B		α			θ		δ	γ	β		
C			α			θ		δ	γ	β	
D				α			θ		δ	γ	β
E	β				α			θ		δ	γ
F	γ	β				α			θ		δ
G	δ	γ	β				α			θ	
H		δ	γ	β				α			θ
I	θ		δ	γ	β				α		
J		θ		δ	γ	β				α	
K			θ		δ	γ	β				α

α, β, γ, δ, and θ denote positions in blocks.

This is one of many YOUDEN Squares that can be constructed for an 11 × 11 × 5 incomplete balanced block. Some of the others may be obtained by interchanging rows and columns of the above table.

Greek letters are used to indicate the YOUDEN Squares for all the symmetrical designs in Appendix 6A.

Non-balanced incomplete blocks, and lattice squares

6·5. There are incomplete block designs other than completely balanced ones for which simplified and systematic methods of analysis are possible without the necessity of analysing the results from first principles, i.e. by the method of Least Squares. These designs are used when the number of treatments to be compared is large and a completely balanced design would require a prohibitive number of replicates. One such type of design is called the Lattice Square. For this design the number of treatments must be a perfect square. Suppose it is required to compare 16 treatments and the conditions of the experiment limit to four the number that can be compared at one time. Applying each treatment once only, an initial design is shown in Table 6·5.

Table 6·5

SIXTEEN TREATMENTS IN BLOCKS OF FOUR. ARRANGEMENT 1

Run	Treatment			
1	1	2	3	4
2	5	6	7	8
3	9	10	11	12
4	13	14	15	16

All treatments within any one row may be compared directly with one another, but the comparison of any two treatments occurring in different rows can only be carried out with a lower degree of precision because of the variation between runs. Assume the experiment is enlarged to include a further set of four runs in which the treatments in each column of Table 6·5 now occur together; the result is shown in Table 6·51.

Table 6·51

SIXTEEN TREATMENTS IN BLOCKS OF FOUR. ARRANGEMENT 2

Run	Treatment			
5	1	5	9	13
6	2	6	10	14
7	3	7	11	15
8	4	8	12	16

Table 6·51 increases the number of pairs of treatments that may be compared directly within runs; in fact the two sets together enable all pairs of treatments to be compared, some directly, some indirectly, using within-row comparisons only. To compare two treatments which do not appear together in any run in either of the two sets above, treatments 1 and 8 for instance, we note that in run 1 treatment 1 is compared with treatment 4 and that in run 8 treatment 8 is compared with treatment 4. The comparison between 1 and 8 is then $(1 - 4) - (8 - 4)$. This comparison does not exhaust all the information on Nos. 1 and 8, but it is sufficient to indicate one property of the design, namely that the comparison of any two treatments that occur together in a block is more precise than a comparison between any that do not occur together.

6·51. With one replicate, i.e. four runs, there will be no degrees of freedom for estimating the error variance; but with two replicates there will in total be 31 degrees of freedom, of which 15 will be due to treatments and 7 due to runs, leaving 9 degrees of freedom for error. The analysis proceeds on the following lines. Denote by x the observations in the first replicate and by y the observations in the second replicate; denote the treatment by a suffix. Arrange the observations as in Tables 6·52 and 6·53.

Table 6·52   Table 6·53

LATTICE SQUARE DESIGN

First Replicate (x) Second Replicate (y)

Run (= block)					Run (= block)			
					5	6	7	8
1	x_1	x_2	x_3	x_4	y_1	y_2	y_3	y_4
2	x_5	x_6	x_7	x_8	y_5	y_6	y_7	y_8
3	x_9	x_{10}	x_{11}	x_{12}	y_9	y_{10}	y_{11}	y_{12}
4	x_{13}	x_{14}	x_{15}	x_{16}	y_{13}	y_{14}	y_{15}	y_{16}

The next step is to form the sums and differences of the two sets of replicates as in Tables 6·54 and 6·55.

Table 6·54

SUMS OF CORRESPONDING PAIRS OF OBSERVATIONS OF TABLES 6·52 AND 6·53

$x_1 + y_1$	$x_2 + y_2$	$x_3 + y_3$	$x_4 + y_4$
$x_5 + y_5$	$x_6 + y_6$	$x_7 + y_7$	$x_8 + y_8$
$x_9 + y_9$	$x_{10} + y_{10}$	$x_{11} + y_{11}$	$x_{12} + y_{12}$
$x_{13} + y_{13}$	$x_{14} + y_{14}$	$x_{15} + y_{15}$	$x_{16} + y_{16}$

Table 6·55

DIFFERENCES OF CORRESPONDING PAIRS OF OBSERVATIONS OF
TABLES 6·52 AND 6·53

$x_1 - y_1$	$x_2 - y_2$	$x_3 - y_3$	$x_4 - y_4$
$x_5 - y_5$	$x_6 - y_6$	$x_7 - y_7$	$x_8 - y_8$
$x_9 - y_9$	$x_{10} - y_{10}$	$x_{11} - y_{11}$	$x_{12} - y_{12}$
$x_{13} - y_{13}$	$x_{14} - y_{14}$	$x_{15} - y_{15}$	$x_{16} - y_{16}$

Write
$$x_1 = T_1 + R_1 + \bar{x} + z \\ y_1 = T_1 + R_5 + \bar{x} + z' \quad \Big\} \quad \dots\dots\dots\dots(6·1)$$

where T_i denotes the treatment effect, that is the (unknown) true difference between the yield of the ith treatment and the mean; R_j denotes the run effect, that is the (unknown) true difference between the yield of the jth run and the mean; $\bar{x}$ denotes the general mean of the 32 observations; and z and z' denote random variates (i.e. experimental error). Then

$$x_1 - y_1 = R_1 - R_5 + (z - z')$$

Similar expressions hold for the other differences; thus, apart from experimental error, each term in the table of differences denotes a difference between two run constants as in Table 6·56.

Table 6·56

TABLE 6·55 EXPRESSED IN TERMS OF RUN CONSTANTS, IGNORING
EXPERIMENTAL ERRORS

$R_1 - R_5$	$R_1 - R_6$	$R_1 - R_7$	$R_1 - R_8$
$R_2 - R_5$	$R_2 - R_6$	$R_2 - R_7$	$R_2 - R_8$
$R_3 - R_5$	$R_3 - R_6$	$R_3 - R_7$	$R_3 - R_8$
$R_4 - R_5$	$R_4 - R_6$	$R_4 - R_7$	$R_4 - R_8$

Now R_1 is common to the first row, R_2 to the second, and so on, and R_5 to the first column, R_6 to the second, and so on. It follows that, regarding Table 6·56 as a two-way table, the remainder sum of squares (obtained by deducting the sums of squares due to rows and columns from the total and dividing by 2, since each entry is a difference between two observations) represents the sum of squares due to error based on nine degrees of freedom. This sum of squares is identical with that obtained by the method of Least Squares and is denoted by Sa [see general Note on Least Squares, Appendix 6B]. The error mean square is then $V = Sa/9$. The above table of differences may also be used to obtain the estimates of the run effects, that is, estimates of

$R_1, R_2, \ldots, R_8$. The row averages are $(R_1 - B)$, $(R_2 - B)$, $(R_3 - B)$, $(R_4 - B)$, where B is the average of R_5, R_6, R_7, and R_8. Subtracting the grand average of the differences from these row averages will then give the effects of runs 1–4 respectively, measured from the mean of the first replicate. Similarly, subtracting the grand average of the difference from the column means will give the effects of runs 5–8, measured from the mean of the second replicate. The appropriate addition or subtraction of one half of the differences between the means of the two replicates will give the estimates of R_1 to R_8. Having calculated the run effects in this way, the corrected treatment means are obtained as follows:

From expressions $(6 \cdot 1)$:

$$x_1 + y_1 = 2\bar{x} + 2T_1 + (R_1 + R_5) + z + z'$$

Therefore, apart from experimental error:

$$T_1 + \bar{x} = (x_1 + y_1)/2 - (R_1 + R_5)/2$$

which on subtracting the values of the R's as calculated above gives an estimate of T_1. The other treatment effects may be estimated similarly.

Comparison of two treatment constants

6·52. Any two treatments may be compared by forming the difference between the corrected treatment means. Owing to the unbalanced nature of the design some treatment comparisons are more precise than others; in fact:

(i) For two treatments which occur in the same run the variance of the difference between the corrected treatment means is $V(p + 1)/p$, where p^2 equals the number of treatments and V the error variance. For $p = 4$ this is $1·25V$.

(ii) For two treatments which do not occur in the same run the variance of the difference is $V(p + 2)/p$. For $p = 4$ this is $1·50V$.

The difference in precision between the two types of comparison is not large, and when p is greater than 3 the mean value $V(p + 3)/(p + 1)$* may be used to give the variance of any comparison with sufficient accuracy for most practical purposes. A full treatment is given in [6·5] and [6·6], from which the above formulae are derived.

Analysis of variance of Tables 6·52 and 6·53

6·53. The significance of the treatment effects as a whole may be assessed by the method given in Appendix 6B for two-way tables with missing values, to which the reader is referred. The procedure is simplified because the error sum of squares has already been obtained, and is given by the remainder sum of squares (divided by 2, since each entry represents a difference between two

* This is not the arithmetic average of the two variances [6·5].

observations) of the table of differences (Table 6·55). This gives the remainder sum of squares denoted above and in Appendix 6B by Sa; it is based on $(p-1)^2$ degrees of freedom. The procedure for assessing the treatment effects as a whole is, first to make the Null Hypothesis that all treatment effects are zero, and then to calculate the sum of squares within the $2p$ runs. Denoting this sum of squares by W, the corresponding number of degrees of freedom is $2p(p-1)$, i.e. $(p-1)$ for each run. The sum of squares due to treatments is then denoted by $(W-Sa)$, which is based on $2p(p-1)-(p-1)^2 = (p-1)(p+1) = p^2-1$ degrees of freedom. The corresponding mean squares are $(W-Sa)/(p^2-1)$ for treatments, and $Sa/(p-1)^2$ for error. The significance of the treatment effects is then assessed by applying the F-test to these two mean squares.

Two replicates of lattice square designs*

6·6. Consider two replications of Tables 6·52 and 6·53.

Table 6·6

FIRST PAIR OF REPLICATES

Run					Run			
					5	6	7	8
I	x_1	x_2	x_3	x_4	y_1	y_2	y_3	y_4
2	x_5	x_6	x_7	x_8	y_5	y_6	y_7	y_8
3	x_9	x_{10}	x_{11}	x_{12}	y_9	y_{10}	y_{11}	y_{12}
4	x_{13}	x_{14}	x_{15}	x_{16}	y_{13}	y_{14}	y_{15}	y_{16}

Table 6·61

SECOND PAIR OF REPLICATES

Run					Run			
					13	14	15	16
9	x_1'	x_2'	x_3'	x_4'	y_1'	y_2'	y_3'	y_4'
10	x_5'	x_6'	x_7'	x_8'	y_5'	y_6'	y_7'	y_8'
11	x_9'	x_{10}'	x_{11}'	x_{12}'	y_9'	y_{10}'	y_{11}'	y_{12}'
12	x_{13}'	x_{14}'	x_{15}'	x_{16}'	y_{13}'	y_{14}'	y_{15}'	y_{16}'

The first step in the analysis is to form the sum over the two replicates. Denoting $x_1 + x_1'$ by X_1, $y_1 + y_1'$ by Y_1, we obtain Tables 6·62 and 6·63.

* Other designs suitable for further replicates are considered in § 6·7.

Table 6·62

X TABLE

Run				
$1 + 9$	X_1	X_2	X_3	X_4
$2 + 10$	X_5	X_6	X_7	X_8
$3 + 11$	X_9	X_{10}	X_{11}	X_{12}
$4 + 12$	X_{13}	X_{14}	X_{15}	X_{16}

Table 6·63

Y TABLE

Run			
$5 + 13$	$6 + 14$	$7 + 15$	$8 + 16$
Y_1	Y_2	Y_3	Y_4
Y_5	Y_6	Y_7	Y_8
Y_9	Y_{10}	Y_{11}	Y_{12}
Y_{13}	Y_{14}	Y_{15}	Y_{16}

The next step is to calculate the sum and difference of the two tables as for single replicates [§ **6·51**]. The estimates of $R_1 + R_9, R_2 + R_{10}$, etc., are obtained from the table of differences between X and Y, and using these values, estimates of the treatment means are derived; thus, for treatment 1 the treatment mean is estimated by $(X_1 + Y_1)/2 - (R_1 + R_9) - (R_5 + R_{13})$.

If separate estimates of R_1 and R_9, etc., are required, then they must be obtained from the first and second replicates treated separately. The expression for the variance of the difference between two treatments is clearly one-half of that obtained for one replicate. It only remains to calculate the experimental error variance. The total number of degrees of freedom is the number of observations less one, i.e. $4p^2 - 1$; there are $(p^2 - 1)$ degrees of freedom for treatments and $(4p - 1)$ for runs, leaving $(3p^2 - 4p + 1)$ $= (3p - 1)(p - 1)$ for error.

Now run 1 is a repeat of run 9, and the results for the two runs may be set out in the form of Table 6·64.

Table 6·64

OBSERVATIONS FOR RUNS 1 AND 9

Run					Sum
1	x_1	x_2	x_3	x_4	R_1
9	x_1'	x_2'	x_3'	x_4'	R_2
Sum ..	X_1	X_2	X_3	X_4	S

This two-way table may be analysed in the usual way, giving a remainder sum of squares based on $(p - 1)$ degrees of freedom. There are $2p$ such two-way tables, whose remainder sum of squares may be added to give a sum of squares based on $2p(p-1)$ degrees of freedom. The remaining $(p-1)^2$ degrees of freedom for error are associated with the remainder sum of squares of the p^2 table corresponding to Table 6·56 formed from the differences between the X and the Y tables. Note that it is necessary to divide this sum of squares by 4, since each entry is derived from four observations. Combining these two sums of squares yields Sa, which divided by $(3p-1)(p-1)$ gives the error variance V. The extension of the analysis of variance to assess the significance of the variation between the treatments as a whole is clear.

When the method is understood there should be no difficulty in extending it to three or more pairs of replicates.

General quasi-factorial designs

6·61. When the number of treatments to be examined cannot be conveniently adjusted to form a perfect square, rectangular designs may be used. These are a little more troublesome, and the reader should consult [6·5] and [6·7] for their description and analysis.

Quasi-Latin Squares

6·7. When the two replicates involved in lattice square designs do not give sufficient precision and a further replicate is required it is usually better to use different arrangements of the treatments in the runs than to repeat the whole design as it stands. For two replicates and 16 treatments in runs of four we use the design of Tables 6·5 and 6·51; but when a further replicate is required the treatments in the third replicate may be allocated as shown in Table 6·7.

Table 6·7

ARRANGEMENT FOR A FURTHER REPLICATE IN LATTICE SQUARE
DESIGN (TABLES 6·5 AND 6·51)

Run	Treatment			
9	1	6	11	16
10	5	10	15	4
11	9	14	3	8
12	13	2	7	12

The resemblance between Table 6·7 and a Latin Square may be shown by writing down the row in which each treatment occurs in the first replicate. Thus treatments 1, 2, 3, and 4 occur in the first row R_1, treatments 5, 6, 7, and 8 in the second row R_2, and so on. The design of Table 6·7 then has the form of Table 6·71.

Table 6·71

TABLE 6·7 ARRANGED AS A LATIN SQUARE

R_1	R_2	R_3	R_4
R_2	R_3	R_4	R_1
R_3	R_4	R_1	R_2
R_4	R_1	R_2	R_3

This is a Latin Square with R_1 to R_4 occupying the "treatment" positions. Further replications would use further Latin Squares orthogonal [§ **5·6**] to one other. When all orthogonal Latin Squares are included we arrive at a balanced incomplete block design, and this in fact provides one way of constructing certain of these designs. For the treatment of quasi-Latin Square designs see [**6·6**].

Applications of quasi-factorial and quasi-Latin Square designs

6·8. Incomplete block designs are used when the number of treatments to be examined is so large as to prohibit a completely balanced design. In addition to the applications mentioned earlier there are cases in which time is an important factor in the variability. It is known that properties of certain manufactured materials undergo secular changes even under controlled laboratory conditions. There are many possible explanations for these secular trends, and until they are removed or allowed for it is necessary to confine comparisons of treatments within relatively short periods of time. A lengthy programme of research work to examine large numbers of treatments should therefore be split up into groups or blocks of fewer treatments capable of being examined together or over short and convenient time intervals, with the object of eliminating components of heterogeneity due to secular changes. In the examination of a large number (say 49) of different types of fillers for rubber the treatments may be divided into seven sets of seven fillers. It is natural to choose those of greatest interest to be examined in the earlier sets. Provided the treatments in each set are examined together or within a relatively short interval the whole programme of work may be spread over any convenient period. This is an important consideration in laboratory work, because a long programme of work on any one problem is likely to cause disorganisation unless it can be divided into smaller parts spaced at intervals of time so that research work on other aspects and normal routine work may also be carried on.

REFERENCES

[6·1] FISHER, R. A., and YATES, F. *Statistical Tables for Biological, Agricultural and Medical Research.* Oliver and Boyd (London and Edinburgh, 1948).

[6·2] YATES, F. "Incomplete Randomised Blocks." *Annals of Eugenics*, **7** (1936), 121–40.

[6·3] SMITH, C. A. B., and HARTLEY, H. O. "Construction of Youden Squares." *Journal of the Royal Statistical Society*, B, **10** (1948), 262–4.

[6·4] GOULDEN, C. H. *Methods of Statistical Analysis.* Wiley (New York, 1939)

[6·5] YATES, F. "A New Method of arranging Variety Trials involving a Large Number of Varieties." *Journal of Agricultural Science*, **26** (1936), 424–55.

[6·6] *Idem.* "A Further Note on the Arrangement of Variety Trials. Quasi-Latin Squares." *Annals of Eugenics*, **7** (4), (1937), 319–31.

[6·7] COCHRAN, W. C., and COX, G. M. *Experimental Designs.* Wiley (New York, 1950).

[6·8] KOLODZIEJCZYK, S. "On an Important Class of Statistical Hypothesis." *Biometrika*, **27** (1935), 161–90.

APPENDIX 6A

TABLES OF BALANCED INCOMPLETE BLOCKS AND YOUDEN SQUARES

6A·1. This appendix gives a selection of balanced incomplete block designs and YOUDEN Squares. It is not exhaustive, but it covers most practical requirements in industrial research. More extensive lists of designs involving larger numbers of treatments are given in [6·1] and [6·7], which should be consulted if required.

Randomisation

6A·11. Before using any of the following designs, the order of the blocks, the allocation of the treatments, and the positions in the blocks should be randomised. If the same design is used repeatedly without randomisation, or if the treatments tend to occupy the same relative position in the different blocks of the same experiment, there is a risk of introducing a bias, particularly when there is the possibility of consecutive observations being correlated [§ 5·1].

Symmetrical designs

6A·12. These are the designs for which the number of treatments is equal to the number of blocks. YOUDEN Squares exist for these designs, and the additional factor (that is, position in the block or some other factor which does not interact with treatments or blocks) is indicated by Greek letters.

The designs are classified first by size of block, i.e. the number of observations per block, and next by number of treatments.

Notation

6A·13. A, B, C, . . . = treatments

$$t = \text{number of treatments}$$
$$k = \text{number of experimental units per block}$$
$$r = \text{number of replications of each treatment}$$
$$N = tr = \text{total number of observations}$$
$$b = tr/k = N/k = \text{number of blocks}$$
$$\lambda = r(k-1)/(t-1) = \text{number of blocks in which any two treatments occur together.}$$

Blocks of two observations

6A·2. A balanced arrangement for t treatments in blocks of two consists of all combinations two at a time, giving $t(t-1)/2$ blocks. The design is symmetrical for $t = 3$.

Treatment	Block		
	I	2	3
A	$X(\alpha)$		$X(\beta)$
B	$X(\beta)$	$X(\alpha)$	
C		$X(\beta)$	$X(\alpha)$

Blocks of three observations

6A·31. Four treatments in four blocks of three.

$$t = 4, k = 3, r = 3$$
$$b = 4, N = 12, \lambda = 2$$

This design is symmetrical.

Treatment	Block			
	I	2	3	4
A	$X(\alpha)$	$X(\beta)$	$X(\gamma)$	
B	$X(\beta)$	$X(\gamma)$		$X(\alpha)$
C	$X(\gamma)$		$X(\alpha)$	$X(\beta)$
D		$X(\alpha)$	$X(\beta)$	$X(\gamma)$

6A·32. Five treatments in 10 blocks of three.

$$t = 5, k = 3, r = 6$$
$$b = 10, N = 30, \lambda = 3$$

This design consists of all treatments taken three at a time, and is not symmetrical.

Treatment	Block									
	1	2	3	4	5	6	7	8	9	10
A	X	X	X	X	X	X				
B	X	X	X				X	X	X	
C	X			X	X		X	X		X
D		X		X		X	X		X	X
E			X		X	X		X	X	X

6A·33. Six treatments in 10 blocks of three.

$$t = 6, k = 3, r = 5$$
$$b = 10, N = 30, \lambda = 2$$

The design is not symmetrical.

Treatment	Block									
	1	2	3	4	5	6	7	8	9	10
A	X			X		X	X	X		
B		X			X		X	X	X	
C			X			X		X	X	X
D	X	X	X				X			X
E	X		X	X	X				X	
F		X		X	X	X				X

6A·34. Seven treatments in seven blocks of three.

$$t = 7, k = 3, r = 3$$
$$b = 7, N = 21, \lambda = 1$$

The design is symmetrical.

Treatment	Block						
	1	2	3	4	5	6	7
A	$X(\alpha)$	$X(\beta)$	$X(\gamma)$				
B			$X(\beta)$	$X(\alpha)$	$X(\gamma)$		
C	$X(\beta)$			$X(\gamma)$		$X(\alpha)$	
D			$X(\alpha)$			$X(\beta)$	$X(\gamma)$
E	$X(\gamma)$				$X(\alpha)$		$X(\beta)$
F		$X(\alpha)$			$X(\beta)$	$X(\gamma)$	
G		$X(\gamma)$		$X(\beta)$			$X(\alpha)$

6A·35. Nine treatments in 12 blocks of three.

$$t = 9, k = 3, r = 4$$
$$b = 12, N = 36, \lambda = 1$$

The design is not symmetrical.

Treatment	Block											
	1	2	3	4	5	6	7	8	9	10	11	12
A	X			X			X			X		
B	X				X			X			X	
C	X					X			X			X
D		X		X					X		X	
E		X			X		X					X
F		X				X		X		X		
G			X	X				X				X
H			X		X				X	X		
I			X			X	X				X	

Blocks of four observations

6A·41. Five treatments in five blocks of four.

$$t = 5, k = 4, r = 4$$
$$b = 4, N = 20, \lambda = 3$$

The design consists of all possible combinations of the five treatments taken in groups of four. It is symmetrical.

Treatment	Block				
	1	2	3	4	5
A	$X(\alpha)$	$X(\beta)$	$X(\gamma)$	$X(\delta)$	
B	$X(\beta)$	$X(\gamma)$	$X(\delta)$		$X(\alpha)$
C	$X(\gamma)$	$X(\delta)$		$X(\alpha)$	$X(\beta)$
D	$X(\delta)$		$X(\alpha)$	$X(\beta)$	$X(\gamma)$
E		$X(\alpha)$	$X(\beta)$	$X(\gamma)$	$X(\delta)$

6A·42. Six treatments in 15 blocks of four.

This design consists of all possible combinations of the six treatments in groups of four at a time. It is not symmetrical.

$$t = 6, k = 4, r = 10$$
$$b = 15, N = 60, \lambda = 6$$

6A·43. Seven treatments in 7 blocks of four.

$$t = 7, k = 4, r = 4$$
$$b = 7, N = 28, \lambda = 2$$

The design is symmetrical.

Treatment	Block						
	1	2	3	4	5	6	7
A		$X(\alpha)$	$X(\beta)$	$X(\gamma)$			$X(\delta)$
B	$X(\alpha)$	$X(\beta)$		$X(\delta)$		$X(\gamma)$	
C	$X(\beta)$		$X(\gamma)$			$X(\delta)$	$X(\alpha)$
D		$X(\delta)$	$X(\alpha)$		$X(\gamma)$	$X(\beta)$	
E				$X(\beta)$	$X(\delta)$	$X(\alpha)$	$X(\gamma)$
F	$X(\gamma)$		$X(\delta)$	$X(\alpha)$	$X(\beta)$		
G	$X(\delta)$	$X(\gamma)$			$X(\alpha)$		$X(\beta)$

6A·44. Eight treatments in 14 blocks of four.

$$t = 8, k = 4, r = 7$$
$$b = 14, N = 56, \lambda = 3$$

This design is not symmetrical.

Treatment	Block													
	1	2	3	4	5	6	7	8	9	10	11	12	13	14
A	X	X	X	X					X	X	X			
B	X	X					X	X	X				X	X
C	X		X			X		X		X		X		X
D	X			X		X	X				X	X	X	
E					X	X	X	X	X	X	X			
F			X	X	X	X				X			X	X
G		X		X	X		X			X		X		X
H		X	X		X			X			X	X	X	

Blocks of five observations

6A·51. Six treatments in 6 blocks of five.

The design consists of all possible combinations of the six treatments in groups of five. It is symmetrical.

$$t = 6, k = 5, r = 5$$
$$b = 6, N = 30, \lambda = 4$$

Treatment	Block					
	1	2	3	4	5	6
A	$X(\alpha)$	$X(\beta)$	$X(\gamma)$	$X(\delta)$	$X(\epsilon)$	
B	$X(\beta)$	$X(\gamma)$	$X(\delta)$	$X(\epsilon)$		$X(\alpha)$
C	$X(\gamma)$	$X(\delta)$	$X(\epsilon)$		$X(\alpha)$	$X(\beta)$
D	$X(\delta)$	$X(\epsilon)$		$X(\alpha)$	$X(\beta)$	$X(\gamma)$
E	$X(\epsilon)$		$X(\alpha)$	$X(\beta)$	$X(\gamma)$	$X(\delta)$
F		$X(\alpha)$	$X(\beta)$	$X(\gamma)$	$X(\delta)$	$X(\epsilon)$

6A·52. Eleven treatments in 11 blocks of five.

$$t = 11, k = 5, r = 5$$
$$b = 11, N = 55, \lambda = 2$$

The design is symmetrical.

Treatment	Block										
	1	2	3	4	5	6	7	8	9	10	11
A	$X(a)$			$X(\epsilon)$		$X(\delta)$	$X(\gamma)$	$X(\beta)$			
B		$X(a)$			$X(\epsilon)$		$X(\delta)$	$X(\gamma)$	$X(\beta)$		
C			$X(a)$			$X(\epsilon)$		$X(\delta)$	$X(\gamma)$	$X(\beta)$	
D				$X(a)$			$X(\epsilon)$		$X(\delta)$	$X(\gamma)$	$X(\beta)$
E	$X(\beta)$				$X(a)$			$X(\epsilon)$		$X(\delta)$	$X(\gamma)$
F	$X(\gamma)$	$X(\beta)$				$X(a)$			$X(\epsilon)$		$X(\delta)$
G	$X(\delta)$	$X(\gamma)$	$X(\beta)$				$X(a)$			$X(\epsilon)$	
H		$X(\delta)$	$X(\gamma)$	$X(\beta)$				$X(a)$			$X(\epsilon)$
I	$X(\epsilon)$		$X(\delta)$	$X(\gamma)$	$X(\beta)$				$X(a)$		
J		$X(\epsilon)$		$X(\delta)$	$X(\gamma)$	$X(\beta)$				$X(a)$	
K			$X(\epsilon)$		$X(\delta)$	$X(\gamma)$	$X(\beta)$				$X(a)$

Blocks of six observations

6A·61. Seven treatments in 7 blocks of six.

$$t = 7, k = 6, r = 6$$
$$b = 7, N = 42, \lambda = 5$$

This design consists of all possible combinations of the seven treatments in groups of six. It is symmetrical.

Treatment	Block						
	1	2	3	4	5	6	7
A	$X(\alpha)$		$X(\theta)$	$X(\epsilon)$	$X(\delta)$	$X(\gamma)$	$X(\beta)$
B	$X(\beta)$	$X(\alpha)$		$X(\theta)$	$X(\epsilon)$	$X(\delta)$	$X(\gamma)$
C	$X(\gamma)$	$X(\beta)$	$X(\alpha)$		$X(\theta)$	$X(\epsilon)$	$X(\delta)$
D	$X(\delta)$	$X(\gamma)$	$X(\beta)$	$X(\alpha)$		$X(\theta)$	$X(\epsilon)$
E	$X(\epsilon)$	$X(\delta)$	$X(\gamma)$	$X(\beta)$	$X(\alpha)$		$X(\theta)$
F	$X(\theta)$	$X(\epsilon)$	$X(\delta)$	$X(\gamma)$	$X(\beta)$	$X(\alpha)$	
G		$X(\theta)$	$X(\epsilon)$	$X(\delta)$	$X(\gamma)$	$X(\beta)$	$X(\alpha)$

6A·62. Nine treatments in 12 blocks of six.

$$t = \ 9, k \ = \ 6, r = 8$$
$$b = 12, N = 72, \lambda = 5$$

The design is not symmetrical.

Treatment	Block											
	1	2	3	4	5	6	7	8	9	10	11	12
A		X	X		X	X		X	X		X	X
B		X	X	X		X	X		X	X		X
C		X	X	X	X		X	X		X	X	
D	X		X		X	X	X	X		X		X
E	X		X	X		X		X	X	X	X	
F	X		X	X	X		X		X		X	X
G	X	X			X	X	X		X	X	X	
H	X	X		X		X	X	X			X	X
I	X	X		X	X			X	X	X		X

6A·63. Eleven treatments in 11 blocks of six.

$$t = 11, k \ = \ 6, r = 6$$
$$b = 11, N = 66, \lambda = 3$$

The design is symmetrical.

Treatment	Block 1	2	3	4	5	6	7	8	9	10	11
A		$X(\theta)$	$X(\epsilon)$		$X(\delta)$				$X(\gamma)$	$X(\beta)$	$X(a)$
B	$X(a)$		$X(\theta)$	$X(\epsilon)$		$X(\delta)$				$X(\gamma)$	$X(\beta)$
C	$X(\beta)$	$X(a)$		$X(\theta)$	$X(\epsilon)$		$X(\delta)$				$X(\gamma)$
D	$X(\gamma)$	$X(\beta)$	$X(a)$		$X(\theta)$	$X(\epsilon)$		$X(\delta)$			
E		$X(\gamma)$	$X(\beta)$	$X(a)$		$X(\theta)$	$X(\epsilon)$		$X(\delta)$		
F			$X(\gamma)$	$X(\beta)$	$X(a)$		$X(\theta)$	$X(\epsilon)$		$X(\delta)$	
G				$X(\gamma)$	$X(\beta)$	$X(a)$		$X(\theta)$	$X(\epsilon)$		$X(\delta)$
H	$X(\delta)$				$X(\gamma)$	$X(\beta)$	$X(a)$		$X(\theta)$	$X(\epsilon)$	
I		$X(\delta)$				$X(\gamma)$	$X(\beta)$	$X(a)$		$X(\theta)$	$X(\epsilon)$
J	$X(\epsilon)$		$X(\delta)$				$X(\gamma)$	$X(\beta)$	$X(a)$		$X(\theta)$
K	$X(\theta)$	$X(\epsilon)$			$X(\delta)$				$X(\gamma)$	$X(\beta)$	$X(a)$

APPENDIX 6B

GENERAL TREATMENT OF TWO-WAY TABLES WITH MISSING VALUES

6B·1. The procedure for the analysis of balanced incomplete blocks is systematic and simple, but in an unbalanced design more complicated methods of analysis are required. Unbalanced designs are sometimes chosen when the number of replicates required in a balanced design is prohibitive or is more than is necessary to give the required precision. In an unbalanced design certain comparisons will be more reliable than others, and naturally the treatments will be allotted to give more weight to the more important comparisons. A design may become unbalanced by accident. When performing a road wear test on tyres, one of the tyres may become faulty and the results may have to be rejected; we are then left with the observations on three tyres, and the design becomes unbalanced. Thus an unbalanced design may be chosen at the outset, or a balanced design may become unbalanced by accident, resulting in missing or obviously abnormal values. Any incomplete block design, whether balanced or not, may be regarded as a two-way table with missing values, and a complete block design may become incomplete by accident. All such cases will therefore be covered by a treatment for $n \times m$ tables from which some values are missing.

General treatment
6B·2. Consider the following $n \times m$ table with t missing values.

Row	Column				
	1	2	3	...	m
1	X	X	—	...	—
2	—	X	X	...	X
3	—	X	—	...	X
·	·	·	·		·
·	·	·	·		·
·	·	·	·		·
n	X	X	—	...	X

The columns could represent treatments and the rows blocks, or vice versa. Alternatively, the rows and columns could represent two factors, one with n and the other with m chosen values of the factors.

There are two ways in which the analysis may be approached: the first is to estimate the missing values from the known values, and the second is to fit constants to the row, column, and mean effects. Both methods are equivalent in the sense that they yield the same results, but in certain circumstances one may be more convenient to use than the other. If there are many fewer missing values than there are rows and columns it is better to estimate the missing values; but if there are many more missing values than there are rows and columns it is better to use the method of fitting constants.

First method. Estimating missing values

6B·3. This method is best illustrated by means of an example.

Example 6B·1

It is required to analyse the following two-way table in which five values (a, β, γ, δ, ϵ) are missing.

Table 6B·1

Row	Column						Sum
	1	2	3	4	5	6	
1	13·4	15·0	13·3	γ	17·4	14·8	73·9 + γ
2	11·0	β	9·7	δ	14·6	10·2	45·5 + β + δ
3	9·8	12·5	12·2	15·2	14·1	12·9	76·7
4	a	18·1	13·1	ϵ	18·8	14·2	64·2 + a + ϵ
5	11·9	12·0	11·3	10·2	12·5	8·8	66·7
Sum ..	46·1 + a	57·6 + β	59·6	25·4 + γ + δ + ϵ	77·4	60·9	327·0 + a + β + γ + δ + ϵ

The basis of the method is so to estimate the missing values as to minimise the residual sum of squares. Following the usual procedure for analysis of variance we derive successively:

(i) Total crude sum of squares. This reduces to $a^2 + \beta^2 + \gamma^2 + \delta^2 + \epsilon^2$ + terms not involving the missing values.

(ii) Correction due to mean $= (327\cdot0 + a + \beta + \gamma + \delta + \epsilon)^2/30$

(iii) Crude sum of squares due to rows. This is

$$[(73\cdot9 + \gamma)^2 + (45\cdot5 + \beta + \delta)^2 + \ldots + 66\cdot7^2]/6$$

(iv) Crude sum of squares due to columns. This is

$$[(46\cdot1 + a)^2 + (57\cdot6 + \beta)^2 + \ldots + 60\cdot9^2]/5$$

The corrected sum of squares in each case is obtained by subtracting the correction (ii). Denote the residual sum of squares when missing values are included by S, thus:

$S =$ Sums of squares due to total — columns — rows

$= a^2 + \beta^2 + \gamma^2 + \delta^2 + \epsilon^2$

$\quad - [(73\cdot9 + \gamma)^2 + (45\cdot5 + \beta + \delta)^2 + (64\cdot2 + a + \epsilon)^2]/6$

$\quad - [(46\cdot1 + a)^2 + (57\cdot6 + \beta)^2 + (25\cdot4 + \gamma + \delta + \epsilon)^2]/5$

$\quad + [327\cdot0 + a + \beta + \gamma + \delta + \epsilon]^2/30$

$\quad +$ terms not involving $a, \beta, \ldots$

The normal equations of Least Squares from which we obtain estimates of $a, \beta, \gamma, \delta, \epsilon$ are given by:

$$\partial S/\partial a = 30a + (327\cdot0 + a + \beta + \gamma + \delta + \epsilon) - 6(46\cdot1 + a)$$
$$- 5(64\cdot2 + a + \epsilon) = 0$$

$$\partial S/\partial \beta = 30\beta + (327\cdot0 + a + \beta + \gamma + \delta + \epsilon) - 6(57\cdot6 + \beta)$$
$$- 5(45\cdot5 + \beta + \delta) = 0$$

$$\partial S/\partial \gamma = 30\gamma + (327\cdot0 + a + \beta + \gamma + \delta + \epsilon) - 6(25\cdot4 + \gamma + \delta + \epsilon)$$
$$- 5(73\cdot9 + \gamma) = 0$$

$$\partial S/\partial \delta = 30\delta + (327\cdot0 + a + \beta + \gamma + \delta + \epsilon) - 6(25\cdot4 + \gamma + \delta + \epsilon)$$
$$- 5(45\cdot5 + \beta + \delta) = 0$$

$$\partial S/\partial \epsilon = 30\epsilon + (327\cdot0 + a + \beta + \gamma + \delta + \epsilon) - 6(25\cdot4 + \gamma + \delta + \epsilon)$$
$$- 5(64\cdot2 + a + \epsilon) = 0$$

The actual partial derivatives have been multiplied by $30/2$ in order to avoid fractional coefficients.

Upon reduction these equations may be set out as follows:

	α	β	γ	δ	ϵ	
(i)	20	1	1	1	-4	270·6
(ii)	1	20	1	-4	1	246·1
(iii)	1	1	20	-5	-5	194·9
(iv)	1	-4	-5	20	-5	52·9
(v)	-4	1	-5	-5	20	146·4

The numbers represent the coefficients in the five linear equations in α, β, γ, δ, ϵ, which may be solved by the usual method of elimination, or alternatively by a method of successive approximation as follows:

The mean value for the values available is 13·08. Take (say) 13·0 as a first estimate for β, γ, δ, and ϵ, and use Equation (i) to find α.

$$20\alpha = 270\cdot6 + 13\cdot0 = 283\cdot6$$
$$\alpha = 14\cdot18$$

Now use this new estimate for α and put γ, δ, and ϵ, each equal to 13·0, to obtain a new estimate for β from (ii), repeating the process on (iii), (iv), and (v) to obtain estimates of γ, δ, and ϵ respectively. For the estimate of β from (ii):

$$20\beta = 246\cdot1 + 26\cdot0 - 14\cdot18$$
$$= 272\cdot1 - 14\cdot18 = 257\cdot92$$
$$\beta = 12\cdot90$$

Repeating this process gives:

			α	β	γ	δ	ϵ
1st cycle	..	..	14·18	12·90	14·89	11·49	16·11
2nd cycle	..	..	14·79	12·33	15·29	12·22	16·54
3rd cycle	..	..	14·85	12·42	15·57	12·41	16·66
4th cycle	..	..	14·84	12·43	15·64	12·46	16·69
5th cycle	..	..	14·84	12·44	15·67	12·48	16·70
6th cycle	..	..	14·84	12·44	15·68	12·49	16·71
7th cycle	..	..	14·84	12·44	15·68	12·49	16·71

The values for α, β, γ, δ, and ϵ rapidly converge to the true values. The missing observations may clearly be given the values

$$\alpha = 14\cdot8, \beta = 12\cdot4, \gamma = 15\cdot7, \delta = 12\cdot5, \epsilon = 16\cdot7$$

Instead of starting with $\alpha = \beta = \gamma = \delta = \epsilon = 13\cdot0$ it is usually possible by inspection of the table to find more plausible initial values; the number of cycles necessary to obtain consistent values will then be less. However, with a calculating machine the process is very rapid; good approximations are usually obtained in the second cycle, and normally it would not be necessary to go beyond the third cycle. This method of successive approximation reduces considerably the labour of solving the equations and makes it practicable to solve for ten or more missing values, for which the method of elimination would involve a large amount of labour. The estimates of the row and column effects are obtained from the completed table; that is, after substituting the estimates of the missing values. Thus any given row effect = row mean — grand mean.

Method of fitting constants

6B·4. Denote the row effects by the constants $b_1, b_2 \ldots, b_k$, the column effects by the constants $a_1, a_2, \ldots, a_p$, and the grand mean by m. By definition $\Sigma b_i = \Sigma a_j = 0$; the number of independent constants to estimate is therefore: number of rows + number of columns — 1.

Let y_{ij} represent the actual observation in the ith row and jth column. The expected value based on the row and column effects is $(a_j + b_i + m)$, and the deviation from the expected value is

$$y_{ij} - (a_j + b_i + m)$$

The quantity to be minimised is given by $S = \Sigma[y_{ij} - (a_j + b_i + m)]^2$ where the summation extends over all the actual observations. (There will clearly be no contribution to the sum from the blanks of the two-way table.) The Normal equations are

$$\tfrac{1}{2}\partial S/\partial m = \Sigma\Sigma(y_{ij} - m - b_i - a_j) \quad = 0$$
$$\tfrac{1}{2}\partial S/\partial b_1 = \Sigma(y_{1j} - m - b_1 - a_j) \quad = 0$$
$$\cdots \qquad \cdots \cdots \cdots$$
$$\tfrac{1}{2}\partial S/\partial b_k = \Sigma(y_{kj} - m - b_k - a_j) \quad = 0$$
$$\tfrac{1}{2}\partial S/\partial a_1 = \Sigma(y_{i1} - m - b_i - a_1) \quad = 0$$
$$\cdots \qquad \cdots \cdots \cdots$$
$$\tfrac{1}{2}\partial S/\partial a_p = \Sigma(y_{ip} - m - b_i - a_p) \quad = 0$$

The summations extend over all available observations.

The constants obtained by solving these equations are identical with the row and column effects and grand mean obtained from the completed table after applying the method of estimating the missing values.

Instead of the conditions $\Sigma b_i = 0$ and $\Sigma a_j = 0$ we could use $\Sigma n_i b_i = 0$ and $\Sigma m_j a_j = 0$, where n_i represents the number of observations in the ith row and m_j the number in the jth column. The result of this is to make the constant m equal to the mean of the actual observations so that there will be one constant less to evaluate. The b's, and similarly the a's, will have the same differences between one another as previously, but all the b's (and also the a's) will be at a higher or a lower level.

When the blanks of the table appear in an ordered pattern as in the case of a balanced incomplete block, the Least Square equations for the constants will also be balanced and usually fairly easy to solve. There are several examples of two-factor experiments in the literature [6·1–6·5], and for further details the reader is referred to these publications. The treatment given above is perfectly general, and it may be applied to tables in which there are different numbers of observations in the cells.

Analysis of variance

6B·5. An approximate method for the analysis of variance is given by inserting the estimated values in the blank spaces and carrying out a formal analysis for a complete two-way table but deducting from the degrees of freedom for the remainder the number of missing values estimated. Table 6B·1 completed by the insertion of the missing values (in brackets) now reads as Table 6B·2.

Table 6B·2

TABLE 6B·1 COMPLETED BY INSERTION OF MISSING VALUES

Row	Column						Total
	1	2	3	4	5	6	
1	13·4	15·0	13·3	(15·7)	17·4	14·8	89·6
2	11·0	(12·4)	9·7	(12·5)	14·6	10·2	70·4
3	9·8	12·5	12·2	15·2	14·1	12·9	76·7
4	(14·8)	18·1	13·1	(16·7)	18·8	14·2	95·7
5	11·9	12·0	11·3	10·2	12·5	8·8	66·7
Total ..	60·9	70·0	59·6	70·3	77·4	60·9	399·1

This gives Table 6B·21.

Table 6B·21

ANALYSIS OF VARIANCE

Source of variation	Sum of squares	Degrees of freedom	Mean squares	Variance ratio
Between rows ..	103·07	4	25·77	13·29
Between columns ..	51·17	5	10·23	5·28
Remainder	29·09	15	1·94	
Total	183·33	24		

The total number of degrees of freedom is $30 - 1 - 5$ (5 being the number of missing values estimated) $= 24$. Both values of the variance ratio F are significant. The remainder or error variance is 1·94.

Exact method

6B·6. The exact method* for the analysis of variance with missing values is as follows.

(i) Determine the minimum sum of squares. Carry out the approximate analysis of variance solely for the purpose of arriving at the remainder sum of squares. The row and column sums of squares obtained in this way are discarded. This gives the remainder of 29·09 based on 15 degrees of freedom (Table 6B·21). Call this remainder sum of squares Sa.

(ii) Calculate the variance due to column effects. If there were no column effects the original table of results (Table 6B·1 with missing values) would be analysed simply as between and within rows. This would give Table 6B·22.

Table 6B·22

Source of variation	Sum of squares	Degrees of freedom	Mean square
Between rows ··	85·01	4	(Discard)
Within rows ·· ··	76·09	20	
Total ·· ·· ··	161·10	24	

The within rows sum of squares will contain the sum of squares due to column effects if the latter exist, and the excess of this quantity over the remainder sum of squares Sa will be the sum of squares due to column effects. We then have:

Sum of squares due
to column effects $= 76·09 - Sa = 76·09 - 29·09$
$= 47·00$, based on 5 degrees of freedom

(iii) Calculate the variance due to row effects. This is calculated in a similar way. Make the initial (Null) Hypothesis that row effects do not exist, and obtain the analysis between and within columns as in Table 6B·23.

* The full theoretical justification for this procedure is given in [6·8].

R

Table 6B·23

Source of variation	Sum of squares	Degrees of freedom	Mean square
Between columns ..	56·50	5	(Discard)
Within columns ..	104·60	19	
Total	161·10	24	

The excess of the within columns sum of squares over the remainder sum of squares Sa will be due to row effects if they exist. We then have:

$$\text{Sum of squares due to rows} = 104·60 - Sa$$
$$= 104·60 - 29·09$$
$$= 75·51$$

The final analysis of variance is then as Table 6B·24.

Table 6B·24

Source of variation	Sum of squares	Degrees of freedom	Mean square	Variance ratio
Row effects	75·51	4	18·88	9·73
Column effects	47·00	5	9·40	4·85
Error	29·09	15	1·94	

Note that in the approximate analysis of variance table the significance of the row and column effects is overestimated. This overestimate may become serious when there are many missing values. Note also that the total of row, column, and error sums of squares does not give the total sum of squares. In other words, where there are values missing the additive property of the sum of squares no longer holds. Applying the method of fitting constants to the orthogonal case, in which there are no values missing, will yield the usual analysis of variance table.

This method could be applied to balanced incomplete blocks, e.g. to Example 6·1, to obtain the same final analysis of variance table. The reader is recommended to work this out as an exercise, estimating the four missing values and applying the above method of analysis.

A further example is worked out in Appendix 6C.

APPENDIX 6C

UNBALANCED INCOMPLETE BLOCKS

6C·1. An example of an unbalanced incomplete block design is obtained by deleting the results for the fourth tyre [§ **6·11**] from the comparison of four compounds in three-part treads. Assume that for some reason the results for the fourth tyre are missing or unreliable. This leaves the data in Table 6C·1.

Table 6C·1
(Derived from Table 6·11)

Compound	Tyre		
	1	2	3
A	238	196	254
B	238	213	—
C	279	—	334
D	—	308	367

The design is now unbalanced, and in order to analyse the data it is necessary either to estimate the missing values or to fit constants to the compound and tyre effects. In this case it is better to estimate the missing values, but for illustrative purposes the method of fitting constants will also be applied.

To estimate missing values

6C·2. Denote the missing values by α, β, and γ, and enter the marginal totals as in Table 6C·11.

Table 6C·11

Compound	Tyre			Total
	1	2	3	
A	238	196	254	688
B	238	213	γ	$451 + \gamma$
C	279	β	334	$613 + \beta$
D	α	308	367	$675 + \alpha$
Total	$755 + \alpha$	$717 + \beta$	$955 + \gamma$	$2{,}427 + \alpha + \beta + \gamma$

Subtracting the sums of squares due to rows and columns from the total sum of squares and allowing for the correction due to the mean gives:

Remainder sum of squares $= S =$ Constant term independent of a, β, γ
$+ a^2 + \beta^2 + \gamma^2 - (451 + \gamma)^2/3 - (613 + \beta)^2/3 - (675 + a)^2/3 - (755 + a)^2/4$
$- (717 + \beta)^2/4 - (955 + \gamma)^2/4 + (2427 + a + \beta + \gamma)^2/12.$

To determine the values of a, β, and γ which will make this remainder sum of squares a minimum, differentiate with respect to a, β, and γ, and equate each differential coefficient to zero.

$\partial S/\partial a = 0$, $\partial S/\partial \beta = 0$, $\partial S/\partial \gamma = 0$ give respectively after reduction the following equations:

$$
\begin{align}
6a + \beta + \gamma &= 2538 \quad .. \quad .. \quad (1) \\
a + 6\beta + \gamma &= 2176 \quad .. \quad .. \quad (2) \\
a + \beta + 6\gamma &= 2242 \quad .. \quad .. \quad (3)
\end{align}
$$

The method of successive approximations could be used if required to solve for a, β, and γ, but in this case it is simpler to solve by ordinary algebra. Summing the three equations gives

$$a + \beta + \gamma = 869 \cdot 5 \quad .. \quad .. \quad (4)$$

Subtracting this equation from (1), (2), and (3) in turn gives the following solutions:

$$a = 333 \cdot 7, \beta = 261 \cdot 3, \gamma = 274 \cdot 5$$

The simplest way of obtaining the remainder sum of squares is to substitute these missing values in the table and carry out the usual analysis of variance. This gives $Sa = 426 \cdot 30$, based on three degrees of freedom, and an error variance of $142 \cdot 1$.

Estimate of compound and tyre effects

6C·3. The estimates of the compound and tyre wear are given by the averages of the rows and columns of the completed table, thus:

Compound .. A $= 229 \cdot 3$, B $= 241 \cdot 8$, C $= 291 \cdot 4$, D $= 336 \cdot 2$
Tyre .. .. (1) $= 272 \cdot 2$, (2) $= 244 \cdot 6$, (3) $= 307 \cdot 4$

The grand mean is $274 \cdot 7$, and the compound and tyre effects are given by subtracting this mean from the compound and tyre means.

Significance of compound and tyre effects

6C·4. Following the procedure of §6·B6, calculate the within tyre sum of squares of the original table, ignoring differences between compounds. This gives:

Total sum of squares of 9 observations $= 26,058 \cdot 00$
Sum of squares between actual tyre totals $= 10,898 \cdot 67$

∴ Sum of squares within tyres $= 15,159 \cdot 33$

In order to determine the sum of squares due to compound effects, deduct the remainder sum of squares, 426·30, from the sum of squares within tyres and obtain 14,733·03. Similarly, to obtain the sum of squares due to tyre effects, subtract the remainder sum of squares from the sum of squares within compounds, thus:

Sum of squares within compounds   = 5,360·17
Remainder sum of squares   =   426·30

Sum of squares due to tyre effects = 4,933·87

The completed analysis of variance table then reads as Table 6C·12.

Table 6C·12

ANALYSIS OF VARIANCE

Source of variation	Sum of squares	Degrees of freedom	Mean square	Variance ratio
Due to compound effects	14,733·03	3	4,911·01	34·56
Due to tyre effects ..	4,933·87	2	2,466·94	17·36
Error	426·30	3	142·10	

Both variance ratios are clearly significant.

Method of fitting constants

6C·5. Denoting the compound effects by a, β, γ, and δ, the tyre effects by a, b, and c, and the mean by m, the expected wear values for the individual part tyres are shown in Table 6C·2.

Table 6C·2

Compound	Tyre		
	1	2	3
A	$m + a + a$	$m + a + b$	$m + a + c$
B	$m + \beta + a$	$m + \beta + b$	—
C	$m + \gamma + a$	—	$m + \gamma + c$
D	—	$m + \delta + b$	$m + \delta + c$

Form the sum of squares of the deviations of the actual values of Table 6C·1 from the expected values of Table 6C·2 and determine the values of the constants which will minimise the sum of squares. The Normal equations are:

$$2427 - 9m - 3(a + b + c) - 3a - 2(\beta + \gamma + \delta) = 0 \quad .. \quad .. \quad (1)$$
$$688 - 3m - 3a - (a + b + c) = 0 \quad .. \quad .. \quad .. \quad .. \quad (2)$$
$$451 - 2m - 2\beta - (a + b) \quad = 0 \quad .. \quad .. \quad .. \quad .. \quad (3)$$
$$613 - 2m - 2\gamma - (a + c) \quad = 0 \quad .. \quad .. \quad .. \quad .. \quad (4)$$
$$675 - 2m - 2\delta - (b + c) \quad = 0 \quad .. \quad .. \quad .. \quad .. \quad (5)$$
$$755 - 3m - 3a - (a + \beta + \gamma) = 0 \quad .. \quad .. \quad .. \quad .. \quad (6)$$
$$717 - 3m - 3b - (a + \beta + \delta) = 0 \quad .. \quad .. \quad .. \quad .. \quad (7)$$
$$955 - 3m - 3c - (a + \gamma + \delta) = 0 \quad .. \quad .. \quad .. \quad .. \quad (8)$$

These equations are not all independent; the sums of (2), (3), (4), and (5) and of (6), (7), and (8) each give Equation (1). There are also the two relations $(a + b + c) = 0$, $(a + \beta + \gamma + \delta) = 0$, which simplify the solution considerably. Thus (1) gives

$$2427 - 9m - a = 0$$

and from (2)
$$688 - 3m - 3a = 0$$

These equations immediately give m and a, and by the exercise of a little ingenuity the equations may be readily solved for the other constants, giving

$$m = 274 \cdot 708, a = - 2 \cdot 533, b = - 30 \cdot 133, c = 32 \cdot 667$$
$$a = - 45 \cdot 375, \beta = - 32 \cdot 875, \gamma = 16 \cdot 725, \delta = 61 \cdot 525$$

The corrected compound and tyre means are obtained by adding the corrected means to the various effects. This gives:

$$A = 229 \cdot 3, B = 241 \cdot 8, C = 291 \cdot 4, D = 336 \cdot 2$$
$$\text{Tyre } (1) = 272 \cdot 2, (2) = 244 \cdot 6, (3) = 307 \cdot 4$$

These values agree with those obtained using the method of estimating missing values. The missing values may be estimated by adding the appropriate constants; thus for tyre (1) and compound D the missing value is $m + \delta + a = 333 \cdot 7$, and so on.

A fuller treatment of the method of Least Squares is given in Appendix 11B.

CHAPTER 7

FACTORIAL EXPERIMENTS: ELEMENTARY PRINCIPLES

MANY experimental situations require the examination of the effects of varying two or more factors. It is shown that in a complete exploration of such a situation it is not sufficient to vary one factor at a time, but that all combinations of the different factor levels must be examined in order to elucidate the effect of each factor and the possible ways in which each factor may be modified by the variation of the others. In the analysis of the experimental results the effect of each factor can be determined with the same accuracy as if only one factor had been varied at a time, and the interaction effects between the factors can also be evaluated. This chapter deals with such experiments, in which each factor is tested at two levels. Several examples are given of the design and the analysis and interpretation of the results of experiments of this kind. The succeeding chapter deals with experiments in which more than two levels of the factors have to be investigated.

Introduction

7·1. Chapter 4 dealt mainly with the design, analysis, and interpretation of experiments for the study of sampling and testing errors. For the study of the variation brought about by deliberate changes in the experimental conditions a generally useful technique is provided by the Factorial Experiment. In the present chapter the basic principles of this class of design will be introduced and illustrated by simple examples. More complex designs are given in Chapters 8, 9, and 10; some of the designs described in Chapters 4 and 5 are special cases of factorial designs.

7·11. Experiments carried out by chemists, physicists, and engineers, whether in the laboratory or on the plant, are in general intended to determine the effects of one or more Factors on the yield or quality of a product, the performance of a machine or measuring instrument, the resistance of a material to chemical attack, the power or fuel consumption of a process, and so on. A considerable advantage is gained if the experiment is so designed that the effect of changing any one variable can be assessed independently of the others. One way of achieving this object is to decide on a set of values, or levels, for each of the factors to be studied, and to carry out one or more trials of the process with each of the possible combinations of the levels of the factors. Such an experiment is termed a Factorial Experiment; the term is extended to modified designs in which the number of trials is restricted in certain well-defined ways. Randomised block and Latin Square designs are special cases of factorial designs.

Note that the term Experiment refers to the whole set of trials carried out, and not to an individual trial.

7·12. The following is a simple illustration of the set-up of a factorial experiment. Table 7·1 shows the results of an experiment in which the effects of three factors were studied. The process was carried out by each of two methods, M_1 and M_2; the main stage was carried out at each of three temperatures, T_1, T_2, and T_3; four batches of raw material, B_1, B_2, B_3, and B_4, representing works manufacture, were used. There were thus $2 \times 3 \times 4 = 24$ different sets of experimental conditions, and two trials were carried out with each set, giving 48 trials in all.

Table 7·1

RESULTS FOR $2 \times 3 \times 4$ FACTORIAL EXPERIMENT

	B_1		B_2		B_3		B_4	
	M_1	M_2	M_1	M_2	M_1	M_2	M_1	M_2
T_1	76·1	80·5	68·6	73·2	67·1	80·2	74·4	77·5
	74·0	79·3	69·4	76·0	71·4	72·9	78·6	75·3
Average	75·0	79·9	69·0	74·6	69·2	76·6	76·5	76·4
T_2	74·0	80·9	70·0	74·4	77·6	76·8	70·2	75·6
	76·1	80·2	73·0	79·3	75·4	80·2	74·5	80·3
Average	75·0	80·6	71·5	76·8	76·5	78·5	72·4	78·0
T_3	74·0	78·2	74·8	81·0	73·6	80·9	78·2	85·8
	82·9	83·8	74·9	79·0	72·8	77·8	77·6	79·6
Average	78·4	81·0	74·8	80·0	73·2	79·4	77·9	82·7

Averages:

$$M_1 = 74\cdot1 \qquad T_1 = 74\cdot7 \qquad B_1 = 78\cdot3$$
$$M_2 = 78\cdot7 \qquad T_2 = 76\cdot2 \qquad B_2 = 74\cdot5$$
$$T_3 = 78\cdot4 \qquad B_3 = 75\cdot6$$
$$B_4 = 77\cdot3$$

Factor

7·2. The term Factor is used in a general sense to denote any feature of the experimental conditions which may be assigned at will from one trial to another. It may represent, for example, the temperature, pressure, or space velocity at which a chemical reaction is carried out; it may be extended to cover different pieces of plant, different operators (especially in analysis or testing), different days or shifts, different batches of raw material, and so on. There are two main types of factor: qualitative and quantitative. A Qualitative Factor is one in which the different levels cannot be arranged in order of magnitude different pieces of plant or materials produced in different factories represent qualitative factors because in general there are no *a priori* reasons for arranging them in any particular order. A Quantitative Factor is one whose values can be arranged in order of magnitude. Such values can usually be associated with points on a numerical scale, e.g. temperatures, pressures, or velocities. So far as design and the initial stages of analysis are concerned, both types may be treated in the same way, but they admit of differences in interpretation.

In Table 7·1 one factor—temperature—is quantitative; the other two are qualitative. The averages for T_1, T_2, and T_3 (which are in ascending order) suggest that the yield increases with increasing temperature; it is natural to infer that a still higher temperature gives a still higher yield, and one lower than T_1 a lower yield; further trials could be carried out to verify this point. The averages also suggest that method 2 gives a higher yield than method 1, but we cannot thence deduce what the yield of a third method would be (assuming, of course, that the three methods are essentially different and not mere variations of a single method). In general no deductions concerning a third method can be made; this is one way in which the interpretation of the effect of a qualitative factor differs from that of a quantitative factor. There is also a distinction between the two factors Method and Batch. The batches may represent a random sample of possible batches, and from the degree of variation among the four batches tested an estimate can be made of the standard deviation associated with batch-to-batch variation and hence of the probable limits within which the yield of a fifth batch will lie, say plus or minus three times the estimated standard deviation from the average of the first four batches. In this sense probable limits can be set for the yield of a subsequent batch but not for the yield of another method. The reason for the distinction is that the batches are assumed to represent a random selection from a universe of batches whose mean and standard deviation can be estimated from the data, while the methods are arbitrarily chosen and do not usually represent a random selection from any universe of methods. A further distinction is that if the experiment is repeated at a later date the same methods and the same temperatures can be used, but perhaps not the same batches of raw material.

Levels of a factor

7·21. The various values of a factor examined in an experiment are known as Levels. The term was first applied to quantitative factors, for which its meaning is clear, but it has been extended by analogy to qualitative factors.

In Table 7·1 the factors Temperature, Method, and Batch have three, two, and four levels respectively.

Treatment

7·22. The set of levels of all factors employed in a given trial is called the Treatment or Treatment Combination. This term originated in fertiliser trials, the treatment being the type and amount of the fertiliser used. The treatment combination gives a full description of the conditions under which the trial is carried out, so far as these are affected by the various factors being studied. In Table 7·1 treatment (B_1, M_2, T_3) means that the trial is carried out on batch 1 by method 2 and at temperature T_3, and a similar notation is used for the other 23 treatments.

Response

7·23. The numerical result of a trial based on a given treatment is called the Response corresponding to that treatment. The response may be the yield of a process, the purity of a chemical, the composition found for a chemical sampled and analysed in a given way, or in general any quantitative expression of the result of a trial.

Effect of a factor

7·24. The Effect of a factor is the change in response produced by a change in the level of the factor. When a factor is examined at two levels only, the effect is simply the difference between the average response of all trials carried out at the first level of the factor and that of all trials at the second level. If there are more than two levels the above definition is incomplete, since the differences between the average responses can be expressed in several ways; this point is discussed in Chapter 8. The effects of the factors of Table 7·1, measured by the differences between the average effects at the various levels, are:

Methods. $78·7 - 74·1 = 4·6$.
Temperature. Differences between the three averages 74·7, 76·2, and 78·4.
Batches. Differences between the four averages 78·3, 74·5, 75·6, and 77·3.

Main effect and interaction

7·25. Each of the averages used in § 7·24 for deriving the effects of a factor is an average over all levels of the other factors. The averages of the two methods, for example, are taken over all levels of temperature and over all batches. It may be that the difference between the two methods is not the same at all temperatures. The average effect is called the Main Effect of the factor, and if the effect of one factor is different at different levels of another the two factors are said to Interact. In chemical experimentation interactions occur frequently and may be very important, especially when the levels of both factors are widely separated and contain maxima or minima. Consider Figure 7·1, which gives hypothetical, but feasible, curves relating the yield of a chemical reaction to temperature at two pressures, the trials being carried out at four temperatures T_1, T_2, T_3, and T_4, and two pressures P_1 and P_2, as shown in Figure 7·1. The effects of changing the pressure from P_1 to P_2 at the four temperatures are seen to be as follows:

At T_1: Very little effect.
At T_2: Large reduction in yield.
At T_3: Large increase in yield.
At T_4: Very little effect.

The effect of one factor thus depends on the level of another factor, and the two factors are said to interact. When T is also at two levels the interaction is defined numerically as the effect of P at T_1 minus the effect of P at T_2. The interaction is symmetrical in the two factors, and its value is the same whether it is expressed as the variation in the effect of P at different levels of T, or as the variation in the effect of T at different levels of P. In Figure 7·1 the interaction between P and T is large and rather complex; if the experiment had been carried out at only two of the temperatures the PT interaction could have been either negligible (T_1 and T_4), large and positive (T_1 and T_2),

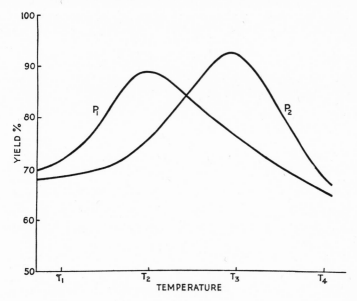

Fig. 7·1. Effect of temperature and pressure on yield. Illustration of interacting factors

or large and negative (T_2 and T_3). The example is exaggerated, since the spacing of the levels of temperature is clearly too wide, but it does illustrate the strong interactions that may occur in chemical experimentation when insufficient attention is paid to the spacing of the factor levels.

The advantages of factorial design

7·26. It can be shown that if the result of changing two or more factors is to be studied, then in general the most efficient method is to use a factorial design. By an efficient method is meant one which obtains the required information with the required degree of precision and with the minimum expenditure of effort. If some *a priori* knowledge of the effects of the factors and of the interactions is available it may be possible to reduce the amount of effort required by using a modified design—some particular part of the full factorial design, such as the Latin Square, or the partial experiments discussed in Chapters 9 and 10. At this stage only complete factorial experiments are considered.

7·27. The advantages of a factorial design can easily be illustrated by means of a simple experiment with two factors, each at two levels. Let the factors be temperature and pressure and denote the levels by T_0, T_1 and P_0, P_1. The minimum amount of experimentation necessary to give information on both factors is three trials, say one at $T_0 P_0$, a second at $T_1 P_0$, involving a change of temperature only, and a third at $T_0 P_1$, involving a change of pressure only. These trials occupy cells (1), (2), and (3) of the following table.

Pressure	Temperature	
	T_0	T_1
P_0	(1)	(2)
P_1	(3)	

The effect of changing the temperature is given by (2) — (1) and that of changing the pressure by (3) — (1). Because of experimental errors some confirmation is desirable, and one way of obtaining this is to duplicate each of the trials, the effects being deduced from the averages of the duplicate responses. This method of approach is known as the One-Factor-at-a-Time Method, since each factor is investigated separately.

Suppose now the table is completed by carrying out a trial with the treatment $T_1 P_1$; denote the response by (4). This completes the factorial design. The effect of temperature is estimated by (2) — (1) at pressure P_0 and by (4) — (3) at pressure P_1. If there is no interaction between temperature and pressure these estimates will differ only because of experimental error, and the average of the two estimates gives the effect of temperature just as precisely as the duplicate observations of (1) and (2). Similarly the effect of pressure is estimated by (3) — (1) and (4) — (2); if there is no interaction this estimate is as precise as one based on duplicate trials of (3) and (1). Thus if there is no interaction the four trials of the factorial design estimate the effects of the two factors with the same precision as the six trials of the duplicated one-factor-at-a-time design. All four observations are used in estimating each effect and the estimate is as precise as though only one factor were involved, whereas in the one-factor-at-a-time design only two-thirds of the observations are used in estimating each effect.

Let us now compare the two designs when the factors interact. If from the design shown in the table it were found that both T_1P_0 and T_0P_1 gave a better result than T_0P_0, a natural conclusion would be that T_1P_1 would be even better. This involves the assumption that T and P do not interact, but, as is shown by Figure 7·1, such an inference may be seriously in error. Again, it might be found that T_1P_0 and T_0P_1 are little, if any, better than T_0P_0, but it is possible that T_1P_1 may be much better—such a state of affairs is quite common. The one-factor-at-a-time design would miss the most favourable treatment. If the factors interact, therefore, the one-factor-at-a-time design may lead to wrong conclusions.

To sum up:

(a) When there are no interactions the factorial design gives the maximum efficiency in the estimation of the effects.

(b) When interactions exist, their nature being unknown, a factorial design is necessary to avoid misleading conclusions.

(c) In the factorial design the effect of a factor is estimated at several levels of the other factors, and the conclusions hold over a wide range of conditions.

These conclusions have been arrived at for two factors only; they hold with even greater emphasis when more than two factors are involved.

Interpretation of main effects and interactions

7·3 The terms Main Effect and Interaction have been defined in § 7·25. Having found, in the light of a significance test, that an effect exists, how do we translate our findings into practical terms, thus enabling the questions asked by the experimenter to be answered or indicating what further experiments are required? It cannot be too strongly emphasised that a statistical analysis, say an analysis of variance, is only a convenient way of detecting and separating the effects of the factors; the process of interpreting the results, that is telling the experimenter what conclusions can properly be drawn or what he should do next, is by no means automatic.

Consider for simplicity the analysis of a two-factor experiment with both factors at two levels only. The responses and the analysis of variance are shown in Tables 7·2 and 7·21. The actual method of deriving the analysis of variance will be given later.

Table 7·2

RESULTS OF A REPLICATED 2 × 2 FACTORIAL EXPERIMENT

	A_0		A_1		Average
		Average		Average	
B_0	108 98	103	120 130	125	114·0
B_1	194 202	198	144 140	142	170·0
Average..		150·5		133·5	142·0

Table 7·21

ANALYSIS OF VARIANCE OF TABLE 7·2

Source of variation	Degrees of freedom	Sum of squares	Mean square
Main effect .. A	1	578	578
Main effect .. B	1	6,272	6,272
Interaction .. AB	1	3,042	3,042
Error..	4	140	35
Total..	7	10,032	—

Comparing the effects A, B, and AB, with the error, all are found to be highly significant; there are real variations corresponding to all. The meanings to be attached to these conclusions are as follows.

Main effect A

7·31. This is the difference between the average response with A at level 0 and that with A at level 1. Alternatively, the difference $A_1 - A_0$ may be considered to be measured twice, once at each level of B, and the main effect of A is defined as the average difference over both levels of B. For Table 7·2 this is − 17.

Main effect B

7·32. This is similarly defined as the difference between the response with B at level 0 and that with B at level 1, averaged over all trials. It is equal to 56.

Interaction AB

7·33. This is the difference between the effects of changing from A_0 to A_1 with B at level 0 and with B at level 1. In this present example:

$$A_1 - A_0 \text{ at } B_1 = 142 - 198 = -56$$
$$A_1 - A_0 \text{ at } B_0 = 125 - 103 = 22$$
$$\text{Difference} \qquad = -78$$

The numerical measure of the interaction is defined as one-half of this quantity; the reason for this will be seen later. Thus

$$\text{Interaction AB} = -39$$

The interaction is symmetrical, i.e. if A and B are interchanged the numerical result is the same.

When an interaction is large the corresponding main effects cease to have much meaning. In the present example it is no advantage to know that on the average (i.e. averaged over both levels of B) A_1 differs from A_0. The existence of a large interaction means that the effect of one factor is markedly dependent on the level of the other, and when quoting the effect of one factor it is necessary to specify the level of the other. If the factors are quantitative, a large interaction usually signifies that the levels of the factors are too widely spaced and further experimental work at intermediate levels is necessary. If one factor is qualitative the results must be examined separately for each level of the qualitative factor.

When the interaction can be assumed negligible it may be inferred that the factors operate independently, and conclusions based on the significance or non-significance of the main effects may legitimately be drawn.

Expectations of mean squares in factorial experiments

7·34. The postulated set-up in a factorial experiment is as follows. The response in a trial with A at the ith level and B at the jth level, for the kth trial of this treatment, is written

$$y_{ijk} = \mu + A_i + B_j + D_{ij} + e_{ijk}$$

where μ denotes the true mean of all trials,

A_i is the true mean of all trials in which A is at its ith level, measured from the true mean of all trials,

B_j is defined similarly for the jth level of B,

D_{ij} measures the extent by which the true response in the trials with the treatment A_iB_j differs from the value $(A_i + B_j + \mu)$, i.e. it measures the lack of independence in the effects of A and B, or the interaction of A and B.

In effect, the analysis of variance estimates from the data the most probable values of A, B, D, and $\sigma_0{}^2$ (the experimental error variance), and assesses by significance tests whether the observed values can be accounted for by experimental error. The methods used in the analysis of variance lead directly to the mean squares, whose expectations are functions of A, B, D, and σ_0^2. If the F-test shows a mean square (say that of A) to be significantly greater than the error mean square, it can be inferred that the terms such as A_i are not all zero, i.e. that changing the level of factor A affects the response.

The expectations of the mean squares in an experiment with two factors, at p and m levels respectively, each treatment being tested n times, are shown in Table 7·3. The derivation is given in Appendix 7A.

Table 7·3

EXPECTATIONS OF MEAN SQUARES IN A TWO-FACTOR EXPERIMENT

Source of variation		Degrees of freedom	Expectation of mean square
Main effect ..	A	$p-1$	$\sigma_0^2 + mn\Sigma A_i^2/(p-1)$
Main effect ..	B	$m-1$	$\sigma_0^2 + pn\Sigma B_j^2/(m-1)$
Interaction ..	AB	$(p-1)(m-1)$	$\sigma_0^2 + n\Sigma D_{ij}^2/\{(p-1)(m-1)\}$
Error..	.. ..	$pm(n-1)$	σ_0^2
Total..	.. ..	$pmn-1$	

The quantities $\Sigma A_i^2/(p-1)$, etc., are sums of squares divided by degrees of freedom; they are analogous to variances, but they are not estimates of any actual variance, because the quantities A_i, etc., are not random drawings from a universe but are fixed by the arbitrary choice of levels and remain the same in every trial.

If variations in A and B have no effect on the response, then all the mean squares are independent estimates of σ_0^2, but if A and/or B affect the response, the relevant mean squares have expectations greater than σ_0^2.

7·35. It is clear from the expectations that all main effects and interactions should be tested against the residual by the F-test; if F exceeds the tabulated value at the level of significance chosen, we conclude that the expression ΣA_i^2 (for example) exists and that the factor in question affects the response, Note, however, that if AB is significant and A is not significant we cannot conclude that A has no effect. The existence of AB means that both A and B affect the response, but not independently. The non-existence of A simply means that A affects the response in different ways at the various levels of B and that when its effect is averaged over the values of B used in the experiment the average effect is small. In quoting the effect of A it is thus necessary to state also the level of B, and vice versa.

The assumption of Normality

7·36. The tabulated significance levels for the tests used in the analysis of variance—the F- and t-tests—are based on the assumption that the observed responses in repeated trials of one treatment are distributed Normally, with the true response as mean, and variance σ_0^2. The F-test in an analysis of variance is really an extension of the t-test for the comparisons of means, and such a test is not very sensitive to departures from Normality. This question has been discussed more fully in §2·6 *et seq*.

Designs with factors at two levels only

7·4. The simplest class of factorial design is that involving factors at two levels, that is, the 2^n class, n being the number of factors. This is the class that has received most attention in the literature, and the theory has been extensively developed.

Notation

7·41. For convenience a factor is denoted by a capital letter, and the two levels of the factor by (1) and the corresponding small letter. The levels of a factor A are thus denoted by (1) and a. By convention (1) refers to the lower level, the normal condition or the absence of a condition, while a refers to the higher level, the change from normal, or the presence of a condition, and so on.

Before giving a general treatment of the 2^n factorial designs it will assist in the presentation and understanding of the subject to consider an example with $n = 3$ first, that is, three factors each at two levels.

7·42. Denote the factors by A, B, and C, and their levels by (1), a; (1), b; and (1), c respectively. There are $8 (= 2^3)$ possible combinations of the levels of these three factors, as shown in Table 7·4.

Table 7·4

SYMBOLS FOR TREATMENT COMBINATIONS

Symbol for treatment combination	Level of factors A	B	C
(1)	—	—	—
a	+	—	—
b	—	+	—
ab	+	+	—
c	—	—	+
ac	+	—	+
bc	—	+	+
abc	+	+	+

+ means that the factor is at its higher level.
− means that the factor is at its lower level.

S

The symbols in the first column give the conventional representations of the treatment combinations; the presence of a small letter means that the factor it represents stands at its higher level, while absence of a letter means that the factor stands at its lower level. Thus (1) denotes the treatment combination in which every factor is at its lower level; the treatment a represents the higher level of A and the lower levels of B and C; the treatment bc the higher levels of B and C and the lower level of A; the treatment abc the higher levels of all three factors, and so on.

Example 7·1. Investigation of a nitration process

7·43. This example represents part of a laboratory investigation of the yield of a nitration process, the resulting product forming the base material for a wide range of dyestuffs and medicinal products. This part of the investigation dealt with the effect of the following factors:

1. Time of addition of nitric acid.
2. Time of stirring.
3. Effect of heel.

The term "heel" is a colloquial expression sometimes used in the large-scale plant manufacture of chemical products. In a batch process the batches are prepared in succession, and after the reaction is complete the product is discharged from the pan. It is not always convenient, or even economic, to clear the pan of the last traces of the batch, and frequently a small quantity is left behind and mixed in with the succeeding batch. This residuum is known as heel. Although the quantity is usually small it is conceivable that the presence of heel may affect the yield or quality of the succeeding batch. The factor was included in the investigation to assess this possibility.

The actual levels of the factors (with notation) are as follows:

A = time of addition of nitric acid. 2 hours = (1) or (−) and 7 hours* = a or (+).

B = time of stirring. $\frac{1}{2}$ hour = (1) or (−) and 4 hours* = b or (+).

C = heel. Absence of heel = (1) or (−); presence of heel = c or (+).

The three factors generate eight treatment combinations. The yields (as per cent of theoretical) corresponding to these eight sets of conditions are given in Table 7·5.

This table illustrates both the factor combinations and a convenient method of presenting the results.

---

* These are much longer than the standard times; they represent times at which the process must be complete.

Table 7·5

PER CENT YIELD FROM NITRATION EXPERIMENT

Time of stirring	No heel (1)			With heel c		
	Time of addition of HNO_3			Time of addition of HNO_3		
	2 hours		7 hours	2 hours		7 hours
½ hour ..	(1)	87·2	a 88·4	c	86·7	ac 89·2
4 hours ..	b	82·0	ab 83·0	bc	83·4	abc 83·7

Symbolic expressions for the effects

7·44. It will simplify later discussions if at this stage we introduce symbolic expressions for the effects. To find the main effect of one factor, say A, we average the responses corresponding to all treatments containing a (i.e. at the higher level of factor A), and all those not containing a (i.e. at the lower level of A), and determine the difference. Referring to Table 7·5, we subtract the average of the treatments (1), b, c, bc (indicated by ($-$) in the A column of Table 7·4) from the average of treatments a, ab, ac, abc (indicated by ($+$) in the A column of Table 7·4). Substituting the responses of Table 7·5, we have:

Average yield at higher level of A

$$= \tfrac{1}{4}(88\cdot4 + 83\cdot0 + 89\cdot2 + 83\cdot7) = 86\cdot1$$

Average yield at lower level of A

$$= \tfrac{1}{4}(87\cdot2 + 82\cdot0 + 86\cdot7 + 83\cdot4) = 84\cdot8$$

∴ Main effect of $A = 86\cdot1 - 84\cdot8 = 1\cdot3$

When this operation is carried out on the symbols representing the treatment combinations we have:

Average with A at higher level $= \tfrac{1}{4}(a + ab + ac + abc)$*

Average with A at lower level $= \tfrac{1}{4}((1) + b + c + bc)$

∴ Main effect of A $= \tfrac{1}{4}(a + ab + ac + abc)$

$\qquad\qquad\qquad\qquad - \tfrac{1}{4}((1) + b + c + bc)$

By treating (1), a, b, c as algebraic symbols the expression can be rearranged as follows:

$$A = \tfrac{1}{4}\{(a - 1) + (ab - b) + (ac - c) + (abc - bc)\}$$
$$= \tfrac{1}{4}(a - 1)(b + 1)(c + 1)$$

* Some authors write these expressions without the divisors, which are unnecessary for some purposes.

Note that these expressions are purely symbolic; they cannot be used as they stand but must be expanded before numerical results can be substituted. Similarly

$$B = \tfrac{1}{4}(a + 1)(b - 1)(c + 1)$$
$$C = \tfrac{1}{4}(a + 1)(b + 1)(c - 1)$$

Consider now the interactions of the factors. The interaction between A and B, denoted by AB, is defined as one-half of the difference between the effect of A when B is at the higher level, and the effect of A when B is at the lower level. The reason for using half the difference will be made clear later. The effect of A with B at the higher level is

$$A_1 = \tfrac{1}{2}(abc + ab) - \tfrac{1}{2}(bc + b)$$
$$= \tfrac{1}{2}b(a - 1)(c + 1)$$

The effect of A with B at the lower level is

$$A_0 = \tfrac{1}{2}(ac + a) - \tfrac{1}{2}(c + (1))$$
$$= \tfrac{1}{2}(a - 1)(c + 1)$$

The difference is

$$A_1 - A_0 = \tfrac{1}{2}(a - 1)(b - 1)(c + 1)$$

and the interaction, defined as one-half of this difference, is

$$AB = \tfrac{1}{4}(a - 1)(b - 1)(c + 1)$$

Similarly it may be shown that

$$AC = \tfrac{1}{4}(a - 1)(b + 1)(c - 1)$$
$$BC = \tfrac{1}{4}(a + 1)(b - 1)(c - 1)$$

The interaction ABC is defined as one-half of the difference between the interaction AB when C is at its higher level and when C is at its lower level. For the trials with C at the higher level we have:

Effect of A with B at higher level

$$A_{11} = (abc - bc)$$

With B at the lower level

$$A_{01} = (ac - c)$$

∴   Interaction AB with C at higher level

$$(AB)_1 = \tfrac{1}{2}(abc - bc - ac + c)$$
$$= \tfrac{1}{2}c(a - 1)(b - 1)$$

The corresponding interaction for the trials with C at the lower level is

$$(AB)_0 = \tfrac{1}{2}(a - 1)(b - 1)$$

Interaction ABC is one-half of the difference between $(AB)_1$ and $(AB)_0$, i.e.

$$ABC = \tfrac{1}{4}(a - 1)(b - 1)(c - 1)$$

The reason for introducing the factor $\frac{1}{2}$ into the definition of the interactions now becomes apparent; for reasons of symmetry all seven expressions must stand on the same footing, and hence require the same external multiplier.

To sum up, we have obtained the following symbolic expressions for a 2^3 design:

$$
\left.
\begin{aligned}
A &= \tfrac{1}{4}(a-1)(b+1)(c+1) \\
B &= \tfrac{1}{4}(a+1)(b-1)(c+1) \\
C &= \tfrac{1}{4}(a+1)(b+1)(c-1) \\
AB &= \tfrac{1}{4}(a-1)(b-1)(c+1) \\
AC &= \tfrac{1}{4}(a-1)(b+1)(c-1) \\
BC &= \tfrac{1}{4}(a+1)(b-1)(c-1) \\
ABC &= \tfrac{1}{4}(a-1)(b-1)(c-1)
\end{aligned}
\right\} \quad \dots\dots\dots\dots(7\cdot1)
$$

The method may easily be generalised to cover any 2^n factorial design. For n factors, $A, B, C, \dots, Q$, each at 2 levels, the corresponding expressions are:

$$
\begin{aligned}
A &= (\tfrac{1}{2})^{n-1}(a-1)(b+1)(c+1)\dots(q+1) \\
AB &= (\tfrac{1}{2})^{n-1}(a-1)(b-1)(c+1)\dots(q+1) \\
ABC\dots Q &= (\tfrac{1}{2})^{n-1}(a-1)(b-1)(c-1)\dots(q-1)
\end{aligned}
$$

Standard order of treatment combinations and effects

7·441. There is a convenient order in which to write the treatment combinations and effects. For one factor we simply have (1), a. For two factors add b, ab, derived by multiplying the first two by the additional letter b. For three factors add c, ac, bc, abc, derived by multiplying the first four by the additional factor c, and so on.

For three factors the standard order is

$$(1),\ a,\ b,\ ab,\ c,\ ac,\ bc,\ abc.$$

Expansion of the expression for A in Equation $(7\cdot1)$ (omitting the multiplier $\frac{1}{4}$) gives, when the terms are arranged in standard order:

$$-1+a-b+ab-c+ac-bc+abc$$

Preserving the standard order, the successive signs are

$$-\quad+\quad-\quad+\quad-\quad+\quad-\quad+$$

In a similar way the expressions for the other main effects and interactions may be expanded to give the appropriate signs. The signs for all the effects in a 2^3 experiment are given in Table 7·6.

Table 7·6

TABLE OF SIGNS FOR CALCULATING EFFECTS IN A 2^3 EXPERIMENT

Treatment combination	Effect							
	Total	A	B	AB	C	AC	BC	ABC
(1)	+	−	−	+	−	+	+	−
a	+	+	−	−	−	−	+	+
b	+	−	+	−	−	+	−	+
ab	+	+	+	+	−	−	−	−
c	+	−	−	+	+	−	−	+
ac	+	+	−	−	+	+	−	−
bc	+	−	+	−	+	−	+	−
abc	+	+	+	+	+	+	+	+

The value of Table 7·6 will become apparent later, but some interesting observations can be made at this stage. The signs for the treatment combinations for the main effects are obvious; in the expansion of A we note that all treatment combinations containing a have the plus sign and all not containing a the minus sign; all other main effects may be written out in the same way. The signs for any interaction are equal to those obtained by multiplying together the signs for the main effects corresponding to the letters in the interaction. The signs for A and B corresponding to treatment (1) are both minus; their product is plus, which agrees with the sign for AB in Table 7·6. The signs for A and B corresponding to treatment a are plus and minus respectively; their product is minus, which agrees with the sign for AB; and so on. For ABC we multiply the three signs for A, B, and C or, what amounts to the same thing, multiply the two signs, one corresponding to AB and the other to C. This is a convenient method of constructing Table 7·6. An extended form of the table up to six factors is given at the end of the volume (Table M). It is required mainly for the chapter on Confounding but has some uses in the present chapter. It is interesting to note that the signs of A, B, and C in Table 7·6 serve two purposes:

(i) They give the levels of the factors in each treatment combination;

(ii) They give the appropriate signs to apply to the responses for the purpose of estimating the main effects.

Calculation of effects and analysis of variance

7·45. There are several ways of calculating the effects and mean squares. The most straightforward way is to write the yields in standard order and use the signs of Table 7·6. In Example 7·1 the yields in standard order are

(1)	a	b	ab	c	ac	bc	abc
87·2	88·4	82·0	83·0	86·7	89·2	83·4	83·7

Applying the signs of Table 7·6:

$$\text{Total} = 87·2 + 88·4 + 82·0 + 83·0 + 86·7 + 89·2 + 83·4 + 83·7 = 683·6$$
$$4A = -87·2 + 88·4 - 82·0 + 83·0 - 86·7 + 89·2 - 83·4 + 83·7 = 5·0$$
$$4B = -87·2 - 88·4 + 82·0 + 83·0 - 86·7 - 89·2 + 83·4 + 83·7 = -19·4$$

and so on.

In calculating these quantities there is no need to write the observations down every time, and any constant quantity may be deducted from each result without affecting the results other than the total, since in each expression other than that for the total, half of the signs are positive and half negative.

YATES [7·1] has developed a systematic tabular method which is particularly convenient when there are four or more factors. Write down the treatment combinations and the observations in standard order, as in the first two columns of Table 7·61.

The column marked (1) is derived from the response column as follows. The first entry in column (1) is the sum of the first two yields (7·2 + 8·4); the second entry is the sum of the second pair of yields (2·0 + 3·0); the third and fourth entries are the sums of the succeeding pairs (6·7 + 9·2), (3·4 + 3·7) respectively. This completes the top half of column (1). The lower half is derived from the response column by taking the differences of the same pairs, the first from the second in every case. Thus the first entry in the lower half is (8·4 − 7·2), the second (3·0 − 2·0), and the other two (9·2 − 6·7) and (3·7 − 3·4). Column (2) is derived from column (1), and column (3) is derived from column (2), in exactly the same way as column (1) was derived from the response column, by summing and differencing the pairs of values. These operations yield exactly the same figures as would have been obtained using the signs of Table 7·6. The actual effects are then obtained by dividing the entries in column (3) by 4. The number of operations of summing and differencing is equal to the number of factors. The

Table 7·61

CALCULATION OF EFFECTS AND MEAN SQUARES BY
YATES'S METHOD

Treatment combination	Response = (Yield minus 80)	(1)	(2)	(3)	Sum of squares = Mean square = (3)²/8
(1)	7·2	15·6	20·6	43·6 = total	
a	8·4	5·0	23·0	5·0 = 4A	3·125
b	2·0	15·9	2·2	− 19·4 = 4B	47·045
ab	3·0	7·1	2·8	− 2·4 = 4AB	0·720
c	6·7	1·2	− 10·6	2·4 = 4C	0·720
ac	9·2	1·0	− 8·8	0·6 = 4AC	0·045
bc	3·4	2·5	− 0·2	1·8 = 4BC	0·405
abc	3·7	0·3	− 2·2	− 2·0 = 4ABC	0·500
Total ..	43·6			Total ..	52·560

reader is recommended to verify the method by inserting the appropriate symbols in place of the numerical data.

The seven effects, A, B, AB, ..., ABC, involve seven independent comparisons between the eight yields. It is possible to obtain many other sets of seven independent comparisons, but the above happens to be the only one of interest in the sense that each comparison represents a recognisable effect of practical significance. Since each of the quantities in column (3) of Table 7·61 is the algebraic sum of eight observations (in fact a difference between two sums of four), the sums of squares (equal in this case to the respective mean squares, there being only one degree of freedom for each effect) are obtained by squaring the corresponding quantities in column (3) and dividing by 8, yielding identically the same results as those obtained by the method usually given for analysis of variance [*S.M.*, Chapter 6]. It is convenient to retain the term Sum of Squares, though no actual summing of squares takes place in this method of analysis. These quantities are given in the final column of Table 7·61. Their total is 52·560, which should agree with the corrected sum of squares for the second column, viz.:

$$\text{Corrected sum of squares} = 7\cdot2^2 + 8\cdot4^2 + \ldots + 3\cdot7^2 - 43\cdot6^2/8$$
$$= 290\cdot18 - 237\cdot62 = 52\cdot56$$

This check is usually sufficient, since compensating errors are unlikely to occur. A more detailed check on the computation is given by YATES [7·1]; it is particularly useful in designs with many factors, since it checks each sum and difference column and mistakes can be detected before any further working is done. The check is hardly necessary with only three factors, but with (say) five or six it is worth while, since if the sum of the entries in the final column does not agree with the corrected sum of squares, which itself needs a lengthy computation in a 2^6 design, the only course is to repeat the computations from the beginning. Details of the check are given in Appendix 7B.

Interpretation of the results of Example 7·1

7·46. It is convenient to present the statistical analysis in the form of Table 7·62.

Table 7·62

ANALYSIS OF VARIANCE OF TABLE 7·5

Source of variation	Sum of squares	Degrees of freedom	Mean square
Main effects:			
Increase in time of addition of HNO_3 (A)	3·125	1	3·125*
Increase in time of stirring (B)	47·045	1	47·045†
Presence of heel (C)	0·720	1	0·720
Interactions:			
AB	0·720 ⎫	1 ⎫	0·720 ⎫
AC	0·045 ⎬ 1·67	1 ⎬ 4	0·045 ⎬ 0·417
BC	0·405 ⎪	1 ⎪	0·405 ⎪
ABC	0·500 ⎭	1 ⎭	0·500 ⎭
Total	52·560	7	

* = possibly significant (5% < P < 10%)
† = highly significant (P < 1%)

Since each treatment was tested only once, there is no direct estimate of the experimental error variance by which the significance of the effects may be judged. It is common to find in non-replicated experiments such as this that some or all of the interaction mean squares are used to give an estimate of the error variance. This procedure may sometimes be used legitimately, but caution is necessary. A general discussion of this question is given in Appendix 7D.

In the present example there was considerable prior knowledge of the chemical reaction, and it was thought unlikely that the factors would interact to any serious extent, so that the interaction mean squares could, if necessary, be combined to supply an estimate of error variance. As was shown in § 7·34, the expected value of an interaction mean square in the absence of any true interaction is the error variance σ_0^2.

Combining all four interactions, we obtain an estimate of error variance of 0·417, based on four degrees of freedom. The 5% value of F for $\phi_1 = 1$, $\phi_2 = 4$ is 7·71, so that using the estimate of error variance, mean squares of 7·71 × 0·417 = 3·21 are significant at the 5% level. The effect of time of stirring is significant (in fact highly significant); that of increase in time of addition of acid is almost significant at the 5% level, and it may be provisionally concluded that this factor probably has a real effect and requires fuller examination. The presence of heel has no appreciable effect, and in further experimental work on this process heel may be disregarded. Since it has been shown that time of stirring and (probably) time of addition of acid have appreciable effects on the yield, both factors should be examined in greater detail.

The main objection to any self-contained experiment of this size is that even in the most favourable conditions, when all interactions are judged non-existent, only four degrees of freedom are available for the estimate of error. But when the experiment is not self-contained the same objection does not equally apply. Frequently an estimate of error based on a larger number of degrees of freedom is available from previous work on the same (or a similar) process, and in fact some laboratories now collect such information as a matter of course for all testing methods and laboratory and plant processes as it becomes available—a practice which is highly recommended. In this particular nitration process much laboratory work had been carried out in the past, and lthis gave a standard error of 0·8 for yields in circumstances similar to those of this experiment, based on a number of degrees of freedom sufficienty large to be treated as infinite. The variance corresponding to this standard deviation is 0·64, and a mean square of 3·84 × 0·64 = 2·46 based on one degree of freedom ($\phi_1 = 1$) would be required for significance at the 5% level (3·84 = value of F for $\phi_1 = 1$, $\phi_2 = \infty$). Using this variance we find that the effect of increase in time of addition of nitric acid is significant, that of increased time of stirring being of course highly significant. We are also able to assess the interactions for significance: clearly no interaction is significant even at the 10% level.

The actual magnitudes of the significant effects are (see Table 7·61):

Effect of increase in time of addition of nitric acid $A = 1·25$

Effect of increase in time of stirring   ..   .. $B = -4·85$

The first had a beneficial effect, but the second produced a marked drop in yield.

Knowing from past experiments that the standard error of the preparations is 0·8, it is of interest to consider what order of effect would probably be detected from an experiment of this size. An effect is the algebraic sum of eight observations divided by 4, and has therefore a standard error of

$0.8 \times \frac{1}{4}\sqrt{8} = 0.57$. The 95% confidence limits for each effect are obtained by multiplying this quantity by the 5% value of $t(\phi = \infty)$, i.e. 1·96. This gives ± 1.11 as the limits to be associated with the above effects.

We shall now consider the experiment in retrospect and show the type of reasoning employed to control the size of the experiment. The chemist wished to ensure that he would not miss a yield difference of $2\frac{1}{2}\%$, so let us fix the chance of missing this, i.e. of committing an error of the second kind (see Chapter 2), at 0·01. In this particular experiment an error of the second kind is more serious than an error of the first kind, that is, of asserting a difference when none exists, because a wrong decision to carry out further experiments would be less serious than a wrong decision to abandon the investigation altogether. We therefore fix the chance of an error of the first kind at 0·1. We are interested in both positive and negative changes in the factors, and this implies the double-sided test. To derive the number of experiments we require the quantity δ, that is $2.5/0.8 = 3.1$. Entering Table E·1, we find $n = 5$. This n refers to the size of group, and since each effect is the difference between the means of two groups of n, the number of observations should be 10. In a 2^3 experiment the number of trials must be a multiple of 8, and since 8 is nearly sufficient on this basis only a single replication was used.

7·47. To complete our consideration of this example, much useful information can be gained from pairing the results. For instance, the effect of increased time of addition of nitric acid is given by the individual comparisons

$$88.4 - 87.2 = + 1.2$$
$$89.2 - 86.7 = + 2.5$$
$$83.0 - 82.0 = + 1.0$$
$$83.7 - 83.4 = + 0.3$$

$$\text{Mean} = + 1.25$$

We could, if we wished, apply the t-test to the mean of the four differences in the usual way. Thus the estimated variance of a difference is $(1.2^2 + 2.5^2 + 1.0^2 + 0.3^2 - 5^2/4)/3 = 0.843$, based on 3 degrees of freedom. The variance of the mean difference is 0·211, which corresponds to a standard error of 0·46. The ratio of the mean difference to its standard error is $1.25/0.46 = 2.72$, which fails to reach significance at the 5% level. The two other main effects can be treated in the same way. This method of analysis, although sometimes adequate, is not as satisfactory as the fuller method given above owing to the loss of one degree of freedom for error. The method shows in a direct way the large amount of information that can be gained even from a small factorial experiment. The eight results furnish four comparisons for each main effect.

Analysis of general 2^n factorial design

7·5. The analysis of designs of higher order is similar to that of the 2^3 design [Table 7·61]; the observations are written down in standard order and the sums and differences are calculated, columns (1), (2), (3), etc., being derived in turn. For a 2^n design the calculation of sums and differences must be carried out n times, giving columns (1), (2), (3), (4), . . . , (n). The divisor used to deduce the effects is 2^{n-1}, and in order to derive the mean squares the entries in column (n) (other than the total) are squared and divided by 2^n. The higher-order interaction mean squares are used as estimates of error variance except when an independent estimate is available, e.g. from past experiments or from replication.

Estimation of responses from effects

7·51. The response obtained with a given treatment combination is an estimate, subject to experimental error, of the true value, that is, the expected value, or the average of a long series of trials, which may be called the True Response. Having inferred from a factorial experiment that a certain treatment combination is the best of those tested, we may wish to estimate, as precisely as possible, what response is to be expected with this optimum treatment. If it is assumed that none of the factors has any effect, the best estimate of the response is clearly the mean of all trials. Similarly, if it is assumed that some factors have no effect, an estimate obtained by averaging over all levels of these factors is a better estimate than the single response under a given treatment. The following is a general method of estimating the responses from the effects. If the values of the effects are taken to be those calculated from the responses, reversal of the calculation must lead back to the original data; but if some effects are assumed to be zero the calculated responses will differ from those observed, and if the assumption is true they will furnish better estimates of the true responses.

Referring to the data of Table 7·61, the calculation is as follows. Apply the signs given in the rows of Table 7·6 to the figures in column (3) of Table 7·61, including the total. Find the algebraic sum and divide by $2^3 = 8$. Thus

$$(1) = \tfrac{1}{8}[43 \cdot 6 - 5 \cdot 0 - (- 19 \cdot 4) + (- 2 \cdot 4) - 2 \cdot 4 + 0 \cdot 6 + 1 \cdot 8 - (- 2 \cdot 0)]$$
$$= 57 \cdot 6/8 = 7 \cdot 2 \qquad\qquad \text{Yield} = 87 \cdot 2$$
$$a = \tfrac{1}{8}[43 \cdot 6 + 5 \cdot 0 - (- 19 \cdot 4) - (- 2 \cdot 4) - 2 \cdot 4 - 0 \cdot 6 + 1 \cdot 8 + (- 2 \cdot 0)]$$
$$= 67 \cdot 2/8 = 8 \cdot 4 \qquad\qquad \text{Yield} = 88 \cdot 4$$

and so on. The results agree with the initial responses, as they must. But if it is assumed that the non-significant effects are zero, the results are different. To find the best estimate of the response under treatment a (longer time of adding nitric acid) on the assumption that the only real effects are A and B, we have

$$(1) = \tfrac{1}{8}[43 \cdot 6 - 5 \cdot 0 - (-19 \cdot 4) + 0 - 0 + 0 + 0 - 0]$$
$$= 58 \cdot 0/8 = 7 \cdot 25 \qquad\qquad\qquad \text{Yield} = 87 \cdot 25$$
$$a = \tfrac{1}{8}[43 \cdot 6 + 5 \cdot 0 - (-19 \cdot 4) - 0 - 0 - 0 + 0 + 0]$$
$$= 68 \cdot 0/8 = 8 \cdot 50 \qquad\qquad\qquad \text{Yield} = 88 \cdot 50$$

Similarly for the higher level of factor B (increase in time of stirring):

$$b = \tfrac{1}{8}[43 \cdot 6 - 5 \cdot 0 + (-19 \cdot 4) - 0 - 0 + 0 - 0 + 0]$$
$$= 19 \cdot 2/8 = 2 \cdot 40 \qquad\qquad\qquad \text{Yield} = 82 \cdot 40$$
$$ab = \tfrac{1}{8}[43 \cdot 6 + 5 \cdot 0 + (-19 \cdot 4) + 0 - 0 - 0 - 0 - 0]$$
$$= 29 \cdot 2/8 = 3 \cdot 65 \qquad\qquad\qquad \text{Yield} = 83 \cdot 56$$

These results are summarised in the following 2×2 table.

Table 7·63

CALCULATED RESPONSES, ASSUMING ALL EFFECTS ZERO EXCEPT
A AND B

	(1)	a	Difference
(1) b	87·25 82·40	88·50 83·65	+ 1·25 + 1·25
Difference ..	− 4·85	− 4·85	

The difference caused by changing one factor is the same for both levels of the other factor; there is thus no interaction, the reason being, of course, that all interaction terms have been given a value of zero in calculating the responses.

Expressions similar to Equations (7·1) may be used instead of the table of signs. These are as follows:

$$(1) = (1 - A')(1 - B')(1 - C')$$
$$= 1 - A' - B' - C' + A'B' + A'C' + B'C' - A'B'C'$$
$$a = (1 + A')(1 - B')(1 - C')$$
$$b = (1 - A')(1 + B')(1 - C')$$
$$ab = (1 + A')(1 + B')(1 - C')$$
$$abc = (1 + A')(1 + B')(1 + C')$$

The term 1 in the expansion represents the mean of all the results. A', B', ..., $A'B'C'$ are the effects divided by 2. The formation of the expressions is obvious, the signs being the reverse of those in Equations (7·1). As before, the expressions are purely symbolic, and the numerical values are substituted only after expansion.

Effects and mean squares in 2^n experiments

7·52. It has been shown how the main effects and interactions of factors at two levels may be calculated from the data by a simple process of addition and subtraction of the yields. In the analysis of variance the quantities that appear and are used in the significance test are not effects but mean squares. The relation between effects and mean squares in 2^n experiments is simple, but in the normal treatment of the analysis of variance this simplicity is not brought out, the apparently arbitrary method of derivation giving little clue to the physical meaning of the analysis. If the variation is purely random no difficulty arises; the expression for the Expected Mean Square shows at once its physical interpretation. But in a factorial experiment such as Example 7·1 the mean square has a less obvious interpretation, and when it has been used to test the significance of an effect we still require some measure of that effect to answer the question, What change in yield will result from changing a factor from one level to the other? The effect as defined in this chapter is the appropriate measure: it expresses quantitatively the result of making the change. Why then does the mean square appear? In fact, when there are only two levels there is no need to introduce it; instead of using the mean square and the F-test to examine the significance we may equally well use the effect and the t-test, since for $\phi_1 = 1$, $F = t^2$ (compare Table C·2 with Table D, $\phi = 1$).

In order to apply the t-test we must calculate

$$t = \frac{Effect}{\text{S.E. (effect)}}$$

or the equivalent

$$t = \frac{Effect\ Total}{\text{S.E. (effect total)}}$$

The Effect Total is the entry in column (3) of Table 7·61; division by 4 gives the Effect.

We thus require to know the standard error. In the 2^3 experiment, Example 7·1, each effect total is the algebraic sum of eight observations, and its variance is therefore

$$\text{V (effect total)} \quad = 8V_0$$

where V_0 is the variance of a single observation. The effect is obtained by dividing the total by 4, so that

$$\text{V (effect)} \quad = 8V_0/4^2 = V_0/2$$

In general, for a 2^n experiment:

$$\text{V (effect total)} \quad = 2^n V_0$$
$$\text{V (effect)} \quad = V_0/2^{n-2}$$
$$\therefore \quad \text{S.E. (effect total)} = \sqrt{(2^n V_0)}$$
$$\text{S.E. (effect)} \quad = \sqrt{(V_0/2^{n-2})} = 2\sqrt{(V_0/2^n)}$$

If V_0 is known beforehand or can be found directly, e.g. from the differences between duplicate tests, it is unnecessary to calculate the mean squares; instead the effect totals can be tested for significance. In Example 7·1, however, the mean squares must be calculated to find V_0, which is based on the interactions, and it is equally easy to test them for significance.

In 2^n experiments an effect and a mean square are completely equivalent, in fact

$$\text{Mean square} = 2^{n-2}(\text{effect})^2$$

But if the factors are at more than two levels the effects can be defined in several ways, whereas the mean square is uniquely defined and easily calculated.

Orthogonality

7·53. Chapter 4 stressed the desirability of making the experiment symmetrical in all the factors by testing all possible treatment combinations the same number of times, thus simplifying both the calculations and the interpretation of the results, in addition to giving maximum efficiency. The property of the designs giving these advantages is known as Orthogonality. As will appear in later chapters, orthogonality can also be achieved by other methods, but in this chapter we consider only experiments in which every treatment combination is tested the same number of times, i.e. complete factorial experiments, with or without replication. Orthogonality ensures that all the main effects and interactions can be independently estimated without entanglement. If the experiment covers measurements of the yield of a reaction at four temperatures, say, 40°, 60°, 80°, and 100° C., and at three pressures, say, 1 atm., 2 atm., and 3 atm., then every combination is tested once, or the same number of times. If we form the averages for each of the three pressures the comparisons between these averages are independent of temperature, since every temperature is equally represented in every average. But if one combination is omitted, say, 40° C. and 2 atm., the averages for $p = 1$ and 3 atm. are taken over all four temperatures, while the average for 2 atm. is taken over only three temperatures, and any comparison is invalidated. Such an experiment is non-orthogonal; it is non-orthogonal with respect to temperature as well as pressure, since the 40° C. average is taken over two pressures instead of three. The same reasoning applies if the different combinations are tested different numbers of times, since an average which includes more tests at a given level of one factor is affected to a greater extent by that factor than an average which includes fewer tests.

7·531. Consider two linear functions of the observations $x_1, x_2, \ldots, x_n$:

$$\left. \begin{array}{l} E_1 = a_1x_1 + a_2x_2 + \ldots + a_nx_n \\ E_2 = b_1x_1 + b_2x_2 + \ldots + b_nx_n \end{array} \right\} \quad \ldots\ldots\ldots\ldots(7\cdot2)$$

where a and b may assume any values, not all zero. A main effect or interaction calculated from the data is seen to be a linear function of the observations with coefficients ± 1. The necessary and sufficient condition for the two linear functions to be orthogonal to each other is

$$\Sigma ab = a_1 b_1 + a_2 b_2 + \ldots + a_n b_n = 0 \quad \ldots\ldots\ldots\ldots(7 \cdot 3)$$

The effect functions used in the analysis of factorial experiments are all orthogonal to one another; it may easily be verified from Table 7·6 that for any pair of effects $\Sigma ab = 0$. The effect functions are subject to another condition. One of the effects is the mean, and since all the effect functions must be orthogonal to one another they must all be orthogonal to the mean. This implies that if the general average changes, the effects other than the mean are unaltered; such a change might for example be simply a change in the origin of measurement, made to simplify the computations. The general mean is

$$\bar{x} = \frac{1}{n}(x_1 + x_2 + \ldots + x_n)$$

Each coefficient is $1/n$, so that, comparing $\bar{x}$ and E_1, using condition $(7 \cdot 3)$:

$$\frac{a_1}{n} + \frac{a_2}{n} + \ldots + \frac{a_n}{n} = 0$$

$$\therefore \quad \Sigma a = 0, \text{ and similarly } \Sigma b = 0$$

7·532. It is clear that any function in an orthogonal set may be multiplied by an arbitrary constant without affecting the orthogonality. As explained in § 7·44, the divisor 2^{n-1} is introduced into every effect function; this ensures that they all have the same variance. If each x in Equation $(7 \cdot 2)$ is subject to error, with variance σ_0^2, the variance of E_1 is

$$V(E_1) = \sigma_0^2(a_1^2 + a_2^2 + \ldots + a_n^2) = \sigma_0^2 \Sigma a^2$$

and $\qquad\qquad V(E_2) = \sigma_0^2 \Sigma b^2$

E_1 and E_2 thus have equal variances if $\Sigma a^2 = \Sigma b^2$, and in the effect functions this is ensured by using appropriate divisors.

To sum up, effect functions in factorial experiments are subject to three conditions, viz.:

$$\Sigma ab = 0 \text{ for every pair of functions}$$

$$\Sigma a \;\;= \Sigma b = \text{etc.} = 0$$

$$\Sigma a^2 = \Sigma b^2 = \text{etc.}$$

Only the first condition is necessary for orthogonality.

In 2^n factorial experiments each effect contains 2^n terms, the coefficients, apart from the divisor, being $+ 1$ and $- 1$ in equal numbers, so that $\Sigma a = \Sigma b = \ldots = 0$, and $\Sigma a^2 = \Sigma b^2 = \ldots = 2^n$, since the divisor is the same for all.

7·533. The physical implication of orthogonality is that the estimate of any effect is unaltered by changes in one or more of the other effects. The independence of the effects in an orthogonal experiment may be shown for a 2^2 design by means of a 2×2 table of responses:

$$
\begin{array}{cc}
y_1 & y_a \\
y_b & y_{ab}
\end{array}
$$

The main effects and interaction are given by

$$A = \tfrac{1}{2}(-y_1 + y_a - y_b + y_{ab})$$
$$B = \tfrac{1}{2}(-y_1 - y_a + y_b + y_{ab})$$
$$AB = \tfrac{1}{2}(y_1 - y_a - y_b + y_{ab})$$

Now suppose the main effect of A to be increased by an amount f, and that of B by an amount g, the interaction remaining unchanged. The result is that all responses at the higher level of A are increased by f and all at the higher level of B by g, and (assuming no experimental error) the responses are:

$$
\begin{array}{c|c}
y_1 & y_a + f \\
y_b + g & y_{ab} + f + g
\end{array}
$$

The effects calculated as before are

$$A_1 = A + f$$
$$B_1 = B + g$$
$$A_1 B_1 = AB$$

The changes in the effect of A leave the calculated effect of B unaltered, and vice versa. The interaction is also unaltered. This is true of all factorial experiments, but if some treatments are not tested, or if the number of trials is not the same for all, the effect functions cease to be orthogonal and the effects are not independent.

Non-orthogonal data can be treated by special methods, but the calculations are laborious, and fully orthogonal experiments are more efficient, that is, for a given number of trials they estimate the effects with greater precision. Whenever possible, therefore, the experiment should be made orthogonal. In some investigations it may be impossible to ensure this; in others the orthogonality may be destroyed by accidents which cause the loss of one or more of the results. The method of analysis to use is that of fitting constants by the method of Least Squares, which is discussed in Appendix 11B.

T

Randomisation

7·54. In any experiment the factors which cause variation in the yield are of two types:

(a) Those deliberately varied.

(b) Those which cannot be controlled and which give rise to the residual variance, or experimental error.

The error, or uncontrolled variation, is treated as a random variable, that is to say, it is assumed uncorrelated with any of the controlled variations. On the assumption that errors are distributed at random among the results it is possible to calculate the odds against a given apparent effect of a factor being due entirely to error variations; such an assumption is implied by the tests of significance. If for some reason the error is not distributed at random but a surplus of positive errors occurs when factor A is at level 1 and of negative errors when it is at level 0, there will be an apparent positive effect for factor A. Unless therefore the errors are distributed at random the whole basis of the analysis, and of the tests of significance, is invalidated. In agricultural trials soil fertility may vary in a systematic way across a field; to ensure that any such variation does not bias the results of the trials the treatments are allotted at random to the plots over the field. In trials of a chemical process it is always possible that some uncontrolled feature of the process is causing a trend or systematic change in efficiency. If all the trials with factor A at level 0 are carried out first and all those with A at level 1 are carried out subsequently, a change with time will appear as an effect of factor A. But if the treatments are allocated at random it is highly unlikely that the plant efficiency will change in step with the trials; the error, i.e. the uncontrolled variation in efficiency, is not correlated with the treatments, and tests of significance are valid.

Whenever trials must be spread over time or space it is a wise precaution to allot them at random to the times and places, say, by the use of random numbers [Table N]. If the experiment is repeated it must be randomised afresh; if the layout is copied from a previous experiment it is no longer random.

Example 7·2. 2^4 factorial design
Preparation of an isatin derivative from an isonitrosoacetylamine derivative

7·6. In a laboratory investigation of the yield of an isatin derivative prepared from an isonitrosoacetylamine derivative (this will be referred to as the base material) the chemist was interested in the effect of the factors

(i) Acid strength (denoted by A).

(ii) Time of reaction (denoted by B).

(iii) Amount of acid (denoted by C).

(iv) Temperature of reaction (denoted by D).

In a preliminary survey of these factors it was decided to examine two levels of each in all combinations. The actual levels were

A (1, a): acid strength; 87%, 93%
B (1, b): reaction time; 15 minutes, 30 minutes
C (1, c): amount of acid; 35 ml., 45 ml.
D (1, d): reaction temperature; 60° C., 70° C.

Each combination was tested once only. In order to eliminate any possible trend in yield with time the tests were performed in random order.
Table 7·7 shows the data in tabular form.

Table 7·7

YIELD OF ISATIN DERIVATIVE

g. per 10 g. of base material

A Acid strength	B Reaction time	Temperature of reaction (D)			
		60 ± 1 (1)		70 ± 1 (d)	
		Amount of acid (C)		Amount of acid (C)	
		35 ml. (1)	45 ml. (c)	35 ml. (1)	45 ml. (c)
87 (1)	15 min. (1)	6·08 (1)	6·31 (c)	6·79 (d)	6·77 (cd)
	30 min. (b)	6·53 (b)	6·12 (bc)	6·73 (bd)	6·49 (bcd)
93 (a)	15 min. (1)	6·04 (a)	6·09 (ac)	6·68 (ad)	6·38 (acd)
	30 min. (b)	6·43 (ab)	6·36 (abc)	6·08 (abd)	6·23 (abcd)

Statistical analysis

7·61. The first step is to arrange the yields in standard order, as in column (2) of Table 7·71, and then derive in turn columns (3), (4), (5), and (6). Column (3) is derived from the response column (2) by summing and differencing successive pairs, and the other columns are each derived from the previous one in the same way. A constant quantity (6 g.) has been deducted from each yield to simplify the arithmetic. The construction of the lower half of the table, which gives a check on the calculations, is explained in Appendix 7B.

Table 7·71

ANALYSIS OF DATA IN TABLE 7·7. YATES'S METHOD

Treatment combination	Yield less 6·00 g.	(1)	(2)	(3)	(4)	Effect = (Col. 4) / 8	Sum of squares = mean square = (Col. 4)² / 16
(1)	0·08	0·12	1·08	1·96	6·11 = total	—	—
a	0·04	0·96	0·88	4·15	− 1·53 = 8A	− 0·191	0·1463
b	0·53	0·40	2·28	− 0·12	− 0·17 = 8B	− 0·021	0·0018
ab	0·43	0·48	1·87	− 1·41	− 0·01 = 8AB	− 0·001	0·0000
c	0·31	1·47	− 0·14	0·92	− 0·61 = 8C	− 0·076	0·0233
ac	0·09	0·81	0·02	− 1·09	0·27 = 8AC	0·034	0·0046
bc	0·12	1·15	− 0·76	0·40	− 0·53 = 8BC	− 0·066	0·0176
abc	0·36	0·72	− 0·65	− 0·41	1·19 = 8ABC	0·149	0·0885
d	0·79	− 0·04	0·84	− 0·20	2·19 = 8D	0·274	0·2998
ad	0·68	− 0·10	0·08	− 0·41	− 1·29 = 8AD	− 0·161	0·1040
bd	0·73	− 0·22	− 0·66	0·16	− 2·01 = 8BD	− 0·251	0·2525
abd	0·08	0·24	− 0·43	0·11	− 0·81 = 8ABD	− 0·101	0·0410
cd	0·77	− 0·11	− 0·06	− 0·76	− 0·21 = 8CD	− 0·026	0·0028
acd	0·38	− 0·65	0·46	0·23	− 0·05 = 8ACD	− 0·006	0·0002
bcd	0·49	− 0·39	− 0·54	0·52	0·99 = 8BCD	0·124	0·0613
abcd	0·23	− 0·26	0·13	0·67	0·15 = 8ABCD	0·019	0·0014
Total	6·11						1·0451
1st half odds W	1·04	3·14	2·46	3·16	4·80		
1st half evens X	0·92	2·97	2·12	1·24	− 0·08		
2nd half odds Y	2·78	− 0·76	− 0·42	− 0·28	0·96		
2nd half evens Z	1·37	− 0·77	0·24	0·60	− 2·00		
X + W	1·96	6·11	4·58	4·40	4·72		
Z + Y	4·15	− 1·53	− 0·18	0·32	− 1·04		
X − W	− 0·12	− 0·17	− 0·34	− 1·92			
Z − Y	− 1·41	− 0·01	0·66	0·88			
X + W + Z + Y	6·11	4·58	4·40	4·72			
(X − W) + (Z − Y)	− 1·53	− 0·18	0·32	− 1·04			

Check: Corrected sum of squares of the 16 results.

$$= 3·3781 - 6·11^2/16$$
$$= 3·3781 - 2·3333 = 1·0448$$

The last column agrees, within rounding-off errors, with this total.

Interpretation

7·62. An estimate of error variance is required. There was not sufficient background of information on the reaction studied to provide a reliable external estimate, and one must be derived from the experiment itself. There was no true internal estimate of error variance, since only a single replication of the experiment was carried out, but on technical grounds it was thought highly unlikely that interaction of three or four factors would be appreciable; it was decided, subject to experimental confirmation of the validity of the step, to combine the three- and four-factor interactions to give an estimate of error variance. In fact all these interactions are small [Table 7·71] and it was reasonable to use them as an estimate of error variance. Note that an F-test to decide whether the three-factor interaction mean squares are significantly greater than the four-factor would be of little use, a very large value of F being required when both mean squares are based on one degree of freedom. For a fuller discussion on the use of interaction mean squares as estimates of error see Appendix 7D.

The error mean square estimated from the three- and four-factor interactions is given by

$$\text{Sum of squares} = 0{\cdot}1924$$
$$\phi = 5$$
$$\text{Mean square} = 0{\cdot}0385$$

The analysis of variance table in its conventional form becomes Table 7·72.

Table 7·72

ANALYSIS OF VARIANCE OF DATA FROM TABLE 7·7

Source of variation	Degrees of freedom	Mean square
Acid strength .. .. A	1	0·1463
Reaction time .. .. B	1	0·0018
Amount of acid.. .. C	1	0·0233
Reaction temperature .. D	1	0·2998
Interaction .. .. AB	1	0·0000
AC	1	0·0046
AD	1	0·1040
BC	1	0·0176
BD	1	0·2525
CD	1	0·0028
Error (high-order interactions)	5	0·0385
Total	15	

For 1 and 5 degrees of freedom the 5% value of F is 6·61. A mean square based on 1 degree of freedom is thus significant at the 5% level if it is as great as $6·61 \times 0·0385 = 0·2545$. D is the only significant effect but BD nearly reaches significance (mean square $= 0·2525$), and since on technical grounds it was thought that the interaction BD might well exist, any future experiments would be planned on the assumption that it did. There is no evidence that factors A and C have any effect.

If it is decided to combine all interactions other than BD to give an error mean square of 0·0321 based on 10 degrees of freedom, then for $\phi_1 = 1$ and $\phi_2 = 10$ a limit of $4·96 \times 0·0321 = 0·1592$ is required for significance. This test would show BD to be significant, but no other effect except D. The combining of variances after a preliminary test has shown them to be not significant is not a practice which can be defended on strictly logical grounds, and it is necessary to seek other and independent evidence before adopting the procedure.

A factor may sometimes be introduced which on chemical grounds would not be expected to have any appreciable interactions with any of the other factors. In such a case we could decide beforehand to combine, in addition to the higher-order interactions, all interactions involving that factor. For instance, if it had been decided to treat factor C in this way we should have obtained an error variance of 0·0272 based on eight degrees of freedom, with the result that factor A would have appeared significant at the 5% level and the interaction AD significant at the 10% level. In the present experiment this assumption could not be made *a priori*, and it is not legitimate to make it *a posteriori* [Appendix 7D].

7·63. The first conclusion is that temperature and the interaction of temperature with reaction time are significant. The actual magnitudes of these effects are:

$$\text{Temperature} \qquad\qquad\qquad = + \, 0·274$$
$$\text{Interaction temperature} \times \text{time} = - \, 0·251$$

In other words, the higher temperature produces an increase in yield on the average but the negative interaction with time of reaction shows that this increase is greater at the shorter time of reaction. Indeed, further increase of temperature and reduction of reaction time may well produce a still higher yield. Using the signs of Table 7·6 to calculate the yield at the higher temperature and the lower time of reaction (i.e. at the treatment combination d with all effects other than D and BD zero) we obtain:

$$\text{Yield} = 6·00 + \{6·11 + 0 + \ldots$$
$$+ \, 0 + 2·19 - 0 - (- \, 2·01) + 0 + \ldots + 0\}/16$$
$$= 6·00 + 10·31/16 = 6·644$$

In a similar way we may calculate the adjusted yields for other conditions.

If we make allowance for factor A, then we have to introduce the quantity $8A = -1.53$ into the calculation of the adjusted yields. The conditions of main interest are then (1), a, d, and bd, and the adjusted yields are

$$(1) = 6.215 \quad a = 6.024 \quad d = 6.740 \quad bd = 6.489$$

Allowance for factor A increases still further the estimate of the yields with respect to condition d.

To sum up, increase in temperature produces an increase in yield which is greater at the shorter reaction time; there is a weak indication that the lower strength of acid may be more favourable, and the amount of acid does not appear to matter within limits used in this experiment. Further experimental work should examine a wider range of temperatures, shorter reaction times, and possibly also lower acid strengths. Methods for doing this are considered in Chapter 11.

Table 7·8

ANALYSIS OF VARIANCE FOR A REPLICATED 2^n EXPERIMENT

Source of variation	Sum of squares	Degrees of freedom	Mean square
Main effects .. A		1	
B		1	
C		1 $\Big\rbrace n$	
.			
.			
.			
Two-factor interactions .. AB		1	
AC		1	
BC		1 $\Big\rbrace \frac{1}{2}n(n-1)$	
.			
.			
.			
Three-factor interactions .. ABC		1	
ACD		1	
BCD		1 $\Big\rbrace \frac{1}{6}n(n-1)(n-2)$	
.			
.			
.			
Other interactions ..			
Sum for all treatments		$2^n - 1$	
Residual = error ..		$2^n(m-1)$	
Total		$m2^n - 1$	

Further examples

Further examples of the analysis and interpretation of 2^n factorial designs are given in Chapter 9, which deals with Confounding.

2^n factorial designs with replication

7·7. The analysis of 2^n factorial designs with replication presents no difficulty. The first step is to calculate, for each treatment combination, the sum of the replicate observations. If there are m replicates we obtain by this means a 2^n factorial design in which each result is a sum of m observations. These sums are then arranged in standard order and the columns of the sums and differences of pairs are derived in the usual way. Since there are m repeats, the effects obtained in this way have to be divided by m and the mean square for each degree of freedom has also to be divided by m. An additional mean square is supplied by the variation between repeats for each set of conditions, and this is best obtained as a difference between the sum of the sums of squares for the $2^n - 1$ effects and the total sum of squares of all $m \times 2^n$ individual observations. If $m = 2$ we can use the sum of the squares of the differences [S.M., § 3·341]. The final analysis of variance table will have the form of Table 7·8.

The residual mean square represents the error variance, which is used to assess the significance of any of the $2^n - 1$ effects.

If in Table 7·7 factor C is regarded simply as a replication, then the analysis will be as given in Table 7·9. This can be readily verified by the reader.

Table 7·9

ANALYSIS OF VARIANCE OF TABLE 7·7 OMITTING FACTOR C

Source of variation		Sum of squares	Degrees of freedom	Mean square
Main effect	A	0·1463	1	0·1463*
	B	0·0018	1	0·0018
	D	0·2998	1	0·2998†
Two-factor interaction	AB	0·0000	1	0·0000
	AD	0·1040	1	0·1040
	BD	0·2525	1	0·2525*
Three-factor interaction	ABD	0·0410	1	0·0410
Sum		0·8454	7	—
Remainder = error		0·1994	8	0·0249
Total		1·0448	15	

* Significant at 5% level.　　　　† Significant at 1% level.

REFERENCES

[7·1] YATES, F. *Design and Analysis of Factorial Experiments*, Imperial Bureau of Soil Science (London, 1937).
[7·2] FISHER, R. A., and YATES, F. *Statistical Tables for Biological, Agricultural and Medical Research.* Oliver and Boyd (London, 1947).

APPENDIX 7A

EXPECTATIONS OF MEAN SQUARES IN FACTORIAL EXPERIMENTS

7A·1. The procedure is similar to that used in Appendix 5A. Consider for simplicity a two-factor experiment in which

Factor A is tested at p levels: $1, 2 \ldots i \ldots p$
Factor B is tested at m levels: $1, 2 \ldots j \ldots m$
Each treatment is tested n times: $1, 2 \ldots k \ldots n$

Suppose that when the treatment combination A_iB_j is tested for the kth time the response is y_{ijk}, and that if this treatment were tested a large number of times the mean response would tend to the true value $E(y_{ijk}) = \mu_{ij}$.

The responses y_{ij} differ from μ_{ij} because of experimental error, which has a standard deviation σ. The mathematical model used in the analysis of a factorial experiment postulates that μ_{ij} can be written

$$\mu_{ij} = \mu + A_i + B_j + D_{ij} \ldots\ldots\ldots\ldots\ldots(7A\cdot1)$$

That is to say, the true response μ_{ij} is built up from the overall mean μ plus a contribution characteristic of the ith level of A, plus a contribution characteristic of the jth level of B, plus the term D_{ij}. If the effect of changing the level of A were always the same, irrespective of the level of B, and vice versa, the term D_{ij} would be zero. D_{ij} is thus a measure of the lack of independence of factors A and B, that is, of their interaction.

Since μ is the mean of μ_{ij}, and an equal number of trials is made with each treatment:

$$\Sigma A_i = \Sigma B_j = \Sigma\Sigma D_{ij} = 0 \ldots\ldots\ldots\ldots\ldots(7A\cdot2)$$

The expectation of a sum or difference of quantities (whether independent or not) is the sum or difference of the individual expectations. For example:

$$E(x \pm y \pm z \pm \ldots) = E(x) \pm E(y) \pm E(z) \ldots\ldots\ldots(7A\cdot3)$$

Now according to the set-up of Equation $(7A\cdot1)$:

$$E(y_{ijk}) = \mu + A_i + B_j + D_{ij}$$

It can easily be shown that

$$E(\bar{y}) = \mu \qquad E(\bar{y}_j - \bar{y}) = B_j$$
$$\left. E(\bar{y}_i - \bar{y}) = A_i \quad E(\bar{y}_{ij} - \bar{y}_i - \bar{y}_j + \bar{y}) = D_{ij} \right\} \quad \ldots\ldots(7A\cdot4)$$

where $\bar{y}$ is the mean of all results, $\bar{y}_i$ is the mean of all results at the ith level of A, $\bar{y}_j$ the mean for the jth level of B, and $\bar{y}_{ij}$ the mean of all results with the treatment A_iB_j.

7A·2. The analysis of variance table showing the expectations of the mean squares is as Table 7A·1.

Table 7A·1

EXPECTATIONS OF MEAN SQUARES IN A FACTORIAL EXPERIMENT

Source of variation	Degrees of freedom	Sum of squares	Expectation of mean square
Main effect A	$p-1$	$mn\Sigma(\bar{y}_i - \bar{y})^2$	$\sigma^2 + \dfrac{mn\Sigma A_i^2}{p-1}$
Main effect B	$m-1$	$pn\Sigma(\bar{y}_j - \bar{y})^2$	$\sigma^2 + \dfrac{pn\Sigma B_j^2}{m-1}$
Interaction AB	$(p-1)(m-1)$	$n\Sigma\Sigma(\bar{y}_{ij} - \bar{y}_i - \bar{y}_j + \bar{y})^2$	$\sigma^2 + \dfrac{n\Sigma\Sigma D_{ij}^2}{(p-1)(m-1)}$
Error	$pm(n-1)$	$\Sigma\Sigma\Sigma(y_{ijk} - \bar{y}_{ij})^2$	σ^2
Total	$pmn-1$	$\Sigma\Sigma\Sigma(y_{ijk} - \bar{y})^2$	

The procedure for finding the expectation is exactly similar to that used in Appendix 5A.

Main effect A

$$\begin{aligned} E(SS)_A &= E[mn\Sigma(\bar{y}_i - \bar{y})^2] \\ &= mn\Sigma[E(\bar{y}_i - \bar{y})]^2 + mn\Sigma V(\bar{y}_i - \bar{y}) \\ &= mn\Sigma A_i^2 + (p-1)\sigma^2 \end{aligned}$$

Main effect B

Similarly $\qquad\qquad E(SS)_B = pn\Sigma B_j^2 + (m-1)\sigma^2$

Interaction AB

$$E(SS)_{AB} = E[n\Sigma\Sigma(\bar{y}_{ij} - \bar{y}_i - \bar{y}_j + \bar{y})^2]$$
$$= n\Sigma\Sigma[E(\bar{y}_{ij} - \bar{y}_i - \bar{y}_j + \bar{y})]^2 + n\Sigma\Sigma V(\bar{y}_{ij} - \bar{y}_i - \bar{y}_j + \bar{y})$$
$$= n\Sigma\Sigma D^2_{ij} + (p-1)(m-1)\sigma^2$$

$\Sigma\Sigma V(\bar{y}_{ij} - \bar{y}_i - \bar{y}_j + \bar{y})$ is found by the method of Appendix 4A to be

$$(p-1)(m-1)\sigma^2/n$$

Total

The expectation of the total sum of squares is

$$E(TSS) = \Sigma\Sigma\Sigma E(y_{ijk} - \bar{y})^2 = \Sigma\Sigma\Sigma[E(y_{ijk} - \bar{y})]^2 + \Sigma\Sigma\Sigma V(y_{ijk} - \bar{y})$$
$$= mn\Sigma A_i^2 + pn\Sigma B_j^2 + n\Sigma\Sigma D_{ij}^2 + (pmn - 1)\sigma_0^2$$

Error

By subtraction, the expectation of the error sum of squares is

$$E(TSS) - E(SS)_A - E(SS)_B - E(SS)_{AB} = pm(n-1)\sigma^2$$

The expectations of the mean squares are therefore as shown in Table 7A·1.

The second terms in A, B, and AB are similar in form to estimates of variance, but since the variation arising from changes in the levels of factors A and B is systematic and not random there is no universe variance of which the mean squares are estimates. The mean squares vary between replicates of the same experiment only because of random variations in the experimental errors. In a random set-up such as that discussed in Appendix 5A the mean square also varies because of random sampling errors. In the systematic set-up of a factorial experiment each expectation contains only one term apart from σ_0^2, whereas in the random set-up of a sampling experiment this is not the case.

APPENDIX 7B

SYSTEMATIC CHECKING IN YATES'S METHOD FOR THE ANALYSIS OF 2^n DESIGNS

THE method is most easily explained by means of an example. The data from Example 7·1, Table 7·61, are used, and the computation is set out in Table 7B·1.

Table 7B·1

METHOD OF CHECKING ANALYSIS OF 2^3 FACTORIAL DESIGN

		(1)	(2)	(3)	Sum of squares $= (3)^2/8$
Treatment combination	Response				
(1)	7·2	15·6	20·6	43·6 = total	
a	8·4	5·0	23·0	5·0 = 4A	
b	2·0	15·9	2·2	− 19·4 = 4B	
ab	3·0	7·1	2·8	− 2·4 = 4AB	
c	6·7	1·2	− 10·6	2·4 = 4C	
ac	9·2	1·0	− 8·8	0·6 = 4AC	
bc	3·4	2·5	− 0·2	1·8 = 4BC	
abc	3·7	0·3	− 2·2	− 2·0 = 4ABC	
1st half odds* .. W	9·2	31·5	22·8	24·2	
1st half evens .. X	11·4	12·1	25·8	2·6	
2nd half odds .. Y	10·1	3·7	− 10·8	4·2	
2nd half evens .. Z	12·9	1·3	− 11·0	− 1·4	
$X + W$	20·6	43·6	48·6	26·8	
$Z + Y$	23·0	5·0	− 21·8	2·8	
$X − W$	2·2	− 19·4	3·0		
$Z − Y$	2·8	− 2·4	− 0·2		
$X + Z + W + Y$ ..	43·6	48·6	26·8		
$(X − W) + (Z − Y)$	5·0	− 21·8	2·8		

* 1st half odds = sum of odd (1st and 3rd) terms in the first half of the table. Similarly for the other terms.

The checks are as follows:

(i) $(W + X)$ in any column $= (X + W) + (Z + Y)$ in previous column.

(ii) $(Y + Z)$ in any column $= (X − W) + (Z − Y)$ in previous column.

(iii) First entry in column (3) $= (X + W + Z + Y)$ in Response column.

Column	$(X + W)$	$(Z + Y)$	Previous column	
			$(X + W + Z + Y)$	$(X − W) + (Z − Y)$
(1)	43·6	5·0	43·6	5·0
(2)	48·6	− 21·8	48·6	− 21·8
(3)	26·8	2·8	26·8	2·8

Thus any error is detected before the next column is started and a clue to its location is provided. If it is found that $(Z + Y)$ is not equal to $(X - W)$ $+ (Z - Y)$ for the previous column, the error occurs either in adding $(X - W)$ and $(Z - Y)$, which is unlikely, or in forming the second half of the column.

It is advisable to form the corrected total sum of squares to check the formation of the final column, but any disagreement must be either in the formation of this column or in the sum of squares itself, and only these need be re-worked. Without the above check the error might be in any part of the working.

The above check is applicable to any 2^n design, and can be extended to 3^n and other designs [Chapter 8].

APPENDIX 7C

SIGNIFICANCE OF ONE AND OF SEVERAL MEAN SQUARES

IN a factorial experiment the final analysis of variance table contains several mean squares, which must be assessed for significance. A 2^4 experiment gives 15 mean squares, corresponding to the four main effects, six two-factor interactions, four three-factor interactions, and one four-factor interaction. The problem thus arises, How to assess the significance of the individual mean squares ?

The principle underlying the F-test is that, if the only source of variation is the experimental error, the variance ratio F has an expectation of about unity (actually $\phi_2/(\phi_2 - 2)$, where ϕ_2 is the number of degrees of freedom for the denominator of F). Because of sampling variations F varies, and will occasionally be as great as the tabulated values for the 10% significance level, less frequently as great as the 5% value, and very rarely as great as the 1% value. If in a single test F is greater than (say) the 5% value, we infer that experimental error is not the only source of variation and that the factor concerned probably has a real effect. The chance that this inference is wrong is only 5%, since only in 5% of trials would F exceed the tabulated value if the factor had no real effect.

In analysing a 2^4 experiment all fifteen effect mean squares must be tested, and even if none of the factors has any real effect it is quite likely that one or two of the F-tests will give a significant result. There is, in fact, a chance of about one in two that at least one F will reach the tabulated 5% level.

No satisfactory way of dealing with this problem has been suggested. To recalculate the significance levels according to the number of mean squares and find approximate values for the levels required would not be completely satisfactory, and it is probably best to place little reliance on the 5% level of significance if only, say, one out of six or more values of F just reaches the 5% value. Such a value should be regarded as indicative only, and the experiment should be made larger in order to make it more sensitive. If any mean square reaches the 1% level the fact may be taken as sufficient evidence of the existence of a real effect.

There is nothing sacrosanct about the 10%, 5%, and 1% levels of significance; they are commonly used because they work in practice. If the conclusion that an effect is real will entail an expensive alteration to a plant, enough tests should be performed to ensure that an effect considered important will lead to a result which will remain highly significant even when the modifications discussed above are allowed for.

An alternative method of testing a group of mean squares is to use the method described in Appendix 7D in order to establish whether a group of effects taken as a whole shows any variation; this step would be taken if there were no *a priori* reasons for expecting some mean squares to be greater than others, i.e. when all the mean squares are on the same footing. If the test shows that the mean squares collectively do not vary significantly it is concluded that none of the effects exists, even if one of the mean squares on its own appears significant. If the test shows that the mean squares as a whole vary significantly, then certain individual mean squares will also be significant and they are likely to be the larger mean squares.

APPENDIX 7D

THE COMBINATION OF INTERACTION MEAN SQUARES TO FORM AN ESTIMATE OF ERROR VARIANCE

IN factorial experiments in which there is no replication and for which no prior estimate of error is available it is customary to employ an estimate of error variance based on the higher-order interactions. The practice may be justified on the ground that often higher-order effects of this kind are non-existent, or at least negligible. On this assumption the sums of squares corresponding to the higher-order interactions may be added together and divided by the total of their degrees of freedom to give an estimate of σ^2 based on several degrees of freedom.

The level at which the variance ratio F is significant is very sensitive to the number of degrees of freedom of the variance estimate in the denominator when this number is small. If a treatment mean square based on a single degree of freedom were compared with an error variance also based on a single degree of freedom and the 5% level of significance were employed, a ratio of the first to the second of no less than 161 would be required before it would be said that the treatment had a significant effect. For two degrees of freedom the ratio would be 18·5 and for three degrees of freedom 10·1, while if the error variance were exactly known the value would be 3·8.

The large value of F required for significance when the error variance is based on only a few degrees of freedom is a reflection of the fact that such an estimate may differ very markedly from σ^2. In particular it may be very much less than σ^2, tending to make the F ratio very large even when no treatment effect exists.

The experimenter is naturally hopeful that some of the effects in an experiment will be significant, and this might sometimes lead him to adopt doubtful procedures in combining interaction effects to obtain an "improved" estimate of error. In particular, he might exclude one or more of the higher-order interactions on the ground that they were large compared with the rest, and use an estimate of error based on the remainder to test these excluded interactions for significance and also to test the main effects.

The danger of procedures of this sort is best appreciated by an example. The following ten mean squares, each having one degree of freedom, were drawn at random from a population in which there were no real effects at all and the error variance was one unit:

(1) 0·0676	(6) 1·4400
(2) 2·4336	(7) 0·7396
(3) 0·1296	(8) 0·2401
(4) 0·3844	(9) 2·7889
(5) 0·0009	(10) 0·4356

If we combine the ten separate estimates we obtain a value 0·8660 based on ten degrees of freedom; this is near to the true value of unity.

Had these values occurred as the mean squares for a set of interactions in a 2^n factorial experiment the experimenter might be tempted to combine, for example, (1), (3), (4), (5), (8), and (10) to form an estimate 0·2097 based on six degrees of freedom against which (2), (6), and (9) might all have been declared significant. The fallacy is clear enough. It is very important to bear in mind how large may be the differences in mean squares based on small numbers of degrees of freedom owing to chance alone.

The most logical procedure is for the experimenter to decide, before the experiment is performed, which interactions are likely to be small enough to be ignored. He will be guided by the order of the interactions and by his theoretical knowledge of the factors concerned. The hypothesis that the mean squares found are in fact estimates of the same variance and may therefore be used as an estimate of error can be tested by BARTLETT's criterion [7D·3], calculated as follows:

Suppose there are k mean squares, $V_1, V_2 \ldots V_i \ldots V_k$, based on ϕ_1, ϕ_2, etc., degrees of freedom, and ϕ is the total number of degrees of freedom, so that the average variance is $V = \Sigma(\phi_i V_i)/\phi$.

The criterion measuring the divergence in the V's is $M = \phi \ln V - \Sigma \phi_i \ln V_i$.

The significance points for M as obtained by NAIR [7D·1] when each mean square has a single degree of freedom are given in the following table.

SIGNIFICANCE POINTS FOR M

Each estimate has one degree of freedom

Value of k ..	2	3	4	5	6	7	8	9	10
5% point ..	5·1	7·7	10·0	12·0	14·1	15·9	17·9	19·6	21·3
1% point ..	8·3	11·5	14·0	16·5	18·9	21·0	23·1	25·2	27·2

As an example we consider Example 7·2, in which the three- and four-factor interactions were combined to give an estimate of error variance. The calculations are as follows.

Interaction				(M.S.)	log (M.S.)	
ABC	..	..	..	885	2·9469	$\phi_i = 1$
ABD	..	..	..	410	2·6128	$\phi = 5$
ACD	..	..	..	2	0·3010	
BCD	..	..	..	613	2·7875	
ABCD	..	..	..	14	1·1461	

$$1{,}924 \qquad 9{\cdot}7943 = \Sigma \log V_i$$

$$V = \qquad 384{\cdot}8 \qquad 22{\cdot}5522 = \Sigma \ln V_i$$

$$\log V = \qquad 2{\cdot}5852$$
$$\ln V = \qquad 5{\cdot}9526$$
$$5 \ln V = \qquad 29{\cdot}7632$$
$$M = 5 \ln V - \Sigma \ln V_i = 7{\cdot}2110$$

Consulting the table, we see that a value of 12·0 is required for significance at the 5% level. There is therefore no evidence of heterogeneity.

When, as frequently happens, the numbers of degrees of freedom in the estimates to be compared are not the same, no exact significance points are available. An approximation which is sufficiently accurate, even when the estimates are based on small numbers of degrees of freedom, has been supplied by Box [7D·2].

To apply this approximate test, calculate:

(i) $A = \dfrac{1}{3(k-1)}\left(\sum \dfrac{1}{\phi_i} - \dfrac{1}{\phi}\right)$

(ii) $f_1 = k - 1$

(iii) $f_2 = (k+1)/A^2$

(iv) $b = f_2/(1 - A + 2/f_2)$

We then apply the F-test with f_1 and f_2 degrees of freedom to the ratio $f_2 M/\{f_1(b - M)\}$. Note that f_1 corresponds to the degrees of freedom of the greater variance, i.e. to ϕ_1 in the F-tables. In the special case in which the degrees of freedom are the same for all mean squares

$$A = (k+1)/(3\phi)$$

For the example just considered

$$A = 6/3 \times 5 \qquad\qquad = 0.4$$
$$f_1 = k - 1 \qquad\qquad = 4$$
$$f_2 = 6/(0{\cdot}4)^2 \qquad\qquad = 37{\cdot}50$$
$$b = 37{\cdot}50/(1 - 0{\cdot}4 + 2/37{\cdot}5) = 57{\cdot}40$$
$$b - M = 50{\cdot}19$$
$$F = \dfrac{37{\cdot}50 \times 7{\cdot}21}{4 \times 50{\cdot}19} \qquad\qquad = 1{\cdot}35$$

This is not significant and, as was found using NAIR's table, there is no evidence of variation between the five mean squares.

REFERENCES

[7D·1] NAIR, K. R. "The Distribution of the Extreme Deviates from the Sample Mean and its Studentiśed Form." *Biometrika*, **35** (1948), 118.

[7D·2] BOX, G. E. P. "The General Distribution Theory of a Class of Likelihood Criteria." *Ibid.*, **36** (1949), 317.

[7D·3] BARTLETT, M. S. "Properties of Sufficiency and Statistical Tests." *Proc. Royal Soc. A*, **160** (1937), 268.

CHAPTER 8

FACTORIAL EXPERIMENTS WITH FACTORS AT MORE THAN TWO LEVELS

THE discussion of the kind of experiment considered in the preceding chapter, in which the effects of several factors are investigated, is extended to cover experiments in which one or more of the factors are investigated at more than two levels. When the factors are measurable (e.g. temperature, proportion of catalyst, time of reaction) the experiment leads to a curve expressing the results in terms of the levels of the factors. It is shown how the parameters of this curve may be calculated and how their variation with the levels of the other factors may be assessed.

Introduction

8·1. When a factor is examined at two levels its main effect is uniquely defined as the difference between the mean of the results at the higher level and the mean of the results at the lower level. With factors at three or more levels the main effect is represented by differences or comparisons between the means corresponding to different levels of the factors, and it can be expressed in several ways. For three levels with means $\bar{y}_1$, $\bar{y}_2$, $\bar{y}_3$, possible differences are $\bar{y}_1 - \bar{y}_2$, $\bar{y}_2 - \bar{y}_3$, $\bar{y}_1 - \bar{y}_3$, $\bar{y}_1 - \frac{1}{2}(\bar{y}_2 + \bar{y}_3)$, $\bar{y}_2 - \frac{1}{2}(\bar{y}_1 + \bar{y}_3)$, and so on. Between three independent quantities there are two independent comparisons; the comparisons of interest will depend upon the nature of the factors, in particular whether they are qualitative (i.e. discontinuous) or quantitative, as defined in Chapter 7. For qualitative factors in which one level denotes a control with mean $\bar{y}_1$ and the other two denote treatments, the comparisons of interest are either $\bar{y}_2 - \bar{y}_1$ and $\bar{y}_3 - \bar{y}_1$, or $\bar{y}_3 - \bar{y}_2$ and $\bar{y}_1 - \frac{1}{2}(\bar{y}_2 + \bar{y}_3)$. The last comparison measures the extent to which the average of the two treatments differs from the control. For quantitative factors where, by definition, the levels denote points on a numerical scale, e.g. the temperature scale, there may be a functional relation between the responses and the level of the factor, and the comparisons of interest will be those giving the most information on this relation, e.g. the slope and the curvature. It is usually desirable to determine whether or not this relation changes with the different conditions of the other factors.

8·11. In the following, four types of factorial design will be considered:

  (i) A multifactorial experiment with all factors qualitative.
  (ii) A two-factor experiment with one factor qualitative and one quantitative.

(iii) A two-factor experiment with both factors quantitative.

(iv) Experiments with several factors, quantitative or qualitative, all at three levels.

These cover most situations likely to be encountered in industrial research, but if it is required to carry out an experiment with three or more quantitative factors, some or all at more than three levels, the analysis can be performed by a simple extension of the methods given in this chapter.

The first stage in the analysis of a factorial design is the same, whether the factors are qualitative or quantitative. In §§ 8·2–8·27 we give a detailed analysis of two three-factor experiments with all factors qualitative. The general method of analysis for a multifactorial experiment with all factors qualitative is given in Appendix 8A.

Example 8·1. Simple illustration of a three-factor experiment

8·2. The data given in Table 8·1 are taken from the results of an investigation into the effects on the physical properties of vulcanised rubber of varying a number of factors, the property recorded being the wear resistance of the samples, and the factors being:

     A   five qualities of filler

     B   three methods of pretreatment of the rubber

     C   four qualities of the raw rubber

Table 8·1

DATA OF A 5 × 3 × 4 FACTORIAL EXPERIMENT
WEAR RESISTANCE OF VULCANISED RUBBER

Level of factor A	Level of factor C											
	1			2			3			4		
	Level of factor B			Level of factor B			Level of factor B			Level of factor B		
	1	2	3	1	2	3	1	2	3	1	2	3
1	404	478	530	381	429	528	316	376	390	423	482	550
2	392	418	431	239	251	249	186	207	194	410	416	452
3	348	381	460	327	372	482	290	315	350	383	376	496
4	296	291	333	165	232	242	158	279	220	301	306	330
5	186	198	225	129	157	197	105	163	190	213	200	255

Note that, as always in a complete factorial design, all combinations of the levels of the different factors are tested. Note also the order of the factors A, B, and C, in the above arrangement of the table of results; it is usual to regard this as the standard arrangement.

The main effects and two-factor interactions

8·21. The main effect of a factor is measured by the difference between the mean values of the wear resistance of the various levels of the factor. For factor A there are $4 \times 3 = 12$ observations at each of the five levels, given respectively by the rows of Table 8·1. The sum and mean for each row are given in Table 8·11.

Table 8·11

SUM AND MEAN OF EACH LEVEL OF A

(Derived from Table 8·1)

	Level of Factor A					Sum
	1	2	3	4	5	
Sum ..	5,287	3,845	4,580	3,153	2,218	19,083
Mean ..	440·6	320·4	381·7	262·7	184·8	318·1 = Grand mean

Before the statistical significance of the overall variation between the levels of this factor can be assessed it is necessary to calculate the corresponding sum of squares and mean square. This is done in the usual way, thus:

Crude sum of squares $\quad = (5287^2 + 3845^2 + 4580^2 + 3153^2 + 2218^2)/12$
$$= 6,547,811$$
Correction due to mean $\quad = 19,083^2/60 = 6,069,348$
Sum of squares about mean $= 6,547,811 - 6,069,348 = 478,463.$

For the crude sum of squares and the correction due to the mean the divisors are the numbers of observations in each quantity that is squared. More generally, the divisor is the sum of squares of the coefficients of the independent observations involved in the quantity which is squared [Appendix 8D], and when the coefficients are all unity their sum of squares is equal to the number of observations.

An alternative method of calculating the crude sum of squares is to multiply the sum at each level by the corresponding mean, and add. Similarly the correction term is the product of the grand sum and the grand mean. It is often convenient to use this method, but care must be taken to retain sufficient decimal places; in the above table, for example, it would be necessary to retain five places of decimals in the mean for each level and six in the grand mean. This would present no difficulty if a calculating machine were used.

In practice we should merge the calculations of main effects and interactions by constructing two-way tables summing the observations on two factors over the levels of the third factor. Thus, for the two-way table of factors A and B the observations are summed over the four levels of C. This results in Table 8·12.

Table 8·12

TWO-WAY TABLE OF SUMS FOR FACTORS A AND B

(Derived from Table 8·1)

| Level of factor A | Level of factor B | | | Sum | Mean |
	1	2	3		
1	1,524	1,765	1,998	5,287	440·6
2	1,227	1,292	1,326	3,845	320·4
3	1,348	1,444	1,788	4,580	381·7
4	920	1,108	1,125	3,153	262·7
5	633	718	867	2,218	184·8
Sum	5,652	6,327	7,104	19,083	
Mean	282·6	316·4	355·2		318·1

The first entry (1524) is the sum of the four observations (404, 381, 316, and 423) at the lowest levels of A and B, and so on for the other entries. The main effects of A and B are represented by the differences between the row means (or totals) and the column means (or totals) respectively.

Table 8·12 is a two-way table in which each entry is the sum of four observations. The analysis with respect to A, B, and their interaction is a simple extension of the method used for randomised blocks (Appendix 5B) and is carried out as follows:

(i) Total crude sum of squares of Table 8·12 $= \frac{1}{4}$ of the sum of squares of the 15 entries (the divisor 4 being the number of levels of C) $= (1524^2 + 1765^2 + \ldots + 718^2 + 867^2)/4 = 6,617,412$

(ii) Crude sum of squares due to factor A $= \frac{1}{12}$ of the sum of squares of the row totals $= (5287^2 + 3845^2 + \ldots + 2218^2)/12 = 6,547,811$

(iii) Crude sum of squares due to factor B $= \frac{1}{20}$ of the sum of squares of the column totals $= (5652^2 + 6327^2 + 7104^2)/20 = 6,122,142$

The corrected sum of squares in each case is obtained by subtracting the square of the grand total divided by 4×15, i.e. $19,083^2/60 = 6,069,348$, giving 548,064 for the total, 478,463 for factor A, and 52,794 for factor B. The analysis of variance of Table 8·12 then takes the form of Table 8·13.

Table 8·13

ANALYSIS OF VARIANCE OF TABLE 8·12

Source of variation	Sum of squares	Degrees of freedom	Mean square
Factor A $\quad$ .. $\quad$ ..	478,463	4	119,616
Factor B $\quad$ .. $\quad$ ..	52,794	2	26,397
Interaction AB $\quad$ ..	16,807	8	2,101
Total $\quad$ .. $\quad$ ..	548,064	14	

In the general case the interaction sum of squares cannot conveniently be calculated by direct methods and it is usual to derive it by subtraction from the total. The only difference between the analysis here and the analysis used for a randomised block design, which is in fact a simple two-way table, consists in division by 4, the number of observations contained in each entry of Table 8·12.

8·211. The other main effect and two-factor interaction sums of squares are determined in a similar manner. For the interaction AC we form the two-way table of A and C by summing over the levels of factor B; for the interaction BC we form the two-way table of B and C by summing over the levels of factor A. The two-way tables are given in Tables 8·14 and 8·15.

Table 8·14

TWO-WAY TABLE OF SUMS FOR FACTORS A AND C

(Derived from Table 8·1)

Level of factor A	Level of factor C				Total	Mean
	1	2	3	4		
1	1,412	1,338	1,082	1,455	5,287	440·6
2	1,241	739	587	1,278	3,845	320·4
3	1,189	1,181	955	1,255	4,580	381·7
4	920	639	657	937	3,153	262·7
5	609	483	458	668	2,218	184·8
Total ..	5,371	4,380	3,739	5,593	19,083	
Mean ..	358·1	292·0	249·3	372·9		318·1

Table 8·15

TWO-WAY TABLE OF SUMS FOR FACTORS B AND C

(Derived from Table 8·1)

Level of factor B	Level of factor C				Total	Mean
	1	2	3	4		
1	1,626	1,241	1,055	1,730	5,652	282·6
2	1,766	1,441	1,340	1,780	6,327	316·4
3	1,979	1,698	1,344	2,083	7,104	355·2
Total ..	5,371	4,380	3,739	5,593	19,083	
Mean ..	358·1	292·0	249·3	372·9		318·1

From Tables 8·14 and 8·15 we readily calculate:

(i) Sum of squares for C = 150,239.

(ii) Sum of squares for interaction AC = 53,890.

(iii) Sum of squares for interaction BC = 6416.

8·212. The only other quantity required to complete the analysis of variance table is the total sum of squares for the $3 \times 4 \times 5 = 60$ observations of Table 8·1. The crude sum of squares is 6,835,645, and subtracting the correction for the mean gives 766,297 for the total sum of squares about the mean. This leads to the analysis of variance shown in Table 8·16.

Table 8·16

ANALYSIS OF VARIANCE OF TABLE 8·1

Source of variation	Sum of squares	Degrees of freedom	Mean square	Variance ratio
Between levels of factor A ..	478,463	4	119,616	374†
B ..	52,794	2	26,397	82·5†
C ..	150,239	3	50,080	156†
Interactions AB	16,807	8	2,101	6·57†
AC	53,890	12	4,491	14·0†
BC	6,416	6	1,069	3·34*
Remainder = interaction ABC..	7,688	24	320	
Total	766,297	59		

* Denotes significant, that is $F \geqslant 5\%$ value but $< 1\%$ value.

† Denotes highly significant, that is $F \geqslant 1\%$ value.

The remainder is the sum of squares corresponding to the three-factor interaction ABC.

This is the general method of calculating the three-factor interaction sum of squares, viz. subtract from the total corrected sum of squares for the original three-factor table the sums of squares of all main effects and two-factor interactions of A, B, and C. When there are more factors, the full number of three-factor tables is drawn up and the corresponding interaction sum of squares is calculated from each in the above way. The method is used in Appendix 8A.

Interpretation

8·22. In the absence of an independent estimate of error the three-factor interaction mean square is used. Relatively to this criterion all main effects and two-factor interactions in the present example are statistically significant at the 5% level at least. For the interaction BC the ratio of the mean square to the error mean square is $1069/320 = 3·34$; for 6 and 24 degrees of freedom the 5% and 1% values of F obtained from Table D are 2·51 and 3·67 respectively. Thus BC, the interaction between method of pretreatment and quality of raw rubber, is significant at the 5% level, all other effects being significant at the 1% level. The three-factor interaction mean square, which is taken to give an estimate of the error variance, corresponds to a standard error of 17·9. The 95% confidence limits to be attached to the observations of Table 8·1 are therefore $\pm 2·06 \times 17·9 = \pm 36·9$, 2·06 being the 5% value of t for 24 degrees of freedom. Although the two-factor interactions are statistically significant they are quite small compared with the main effects, and a table of means for the levels of each factor (Table 8·11 and the marginal means of Table 8·15) gives an adequate summary of the experimental results. Normally, when two factors interact, it is necessary to express the effects by means of the two-factor table.

Example 8·2. Aluminium alloys. Corrosion resistance

8·23. The following is an example of an experimental design of general utility in many fields. It relates to the testing of nine aluminium alloys for their resistance to corrosion in a chemical plant atmosphere. Four sites in the factory were chosen, and on each of them a plate made from each alloy was exposed for a year. The plates were then submitted to four observers, who assessed their condition visually and awarded marks to each from 0 to 10 according to the degree of resistance to attack. The observers worked independently and the plates were submitted to them in random order; in other words the observers did not assess all plates from one site at the same time. Metallurgical tests were also carried out, but only the results of the visual examinations are considered here. Visual assessment is frequently used for paints and similar coatings, for which no other satisfactory quantitative measure of resistance is available. The aim of the experiment was to decide which, if any, of the alloys were suitable for use in the factory, and especially to select any found to be suitable on all the sites. It was also required to know whether the four observers agreed in their relative assessments. There were nine alloys, four sites, and four observers, making a $9 \times 4 \times 4$ experiment, i.e. 144 observations in all. Both the top and bottom surfaces of the plates were assessed, but the bottom surface was invariably the more severely attacked, and only these results are analysed. The data are given in Table 8·2. If this experiment is analysed in the standard manner as a

Table 8·2

RESISTANCE TO CORROSION OF ALUMINIUM ALLOYS

Site	Observer / Alloy	1	2	3	4	5	6	7	8	9	Total
I	A	5	5	5	4	6	6	1	6	7	45
	B	4	5	5	4	5	3	1	5	7	39
	C	7	7	7	7	8	5	4	7	7	59
	D	6	5	4	5	7	6	3	6	7	49
	Total	22	22	21	20	26	20	9	24	28	192
II	A	8	7	7	7	5	4	5	4	5	52
	B	7	8	6	7	6	5	3	7	8	57
	C	9	9	9	9	8	6	7	8	8	73
	D	8	8	7	7	5	5	7	4	5	56
	Total	32	32	29	30	24	20	22	23	26	238
III	A	4	4	5	3	4	3	0	5	5	33
	B	1	3	3	2	5	2	0	4	5	25
	C	5	5	5	6	6	4	3	7	9	50
	D	3	3	7	2	3	3	1	6	6	34
	Total	13	15	20	13	18	12	4	22	25	142
IV	A	6	5	6	5	6	4	4	7	5	48
	B	1	3	6	5	5	4	3	6	5	38
	C	5	5	7	6	8	7	5	8	8	59
	D	5	3	5	3	5	3	3	7	6	40
	Total	17	16	24	19	24	18	15	28	24	185
Grand total		84	85	94	82	92	70	50	97	103	757

$9 \times 4 \times 4$ factorial design, we shall arrive at the analysis of variance given in Table 8·21. The details of this analysis are given in Appendix 8B as a further illustration of the computations required in a factorial design.

8·231. There are important differences between this experiment and the previous one, the existence of which become apparent when the various sources of error in the experiment are studied. We stress the importance of considering carefully in all experiments the various sources of error and how these relate to the effects measured; without such consideration a mechanical application of the analysis of variance might lead to wrong conclusions.

Table 8·21

FORMAL ANALYSIS OF VARIANCE OF TABLE 8·2

Source of variation		Sum of squares	Degrees of freedom	Mean square
Between sites	S	128·74	3	42·91
Between alloys	A	128·18	8	16·02
Between observers	O	106·24	3	35·41
Interaction	SA	89·32	24	3·72
	SO	12·73	9	1·41
	OA	23·32	24	0·97
	SOA	58·96	72	0·82
Total		547·49	143	

Examination of the sources of error

8·24. In this experiment there were nine alloys, and one plate from each alloy was exposed on each of four sites. This makes four plates per alloy and $9 \times 4 = 36$ plates in all. Two possible kinds of error arise at this stage:

(i) Each alloy may not be entirely uniform; there may be differences, however small, between the four plates cut from the same alloy.

(ii) The exposure on each site may not be entirely uniform for all the plates, since the plates cannot occupy identically the same positions.

It is not possible to separate these two sources of error with the data available, and they will be treated as one source in the subsequent discussion. A direct estimate of joint error might have been obtained by replication, that is, by exposing two or more plates from one or more alloys on one or more sites, and preferably an equal number from each alloy on all the sites. In the absence of replication the error is included in, and is not separable from, any interaction between alloys and sites. It will clearly influence the differences between alloys and the differences between sites, and since it is not separable from any interaction effects, the significance of the differences between alloys and between sites must be assessed against the mean square corresponding to the interaction between them.

8·241. There is in addition an error of assessment of the extent of corrosion of the alloys, and this is also included in the above-mentioned interaction. Unlike the other sources of error, (i) and (ii), the error of assessment may be independently estimated because several assessments have been carried out on every plate, one by each of four observers. All 36 plates have been assessed by each observer, and if for the moment we disregard the relation between the 36 samples the results can be written in the form of the two-way Table 8·22.

Table 8·22

TWO-WAY TABLE OF OBSERVERS AND PLATES

Observer	Plate					
	1	2	3	...	35	36
1	5	5	5	...	7	5
2	4	5	5	...	6	5
3	7	7	7	...	8	8
4	6	5	4	...	7	6

This is a two-way table which yields the analysis of variance of Table 8·221.

Table 8·221

ANALYSIS OF VARIANCE OF TABLE 8·22

Source of variation	Sum of squares	Degrees of freedom	Mean square
Between plates	346·24	35	9·89
Between observers ..	106·24	3	35·41
Remainder	95·01	105	0·905
Total	547·49	143	

The remainder measures the extent to which the observers disagree in their assessments of the relative resistance of the plates to corrosion. The bias of each observer does not matter, because we are interested mainly in the comparison between plates. Since all observers assess the same plates, the variation between observers cannot be affected by the sampling error of the alloys or by the variation in exposure within each site, and the significance of the bias between observers must be assessed against this interaction of observers and plates.

8·242. In the above reasoning no account has been taken of the fact that the 36 samples are related—it is possible that the bias between observers may differ for the various alloys and again for the four sites. The remedy is to subdivide the interaction between plates and observers into that due to alloys and observers, that due to sites and observers, and the remainder, which is the interaction of alloys, sites, and observers. This was done in Table 8·21 by the usual method of analysis applied to factorial designs, but in view of the above discussion the analysis of variance is better presented as Table 8·2

Table 8·23

FURTHER ANALYSIS OF VARIANCE OF TABLE 8·2

Source of variation	Sum of squares	Degrees of freedom	Mean square
Between alloys	128·18	8	16·02
Between sites	128·74	3	42·91
Interaction between alloys and sites ..	89·32	24	3·72
Total between plates	346·24	35	
Between observers	106·24	3	35·41
Interactions between:			
Observers and alloys	23·32	24	0·97
Observers and sites	12·73	9	1·41
Observers, alloys, and sites	58·96	72	0·82
Total interactions of observers and plates	95·01	105	0·90
Total	547·49	143	

Interpretation

8·25. In the absence of repeat assessments by the same observer the three-factor interaction 0·82 is used for assessing the significance of the interaction between observers and alloys, and between observers and sites. These two interactions are not significant, and consequently there is no evidence that the bias between observers varies for the different alloys and the four sites. This is reassuring, because otherwise there would have been an indication that the method of assessment was unsatisfactory. Since there is no evidence of interaction of observers with sites and alloys, and what is more important, no such interaction was expected from general considerations, the three interactions with observers are combined to give an overall estimate of 0·90 for the mean square of the error of assessment. This is the appropriate error variance with which to assess the overall bias between observers. The ratio 35·41/0·90 clearly indicates that the bias between observers is highly significant. The bias is of interest, but its existence does not constitute a serious disadvantage, because in comparing different alloys and sites we average over all four observers, thus cancelling the effect of the bias; the precision of the experiment in relation to the assessment is governed by interaction between observers and plates.

The differences between alloys and between sites are significant, as is seen when the corresponding mean squares are tested for significance against the mean square due to the interaction between alloys and sites, which is the appropriate error variance for these two effects. It is clear that the sites differ considerably in severity of attack, but this would not matter so long as the same alloys performed well on all sites—it would be inconvenient to have to use different alloys in different sites in a factory. Now the interaction between alloys and sites is significant when compared with the assessment error mean square 0·90. This means that either the interaction between alloys and sites, or the error due to variations within alloys and within sites, or both combined, are significant. In the absence of information on the variation within alloys and sites it is not possible to say whether there is any real interaction between these two factors. This could only be determined by a repeat of the experiment, which would supply two additional sources of variation: between replications, and interactions between samples and replications. The latter provide a valid error variance for testing the significance of the interaction between alloys and sites.

From general considerations and detailed knowledge of the preparation of the alloys and arrangement of the plates on each site it was clear that the variation within alloys and sites could not be large. It would be reasonable to conclude that there is real interaction between alloys and sites. This means that the relative performance of the alloys is not the same for all sites, and we must examine the two-factor table, alloys *v.* sites, in greater detail. It is stressed that in a design of this nature we cannot properly test the significance of the interaction; in order to do this it would be necessary to repeat the experiment. Occasionally, as in this particular experiment, it is possible to assign most of the interaction mean square to real interaction, but caution must be exercised in such cases.

8·251. The means over the four observers required to examine the interaction between alloys and sites are given in Table 8·24.

Table 8·24

MEAN ASSESSMENTS FOR ALLOYS AND SITES
(Derived from Table 8·2)

Site \ Alloy	1	2	3	4	5	6	7	8	9	Mean
1	5·50	5·50	5·25	5·00	6·50	5·00	2·25	6·00	7·00	5·33
2	8·00	8·00	7·25	7·50	6·00	5·00	5·50	5·75	6·50	6·61
3	3·25	3·75	5·00	3·25	4·50	3·00	1·00	5·50	6·25	3·94
4	4·25	4·00	6·00	4·75	6·00	4·50	3·75	7·00	6·00	5·14
Mean ..	5·25	5·31	5·88	5·13	5·75	4·38	3·13	6·06	6·44	

The nature of the interaction between alloys and sites is apparent from an inspection of this table, e.g. alloys 1 and 2 rank highest on site 2 but quite low on site 3.

We can clearly reject alloy 7, which is poor on all sites. Alloys 8 and 9 are the best except on site 2; but site 2 is the least severe, and the somewhat lower performance of 8 and 9 on this site might be ignored. Other things equal, alloys 8 and 9 would be chosen as best all round. It was not considered practicable to specify different alloys for different sites unless there were very strong reasons for doing so.

The error variance of 3·72 (interaction SA) for assessing the significance of the differences between alloys corresponds to a standard error of 1·93. The mean for each alloy given in Table 8·24 then has a standard error of 0·97, giving 95% confidence limits of $\pm 2·06 \times 0·97 = \pm 2·00$ to each mean. The degree of confidence we can attach to the selection of alloys 8 and 9 as the best pair is therefore not very high. If a greater degree of confidence were required, further tests would have to be carried out unless other and independent evidence were available.

Notes on design

8·26. The use of four different sites within the factory ensured that any conclusions would be applicable to the whole factory and not merely to one particular part of it. If only one site had been used it would in any case have been necessary to test each alloy at least in duplicate, since a result on one specimen only would not be considered reliable. These repeats are in effect supplied by using different sites. They enable the different sites and the performances of the alloys on the sites to be compared, thus adding to the efficiency of the experiment. By using four observers we place the conclusions on a sounder basis than if only one were used. All alloys were tested on all sites and were assessed by all observers; this balances the experiment, gives maximum efficiency, and simplifies the analysis and interpretation. Although no true duplicates were tested, certain interactions could be used to furnish estimates of the error variances appropriate to test the statistical significance of the effects.

Further steps in the analysis of qualitative factors

8·27. The above examples were introduced mainly to illustrate the first part of the analysis of all factorial experiments, whether for qualitative or for quantitative factors. It was convenient also to consider the subsequent analysis and interpretation. It is sometimes desirable to go a stage further in the analysis of both the main effects and the interaction. If it is possible to divide the alloys into two groups according to some prior resemblance within the groups, if for instance one group of alloys contains an element not present in the rest, then we may wish to test the significance of the difference between the means of the two groups by using the t-test or to calculate the 95% confidence limits for the mean of each group. One way of testing the difference is the following. If the groups contain n and m alloys respectively and if $(\bar{x}_1, \bar{x}_2, \ldots, \bar{x}_n)$, $(\bar{y}_1, \bar{y}_2, \ldots, \bar{y}_m)$ are the means of r observations each for the respective alloys, then the difference we wish to test is

$$D = \frac{\bar{x}_1 + \bar{x}_2 + \ldots + \bar{x}_n}{n} - \frac{\bar{y}_1 + \bar{y}_2 + \ldots + \bar{y}_m}{m}$$

The variance of this difference is $s^2\left(\dfrac{1}{n} + \dfrac{1}{m}\right)\Big/r$, where s^2 is the error variance. The statistic t is then D divided by its standard error $s\left\{\dfrac{1}{r}\left(\dfrac{1}{n} + \dfrac{1}{m}\right)\right\}^{\frac{1}{2}}$

and it has the number of degrees of freedom associated with the error variance s^2.

The comparison may be that of one alloy with the rest or that of one alloy with another. If, for instance, one alloy is treated as a control or standard, we may wish to test whether the mean result found for it differs significantly from the mean result for all the other alloys or from the mean result for a group of alloys having some prior resemblance.

The customary test of significance indicated above applies only to prior classification; we stress that this test of significance does not apply to the comparison of two alloys or to two groups of alloys suggested by the data to respond differently. Although rigorous tests exist or may be devised for such comparisons, much larger differences than are indicated by the t-test will usually be required for significance. If the overall differences, or the differences within certain groups of alloys which have a prior resemblance, are significant, then the alloys which gave the high responses in the groups are the ones most likely to be the best ones of the group, and these will naturally be the ones selected for factory use or for further trials. The application of confidence limits to the mean response for each alloy indicates the degree of confidence which can be attached to such a conclusion.

Quantitative factors. Polynomial representation

8·3. When a factor is quantitative it is desirable to examine the numerical relationship between the observations and the levels of the factor. If the general functional form of this relationship is known the problem reduces to that of estimating from the observations the values of the constants required to specify the function completely. Usually the true functional form is not known, but it is in practice possible to approximate over a finite range of the factor by means of a polynomial, e.g.

$$y = a + bx + cx^2 + dx^3 + \dots$$

For narrow ranges of the factor a few terms of the series may suffice to give a sufficiently accurate representation. The relation between the response and the level of the factor can sometimes be represented more closely by a straight line when logarithms are taken or some other simple transformation is employed.

When only two levels of the factor are used the only functional form which can be uniquely fitted is a straight line, and the tacit assumption must be made that over the range of the factor studied the relation between the expected responses and the corresponding values of the factor is, to a sufficient degree of approximation, linear. Similarly, when only three levels are used, a quadratic function is implied; when four levels are used, a cubic function, and so on.

8·31. Much labour is saved if the levels of the factor fall at equal intervals on the ordinary scale of measurement or on some appropriate transformation of the scale. If we wish to examine the factor at its normal level and also at twice and at one-half this level, then the three levels are represented by equal intervals on a logarithmic scale. Alternatively, it is sometimes an advantage to choose the intervals of the factor so that the responses are likely to change by roughly the same amount between successive levels, and examples of this method arise in investigations on the rate of deterioration of products, e.g. ageing of rubber. The amount of deterioration is likely to be much greater in the earlier stages than in the later, and levels such as 0, 1 month, 6 months, may be found suitable. If the purpose is simply to compare the rates of deterioration of different substances, these levels may for the purpose of analysis be treated as though they were at equal intervals.

The advantage of using equal intervals of the variable or of regarding the levels as being at equal intervals is that it enables the constants to be determined very simply. With three equally spaced levels and observations y_1, y_2, and y_3 respectively, the average response corresponding to constant a when the polynomial is suitably transformed is simply $\frac{1}{3}(y_1 + y_2 + y_3)$. If the relation is represented by a straight line, the slope corresponding to constant b is $\frac{1}{2}(y_3 - y_1)$. If a linear representation is inadequate and a term involving the square of the variable is required, then the coefficient of the additional term is $\frac{1}{2}(y_1 - 2y_2 + y_3)$. This clearly measures the departure from linearity because, if the relations were exactly linear, $(y_3 - y_2)$ would be equal to $(y_2 - y_1)$, that is, the difference between them, $(y_3 - y_2) - (y_2 - y_1)$ $= (y_1 - 2y_2 + y_3)$, would be zero. $(y_1 - 2y_2 + y_3)$ is frequently referred to as the quadratic component, or the curvature. The constant terms and the linear, quadratic, etc., components are all orthogonal to one another. A more detailed consideration of these functions is given in Appendix 8C. A polynomial of this kind is referred to as an Orthogonal Polynomial.

Example 8·3. Analysis of factorial design of two factors, one quantitative and the other qualitative

8·32. The following example of a 4×5 design in which one factor is qualitative and the other quantitative illustrates the examination of the functional form of the relation between the response and the level of the factor. The data are given in Table 8·3, in which factor A at four levels is qualitative and factor B at five levels is quantitative.

Table 8·3

4 × 5 FACTORIAL DESIGN. FACTOR A QUALITATIVE AND FACTOR B QUANTITATIVE

| | | \multicolumn{5}{c}{Level of factor B (quantitative)} | Sum | Mean |
		b_1	b_2	b_3	b_4	b_5		
Level of factor A (qualitative)	a_1	28·2	29·3	33·7	41·2	50·9	183·3	36·66
	a_2	23·5	24·8	24·1	34·7	32·8	139·9	27·98
	a_3	17·4	15·2	17·8	14·7	16·6	81·7	16·34
	a_4	10·1	11·5	15·6	9·9	4·7	51·8	10·36
Sum ..		79·2	80·8	91·2	100·5	105·0	456·7	
Mean..		19·80	20·20	22·80	25·13	26·25		

X

The levels of the quantitative factor B are arranged at equal intervals of the variable. The data of Table 8·3 will be used to describe and illustrate the general method of analysis.

Method of analysis

8·33. The first step is to analyse the data, ignoring the relation between the levels of the quantitative factor, that is, to treat both factors as qualitative in the first instance. This results in the analysis of variance of Table 8·31.

Table 8·31

ANALYSIS OF VARIANCE OF TABLE 8·3

Source of variation	Sum of squares	Degrees of freedom	Mean square
Factor A	2,077·07	3	692·36
Factor B	132·25	4	33·06
Remainder (= interaction)	407·65	12	33·97
Total	2,616·97	19	—

There are no repeat determinations and no independent estimate of the error variance; it is necessary therefore to use the remainder variance for this purpose. Referring to the F-tables, factor A is seen to be highly significant, but factor B is clearly not significant.

8·331. In the overall mean square corresponding to the quantitative factor B no account is taken of the order of the levels, and it is interesting to examine the consequences, because it is possible to have a significant trend in the individual results without the overall variation being significant. The analysis is made more sensitive by taking into account the relation between the response and the levels of factor B. These levels are at equal intervals of the variable, and the linear, quadratic, cubic, etc., components of the effect of factor B are readily determined by means of orthogonal polynomials. (For details see Appendix 8C.) As applied to the present example, the method consists in multiplying the observations of each row of Table 8·3 by appropriate coefficients derived from Table 8C·1. The factor B has five levels, so that the appropriate coefficients are based on $n = 5$. For convenience they are reproduced in Table 8·32.

With five levels it is possible also to calculate the quartic component, but it is hardly ever necessary to go beyond the cubic term in a factorial experiment. The first step is to calculate the sum and the linear, quadratic, and cubic

Table 8·32

COEFFICIENTS TO DETERMINE LINEAR, QUADRATIC, AND
CUBIC TERMS

	Level of factor B					Sum of squares
	1	2	3	4	5	
Linear component ..	− 2	− 1	o	+ 1	+ 2	10
Quadratic component..	+ 2	− 1	− 2	− 1	+ 2	14
Cubic component ..	− 1	+ 2	o	− 2	+ 1	10

components of the effect of B for each level of factor A. Multiplying the
observations of Table 8·3 by the appropriate coefficients of Table 8·32, we
obtain the following results for the first level of factor A:

Sum B $\quad$ = 28·2 + 29·3 + 33·7 + 41·2 + 50·9 $\qquad$ = 183·3

Linear
component $= - 2 \times 28\cdot2 - 1 \times 29\cdot3 + 0 \times 33\cdot7 + 1 \times 41\cdot2 + 2 \times 50\cdot9$
of B $\qquad\qquad\qquad\qquad\qquad\qquad\qquad\qquad\qquad$ = 57·3

Quadratic
component $= + 2 \times 28\cdot2 - 1 \times 29\cdot3 - 2 \times 33\cdot7 - 1 \times 41\cdot2 + 2 \times 50\cdot9$
of B $\qquad\qquad\qquad\qquad\qquad\qquad\qquad\qquad\qquad$ = 20·3

Cubic
component $= - 1 \times 28\cdot2 + 2 \times 29\cdot3 + 0 \times 33\cdot7 - 2 \times 41\cdot2 + 1 \times 50\cdot9$
of B $\qquad\qquad\qquad\qquad\qquad\qquad\qquad\qquad\qquad$ = − 1·1

These operations are carried out at all the other levels of the qualitative
factor A, and we obtain the results given in Table 8·33.

Table 8·33

COMPONENTS OF THE QUANTITATIVE FACTOR B

Level of qualitative factor A	Component of quantitative factor B			
	Sum	Linear	Quadratic	Cubic
(1)	(2)	(3)	(4)	(5)
1	183·3	57·3	20·3	− 1·1
2	139·9	28·5	4·9	− 10·5
3	81·7	− 2·1	2·5	o·2
4	51·8	− 12·4	− 23·0	− 2·2
Sum	456·7	71·3	4·7	− 13·6
Divisor for sum of squares	5	10	14	10

The sums over the four levels of factor A in Table 8·33 should agree exactly with the sum, linear, quadratic, and cubic components of the sum of the actual observations in the columns of Table 8·3. Thus, for example, the linear component of these sums is

$$-2 \times 79{\cdot}2 - 1 \times 80{\cdot}8 + 0 \times 91{\cdot}2 + 1 \times 100{\cdot}5 + 2 \times 105{\cdot}0 = 71{\cdot}3$$

which agrees with the value given in Table 8·33. Application to all components furnishes a check on the calculations up to this stage.

Calculation of sums of squares. Main effects

8·332. The entries of Table 8·33 indicate the shape of the response curves for each level of factor A, but it is necessary to assess their significance and to test whether or not the shape varies from one level of factor A to another. Consider in the first place the general levels of the response curves for each level of factor A, given by the sums in column (2) of Table 8·33. The sum of squares corresponding to the differences between these quantities is

$$(183{\cdot}3^2 + 139{\cdot}9^2 + 81{\cdot}7^2 + 51{\cdot}8^2)/5 - 456{\cdot}7^2/20$$

This, of course, represents the main effect of factor A [Table 8·31]. Consider now the main effect of factor B, which is given by the comparisons or the differences between the column totals (or means) of Table 8·3: the linear, quadratic, and cubic components of the effect calculated from the totals are:

$$\text{Linear} = 71{\cdot}3 \qquad \text{Quadratic} = 4{\cdot}7 \qquad \text{Cubic} = -13{\cdot}6$$

as given in Table 8·33. These components are linear functions of the observations, and in order to derive the appropriate sums of squares for the analysis of variance we divide the square of each component by the sum of squares of the coefficients of the observations composing it [Appendix 8D]. Thus the sum of squares due to the linear component is $71{\cdot}3^2/(10 \times 4) = 127{\cdot}09$, since 10 is the sum of squares of the coefficients of Table 8·32 used to calculate the linear component and 4 is the number of observations contained in the sum for each level of factor B. The sums of squares for the quadratic and cubic components are calculated similarly, and the results are:

Sum of squares for linear B $= 71{\cdot}3^2/40 = 127{\cdot}09$
Sum of squares for quadratic B $= 4{\cdot}7^2/56 = 0{\cdot}39$
Sum of squares for cubic B $= (-13{\cdot}6)^2/40 = 4{\cdot}62$

Interactions

8·333. The above analysis of the main effect of factor B gives the average shape of the curve relating the response to the level of the factor; later it will be shown how to assess the significance of the linear, quadratic, and cubic components of this relation. It is possible, however, for the shape of the curve to change from one level of A to another, such change being reflected in a change in one or more of the linear, quadratic, and cubic components of Table 8·33. Referring to Table 8·33, it is seen that the linear component for the first level of A is positive while that for the fourth level is negative, suggesting that the linear part changes from one level of A to another. The first step in the analysis of this variation is to calculate the sum of squares corresponding to the differences between the linear components. The sum of squares corresponding to the variation of the linear component of factor B over the levels of factor A is

$$[57 \cdot 3^2 + 28 \cdot 5^2 + (-2 \cdot 1)^2 + (-12 \cdot 4)^2]/10$$
$$- 71 \cdot 3^2/(4 \times 10) = 425 \cdot 37 - 127 \cdot 09$$
$$= 298 \cdot 28$$

i.e. one-tenth of the sum of squares about their mean of the linear components of Table 8·33, 10 being the sum of squares of the coefficients for each component. The correction to the crude sum of squares is seen to be identical with the sum of squares corresponding to the linear component of the main effect of factor B. The corrected sum of squares (298·28) measures the extent to which the linear component of B varies from one level of A to another, and it therefore represents the interaction of linear B with A.

The sums of squares corresponding to the interactions of the quadratic and cubic components of B with A are calculated in a similar way:

Quadratic:
$$[20 \cdot 3^2 + 4 \cdot 9^2 + 2 \cdot 5^2 + (-23 \cdot 0)^2]/14 - 4 \cdot 7^2/(4 \times 14) = 69 \cdot 38 - 0 \cdot 39$$
$$= 68 \cdot 99$$

Cubic:
$$[(-1 \cdot 1)^2 + (-10 \cdot 5)^2 + 0 \cdot 2^2 + (-2 \cdot 2)^2]/10 - (-13 \cdot 6)^2/(4 \times 10)$$
$$= 11 \cdot 63 - 4 \cdot 62$$
$$= 7 \cdot 01$$

This leads to the analysis of variance of Table 8·34.

The remainders for the main effect of B and the interaction of A and B are found by subtraction from the corresponding quantities of Table 8·31.

Interpretation of Table 8·34

8·34. In the absence of replication or an independent estimate of the error variance it is necessary to use an interaction mean square as the error variance. The first choice is the remainder 11·12 with 3 degrees of freedom. Compared with this, factor A and linear B are highly significant, and the interaction of linear B with A is almost significant at the 5% level. It is frequently possible to obtain a better estimate of error by combining certain of the mean squares, but caution must be exercised when so doing. In the analysis of Table 8·34

Table 8·34

ANALYSIS OF VARIANCE OF THE DATA OF TABLE 8·3: FACTOR A
QUALITATIVE, FACTOR B QUANTITATIVE

Source of variation	Sum of squares	Degrees of freedom	Mean square
Factor A	2,077·07	3	692·36
Between levels of factor B:			
Linear effect	127·09	1	127·09
Quadratic effect	0·39	1	0·39
Cubic effect	4·62	1	4·62
Remainder (= quartic B) ..	0·15	1	0·15
Total for factor B	132·25	4	
Interactions with factor A of:			
Linear B	298·28	3	99·43
Quadratic B	68·99	3	23·00
Cubic B	7·01	3	2·34
Remainder (= interaction of factor A and quartic B)	33·37	3	11·12
Total interaction	407·65	12	
Total	2,616·97	19	

terms higher than the cubic are not calculated because such terms are not expected to be appreciable; we therefore combine the remainder of the main effect of B with the remainder interaction.

From experience we know that cubic terms are less likely to be appreciable than quadratic, and quadratic terms less likely to be appreciable than linear. In this investigation there is no prior reason for supposing that cubic terms for the main effect and the interaction are appreciable, and certainly no evidence is supplied by Table 8·34 to suggest any such effect. Thus it is legitimate to combine the mean square for the cubic and higher terms for both the main effect B and the interactions to give an error variance of $(4·62 + 0·15 + 7·01 + 33·37)/(1 + 1 + 3 + 3) = 45·15/8 = 5·64$ based on 8 degrees of freedom. If, contrary to our prior expectation, the mean square of the remainder of the main effect of factor B turns out significantly greater than the mean square of the remainder of the interactions, it is clear that factor B must be examined to a higher degree, at least the quartic. In this case there is of course no such evidence. Compared with the error variance of 5·64 the mean square for factor A, linear B, and the interactions of linear B and quadratic B with A, are significant. This information was not revealed by the analysis of Table 8·31 carried out as for qualitative factors, and it shows the need for separating the linear, quadratic, etc., components of the effect of B.

According to the test, quadratic B is not significant, but in view of the significance of the interaction of quadratic B with A, the inclusion of this effect in the error variance would not be justified.

Estimates of the effects

8·35. One further step is required to complete the analysis, and that is to estimate the magnitudes of the significant effects. In view of the interaction of both linear and quadratic effects with factor A, the level of A must be specified when quoting the effect of B. The actual values of the linear and quadratic coefficients are derived from the components of Table 8·33 by multiplying by the corresponding factors $K/\mathcal{J}$ given in Table 8C·1 [Appendix 8C]. For $n = 5$, the factors are 1/10 and 1/14 for the linear and quadratic components respectively, and applying them to the corresponding components of Table 8·33 gives the slope and curvature of factor B. The final table of effects is as Table 8·35.

Table 8·35

TABLE OF EFFECTS

(Derived from Table 8·33)

Levels of qualitative factor A (1)	Components of quantitative factor B		
	Mean (2)	Slope (3)	Curvature (4)
1	36·66	5·73	1·45
2	27·98	2·85	0·35
3	16·34	− 0·21	0·18
4	10·36	− 1·24	− 1·64
Standard error ..	1·06	0·75	0·64

The standard errors given in the last row of Table 8·35 are derived from the error variance of 5·64 based on 8 degrees of freedom. Thus for each level of A the standard error of the mean $= \sqrt{(5\cdot64/5)} = 1\cdot06$, of the slope $= \sqrt{(5\cdot64/10)} = 0\cdot75$, and of the curvature $= \sqrt{(5\cdot64/14)} = 0\cdot63$. (The slopes and curvatures of Table 8·35 are linear functions of the observations and their variances are therefore equivalent to the error variance of 5·64 multiplied by the sum of squares of the coefficients of the observations in each component [S.M., § 3·71].)

The interpretation of Table 8·35 is that the general level of the response drops and the slope and curvature change sign as we move from levels 1 and 2 to 3 and 4 of A. Using the information given in this table it is possible, if required, to construct the curves expressing the relation between the responses and the level of factor B for each level of A.

Example 8·4. Penicillin. Effect of different amounts of various sugars on the production of mycelial inoculum

8·36. This is another example of a two-factor experiment with one factor qualitative and the other quantitative. It differs slightly from the previous example in that estimates of the effects of the two factors are subject to different sources of error. This type of problem is not unusual, and it is introduced in order to emphasise the importance of examining carefully the various errors involved and their effects on the comparisons required by the experiment. The example is taken from laboratory investigations on the production of mycelium, which is required in penicillin manufacture. The inoculum is grown in a medium containing the necessary ingredients under suitable conditions of agitation, aeration, and temperature; special apparatus is required to obtain these conditions. The mycelium is then assessed for its capacity to produce penicillin, and the whole process of mycelium production and assessment occupies one week. This particular investigation examined the effect of different concentrations of various sugars on the amount of mycelium produced and on the subsequent yield of penicillin. Data on mycelium production only are used to illustrate the method of statistical analysis. There were six replicate units available for the investigation, so that it was possible to examine this number of conditions at any given time. Five sugars were to be compared and four concentrations, namely 2%, 4%, 6%, and 8%, were chosen for assessment, involving twenty combinations to be carried out at most six at a time, i.e. at the maximum rate of six per week. In penicillin work there are large variations from week to week due to uncontrolled factors; consequently comparisons between experiments carried out side by side are more precise than comparisons from one week to another. Since only six conditions could be compared at a time it was impossible to compare all twenty conditions with the same degree of precision, and the question arose, What were the most important comparisons? In this case the comparison of the effects of the various sugars was more important than the comparison of the effects of different concentrations of each sugar. Another complication, the significance of which will be appreciated later, was that very little information of a precise nature existed on these sugars, and although it was expected that increasing amounts of the various sugars would have similar effects, it would have been unsafe to rely on this expectation. The design used in these circumstances was to test one concentration of all the sugars in one week, another concentration in another week, and so on for the four weeks, the order of the concentrations over the four weeks and the allocation of the sugars over the units per week being randomised. A control was added each week, and this was the same from week to week, the purpose being to peg the week-to-week variation and enable comparisons to be made of the effects of increasing amounts of each sugar. The observations are given in Table 8·36.

Table 8·36

WET WEIGHTS OF INOCULUM PREPARED WITH DIFFERENT
CONCENTRATIONS OF VARIOUS SUGARS

g./100 ml. of culture

Type of sugar	Concentration of sugar in g./100 ml.			
	2%	4%	6%	8%
Crude lactose ..	2·1	1·6	2·7	3·4
Crude glucose ..	2·7	3·7	2·8	5·6
Sucrose	3·0	3·0	3·3	4·0
Molasses	3·4	3·5	2·9	6·1
Dextrine	3·1	2·9	3·0	4·7
Control	5·2	3·5	2·8	4·2

It was known from past experience that variation from one week to the next affected the results proportionately, that is, if two conditions were repeated from week to week, the ratio and not the difference of the two responses would tend to remain constant, apart from experimental error. For this reason the mycelium weights are converted into logarithms and the logarithm of the control is subtracted from the logarithm of each result for each week in order to eliminate the week-to-week variations. Unity is added to each result to avoid negative logarithms; this does not affect the analysis but simplifies the arithmetic. The results are given in Table 8·37.

Subtraction of the logarithm of the mycelial weight of control effectively removes the week-to-week variation. We must, however, take careful note of the sources of error which affect any given comparison. The subtraction of the logarithm of the response for the control for each column does not in any way affect the error of the comparison within weeks, i.e. between the various sugars. The comparisons of these adjusted responses from week to week, that is, between concentrations of each sugar, are now independent of the week-to-week variation. If σ^2 is the error variance of the logarithm of the responses within weeks, the variance of the difference between the adjusted responses of two sugars in any one week is $2\sigma^2$, and the variance of the

Table 8·37

ADJUSTED RESPONSES

(Derived from Table 8·36)

| Sugar | Concentration of sugar | | | | Sum | Mean |
	2%	4%	6%	8%		
Crude lactose ..	0·606	0·660	0·984	0·908	3·158	0·790
Crude glucose ..	0·715	1·024	1·000	1·125	3·864	0·966
Sucrose	0·761	0·933	1·072	0·979	3·745	0·936
Molasses	0·815	1·000	1·015	1·162	3·992	0·998
Dextrine	0·775	0·918	1·030	1·049	3·772	0·943
Sum	3·672	4·535	5·101	5·223	18·531	
Mean	0·734	0·907	1·020	1·045		

difference of the adjusted responses between any two concentrations of any given sugar, i.e. between weeks, is $4\sigma^2$, since this difference is calculated from four observations instead of two. This, of course, relates to the data of Table 8·37 and not to the data of Table 8·36.

Analysis

8·37. We are interested in the following questions:

(i) Do the sugars differ significantly in their effects on the production of mycelium ?

(ii) What is the effect of varying the concentration for each of the sugars, and does this differ from one sugar to another ?

The first step is to analyse these results as a 5×4 table, ignoring the relationship between the levels of sugars, in other words, as if both factors were qualitative only. The resulting analysis of variance table is found to be as Table 8·371.

Table 8·371

ANALYSIS OF VARIANCE OF TABLE 8·37

Source of variation	Sum of squares	Degrees of freedom	Mean square
Between sugars ..	0·1032	4	0·0258
Between concentrations	0·3000	3	0·1000
Remainder	0·0545	12	0·0045
Total	0·4577	19	

There are no repeat determinations and no independent estimate of the error variance; it is necessary, therefore, to use the remainder mean square for this purpose. The comparisons between sugars are all within weeks, and accordingly the remainder mean square is the appropriate error variance for this factor. The ratio of the mean squares is $0·0258/0·0045 = 5·73$, which is highly significant for four and twelve degrees of freedom. In normal circumstances the remainder mean square would also be the appropriate variance for the other factor, but in this case the control based on one determination having been subtracted from all results, another step has to be introduced into the calculation. The sum of the results of each column of Table 8·37 is the sum of five observations from which is subtracted five times the control, i.e. it is of the form

$$(x_1 + x_2 + x_3 + x_4 + x_5) - 5x_6$$

If σ^2 is the variance of each observation, the variance of the whole expression is σ^2 multiplied by the sum of squares of coefficients $= 30\sigma^2$. In order that the mean square between concentrations may have the expectation σ^2 on the Null Hypothesis that the different concentrations of sugar have no effect, the corrected sum of squares between the column totals must be divided by 30 and not simply by 5 [Appendix 8D]. The corrected mean square between concentrations is then $0·1000/6 = 0·0167$, based on three degrees of freedom as before, and this has to be compared with the remainder mean square of $0·0045$ to test for statistical significance. The ratio is $0·0167/0·0045 = 3·71$, which is just significant at the 5% level. The variance of the mean per sugar is $0·0045/4 = 0·0011$, and this is used to compare the means for any two sugars. The corresponding variance of the means for the individual concentrations, that is of $(x_1 + x_2 + x_3 + x_4 + x_5)/5 - x_6$, is $0·0045(\frac{1}{5} + 1) = 0·0054$.

8·371. So far the analysis is that appropriate to qualitative factors. The next stage is to examine the functional form of the relation between yield of mycelium and per cent sugar for each sugar. The details of the analysis, which follows the same general procedure as the previous example, are given in Appendix 8E. The various components for the per cent sugar for each sugar are given in Table 8·38.

The analysis of variance is given in Table 8·39.

Interpretation

8·38. In the absence of replication or an independent estimate it is necessary to use an interaction mean square as the error variance. The mean square least likely to be appreciable is that of the interaction of the cubic component with the different sugars, and this should be the first choice for the error variance. The linear and quadratic interactions are clearly not significant,

Table 8·38

COMPONENTS OF CONCENTRATION OF SUGAR

(Derived from Table 8·37)

Level of qualitative factor = sugar	Components of quantitative factor (concentration of sugar)			
(1)	(2) Sum	(3) Linear	(4) Quadratic	(5) Cubic
Crude lactose	3·158	1·230	− 0·130	− 0·670
Crude glucose	3·864	1·206	− 0·184	0·482
Sucrose	3·745	0·793	− 0·265	− 0·199
Molasses	3·992	1·056	− 0·038	0·302
Dextrine	3·772	0·934	− 0·124	− 0·062
Sum..	18·531	5·219	− 0·741	− 0·147
Divisor for sum of squares..		20	4	20

Table 8·39

ANALYSIS OF VARIANCE OF TABLE 8·37

Source of variation	Sum of squares	Degrees of freedom	Mean square
Main effects:			
Between sugars	0·1032	4	0·0258
Between concentrations of sugars:			
Linear	0·2724 ⎫	1 ⎫	0·2724
Quadratic	0·0275 ⎬ 0·3001	1 ⎬ 3	0·0275
Cubic	0·0002 ⎭	1 ⎭	0·0002
Interactions with sugars:			
Linear	0·0068 ⎫	4 ⎫	0·0017
Quadratic	0·0070 ⎬ 0·0544	4 ⎬ 12	0·0017
Cubic	0·0406 ⎭	4 ⎭	0·0102
Total	0·4577	19	

and we infer that the shape of the relation connecting yield of mycelium and per cent sugar is the same for all sugars. This result was not unexpected, but provision was made to reveal the interactions if they existed. We are therefore justified in combining all the interaction terms to give an error variance of 0·0045 based on 12 degrees of freedom.* Using the error variance of 0·0045, it is found as before that there is a significant variation between the mean yields for the various sugars.

8·381. If there were no complications due to the control, a straight test of significance would be applied to all the three components of the main effects between concentrations of sugar, but in this case, because of the use of a control for each week, it is necessary to divide the mean square by 6. The mean square of the linear component is thus reduced to 0·0454, which is still highly significant. (Ratio to error mean square $= 0·0454/0·0045 = 10·1$; 1% value of F for 1 and 12 degrees of freedom $= 9·33$.) Neither the quadratic nor the cubic component of the effect is significant. The significance of the linear component of the effect of concentration of sugar was not revealed by the analysis of Table 8·371 carried out as for qualitative factors, and this demonstrates the need for analysing with respect to the linear, quadratic, etc., components of the effects.

The interaction of the linear effect with the sugars represents the variation in the slope from sugar to sugar. The fact that this is not significant supports the hypothesis that all sugars give the same slope, that is to say, the relationship between log yield of mycelium and concentration of sugar is linear and parallel for all the sugars, these differing only in position.

Summary

8·382. The conclusions so far are:

(i) There are significant differences between mean yields of the various sugars.

(ii) There is a significant linear increase in yield with increase in sugar content.

(iii) The quadratic and cubic effects of concentration of sugar are small, so that within the range examined a linear function provides an adequate representation.

(iv) The slope of the line is the same for all sugars. The sugars therefore differ only in the mean log yield produced.

(v) The error variance of individual log yield determinations within weeks is 0·0045.

* If required, it would be possible to go a stage further and combine with this the higher main effects, such as the cubic term, which are usually not expected to be appreciable.

8·383. The next step is to determine the slope of the line, i.e. the regression coefficient of log yield on per cent sugar. This is calculated as follows.

The linear component of the sum over all the five sugars is 5·219 [Table 8·38], giving a mean of 5·219/5 = 1·044. The slope is then 1·044 × 2/20 = 0·1044 [Appendix 8C]. The interval is 2% sugar; therefore the final value of the slope is 0·0522. In other words, there is an increase of 0·0522 in log yield for each unit per cent increase in sugar content. The antilog of 0·0522 is 1·128, corresponding to an increase of 12·8% yield of mycelium for each unit per cent increase in sugar concentration within the range 2–8% sugars.

The standard error of the slope is calculated as follows. The sum of squares of the constants used to derive the linear effects of Table 8·38 is 20. A multiplier 2/20 has been applied in order to convert the linear effects to the slope of the line, and again a further multiplier 1/2 has been used to express the slope in terms of unit per cent sugar content. The combined multiplier is then 1/20, and the slope is

$$(- 3\bar{y}_1 - \bar{y}_2 + \bar{y}_3 + 3\bar{y}_4)/20$$

where $\bar{y}_1, \bar{y}_2, \bar{y}_3$, and $\bar{y}_4$ are respectively the means of the observations of Table 8·37 for the various per cent sugars. The variance of this expression is the sum of squares of the coefficients of the $\bar{y}$'s multiplied by the variance of each $\bar{y}$, that is $1/20 \times V(\bar{y}_i)$. The variance of each $\bar{y}$ is $0\cdot0045(1 + \frac{1}{5}) = 0\cdot0054$. The variance of the slope is then 0·00027, which corresponds to a standard error of 0·0164, and is based on 12 degrees of freedom. The 5% value of t for 12 degrees of freedom is 2·179; therefore the 95% confidence limits of the log slope are 0·0522 ± 0·0357 = 0·0165 and 0·0879. The antilogs of these limits are 1·039 and 1·224. It follows that for each unit increase in per cent sugar concentration the expected increase in mycelium yield is 12·8% with the 95% confidence limits of 3·9 and 22·4%. The wide confidence range is a reflection of the large error that occurs when comparing the observations from different concentrations of sugar.

8·384. Finally, it is necessary to examine the differences between the sugars. It is appropriate to compare the means over all the concentrations, since it has already been established that the slope of the curve does not differ significantly between sugars, and we accept the hypothesis that the slope is the same for all sugars. The mean log mycelium yields are:

Crude lactose	= 0·790	Crude glucose	= 0·966
Sucrose	= 0·936	Molasses	= 0·998
Dextrine	= 0·943		

The standard error of each of these is $\sqrt{(0\cdot0045/4)} = 0\cdot034$, and differences of 0·103 are required between any two sugars for significance at the 5% level.

The test discriminates clearly between crude lactose and the rest, but it does not discriminate between glucose, sucrose, molasses, and dextrine. The 95% confidence limits to be attached to each mean are $\pm$ 0·074.

Comment on the design

8·39. One purpose of this example was to illustrate the method of analysis for factors with levels measurable by continuous variables. A complication arose from the existence of a control to correct for week-to-week variation. This example was chosen intentionally as a warning that every example must be considered carefully from the point of view of the appropriate error variance. The design is open to criticism because the week-to-week variation is estimated by one single result per week. If the experimenter had been sufficiently confident at the outset that the shape of the curve would not differ appreciably from one sugar to another a better design would have been provided by a Latin Square with respect to weeks, sugars, and concentrations of sugar, in which all comparisons of practical interest would have been made with the same and maximum degree of precision [Chapter 5]. An additional level for concentrations of sugar would be required to do this. When the shape of the curve, apart from position, is the same for all sugars, it follows that there is no interaction between concentration and type of sugar. Absence of appreciable interactions between the factors is the essential condition which must be satisfied before full advantage may be taken of the Latin Square designs. This point will be dealt with more fully in Chapter 10.

$m \times n$ factorial designs with both factors quantitative

8·4. The examples just considered were those in which one factor was quantitative and the other qualitative. Because of the quantitative nature of one of the factors it was possible, and indeed desirable, to determine whether the response to different concentrations could be satisfactorily represented by a linear relation, or whether a quadratic or higher-order curve was required; and also to determine whether the relation found was the same for all levels of the other factor, or whether relations differing in form were necessary to express the effect of the quantitative factor at different levels of the other factor. When two factors are involved and both are quantitative, not only can a similar assessment be made of the nature of the relation between the average responses and the levels of each of the factors, but also the interaction can, as shown later, be separated into the individual interactions between the several components (linear, quadratic, cubic, . . .) of one factor and the several components of the other. This separation of the various components of the interaction tends to make the experiment more sensitive by revealing as significant interactions which might otherwise be overlooked.

If one of the components is large and the others are small, the large component will probably be masked in the average over all the components.

A straightforward analysis of an $m \times n$ table without resolving the main effects and interactions takes the form of Table 8·4.

Table 8·4

ANALYSIS OF VARIANCE OF AN $m \times n$ TABLE: BOTH FACTORS ASSUMED QUALITATIVE

Source of variation	Sum of squares	Degrees of freedom	Mean square
Main effects*:			
Factor A		$m - 1$	
Factor B		$n - 1$	
Interaction		$(m - 1)(n - 1)$	
Total		$mn - 1$	

* The factor at m levels is denoted by A and that at n levels by B.

By means of the orthogonal polynomials given in Table 8C·1 we may resolve the $(m - 1)$ degrees of freedom for the main effect of A, and similarly the $(n - 1)$ for the main effect of B, as follows.

A (main effects). Linear component, quadratic component, cubic component, with one degree of freedom each; the remaining components with $(m - 4)$ degrees of freedom.

B (main effects). Linear component, quadratic component, cubic component, with one degree of freedom each; the remaining components with $(n - 4)$ degrees of freedom.

Analysis of interaction

8·41. The above completes the analysis of the two main effects. The next stage is to subdivide the interaction into its components, the method representing a simple extension of that used for Examples 8·3 and 8·4. In the first place we carry out the analysis in the same way as for one factor qualitative and the other quantitative; that is to say, we calculate the linear, quadratic, and cubic components for one factor (say A) for each level of the other factor, and produce a table such as Table 8·41.

Table 8·41

Level of B	Sum	Components of A Linear Quadratic Cubic		
1	S_1	L_1	Q_1	C_1
2	S_2	L_2	Q_2	C_2
3	S_3	L_3	Q_3	C_3
.	.	.	.	.
.	.	.	.	.
.	.	.	.	.
n	S_n	L_n	Q_n	C_n

Since the levels of B are also points on a numerical scale there may be trends in the linear, quadratic, and cubic components. Since the $L_1, L_2, \ldots,$ L_n components when plotted on a graph against the levels of B trace out a curve which may be either linear or curvilinear, we can treat the L's as though they were responses for given levels of a quantitative factor and determine the linear, quadratic, and cubic components. For example, if $n = 4$, the linear component of the L's will be, apart from a numerical factor,

$$(-3L_1 - L_2 + L_3 + 3L_4)$$

The linear component with respect to B of the linear component of factor A is called the linear A × linear B interaction. Similarly there exists a linear A × quadratic B interaction, i.e. the quadratic component of linear A with respect to B. The quadratic and cubic components of A may be treated similarly, giving the effects: quadratic A × quadratic B, cubic A × linear B, cubic A × cubic B, etc.

The interaction of quadratic A with quadratic B, and higher-degree interactions, are difficult to interpret; if they are appreciable in magnitude a rather complex situation is indicated, and the experimenter will have to rely mainly on an inspection of the data or on other methods for his conclusions [Chapter 11]. Such would be the case if factor A passed through an optimum for each level of B and this optimum changed in position and magnitude with the levels of B.

The analysis of variance table up to the cubic terms will have the form of Table 8·42.

Calculation of main effects and interactions
8·42. The steps in the calculation will be illustrated by means of the 5 × 4 table of results given in Table 8·3, but for the present purpose both factors A

Y

Table 8·42

ANALYSIS OF VARIANCE OF TWO-WAY TABLE: BOTH FACTORS QUANTITATIVE

Source of variation	Sum of squares	Degrees of freedom	Mean square
Main effects:			
Linear A		1	
Quadratic A..		1	
Cubic A		1	
Linear B		1	
Quadratic B		1	
Cubic B		1	
Interactions:			
Linear A × linear B		1	
Linear A × quadratic B		1	
Quadratic A × linear B		1	
Remainder		$nm - 10$	
Total		$nm - 1$	

and B are considered as quantitative. The analysis of variance regarding both factors as qualitative is given in Table 8·31, from which it is seen that factor A is highly significant. In order to analyse the main effects and interaction further, we use the orthogonal polynomials given in Table 8C·1 for $n = 4$ and $n = 5$, which are reproduced for convenience in Table 8·43.

Table 8·43

ORTHOGONAL POLYNOMIALS FOR 4 AND 5 LEVELS

(a) 5 levels

	Linear	Quadratic	Cubic
	−2	+2	−1
	−1	−1	+2
	0	−2	0
	+1	−1	−2
	+2	+2	+1
Sum of squares ..	10	14	10

Table 8·43 (*continued*)

(*b*) 4 levels

	Linear	Quadratic	Cubic
	− 3	+ 1	− 1
	− 1	− 1	+ 3
	+ 1	− 1	− 3
	+ 3	+ 1	+ 1
Sum of squares ..	20	4	20

Calculation of main effects

8·43. The main effect of A is derived from the row sums of Table 8·3 by multiplying by the coefficients of Table 8·43(*b*). Thus:

Linear effect: $- 3 \times 183{\cdot}3 - 1 \times 139{\cdot}9 + 1 \times 81{\cdot}7 + 3 \times 51{\cdot}8 = - 452{\cdot}7$
Quadratic effect: $1 \times 183{\cdot}3 - 1 \times 139{\cdot}9 - 1 \times 81{\cdot}7 + 1 \times 51{\cdot}8 = 13{\cdot}5$
Cubic effect: $- 1 \times 183{\cdot}3 + 3 \times 139{\cdot}9 - 3 \times 81{\cdot}7 + 1 \times 51{\cdot}8 = 43{\cdot}1$

The contributions to the sum of squares are obtained by dividing the square of each of these effects by five times the sum of squares of the relevant coefficients of Table 8·43(*b*). The factor five is introduced because five observations are contained in the sum for each level of A.

The contributions to the sum of squares are therefore:

Sum of squares corresponding to the linear component of the effect A
$$= (- 452{\cdot}7)^2/(5 \times 20) = 2049{\cdot}37$$
Sum of squares corresponding to the quadratic component of the effect A
$$= 13{\cdot}5^2/(5 \times 4) = 9{\cdot}11$$
Sum of squares corresponding to the cubic component of the effect A
$$= 43{\cdot}1^2/(5 \times 20) = 18{\cdot}58$$

The above components are each based on one degree of freedom, and thus account for all the variation due to the main effect A. The total of the sum of squares of these components is 2077·06, agreeing within rounding-off errors with the sum of squares for the main effect of A given in Table 8·31.

The components for the main effect of B are calculated similarly. This was done in Example 8·3, but for completeness the results are reproduced here:

Linear effect of B:
　Contribution to sum of squares $= 71{\cdot}3^2/(4 \times 10) = 127{\cdot}09$
Quadratic effect of B:
　Contribution to sum of squares $= 4{\cdot}7^2/(4 \times 14) = 0{\cdot}39$

Cubic effect of B:

Contribution to sum of squares $= (- 13\cdot6)^2/(4 \times 10) = 4\cdot62$

Remainder $\qquad\qquad\qquad\qquad = 0\cdot15$

Total $\qquad\qquad\qquad\qquad\quad\; = 132\cdot25$

There are four degrees of freedom for the main effects of B, and therefore the remainder based on one degree of freedom is the quartic component of the main effect.

The next step is to analyse the 12 degrees of freedom for interaction. The individual degrees of freedom could all be calculated separately, but the only ones that are at all likely to be appreciable are linear A $\times$ linear B, linear A $\times$ quadratic B, and quadratic A $\times$ linear B. The remainder will be pooled, and derived as a difference from the tota interaction sums of squares given in Table 8·31.

Calculation of interactions

8·44. The first step is to calculate the linear and quadratic components for each row, i.e. each level of A of Table 8·3, by using the coefficients given in Table 8·43. This was done in the analyses of Example 8·3 (Table 8·33), but for completeness the results are reproduced in Table 8·44.

Table 8·44

LINEAR AND QUADRATIC COMPONENTS OF QUANTITATIVE FACTOR B

Level of factor A	Linear B	Quadratic B
I	57·3	20·3
2	28·5	4·9
3	− 2·1	2·5
4	− 12·4	− 23·0
Sum ..	71·3	4·7

The sums agree with those obtained for the linear and quadratic components of the main effect of B derived above, and this provides an arithmetical check. The linear and quadratic effects vary from one level of A to another. These effects may be analysed in exactly the same way as though they were yields, that is, we may calculate the linear, quadratic, and cubic components using the coefficients of Table 8·43(b) for four levels. Thus: Linear component of linear B with respect to levels of A, i.e. linear B $\times$ linear A $= - 3 \times 57\cdot3 - 1 \times 28\cdot5 + 1 \times (- 2\cdot1) + 3 \times (- 12\cdot4) = - 239\cdot7$.

The quadratic component of linear B, i.e. quadratic A × linear B, may be calculated in a similar way. The same operation may be used for both columns of Table 8·44, giving the results shown in Table 8·441.

Table 8·441

COMPONENTS OF INTERACTION A × B

	Linear A	Quadratic A
Linear B ..	− 239·7	18·5
Quadratic B ..	− 132·3	− 10·1

The same results will be obtained if the components of A are calculated first.

8·45. In order to determine the contributions to the sum of squares it is necessary to divide the squares of the above quantities by the appropriate divisors, which are given by the sums of the squares of the coefficients of the observations used to derive the quantities. It can be shown that the sum of squares of the coefficients of linear B × linear A is simply the product of the sums of squares of the coefficients in Table 8·43 used to derive linear A and linear B separately, viz. $10 \times 20 = 200$. Similarly the sum of squares of the coefficients of the observations in the expression linear B × quadratic A is the product of the sums of squares of the coefficients in Table 8·43 used to derive linear B and quadratic A separately, viz. $10 \times 4 = 40$; and so on for the other components. These may be conveniently expressed in the form of Table 8·45.

Table 8·45

DIVISORS FOR INTERACTION SUMS OF SQUARES

Divisor for B	Divisors for A	
	Linear $= 20$	Quadratic $= 4$
Linear $= 10$ ..	200	40
Quadratic $= 14$ ..	280	56

The divisors for the various interactions are the products of the corresponding divisors of the components. The reader can readily satisfy himself that these are the correct divisors by carrying out the procedure of deriving the linear A, linear B, etc., effects, using the symbols $y_1, y_2, \ldots, y_n$ for the individual observations, and summing the squares of the coefficients of these observations in the final expression.

8·46. The following are the sums of squares in the analysis of variance of the interactions:

$$
\begin{aligned}
\text{Linear A} \times \text{linear B} &= (-239\cdot7)^2/200 = 287\cdot28 \\
\text{Linear A} \times \text{quadratic B} &= (-132\cdot2)^2/280 = 62\cdot51 \\
\text{Quadratic A} \times \text{linear B} &= 18\cdot5^2/40 = 8\cdot56 \\
\text{Quadratic A} \times \text{quadratic B} &= (-10\cdot1)^2/56 = 1\cdot82
\end{aligned}
$$

The last component, quadratic A × quadratic B, is rarely required and is included in the remainder of the interaction, which is $407\cdot65 - (287\cdot28 + 62\cdot51 + 8\cdot56) = 49\cdot30$, based on $(12 - 1 - 1 - 1) = 9$ degrees of freedom. The total interaction sum of squares of $407\cdot65$ is derived from Table 8·31. This leads to the analysis of variance shown in Table 8·46.

Table 8·46

FINAL ANALYSIS OF VARIANCE OF 5 × 4 TABLE: BOTH FACTORS QUANTITATIVE

(Derived from Table 8·3)

Source of variation		Sum of squares		Degrees of freedom		Mean square	Variance ratio
Main effects:							
A =	Linear	2,049·37		1		2,049·37	373·97
	Quadratic	9·11	2,077·06	1	3	9·11	1·66
	Cubic	18·58		1		18·58	3·39
B =	Linear	127·09		1		127·09	23·19
	Quadratic	0·39	132·25	1	4	0·39	0·07
	Cubic	4·62		1		4·62	0·84
	Remainder (= quartic)	0·15		1		0·15	0·03
Interactions:							
Linear A × linear B		287·28		1		287·28	52·42
Linear A × quadratic B		62·51		1		62·51	11·41
Quadratic A × linear B		8·56	407·65	1	12	8·56	1·56
Remainder = error		49·30		9		5·48	
Total		2,616·97		19			

Interpretation

8·47. In the absence of replication or an independent estimate of the error variance the remainder interaction mean square is used. The largest single effect is that of linear A, but the significant interactions of linear A with linear B and quadratic B show that the linear effect of A differs for different levels of B. There is an overall increase in the linear effect of A when the level of B increases from 1 to 5. We should usually be justified in combining 0·15, the remainder sum of mean squares of the main effect B, with 49·30, the sum of squares of the remainder of the interaction, to give an error variance based on ten degrees of freedom, because these effects are not expected to exist. If also the cubic and higher effects are not expected to exist, and if, as in this case, the expectation is not contradicted by the results, the sums of squares for the cubic effects may also be combined with the remainder interaction mean square, giving in this case an estimate of the error variance based on 12 degrees of freedom.

8·48. It is interesting to note the significant interactions which have emerged, for these would have been missed in the analysis of Table 8·31. This illustrates the point made early in this chapter, that the analysis by components of responses to quantitative factors renders the experiment more sensitive than if such factors are treated as qualitative. From Table 8·31 it would be possible to conclude only that factor A had a marked effect. The point that factor B had a marked effect would have been missed, though by dividing the main effect B into its components without the analysis of the interactions it would have established that there was a real effect (variance ratio 23·19, with 1 and 9 degrees of freedom; 5% significance level requires 5·12 or greater). The analysis of the interactions shows not only that the effect of B reaches a more significant level but also that there is a considerable amount of interaction between the two factors.

Factorial designs with all factors at three levels

8·5. When more than two factors are involved the experiment becomes rather large if more than three levels of each factor are to be examined. When the factors are all quantitative it is preferable at the outset to examine them at two, or at most three, levels; if the initial experiment does not give sufficient information it will at least indicate what further experiments are required. These will usually be smaller ones, with new levels for some or all of the factors. This is a form of sequential approach to the problem, and systematic methods of designing such experiments are discussed in Chapter 11. Provided the sequential approach is employed it is usually sufficient to restrict the design to only two levels of the factors, but there is sometimes an advantage in using three levels of the factors, because with three levels information is supplied on both the linear and the quadratic components of the effects. A quadratic component may imply a maximum or minimum response at some intermediate factor combination, or at a point outside the range examined for some or all of the factors, indicating a need for further experimental work at a different set of levels. There is thus special interest in designs with factors at three levels when quantitative factors are involved, and they have received considerable study for this reason. For n factors these designs are usually denoted by 3^n. The simplest member of this class of design is that in which only two factors occur, and though this is but a special case of the $m \times n$ design already considered it is convenient to use it to introduce some special nomenclature which is used in discussing 3^3 and higher designs.

Notation used in 3^n factorial designs

8·51. It is usual to represent the factors by capital letters and the three levels by 0, 1, 2, or by the corresponding small letters with these numbers as suffixes. For example, (a_0, a_1, a_2) may be used to represent the levels of a factor A, and (b_0, b_1, b_2) the levels of a second factor B, and so on. The lowest member of this class of design, that with two factors each at three levels, contains nine combinations, which may be represented in tabular form as Table 8·5.

Table 8·5

3 × 3 FACTORIAL DESIGN

Level of factor A	Level of factor B		
	0	1	2
0	a_0b_0	a_0b_1	a_0b_2
1	a_1b_0	a_1b_1	a_1b_2
2	a_2b_0	a_2b_1	a_2b_2

There is no ambiguity in representing the factor combinations by the suffixes, the first representing the level of A and the second the level of B; thus a_0b_0 may be represented by (00), a_1b_2 by (12), etc. A still more convenient method is to regard the above table in which A appears on the left-hand margin and B on the upper margin as a standard form and denote the combinations simply by the numbers 1–9 as in Table 8·51.

Table 8·51

NOTATION FOR 3 × 3 TABLE

Level of factor A	Level of factor B		
	0	1	2
0	1	4	7
1	2	5	8
2	3	6	9

This is the notation used by YATES [8·1]. The nine treatment combinations may then be represented in any of the three ways shown in Table 8·52.

Table 8·52

VARIOUS REPRESENTATIONS OF THE TREATMENT COMBINATIONS
IN A 3^2 FACTORIAL DESIGN

1	2	3
a_0b_0	00	1
a_1b_0	10	2
a_2b_0	20	3
a_0b_1	01	4
a_1b_1	11	5
a_2b_1	21	6
a_0b_2	02	7
a_1b_2	12	8
a_2b_2	22	9

These notations may be extended to several factors. With respect to four factors, A, B, C, and D, the particular combination $a_1b_2c_0d_2$ may be represented by 1202, the factors being taken in the order A, B, C, and D. The combination of the levels of the first two factors (12) correspond to 8 and the second two factors (02) to 7, and therefore the combination 1202 may be represented more concisely by the number 87.

8·52. The analysis for two factors, one or both quantitative, is a special case of the general $m \times n$ factorial designs considered in the previous sections. For three levels there are only three constants to represent the position and shape of the response curve for a quantitative factor; these are the mean, slope, and curvature. If the three observations are denoted by y_0, y_1, and y_2, at equal unit intervals of the variable, the three constants are represented by the following three orthogonal expressions:

$$(y_0 + y_1 + y_2)/3 = \text{mean}$$
$$(- y_0 + 0 + y_2)/2 = \text{linear component or slope}$$
$$(y_0 - 2y_1 + y_2)/2 = \text{quadratic component or curvature}$$

As in the previous examples, it is convenient to drop the divisors 3, 2, 2 for the purpose of deriving the analysis of variance table, but these divisors must be reintroduced later in order to give estimates of the magnitudes of the effects.

The main effects and interactions are all linear combinations of the observations, and a convenient method of estimating these effects for a 3×3 design is to derive a table of the appropriate multipliers to be applied to the observations. First denote the observations by the entries in Table 8·53.

Table 8·53

3×3 TABLE

Level of factor A	Level of factor B			Total
	0	1	2	
0	y_1	y_4	y_7	R_0
1	y_2	y_5	y_8	R_1
2	y_3	y_6	y_9	R_2
Total ..	C_0	C_1	C_2	T

By carrying out the general method given above on the y's of Table 8·53 we derive the linear functions representing the effects. The coefficients of the y's for each effect are given in Table 8·54.

Table 8·54

MULTIPLIERS FOR DERIVATION OF THE EFFECTS IN A 3^2 FACTORIAL DESIGN

		Observation									Divisor for sum of squares
		y_1	y_2	y_3	y_4	y_5	y_6	y_7	y_8	y_9	
Main effects	Linear A ..	-1	0	$+1$	-1	0	$+1$	-1	0	$+1$	$6r$
	Quadratic A ..	$+1$	-2	$+1$	$+1$	-2	$+1$	$+1$	-2	$+1$	$18r$
	Linear B ..	-1	-1	-1	0	0	0	$+1$	$+1$	$+1$	$6r$
	Quadratic B ..	$+1$	$+1$	$+1$	-2	-2	-2	$+1$	$+1$	$+1$	$18r$
Interactions	Linear A and linear B	$+1$	0	-1	0	0	0	-1	0	$+1$	$4r$
	Linear A and quadratic B	-1	0	$+1$	$+2$	0	-2	-1	0	$+1$	$12r$
	Quadratic A and linear B	-1	$+2$	-1	0	0	0	$+1$	-2	$+1$	$12r$
	Quadratic A and quadratic B	$+1$	-2	$+1$	-2	$+4$	-2	$+1$	-2	$+1$	$36r$ (r = number of replicates)

The reader is recommended to carry out these operations and derive Table 8·54 as an exercise.

To calculate the main effects and interactions the observations are multiplied by the appropriate coefficients in the above table and summed. The square of the sum thus formed divided by the sum of squares of the coefficients used in deriving it gives the contribution of the relevant degree of freedom to the sum of squares.

In the absence of an independent estimate of error the three interactions involving a quadratic component would be combined. For a 3×3 experiment it is usual to replicate at least twice in order to obtain a sufficient degree of precision. In the analysis of a replicated set we sum over all the replicates and analyse the 3×3 table so formed in the above manner, with the difference that the sum of squares is divided by a further factor equal to the number of replicates. The remainder variance, which is then used as the error variance, is obtained by subtracting the aggregate sum of squares of the 3×3 table formed in the above manner from the total sum of squares of the $r \times 3 \times 3$ individual observations, where r is the number of replicates.

3^3 factorial designs

8·6. The analysis and interpretation of a 3^3 factorial design involves a simple extension of the method used for a 3^2 design. The results may be conveniently represented in the form of Table 8·6.

Table 8·6

STANDARD FORM FOR $3 \times 3 \times 3$ TABLE

		Factor C						
		c_0			c_1			c_2		
		Factor B			Factor B			Factor B		
		b_0	b_1	b_2	b_0	b_1	b_2	b_0	b_1	b_2
Factor A	a_0 a_1 a_2									

This is the standard form for three factors A, B and C. There are two degrees of freedom for each main effect, and four for each of the three two-factor interactions. This accounts for 18 degrees of freedom, leaving eight for the three-factor interactions.

One way* to analyse a $3 \times 3 \times 3$ experiment is to form three 3×3 tables each of which corresponds to one of the three pairs of factors AB, BC,

---

* Another systematic method is considered later and is given in detail in Appendix 8G.

AC. Each table so formed is analysed in the usual way, but an additional divisor of 3 is used in the sum of squares, since each result is the sum of three observations. From these 3×3 tables we obtain the sums of squares corresponding to A, B, and C (each based on two degrees of freedom), and to the interactions AB, BC, and AC (each based on four degrees of freedom). The sum of these corresponds to 18 degrees of freedom; this leaves a remainder of eight degrees of freedom, which corresponds to the three-factor interactions. The combined sum of squares for all the three-factor interactions is obtained by subtracting the sum of squares for the main effects and two-factor interactions from the sum of squares for all the 27 individual observations. The extension of the analysis when the design has been replicated is the same as for any replicated factorial design; the sum over all the replicates is formed and analysed in the usual way, except that an additional divisor equal to the number of replicates is used for each sum of the squares. The replication sum of squares and degrees of freedom may be obtained by subtraction from the total sum of squares and degrees of freedom of the individual observations; the corresponding mean square gives the error mean square to test the significance of the other effects. In the absence of replication or an independent estimate of the error variance it is necessary to use the three-factor interaction variance for this purpose. All the steps in the above analysis will be brought out in the following example.

Example 8·5. 3³ factorial design replicated twice
8·7. This example relates to a cotton dyestuff of which the output is fairly large. The chemical process is a simple one, involving essentially three reactants, viz. the base material or intermediate, and two inorganic materials which we shall denote by A and B. A change was made in the process of manufacture of the base material, and this was followed by a drop in yield of the dyestuff made from it. On chemical considerations the two events did not appear to be related since the quality of the intermediate appeared unchanged. A laboratory investigation was put in hand to examine three possible factors:

C, the concentration of A in the free water present in the reaction mixture.
V, the volume of free water present in the reaction mixture.
N, the amount of B in the reaction mixture.

It was decided to examine all combinations of three levels of each of these factors, and the whole experiment was repeated in order to give sufficient precision. In the data given in Table 8·61 a constant amount has been deducted from each yield.

Analysis
8·71. All the factors in this example denote variables, and the levels for each are at equal intervals of the variable. The analysis should therefore relate the

Table 8·61

YIELDS OF A DIRECT COTTON DYESTUFF

Levels of factor C	n_0 Levels of factor V			n_1 Levels of factor V			n_2 Levels of factor V		
	v_0	v_1	v_2	v_0	v_1	v_2	v_0	v_1	v_2
c_0	74 (α_1) 85 (α_2)	13 (γ_1) 12 (β_2)	69 (β_1) 115 (γ_2)	112 (γ_1) 148 (γ_2)	46 (β_1) 52 (α_2)	130 (α_1) 107 (β_2)	71 (β_1) 75 (β_2)	56 (α_1) 47 (γ_2)	125 (γ_1) 70 (α_2)
Sum ..	159	25	184	260	98	237	146	103	195
c_1	211 (β_1) 184 (β_2)	110 (α_1) 145 (γ_2)	199 (γ_1) 164 (α_2)	166 (α_1) 288 (α_2)	218 (γ_1) 204 (β_2)	220 (β_1) 142 (γ_2)	201 (γ_1) 216 (γ_2)	216 (β_1) 239 (α_2)	227 (α_1) 265 (β_2)
Sum ..	395	255	363	454	422	362	417	455	492
c_2	74 (γ_1) 75 (γ_2)	147 (β_1) 104 (α_2)	195 (α_1) 183 (β_2)	47 (β_1) 65 (β_2)	146 (α_1) 124 (γ_2)	198 (γ_1) 165 (α_2)	90 (α_1) 60 (α_2)	102 (γ_1) 70 (β_2)	164 (β_1) 114 (γ_2)
Sum ..	149	251	378	112	270	363	150	172	278

Levels of factor N

The Greek letters in brackets following each observation are introduced for a purpose to be described in a later chapter.

Table 8·62

ANALYSIS OF VARIANCE OF TABLE 8·61: ALL FACTORS QUANTITATIVE

Source of variation	Sum of squares	Degrees of freedom	Mean square
Main effects:			
C			
Linear	14,241	1	14,241†
Quadratic	126,759	1	126,759†
(Sum)	(141,000)	(2)	(70,500)
V			
Linear	10,336	1	10,336†
Quadratic	9,112	1	9,112†
(Sum)	(19,448)	(2)	(9,724)
N			
Linear	1,723	1	1,722
Quadratic	3,212	1	3,212‡
(Sum)	(4,935)	(2)	(2,468)
Two-factor interactions:			
C × V			
Linear V × linear C	12,927	1	12,927†
Linear V × quadratic C	7,959	1	7,959†
Quadratic V × linear C	6,517	1	6,517†
Quadratic V × quadratic C	520	1	520
(Sum)	(27,923)	(4)	(6,981)
C × N			
Linear N × linear C	2,688	1	2,688‡
Linear N × quadratic C	8,978	1	8,978†
Quadratic N × linear C	983	1	983
Quadratic N × quadratic C	395	1	395
(Sum)	(13,044)	(4)	(3,261)
V × N			
Linear N × linear V	38	1	38
Linear N × quadratic V	1,682	1	1,682
Quadratic N × linear V	567	1	567
Quadratic N × quadratic V	627	1	627
(Sum)	(2,914)	(4)	(729)
Three-factor interaction:			
C × V × N	9,746	8	1,218
Remainder (error)	21,036	27	779
Total	240,046	53	—

† Highly significant; $P \leqslant 1\%$
* Significant; $1\% < P \leqslant 5\%$
‡ Possibly significant; $5\% < P \leqslant 10\%$

effects at the different levels, and this is done by calculating the linear and quadratic components and their interactions. The details are given in Appendix 8F, from which we obtain the analysis of variance of Table 8·62.

The linear and quadratic effects for C and V are all highly significant. Neither effect for N is significant, but the quadratic effect approaches significance at the 5% level. All interactions of CV involving a linear component are significant. As expected, quadratic V × quadratic C is not significant. The only component of the interaction CN which is significant is linear N × quadratic C. None of the VN interactions are significant, and all the three-factor interactions are not significant. It is sufficient therefore to consider the two-way tables of C × V and C × N. These are given in Table 8·63, from

Table 8·63

TWO-WAY TABLES OF C AND V, AND C AND N

	CV			Mean		CN			Mean
	v_0	v_1	v_2			n_0	n_1	n_2	
c_0	94·2	37·7	102·7	78·2	c_0	61·3	99·2	74·0	78·2
c_1	211·0	188·7	202·8	200·8	c_1	168·8	206·3	227·3	200·8
c_2	68·5	115·5	169·8	117·9	c_2	129·7	124·2	100·0	117·9
Mean ..	124·6	113·9	158·4			119·9	143·2	133·8	

which it is seen that the best condition of factor C is at c_1, whatever the condition of the other factors. There is a sharp peak at this level which is responsible for the large quadratic component of C; in fact, this is the largest single effect. The yield is very sensitive to changes in the level of C, a higher or lower value than c_1 producing a marked drop in yield. This drop is sharper for lower values than for higher values of C. From the CV table (Table 8·63) it is seen that the lowest value of V is to be preferred, and from the CN table the best results are obtained from the highest level of N. The interaction between N and C is of considerable interest because although on the average there is no appreciable difference between n_1 and n_2, for the condition c_1 a change to n_2 produces an increase in yield, while for both conditions of c_0 and c_2 an increase in N results in a drop in yield. The error variance is 779, from which we deduce that the standard error of each result of Table 8·63 is $\sqrt{(779/6)} = 11\cdot4$, giving 95% confidence limits of $2\cdot05 \times 11\cdot4 = 23\cdot4$ to be attached to each result.

8·72. This experiment gave valuable information on the reaction leading to the product under investigation. The paramount importance and the critical nature of the factor C had not previously been suspected. The interaction between C and N was most revealing, because on the plant (but not in these laboratory experiments) the two factors were linked by a mechanical manipulative effect which was unsuspected. Briefly, N had been decreased in the last two years by an alteration of the process in the manufacture of the intermediate and consequently it was possible that C had been altered unwittingly following the change. Attention on the plant to this point showed an immediate improvement in yield. In addition, the laboratory experiments indicated that by suitable adjustment of C and V the yield might be increased above normal and a saving in materials might be effected concurrently.

3^4 and higher designs

8·8. The method of analysis described for 3^2 and 3^3 designs may be readily extended to 3^4 and higher designs, the main effects and two-factor interactions being calculated as for 3^3 designs. There is usually no point in subdividing the three- and four-factor interactions, since they are rarely important; therefore, as in the case of the 3^3 design analysed in the previous section, the eight degrees of freedom for three-factor interactions for each set of three factors are derived as a whole. Similar considerations apply to the higher-order interactions.

Systematic method of analysing 3^n factorial design when all factors are quantitative

8·9. A systematic method exists for deriving the components of the main effects and all interactions in 3^n designs (all factors assumed quantitative and levels equally spaced). This corresponds to the method given in Chapter 7 for 2^n designs and involves writing the treatment combinations in a standard order, dividing into sets of three and performing three operations:
   (i) Adding the three numbers.
   (ii) Subtracting the first from the third (linear).
   (iii) Subtracting twice the middle term from the sum of the other two (quadratic).

The operations correspond to finding the sum and linear and quadratic components of each set of three. This is seen to be an extension of the method used for 2^n designs, the extension involving the third operation of finding the quadratic component. The method is described and illustrated in Appendix 8G.

REFERENCES

[8·1] YATES, F. The Design and Analysis of Factorial Experiments. Imperial Bureau of Soil Science (Harpenden, 1937).

[8·2] STEVENS, W. L. "Statistical Analysis of a Non-orthogonal Tri-factorial Experiment." Biometrika, 35 (1948), 346.

[8·3] FISHER, R. A., and YATES, F. Statistical Tables for Biological, Agricultural and Medical Research. Oliver & Boyd (Edinburgh and London, 1948).

Appendix 8A

GENERAL METHOD OF ANALYSIS OF FACTORIAL DESIGNS FOR QUALITATIVE FACTORS

8A·1. Consider the general factorial design for k qualitative factors with $m, n, p, \ldots, t$ levels respectively. The total number of observations involved is $N = mnp \ldots t$. The numbers of levels for some of the factors may be equal, but this will not affect the generality of the analysis.

Calculation of the main effects

8A·2. Denote the first factor by A. Each of its m levels will appear with all the different combinations of the levels of the other $(k - 1)$ factors representing $np \ldots t$ different treatment combinations. Denote by T_1 the sum of all the observations at the first level of factor A and by T_2, T_3, T_4, etc., the sums of all the observations at the second, third, fourth, etc., levels respectively. Denote the corresponding means by X_1, X_2, X_3, etc., and construct Table 8A·1.

Table 8A·1

MAIN EFFECT OF A

		Level of factor A						Total
		1	2	3	...	i	...	m	
Total	..	T_1	T_2	T_3	...	T_i	...	T_m	T
Mean	..	X_1	X_2	X_3	...	X_i	...	X_m	Grand mean $= X$

The main effect of factor A is represented by the differences between the means $X_1, X_2, \ldots, X_m$ of the above table, and in order to assess the significance of the main effect as a whole it is necessary to calculate the appropriate sum of squares and the corresponding mean square. To obtain the sum of squares, $\Sigma T_i^2/(np \ldots t) - T^2/N$, square each total, add, divide by the number of observations in each, then subtract the correction for the mean. An equivalent expression is $\Sigma T_i X_i - TX$.

If the latter expression is used, an adequate number of significant places must be retained in each mean. This sum of squares is based on $(m - 1)$ degrees of freedom. An identical operation may be performed on each of the remaining $(k - 1)$ factors. In practice the main effects are best derived as part of the procedure for calculating the two-factor interactions, as shown in the next section.

z

Calculation of the two-factor interactions

8A·3. The procedure for calculating the two-factor interactions will now be given in relation to the first two factors, A and B, with m and n levels respectively. A two-factor table may be set up for A and B in which the upper margin represents the levels of one factor and the left-hand margin the levels of the other, as in Table 8A·2. The entries represent the sums of all the $pq \dots t$ observations for each of the given combinations of the levels of A and B. Thus T_{ij} represents the sum of the observations involving the ith level of A and the jth level of B. The analysis of variance of Table 8A·2 is given in Table 8A·3.

Table 8A·2

TWO-WAY TABLE FOR FACTORS A AND B

Level of first factor A	Level of second factor B					Total	Mean
	1	2	3	...	n		
1	T_{11}	T_{12}	T_{13}	...	T_{1n}	$T_{1.}$	$X_{1.}$
2	T_{21}	T_{22}	T_{23}	...	T_{2n}	$T_{2.}$	$X_{2.}$
3	T_{31}	T_{32}	T_{33}	...	T_{3n}	$T_{3.}$	$X_{3.}$
.	.	.	.		.	.	.
.	.	.	.		.	.	.
.	.	.	.		.	.	.
m	T_{m1}	T_{m2}	T_{m3}	...	T_{mn}	$T_{m.}$	$X_{m.}$
Total ..	$T_{.1}$	$T_{.2}$	$T_{.3}$	...	$T_{.n}$	T	
Mean ..	$X_{.1}$	$X_{.2}$	$X_{.3}$	...	$X_{.n}$		

Table 8A·3

ANALYSIS OF VARIANCE OF TWO-FACTOR TABLE A AND B

Source of variation	Sum of squares	Degrees of freedom
Factor A	$\Sigma T_{i.}{}^2/(np \dots t) - T^2/N$	$m - 1$
Factor B	$\Sigma T_{.j}{}^2/(mp \dots t) - T^2/N$	$n - 1$
Interaction	Remainder	$(m - 1)(n - 1)$
Total	$\Sigma T_{ij}{}^2/(pq \dots t) - T^2/N$	$mn - 1$

The calculation of the sums of squares for the main effects A and B has already been explained, and the only new quantity to be calculated is the total sum of squares for the two-factor table, which is

$$\Sigma T_{ij}^2/(pq \ldots t) - T^2/N$$

The sum of squares for the interaction AB is then obtained by subtraction,* and the degrees of freedom, which may also be obtained by subtraction, are $(m - 1)(n - 1)$. There are $k(k - 1)/2$ pairs of factors, and therefore the same number of two-factor interactions, and all of these are dealt with in the same way. The divisor for each quantity squared when deriving the sum of squares is the number of observations contained in the quantities which are squared, e.g. $pq \ldots t$ for each T_{ij}^2 and N for T^2.

Calculation of the three-factor interactions

8A·4. Denote the first three factors with levels m, n, and p by A, B, and C respectively. There are mnp combinations of the levels of these factors, each of which appears $q \ldots t$ times. Sum the $q \ldots t$ observations for each combination of the levels of factors A, B, and C. If required, these sums may be set out in the form of a three-factor table. Let the sum of all observations for the ith level of factor A, the jth level of factor B, and the kth level of factor C, be T_{ijk}. Then the total sum of squares for the three-way table is

$$\Sigma T_{ijk}^2/(q \ldots t) - T^2/N$$

Deducting from this the sums of squares due to the main effects of A, B, and C, and the three two-factor interactions AB, AC, and BC, we obtain the sum of squares for the three-factor interaction ABC, and this will be based on $(m - 1)(n - 1)(p - 1)$ degrees of freedom. This procedure must be repeated for all the $k(k - 1)(k - 2)/6$ different three-factor interactions.

8A·5. If it is necessary to calculate the four-factor interactions, the procedure is a simple extension of the above, that is, all the observations for every one of the combinations of the levels of the four factors concerned are summed, preferably with the formation of a four-factor table of these sums. The total corrected sum of squares of these quantities is calculated and the four-factor interaction sum of squares is obtained by subtracting from this the sums of squares for all the main effects and for all the two-factor and three-factor interactions between the four factors involved. Usually, however, the four-factor and all higher-order interactions may be combined and derived as a remainder after subtracting all main effects and two-factor and three-factor interactions from the total corrected sum of squares of all N individual observations.

* It is possible to obtain the sum of squares for the interaction directly, but this is usually inconvenient and it is simpler to derive it by subtraction.

Replication

8A·6. If replication occurs, it is important that all the factor combinations are replicated to the same extent, for otherwise the effects will not be orthogonal and the analysis will be laborious and beyond the scope of this book. A method for three factors in which the combinations are not all replicated to the same extent is considered in detail in [8·2].

When all the combinations are replicated the same number of times, the first step in the analysis is to sum the observations over all the replicates. The resulting table may be analysed for main effects and interactions as above, but with the difference that an additional divisor r ($=$ the number of replicates) is required for the crude sums of squares and correction. A further effect "within replicates" is calculated, and this is best derived as a remainder from the total sum of squares of the rN individual observations. It will be based on $(r-1)N$ degrees of freedom.

8A·61. Alternatively, the sum of squares within each group of r repeat observations may be calculated directly, and these sums may be totalled to give the "within replicates" sum of squares. When $r = 2$ this is simple: the sum of squares within replicates is then $\Sigma w_i{}^2/2$ where $w_1, w_2, w_3, \ldots$ are the differences between the duplicate results.

Significance of effects

8A·7. When there are no repeats, the remainder mean square representing the higher-order interactions is used as an estimate of the error variance to test the significance of the effects calculated. If a two-factor interaction is significant, it means that the effect of one of the factors depends upon the condition of the other factor, and it may be necessary to examine in detail the two-way table of the factors concerned by forming a table of means analogous to Table 8A·2. When a three-factor interaction is significant and appreciable in magnitude the three-way table must be examined in detail because the effect of any one of the factors will depend upon the particular condition of the other two factors. When there is replication, the mean square due to replication is used as an estimate of the error variance.

Appendix 8B

DETAILS OF ANALYSIS OF RESULTS OF EXAMPLE 8·2

Calculation of main effects and two-factor interactions

8B·1. The complete data are given in Table 8·2, to which we refer. It is convenient to calculate the main effects at the same time as the two-factor interactions. There are three factors, and therefore three sets of two-factor interactions, which are:

(i) Alloy $\times$ observer, (ii) Alloy $\times$ site, (iii) Observer $\times$ site

The main effects of alloys and observers and the interaction between them are calculated as follows.

Alloys and observers

8B·2. Form the appropriate two-way table by summing over the sites. This results in Table 8B·1.

Table 8B·1

TWO-WAY TABLE OF ALLOYS AND OBSERVERS

Observer \ Alloy	1	2	3	4	5	6	7	8	9	Total
A	23	21	23	19	21	17	10	22	22	178
B	13	19	20	18	21	14	7	22	25	159
C	26	26	28	28	30	22	19	30	32	241
D	22	19	23	17	20	17	14	23	24	179
Total	84	85	94	82	92	70	50	97	103	757

Each entry is the sum of the four observations made by the given observer on the given alloy at the four sites; for example, the first entry is given by $5 + 8 + 4 + 6 = 23$.

Calculation of main effects of alloys and observers

8B·3. The main effect for alloys is represented by the differences between the averages for each column. Since each entry is a sum of four observations, the divisor to obtain the average of each column is 16, and that for each row is 36.

For the alloy main effect:

Crude sum of squares
$\quad$ = (sum of squares of column totals)/(No. of observations in each total)
$\quad$ = $(84^2 + 85^2 + 94^2 + \ldots + 103^2)/16$
$\quad$ = $4107\cdot69$

Correction
$\quad$ = (square of grand total)/(total No. of observations)
$\quad$ = $757^2/144 = 3979\cdot51$

Corrected sum of squares = $4107\cdot69 - 3979\cdot51 = 128\cdot18$

Similarly the sum of squares between observers is:

Corrected sum of squares = $(178^2 + 159^2 + 241^2 + 179^2)/36 - 757^2/144$
$\quad$ = $4085\cdot75 - 3979\cdot51 = 106\cdot24$.

To derive the interaction sum of squares we must first calculate the total sum of squares between the 36 entries of Table 8B·1.

$$\text{Total corrected sum of squares} = (23^2 + 21^2 + 23^2 + \ldots + 14^2 + 23^2 + 24^2)/4 - 757^2/144$$
$$= 4237\cdot25 - 3979\cdot51 = 257\cdot74$$

Analysis of variance

8B·4. The formal analysis of variance table for alloys and observers is then as Table 8B·2.

Table 8B·2

ANALYSIS OF VARIANCE OF TABLE 8B·1

Source of variation	Sum of squares	Degrees of freedom	Mean square
Between alloys	128·18	8	16·023
Between observers ..	106·24	3	35·413
Interaction of alloys and observers	23·32	24	0·972
Total	257·74	35	

The sums of squares and degrees of freedom for the interaction of alloys and observers are obtained by subtraction from the total.

The interactions between alloys and sites, and between observers and sites, are obtained similarly.

Interaction between alloys and sites

8B·5. The corresponding two-way table obtained by summing over the four observers is shown in Table 8B·3.

Table 8B·3

TWO-WAY TABLE OF ALLOYS AND SITES

Site \ Alloy	1	2	3	4	5	6	7	8	9	Total
1	22	22	21	20	26	20	9	24	28	192
2	32	32	29	30	24	20	22	23	26	238
3	13	15	20	13	18	12	4	22	25	142
4	17	16	24	19	24	18	15	28	24	185
Total	84	85	94	82	92	70	50	97	103	757

The main effect between alloys has already been calculated, and the corrected sum of squares for sites is

$$(192^2 + 238^2 + 142^2 + 185^2)/36 - 757^2/144 = 4108\cdot25 - 3979\cdot51$$
$$= 128\cdot74$$

The total corrected sum of squares for Table 8B·3 is

$$(22^2 + 22^2 + 21^2 + \ldots + 15^2 + 28^2 + 24^2)/4 - 757^2/144$$
$$= 4325\cdot75 - 3979\cdot51 = 346\cdot24$$

The interaction sum of squares is then

$$346\cdot24 \text{ (total)} - 128\cdot74 \text{ (sites)} - 128\cdot18 \text{ (alloys)} = 89\cdot32$$

This is based on $3 \times 8 = 24$ degrees of freedom.

Interaction between observers and sites

8B·6. The two-way table for the remaining two-factor interaction is Table 8B·4.

Table 8B·4

TWO-WAY TABLE OF SITES AND OBSERVERS

Observer Site	A	B	C	D	Total
1	45	39	59	49	192
2	52	57	73	56	238
3	33	25	50	34	142
4	48	38	59	40	185
Total	178	159	241	179	757

Each entry is now a sum of nine observations and the total corrected sum of squares is

$$(45^2 + 39^2 + 59^2 + \ldots + 38^2 + 59^2 + 40^2)/9 - 757^2/144$$
$$= 4227\cdot22 - 3979\cdot51 = 247\cdot71$$

The interaction sum of squares is then

$$247\cdot71 \text{ (total)} - 106\cdot24 \text{ (observers)} - 128\cdot74 \text{ (sites)} = 12\cdot73$$

This is based on $3 \times 3 = 9$ degrees of freedom.

Calculation of three-factor interaction

8B·7. There are only three factors in this experiment, and the sum of squares for the three-factor interaction is obtained by subtracting the sums of squares for the three main effects and the three two-factor interactions from the total corrected sum of squares of all 144 individual observations.

The total sum of squares of the observations of Table 8·2 is

$$(5^2 + 5^2 + 5^2 + \ldots + 3^2 + 7^2 + 6^2) - 757^2/144 = 4527 - 3979 \cdot 51$$
$$= 547 \cdot 49$$

Final analysis of variance table

8B·8. The final analysis of variance table is then as Table 8B·5.

Table 8B·5

ANALYSIS OF VARIANCE OF TABLE 8·2

Source of variation	Sum of squares	Degrees of freedom	Mean square
Between alloys	128·18	8	16·023
Between observers	106·24	3	35·413
Between sites..	128·74	3	42·913
Interactions:			
Alloys × observers	23·32	24	0·972
Alloys × sites	89·32	24	3·722
Sites × observers	12·73	9	1·414
Alloys × observers × sites ..	58·96	72	0·819
Total	547·49	143	

APPENDIX 8C

PARTITIONING OF DEGREES OF FREEDOM FOR QUANTITATIVE FACTORS BY MEANS OF ORTHOGONAL POLYNOMIALS

A QUANTITATIVE factor is a factor for which the levels may be represented by points on a scale. An example is the factor temperature when the levels examined are given temperatures. The effect of such a factor will be a mathematical function of the levels of the factor, and usually this can be represented by a polynomial expression:

$$y = a_1 + a_2x + a_3x^2 + a_4x^3 + \ldots \quad \ldots\ldots\ldots\ldots(8C\cdot1)$$

where x denotes the level of the factor and y the response.

Given the values $x_1, x_2, x_3, \ldots, x_n$ and the corresponding values of y, then the constants of the polynomial expression may be estimated by the method of Least Squares [Appendix 11B and *S.M.*, Chapter 8]. The least squares solution gives these constants as linear combinations of the observations. Thus, if there are n observations, $y_1, y_2, y_3, \ldots, y_n$ corresponding respectively to the n values $x_1, x_2, x_3, \ldots, x_n$ of the factor, the estimated values of the constants of the polynomial will have the form

$$a_1 = a_{11}y_1 + a_{12}y_2 + a_{13}y_3 + \ldots + a_{1n}y_n$$
$$a_2 = a_{21}y_1 + a_{22}y_2 + a_{23}y_3 + \ldots + a_{2n}y_n$$
$$a_3 = a_{31}y_1 + a_{32}y_2 + a_{33}y_3 + \ldots + a_{3n}y_n$$

etc.

where the a's are another set of constants independent of the y's, and are functions of the x's. For example, the first two constants are simply

$$a_1 = \text{mean} = \Sigma y_i/n = \frac{y_1}{n} + \frac{y_2}{n} + \ldots + \frac{y_n}{n} \quad \ldots\ldots\ldots\ldots\ldots\ldots\ldots(8C\cdot2)$$

$$a_2 = \text{slope} = \frac{\Sigma(x - \bar{x})y}{\Sigma(x - \bar{x})^2}$$

$$= \frac{(x_1 - \bar{x})}{\Sigma(x - \bar{x})^2}y_1 + \frac{(x_2 - \bar{x})}{\Sigma(x - \bar{x})^2}y_2 + \ldots + \frac{(x_n - \bar{x})}{\Sigma(x - \bar{x})^2}y_n \quad ..(8C\cdot3)$$

The coefficients for a_3, a_4 and those of higher powers are somewhat more complicated functions of the x's. The constants $a_1, a_2, a_3, \ldots$ are not all mutually orthogonal, but it is possible to transform the polynomial *(8C·1)* into another polynomial:

$$y = A + BX_1 + CX_2 + DX_3 + \ldots \quad \ldots\ldots\ldots\ldots(8C\cdot4)$$

in which the constants $A, B, C, D, \ldots$ are now mutually orthogonal linear functions of the observations and $X_1, X_2, X_3, \ldots$ are respectively linear, quadratic, cubic, etc., functions of the variable x. We shall not be concerned in this book with the derivation of the expressions X_1, X_2, X_3, etc., and the coefficients A, B, C, D, etc., in the general case, but when the levels of the factor, i.e. $x_1, x_2, \ldots, x_n$, are at equally spaced intervals, the coefficients A, B, C, D, etc., and the expressions X_1, X_2, X_3, etc., simplify, as already shown [*S.M.*, Chapter 8]. The only points that we need be concerned with here are:

(i) A is the mean, B is known as the linear component, C as the quadratic component, D as the cubic component, etc.

(ii) All these constants are linear functions of the observations y_i, i.e. we may write

$$A = \Sigma ay \qquad\qquad B = \Sigma \beta y$$
$$C = \Sigma \gamma y \qquad\qquad D = \Sigma \delta y, \text{ etc.}$$

and all are mutually orthogonal.

(iii) a is $1/n$, since A is the mean. The constants β, γ, etc., up to those for the quintic component, may be readily derived from tables covering a wide range of values of n, the number of levels [8·3]. The actual values tabulated are proportional to the constants α, β, . . . required in the expression under (ii).

These tables of values of the orthogonal coefficients make the work of calculating the linear, quadratic, cubic, etc., components a simple matter. More than six levels and higher terms than the cubic are rarely encountered in experimental work, and a suitably condensed form of the tables of orthogonal polynomial coefficients is given in Table 8C·1 at the end of this appendix. For four levels the table of coefficients is:

Observation	Linear β'	Quadratic γ'	Cubic δ'
y_1	-3	$+1$	-1
y_2	-1	-1	$+3$
y_3	$+1$	-1	-3
y_4	$+3$	$+1$	$+1$
$\mathcal{J}$	20	4	20
K	2	1	10/3

$\mathcal{J}$ is the sum of squares of the coefficients and K a scale factor. The quantities β', γ', δ' are tabulated as integral values in order to simplify the calculations still further, and the factor K is subsequently applied as a correction. In practice the quantity $B' = \Sigma\beta'y$ is termed the linear component; similarly $C' = \Sigma\gamma'y$ and $D' = \Sigma\delta'y$ are termed the quadratic and cubic components. The actual values of the constants in the orthogonal form of the polynomial are derived from B', C', and D' by multiplying by the corresponding quantity $K/\mathcal{J}$. Thus $B = (K/\mathcal{J})\Sigma\beta'y$.

When carrying out an analysis of variance it is convenient to drop the multiplier $K/\mathcal{J}$, which need only be introduced when the actual numerical values of the constants B, C, and D are required. Omitting these multipliers, the following expressions are obtained for $n = 4$.

$$\begin{aligned}
\text{Sum} &= y_1 + y_2 + y_3 + y_4 &&= 4A \\
\text{Linear component} &= -3y_1 - y_2 + y_3 + 3y_4 &&= B' = 10B \\
\text{Quadratic component} &= y_1 - y_2 - y_3 + y_4 &&= C' = 4C \\
\text{Cubic component} &= -y_1 + 3y_2 - 3y_3 + y_4 &&= D' = 6D
\end{aligned}$$

It can readily be verified that all these linear functions are orthogonal to one another, e.g. for the linear and quadratic components the sum of the products of the coefficients of the observations is $-3 + 1 - 1 + 3 = 0$, which is the condition required for orthogonality.

There are other ways of representing the observations by orthogonal effects, e.g.

$$y_1 + y_2 + y_3 + y_4 \qquad\qquad y_1 + y_2 + y_3 + y_4$$
$$y_1 - y_2 - y_3 + y_4 \quad \text{or} \quad y_1 - y_2$$
$$y_1 - y_2 + y_3 - y_4 \qquad\qquad y_3 - y_4$$
$$y_1 + y_2 - y_3 - y_4 \qquad\qquad y_1 + y_2 - y_3 - y_4$$

However, the set giving the linear, quadratic, cubic, etc., components is more useful for quantitative factors, because it is capable of a simple interpretation in terms of the shape constants of the response curve. If the observations may be represented by a straight line, $B = B'/10$ gives the slope or regression coefficient and $y = \bar{y} + BX_1 = \bar{y} + B(x - \bar{x})$, since $X_1 = x - \bar{x}$ [*S.M.*, Chapter 6]. When the points fall exactly on a straight line the quadratic component is seen to be zero. If a quadratic expression is required to represent the relationship, then an additional term $CX_2 = C'X_2/4$ is required. The expression X_2 is given by $X_1^2 - (n^2 - 1)/12 = X_1^2 - 1 \cdot 25$ for $n = 4$ [*S.M.*, Chapter 6], and the regression equation is

$$y = \bar{y} + B(x - \bar{x}) + C\{(x - \bar{x})^2 - 1 \cdot 25\}$$
$$= (\bar{y} - 1 \cdot 25C) + B(x - \bar{x}) + C(x - \bar{x})^2$$

If the points fall exactly on a quadratic curve the cubic component must be zero. Using the coefficients of Table 8C·1, the cubic component is seen to be $(-y_1 + 3y_2 - 3y_3 + y_4)$, and as expected, this is the difference between the quadratic components for (y_1, y_2, y_3) and (y_2, y_3, y_4), i.e. $(y_2 - 2y_3 + y_4) - (y_1 - 2y_2 + y_3) = -y_1 + 3y_2 - 3y_3 + y_4$.

Table 8C·1

TABLE OF ORTHOGONAL POLYNOMIALS FOR THE LINEAR, QUADRATIC, AND CUBIC COMPONENTS FOR $n = 3$ to 6

Based on [8·3]

| $n = 3$ | | $n = 4$ | | | $n = 5$ | | | $n = 6$ | | |
| Linear | Quad-ratic | Linear | Quad-ratic | Cubic | Linear | Quad-ratic | Cubic | Linear | Quad-ratic | Cubic |
β'	γ'	β'	γ'	δ'	β'	γ'	δ'	β'	γ'	δ'
								-5	$+5$	-5
					-2	$+2$	-1	-3	-1	$+7$
		-3	$+1$	-1	-1	-1	$+2$	-1	-4	$+4$
-1	$+1$	-1	-1	$+3$	0	-2	0	$+1$	-4	-4
0	-2	$+1$	-1	-3	$+1$	-1	-2	$+3$	-1	-7
$+1$	$+1$	$+3$	$+1$	$+1$	$+2$	$+2$	$+1$	$+5$	$+5$	$+5$
J 2	6	20	4	20	10	14	10	70	84	180
K 1	3	2	1	$\frac{10}{3}$	1	1	$\frac{5}{6}$	2	$\frac{3}{2}$	$\frac{5}{3}$

DIVISORS FOR SUMS OF SQUARES IN AN ANALYSIS OF VARIANCE

8D·1. In an analysis of variance of a factorial experiment, and in other cases such as regression analysis, it is frequently required to determine the sums of squares and mean squares of quantities which are linear functions of the observations. In an $n \times m$ factorial design the sum of squares between rows or between columns is derived by first summing the squares of the totals (or means) of the rows of the columns. Again, when deriving the sum of squares of the components of interaction between two factors, e.g. linear B and A, the linear components of B for each level of A are calculated, squared, and totalled [§ 8·33 *et seq.*]. In a regression analysis the linear or any other component of the regression is a linear function of the observations, and it is necessary to know the correct divisor to use when calculating the sum of squares.

Briefly, for the square of any quantity which is a linear function of the observations the appropriate divisor is the sum of squares of the coefficients, this divisor being introduced so that all the mean squares are on a comparable basis with respect to the error variance.

In more detail, let $y_1, y_2, \ldots, y_n$ be n observations taken respectively at n levels of a continuous factor, e.g. the yield of a chemical preparation at different temperatures, and consider the linear function

$$Q_1 = a_1 y_1 + a_2 y_2 + \ldots + a_n y_n$$

where the a's are constants. Assume the error variance σ^2 is the same for all the y's and let its estimated value be s^2, based on ϕ degrees of freedom. The variance of Q_1 is

$$V(Q_1) = \Sigma a^2 \sigma^2$$

estimated by $\Sigma a^2 s^2$ [*S.M.*, § 3·71]. This simply means that if the observations are repeated at the same levels indefinitely and a value of Q is calculated for each replication, the variance of these values will tend to $\Sigma a^2 \sigma^2$. Accordingly if $V(Q_1)$ is divided by Σa^2 the result will be an estimate of σ^2. If it is required to test whether Q_1 differs significantly from zero, then we make the Null Hypothesis that the universe value of Q is zero. We have then one sample or one determination of Q, that is Q_1, with expected value zero, and an estimate of the variance of Q is then Q_1^2 based on one degree of freedom. The quantity $Q_1^2/\Sigma a^2$ will have σ^2 as its expected value, and a test of the Null Hypothesis is supplied by comparing $Q_1^2/\Sigma a^2$ with s^2 by means of the F-test with one and ϕ degrees of freedom. $Q_1^2/\Sigma a^2$ is also the sum of squares, whence it is seen that Q_1^2 has to be divided by the sum of squares of the coefficients of the observations in order that the resulting variance may have the same expectation as the error variance on the Null Hypothesis.

For appropriate values of the a's Q could represent the mean or the linear, quadratic, etc., components of the regression of y. The $(n-1)$ degrees of freedom between the n observations may be represented by the linear, quadratic, $\ldots$, $(n-1)$th power components; the square of each component is divided by the appropriate Σa^2 to give the corresponding sum of squares and the total of those sums of squares.

8D·2. Another problem which requires to be considered is based on an $m \times n$ factorial table as in Table 8D·1.

Table 8D·1

$m \times n$ FACTORIAL DESIGN

Level of factor A	Level of factor B				
	1	2	3	$\ldots$	n
1	y_{11}	y_{12}	y_{13}	$\ldots$	y_{1n}
2	y_{21}	y_{22}	y_{23}	$\ldots$	y_{2n}
3	y_{31}	y_{32}	y_{33}	$\ldots$	y_{3n}
.	.	.	.		.
.	.	.	.		.
.	.	.	.		.
m	y_{m1}	y_{m2}	y_{m3}	$\ldots$	y_{mn}

Suppose that Q is a particular component of factor B and that we wish to test the significance of Q and whether or not Q varies for different levels of A. We calculate Q for each level of A and obtain

$$Q_1 = a_1 y_{11} + a_2 y_{12} + a_3 y_{13} + \ldots + a_n y_{1n}$$
$$Q_2 = a_1 y_{21} + a_2 y_{22} + a_3 y_{23} + \ldots + a_n y_{2n}$$

.

.

.

$$Q_m = a_1 y_{m1} + a_2 y_{m2} + a_3 y_{m3} + \ldots + a_n y_{mn}$$

$$\text{Sum} = a_1 S_1 + a_2 S_2 + a_3 S_3 + \ldots + a_n S_n$$

where $S_j = \Sigma_i y_{ij}$.

To test Q_i for significance we simply compare $Q_i^2 / \Sigma a^2$ with the error variance. The average value of Q is

$$\bar{Q} = (a_1 S_1 + a_2 S_2 + \ldots + a_n S_n)/m$$

and to test this for significance we divide $\overline{Q}^2$ by the sum of squares of the coefficients of the observations. The coefficient of y_{ij} is a_j/m, and there are m observations with this value for the coefficient. The sum of squares of the coefficients is then $\Sigma a^2/m$ and the appropriate variance based on one degree of freedom is $m\overline{Q}^2/\Sigma a^2$. We could have taken the expression for the sum of the Q's instead of the mean, and this is usually more convenient in an analysis of variance. This would give $(\Sigma Q)^2/(m\Sigma a^2)$. Since $\overline{Q} = \Sigma Q/m$, the expressions are equivalent.

To test the significance of the variation between the Q_i's we could first calculate the actual variance between the Q's. Thus the sum of squares equals $(Q_1{}^2 + Q_2{}^2 + \ldots + Q_m{}^2) - (\Sigma Q)^2/m$ with $(m-1)$ degrees of freedom. Now each Q has a variance of $(\Sigma a^2)\sigma^2$, and on the assumption that the variation between the Q's is due to experimental error then the expectation of the variance between the Q's will be $\Sigma a^2\sigma^2$. To reduce this in order to give an expectation of σ^2 we must divide by (Σa^2), and we obtain the following sum of squares:

$$(Q_1{}^2 + Q_2{}^2 + \ldots + Q_m{}^2)/\Sigma a^2 - (\Sigma Q)^2/(m\Sigma a^2)$$

We note that the correction term is the same as that which would be used to test the significance of the mean value of Q_i.

In the most general case each Q_i will have a different set of a's, e.g.

$$Q_i = a_{i1}y_{i1} + a_{i2}y_{i2} + \ldots + a_{in}y_{in}$$

and the sum of squares between the Q's will then be

$$Q_1{}^2/\Sigma a_{1i}{}^2 + Q_2{}^2/\Sigma a_{2i}{}^2 + \ldots + Q_m{}^2/\Sigma a_{mi}{}^2 - (\Sigma Q_i)^2/\Sigma\Sigma a_{ij}{}^2$$

The divisors are seen to be the sums of squares of the coefficients of the observations in the corresponding linear expressions Q_i, or ΣQ_i.

In the simplest case all the a's are equal to ± 1, and the divisor for the sum of squares is equal to the number of observations.

Appendix 8E

DETAILS OF ANALYSIS OF THE RESULTS OF EXAMPLE 8·4

8E·1. The data for analysis are given in Table 8·37.

The steps in the overall analysis of variance are:
  (i) Total crude sum of squares $= 17\cdot6276$
      Correction due to mean $= 18\cdot531^2/20 = 17\cdot1699$
      Total corrected sum of squares $= 17\cdot6276 - 17\cdot1699 = 0\cdot4577$
  (ii) Corrected sum of squares between different sugars
      $= (3\cdot158^2 + 3\cdot864^2 + 3\cdot745^2 + 3\cdot992^2 + 3\cdot772^2)/4 - 18\cdot531^2/20$
      $= 17\cdot2731 - 17\cdot1699$
      $= 0\cdot1032$

(iii) Corrected sum of squares between concentrations
$$= (3 \cdot 672^2 + 4 \cdot 535^2 + 5 \cdot 101^2 + 5 \cdot 223^2)/5 - 18 \cdot 531^2/20$$
$$= 17 \cdot 4699 - 17 \cdot 1699 = 0 \cdot 3000$$

(iv) Interaction sum of squares
$$= 0 \cdot 4577 - 0 \cdot 1032 - 0 \cdot 3000 = 0 \cdot 0545.$$

This leads to the analysis of variance shown in Table 8·371.

8E·2. This is the analysis appropriate for qualitative factors, but since one of the factors—concentration of sugar—is quantitative, it is desirable to analyse its effect further into its linear, quadratic, and cubic components, and their interactions with the other factor. There are four concentrations, and the appropriate constants to use in the calculations of the various components are given in Table 8C·1. Denoting the observations at the four levels for any given sugar by y_1, y_2, y_3, and y_4 respectively, the various components are:

$$\text{Linear: } -3y_1 - y_2 + y_3 + 3y_4$$
$$\text{Quadratic: } y_1 - y_2 - y_3 + y_4$$
$$\text{Cubic: } -y_1 + 3y_2 - 3y_3 + y_4$$

Substituting in these expressions the observations of Table 8·37 for each sugar and for the totals over all sugars gives the results of Table 8·38.

The sums over the five sugars given in Table 8·38 agree exactly with the sum, linear, quadratic, and cubic components of the sums of the actual observations of Table 8·37, and this furnishes a complete check on the calculations up to this stage.

Calculation of sums of squares for main effect of quantitative factor

8E·3. The linear, quadratic, and cubic components of the main effects of concentration of sugar are given in the row marked "Sum" in Table 8·38. The contribution to the sum of squares for each component is the square of the component divided by the sum of squares of the coefficients of the observations [Appendix 8D]. The divisor for the linear component for each sugar is then 20, and that for the linear component of the main effect of concentration of sugar is 5×20, since the components of the main effect are derived by applying the polynomial constants to the sums over the five sugars. The divisors for the quadratic and cubic components are derived similarly. The sums of squares required for the main effect of concentration of sugar are therefore:

Sum of squares for linear component $\quad = 5 \cdot 219^2/(5 \times 20) \quad = 0 \cdot 2724$
Sum of squares for quadratic component $= (-0 \cdot 741)^2/(5 \times 4) = 0 \cdot 0275$
Sum of squares for cubic component $\quad = (-0 \cdot 147)^2/(5 \times 20) = 0 \cdot 0002$

These correspond to the three degrees of freedom for the main effect, i.e. between the means for the four levels; and the total of the three sums of squares is 0·3001, which, as expected, agrees within rounding-off errors with the corresponding sum of squares of Table 8·371. This provides a check on the calculations up to this stage.

Analysis of interaction

8E·4. The variation between the sums for each sugar given in column 2 of Table 8·38 represents the variation between sugars, and the corresponding sum of squares is given in Table 8·371. The linear component of the interaction between concentration and type of sugar is the variation between the quantities in column (3) of Table 8·38, and the corresponding sum of squares is the corrected sum of squares of those quantities divided by 20, this being the sum of squares of the coefficients of the observations in the linear component for each sugar. The sums of squares for the quadratic and cubic interactions are derived similarly. The various sums of squares are:

Component	Sum of squares
Linear ..	$[1·230^2 + 1·206^2 + 0·793^2 + 1·056^2 + 0·934^2 - 5·219^2/5]/20$ $= 0·0068$
Quadratic ..	$[(- 0·130)^2 + (- 0·184)^2 + (- 0·265)^2 + (- 0·038)^2$ $+ (- 0·124)^2 - (- 0·741)^2/5]/4 = 0·0070$
Cubic ..	$[(- 0·670)^2 + 0·482^2 + (- 0·199)^2 + 0·302^2 + (- 0·062)^2$ $- (- 0·147)^2/5]/20 = 0·0406.$

These exhaust all the degrees of freedom of the interaction between the two factors, and the sum of the sums of squares in the second column agrees, within rounding-off errors, with the total of the interaction sum of squares in Table 8·371.

The complete analysis of variance table is then as Table 8·39.

APPENDIX 8F

STATISTICAL ANALYSIS OF A 3^3 FACTORIAL DESIGN

8F·1. To save space, the data of Example 8·5 will be used to illustrate the methods of analysis appropriate to experiments both with and without replication for both qualitative and quantitative factors.

Table 8F·1 shows the table of the sums of the pairs of results of Table 8·61.

Table 8F·1

DATA FOR 3 × 3 × 3 FACTORIAL EXPERIMENT

Levels of factor C	Levels of factor N								
	n_0			n_1			n_2		
	Levels of factor V			Levels of factor V			Levels of factor V		
	v_0	v_1	v_2	v_0	v_1	v_2	v_0	v_1	v_2
c_0	159	25	184	260	98	237	146	103	195
c_1	395	255	363	454	422	362	417	455	492
c_2	149	251	378	112	270	363	150	172	278

In order to illustrate the method of analysis for an experiment without replication the entries of Table 8F·1 will be treated as the original observations.

Method for qualitative factors

8F·2. In the first place we will assume that the factors C, V, and N are qualitative and carry out the appropriate analysis. The steps in the analysis are as follows:

(i) Calculate total sum of squares about the mean:

Sum of all 27 observations   =   7145
Crude sum of squares   = 2,328,793
Correction for mean = $7145^2/27$ = 1,890,779.
Total sum of squares about mean =   438,014

(ii) Obtain the two-way table for each pair of factors by summing over the levels of the third factor.

Table 8F·2

C × V (8F·21)

	v_0	v_1	v_2	Sum
c_0	565	226	616	1,407
c_1	1,266	1,132	1,217	3,615
c_2	411	693	1,019	2,123
Sum	2,242	2,051	2,852	7,145

C × N (8F·22)

	n_0	n_1	n_2	Sum
c_0	368	595	444	1,407
c_1	1,013	1,238	1,364	3,615
c_2	778	745	600	2,123
Sum	2,159	2,578	2,408	7,145

A2

Table 8F·2 (continued)

V × N (8F·23)

	n_0	n_1	n_2	Sum
v_0	703	826	713	2,242
v_1	531	790	730	2,051
v_2	925	962	965	2,852
Sum	2,159	2,578	2,408	7,145

(iii) For each table separately calculate the total sum of squares of the 9 entries about the grand mean. Note that each entry is the sum of three observations, so that the sums of squares must therefore be divided by 3.

For C × V (Table 8F·21):

Crude total sum of squares $= (565^2 + 226^2 + \ldots + 1019^2)/3$
$= 6{,}802{,}557/3 = 2{,}267{,}519$

Correction for mean $= 1{,}890{,}779$

Total sum of squares of
C × V table about mean $= 376{,}740$

Similarly, the total sum of squares of C × N table about mean $= 317{,}955$

and the total sum of squares of V × N table about mean $= 54{,}591$

(iv) Calculate sums of squares for the main effects.

From the C × V table, the sums over c_0, c_1, and c_2 are respectively 1407, 3615, and 2123. The crude sum of squares for C is 1/9 times the sum of squares of these three totals. Subtracting the correction for the mean gives the sum of squares for the main effect of C. The results obtained for C, V, and N are:

Sum of squares for C $= 2{,}172{,}778 - 1{,}890{,}779 = 281{,}999$

Sum of squares for V $= 1{,}929{,}674 - 1{,}890{,}779 = 38{,}895$

Sum of squares for N $= 1{,}900{,}648 - 1{,}890{,}779 = 9{,}869$

(v) Calculate the sums of squares for the interactions between the pairs of factors.

These are obtained by difference. Thus the C × V interaction sum of squares is obtained by subtracting from the total sum of squares for the C × V table the sum of squares for the main effects of C and V.

Interaction sum of squares for $= 376{,}740 - 281{,}999 - 38{,}895$
$\quad$ C × V $\qquad\qquad\qquad\qquad\qquad = 55{,}846$
Interaction sum of squares for $= 317{,}955 - 281{,}999 - 9869$
$\quad$ C × N $\qquad\qquad\qquad\qquad\qquad = 26{,}087$
Interaction sum of squares for $= 54{,}591 - 38{,}895 - 9869$
$\quad$ V × N $\qquad\qquad\qquad\qquad\qquad = 5827$

(vi) Calculate the sum of squares for the three-factor interaction.

This is obtained by subtracting from the total sum of squares about the mean of all 27 observations all sums of squares for the main effects and two-factor interactions.

(vii) Construct the analysis of variance table as Table 8F·3.

Table 8F·3

ANALYSIS OF VARIANCE OF 3^3 DESIGN: BOTH FACTORS CONSIDERED QUALITATIVE

Source of variation	Sum of squares	Degrees of freedom	Mean square	Variance ratio
Main effects:				
C	281,999	2	141,000	57·9
V	38,895	2	19,448	7·98
N	9,869	2	4,935	2·03
Two-factor interactions:				
C × V	55,846	4	13,962	5·73
C × N	26,087	4	6,522	2·68
V × N	5,827	4	1,457	0·60
Three-factor interaction:				
C × V × N	19,491	8	2,436	
Total	438,014	26		

Method for quantitative factors: without replication

8F·3. The factors in this example are in fact quantitative, the levels being equally spaced. The appropriate analysis is as follows. Carry out the full analysis for qualitative factors as in the previous section. The additional calculations required are for the linear and quadratic components and their interactions.

We apply the coefficients of Table 8·54 to each two-way table in turn in Table 8F·2. For example, to calculate $L_C L_V$ we use the two-way table (Table 8F·21), and applying the multipliers to the entries of this table we obtain

$$(1 \times 565 + 0 \times 226 - 1 \times 616) + (0 \times 1266 + 0 \times 1132$$
$$+ 0 \times 1217) + (-1 \times 411 + 0 \times 693 + 1 \times 1019) = +557$$

The contribution to the sum of squares is obtained by squaring 557 and dividing by the sum of squares of the coefficients multiplied by the number of observations in each result of the two-way table, i.e. by the divisor of Table 8·54, which for $L_C L_V$ is $4 \times 3 = 12$. The contribution to the sum of squares is then $557^2/12 = 25,854$.

For $Q_C \times Q_V$ we obtain

$$(1 \times 565 - 2 \times 226 + 1 \times 616) + (-2 \times 1266 + 4 \times 1132$$
$$- 2 \times 1217) + (1 \times 411 - 2 \times 693 + 1 \times 1019) = +335$$

and the contribution to the sum of squares is $335^2/(36 \times 3) = 1039$.

The results are tabulated in Tables 8F·4 to 8F·6.

Table 8F·4

MAIN EFFECTS

Factor	Linear component	Quadratic component	Sum of squares Linear component	Sum of squares Quadratic component	Total of sum of squares
C	716	− 3,700	28,481	253,519	282,000
V	610	+ 992	20,672	18,223	38,895
N	249	− 589	3,445	6,424	9,869

Table 8F·5

COMPONENTS OF INTERACTION

Interaction AB	$L_A L_B$	$Q_A L_B$	$L_A Q_B$	$Q_A Q_B$
CV	557	757	− 685	335
CN	− 254	− 804	266	− 292
VN	30	− 348	202	368

Table 8F·6

CONTRIBUTIONS TO SUM OF SQUARES

Interaction AB	$L_A L_B$	$Q_A L_B$	$L_A Q_B$	$Q_A Q_B$	Total
CV	25,854	15,918	13,034	1,039	55,845
CN	5,376	17,956	1,965	789	26,086
VN	75	3,364	1,133	1,254	5,826

We note that the totals agree within rounding-off errors with the sum of squares of Table 8F·3. This provides a check.

It is not usually required to separate the three-factor interactions. The total is given in Table 8F·3. The complete analysis of variance table may now be constructed as Table 8F·7.

Table 8F·7

COMPLETE ANALYSIS OF VARIANCE OF TABLE 8F·1

Source of variation	Sum of squares	Degrees of freedom	Mean square	Variance ratio
Main effects:				
C $\{$ Linear	28,481	1		11·69†
C $\{$ Quadratic	253,519	1		104·07†
V $\{$ Linear	20,672	1		8·49*
V $\{$ Quadratic	18,223	1		7·48*
N $\{$ Linear	3,445	1		1·41
N $\{$ Quadratic	6,424	1		2·64
Two-factor interactions:				
$L_C L_V$	25,854	1		10·61*
$Q_C L_V$	15,918	1		6·53*
$L_C Q_V$	13,034	1		5·35*
$Q_C Q_V$	1,039	1		0·43
$L_C L_N$	5,376	1		2·21
$Q_C L_N$	17,956	1		7·37*
$L_C Q_N$	1,965	1		0·81
$Q_C Q_N$	789	1		0·32
$L_V L_N$	75	1		0·03
$Q_V L_N$	3,364	1		1·38
$L_V Q_N$	1,133	1		0·47
$Q_V Q_N$	1,254	1		0·51
Three-factor interactions	19,491	8	2,436	
Total	438,012	26		

* Significant, $1\% < P \leqslant 5\%$.   † Highly significant, $P \leqslant 1\%$.

Analysis of 3^3 factorial design with replications

8F·4. Table 8·61 is an example of a 3^3 factorial design with two replications. The data of this table will be used to illustrate step by step the method of analysis.

Qualitative factors

(i) Sum over the two replicates, i.e. the pairs of values for each set of conditions, and form Table 8F·1. The first stage of the analysis is similar to that given in § **8F·2**, the only difference being that since each result is now the sum of two observations it is necessary to divide the crude sum of squares corresponding to each effect by 2. The result will be the analysis of variance Table 8F·3, in which each sum of squares and mean square is divided by 2.

(ii) Calculate the total sum of squares of all 54 observations about the mean:

$$\begin{array}{ll}
\text{Sum of all 54 observations of Table 8·61} & = \quad\ \ 7{,}145 \\
\text{Crude sum of squares of all 54 observations} & = 1{,}185{,}435 \\
\text{Correction for the mean} = 7145^2/54 & = \quad 945{,}389 \\
\hline
\text{Total sum of squares about mean} & = \quad 240{,}046
\end{array}$$

(iii) Calculate the sum of squares for error.

This is the sum of squares within groups, i.e. within duplicates, and may be derived by subtraction from the total sum of squares.

(iv) Construct the analysis of variance table.

Table 8F·8

ANALYSIS OF VARIANCE FOR 3^3 DESIGN WITH REPLICATIONS: BOTH FACTORS CONSIDERED QUALITATIVE

Source of variation	Sum of squares	Degrees of freedom	Mean square	Variance ratio
Main effects:				
C	141,000	2	70,500	90·5
V	19,448	2	9,724	12·5
N	4,935	2	2,468	3·2
Two-factor interactions:				
C × V	27,923	4	6,981	9·0
C × N	13,044	4	3,261	4·2
V × N	2,914	4	729	0·9
Three-factor interactions:				
C × V × N	9,746	8	1,218	1·6
Remainder = error ..	21,036	27	779	
Total	240,046	53		

Interpretation

8F·5. The three-factor interaction is not statistically significant, but all other effects, apart from V × N, are. The dependence of yield on these factors must therefore be examined by means of the two-way tables C × V and C × N.

All factors quantitative

8F·6. The analysis will be as given in Table 8F·7 but with the sums of squares and mean squares divided by 2. In addition there will be the remainder or error variance as given in Table 8F·8.

Detailed analysis of the interaction of Table 8F·1 when the factors are regarded as qualitative*

8F·7. The purpose of this analysis is to show how to calculate the I- and J-components [Chapter 5] of the two-factor interactions, and also the W, X, Y, and Z components of the three-factor interactions. We will treat the figures of Table 8F·1 as individual observations.

Interaction C × V

To calculate this we refer to Table 8F·21. The I-components are

$$i_0 = \;\;565 + 1132 + 1019 = 2716$$
$$i_1 = 1266 + \;\;693 + \;\;616 = 2575$$
$$i_2 = \;\;411 + \;\;226 + 1217 = 1854$$

The sum of squares for the I-component of the interaction is

$$(2716^2 + 2575^2 + 1854^2)/9 - 7145^2/27 = 1{,}938{,}289 - 1{,}890{,}779 = 47{,}510$$

We divide the squares of each i by 9 because each i represents the sum of 9 observations of Table 8F·1.

The J-components are

$$j_0 = \;\;565 + \;\;693 + 1217 = 2475$$
$$j_1 = 1266 + \;\;226 + 1019 = 2511$$
$$j_2 = \;\;411 + 1132 + \;\;616 = 2159$$

The sum of squares for the J-component of the interaction is

$$(2475^2 + 2511^2 + 2159^2)/9 - 7145^2/27 = 1{,}899{,}114 - 1{,}890{,}779 = 8335$$

The total of the sums of squares for the I- and J-components of C and V is 55,845, which agrees within rounding-off errors with the figure given in Table 8F·3.

---

* This should be read after Chapter 9.

Interaction C × N

Refer to Table 8F·22. The I-components are

$$i_0 = \;\; 368 + 1238 + \;\; 600 = 2206$$
$$i_1 = 1013 + \;\; 745 + \;\; 444 = 2202$$
$$i_2 = \;\; 778 + \;\; 595 + 1364 = 2737$$

The sum of squares for the I-components of interaction C × N is

$$(2206^2 + 2202^2 + 2737^2)/9 - 7145^2/27 = 1{,}911{,}823 - 1{,}890{,}779 = 21{,}044$$

The J-components are

$$j_0 = \;\; 368 + \;\; 745 + 1364 = 2477$$
$$j_1 = 1013 + \;\; 595 + \;\; 600 = 2208$$
$$j_2 = \;\; 778 + 1238 + \;\; 444 = 2460$$

The corresponding sum of squares is

$$(2477^2 + 2208^2 + 2460^2)/9 - 7145^2/27 = 1{,}895{,}821 - 1{,}890{,}779 = 5042$$

The total sum of squares for the I- and J-components $= 26{,}086$, which agrees within rounding-off errors with the result of Table 8F·3.

Interaction V × N

Refer to Table 8F·23. The I-components are

$$i_0 = 703 + 790 + 965 = 2458$$
$$i_1 = 531 + 962 + 713 = 2206$$
$$i_2 = 925 + 826 + 730 = 2481$$

The sum of squares is

$$(2458^2 + 2206^2 + 2481^2)/9 - 7145^2/27 = 1{,}895{,}951 - 1{,}890{,}779 = 5172$$

The J-components are

$$j_0 = 703 + 962 + 730 = 2395$$
$$j_1 = 531 + 826 + 965 = 2322$$
$$j_2 = 925 + 790 + 713 = 2428$$

The sum of squares is

$$(2395^2 + 2322^2 + 2428^2)/9 - 7145^2/27 = 1{,}891{,}433 - 1{,}890{,}779 = 654$$

The total sum of squares due to the I- and J-components is 5826, which agrees within rounding-off errors with the result of Table 8F·3.

Calculation of the three-factor interactions

The first step is to calculate the I- and J-totals for C × V for each level of N in Table 8F·1. For instance, the first set of nine observations is a two-way table for factors C and V at the zero level of factor N. The i- and j-components of this table are:

$$i_0 = 159 + 255 + 378 = 792$$
$$i_1 = 395 + 251 + 184 = 830$$
$$i_2 = 149 + 25 + 363 = 537$$
$$j_0 = 159 + 251 + 363 = 773$$
$$j_1 = 395 + 25 + 378 = 798$$
$$j_2 = 149 + 255 + 184 = 588$$

Similarly for the interaction $C \times V$ at n_1:

$$i_0 = 260 + 422 + 363 = 1045$$
$$i_1 = 454 + 270 + 237 = 961$$
$$i_2 = 112 + 98 + 362 = 572$$
$$j_0 = 260 + 270 + 362 = 892$$
$$j_1 = 454 + 98 + 363 = 915$$
$$j_2 = 112 + 422 + 237 = 771$$

Again for the interaction $C \times V$ at n_2:

$$i_0 = 146 + 455 + 278 = 879$$
$$i_1 = 417 + 172 + 195 = 784$$
$$i_2 = 150 + 103 + 492 = 745$$
$$j_0 = 146 + 172 + 492 = 810$$
$$j_1 = 417 + 103 + 278 = 798$$
$$j_2 = 150 + 455 + 195 = 800$$

The next step is to arrange the i's and j's in the form of two 3×3 tables as Table 8F·9.

Table 8F·9

THE I- AND J-COMPONENTS OF INTERACTION $C \times V$ FOR EACH LEVEL OF N

Table A					Table B			
	Level of N			Sum		Level of N			Sum
	0	1	2	Sum		0	1	2	Sum
i_0	792	1,045	879	2,716	j_0	773	892	810	2,475
i_1	830	961	784	2,575	j_1	798	915	798	2,511
i_2	537	572	745	1,854	j_2	588	771	800	2,159
Sum	2,159	2,578	2,408	7,145	Sum	2,159	2,578	2,408	7,145

We note that the row totals agree with the components for the interaction C × V calculated above. The column totals are the totals for n_0, n_1, and n_2, which agree with the column totals in Table 8F·22.

Table 8F·9 consists of two 3 × 3 tables, and we may calculate the I- and J-components of these tables in the usual way. Denoting the left-hand table by A and the right-hand table by B, we obtain:

Table A

I-components

$$i_0 = \ \ 792 + 961 + 745 = 2498$$
$$i_1 = 1045 + 784 + 537 = 2366$$
$$i_2 = \ \ 879 + 830 + 572 = 2281$$

J-components

$$j_0 = \ \ 792 + 784 + 572 = 2148$$
$$j_1 = 1045 + 830 + 745 = 2620$$
$$j_2 = \ \ 879 + 961 + 537 = 2377$$

Table B

I-components

$$i_0 = 773 + 915 + 800 = 2488$$
$$i_1 = 892 + 798 + 588 = 2278$$
$$i_2 = 810 + 798 + 771 = 2379$$

J-components

$$j_0 = 773 + 798 + 771 = 2342$$
$$j_1 = 892 + 798 + 800 = 2490$$
$$j_2 = 810 + 915 + 588 = 2313$$

Table A is a table of the I-components of interaction C × V for each level of N and may be written as $I[(CV) \times N]$. The I- and J-components of this table are in fact the W- and X-interactions, that is:

$$I[I(CV) \times N] = W(CVN)$$
$$J[I(CV) \times N] = X(CVN)$$

Table B is a table of the J-components of the interaction C × V for each level of N and may be written as $J[(CV) \times N]$. The I- and J-components of this table are the Y- and Z-interactions, that is:

$$I[J(CV) \times N] = Y(CVN)$$
$$J[J(CV) \times N] = Z(CVN)$$

The sum of squares for these may be calculated in the usual way from the I- and J-totals, and this gives:

$$\text{Sum of squares of } W(\text{CVN}) = 2{,}657$$
$$\text{Sum of squares of } X(\text{CVN}) = 12{,}380$$
$$\text{Sum of squares of } Y(\text{CVN}) = 2{,}451$$
$$\text{Sum of squares of } Z(\text{CVN}) = 2{,}002$$

The total of these sums of squares is 19,490, which agrees within rounding-off errors with the result given in Table 8F·3.

APPENDIX 8G

SYSTEMATIC METHOD FOR THE ANALYSIS OF A 3^n DESIGN WHEN ALL FACTORS ARE QUANTITATIVE AND THE LEVELS OF EACH FACTOR ARE EQUALLY SPACED

THE method will be illustrated on the 3^3 design of Example 8·5, which for this purpose will be treated as an experiment without replication.

The factors are denoted by C, V, and N and (for this purpose) the three levels by (1), c_1, c_2; (1), v_1, v_2; (1), n_1, n_2 respectively (*cf.* Table 8F·1).

The 27 treatment combinations are written down in the order given in column (1) of Table 8G·1 below. This order is known as the standard order for the application of the systematic method of analysis. The standard order for one factor C, involving three treatment combinations, is

$$(1), c_1, c_2 \quad \dots\dots\dots\dots\dots\dots\dots\dots\dots(8G\cdot1)$$

corresponding to the first three entries in column (1) of Table 8G·1. For two factors there are nine treatment combinations, and to introduce the second factor V with levels (1), v_1, v_2, two more sets of three formed by multiplying sequence $(8G\cdot1)$ above by v_1 and v_2 respectively all in the same order are added. The resulting nine treatment combinations

$$(1), c_1, c_2, v_1, c_1v_1, c_2v_1, v_2, c_1v_2, c_2v_2 \quad \dots\dots\dots(8G\cdot2)$$

correspond to the first 9 entries in column (1) of Table 8G·1.

For three factors there are 27 treatment combinations, and the third factor N, with levels (1), n_1, and n_2, is introduced by adding to sequence $(8G\cdot2)$ two further sets of nine treatment combinations obtained by multiplying these treatment combinations by n_1 and n_2, again retaining the same order. The 27 treatment combinations correspond in order to those given in column (1) of Table 8G·1.

The extension to four or more factors is obvious.

The systematic method for the calculation of the effects and their sums of squares which will now be described is a simple extension of the method introduced by YATES for 2^n factorial designs. For 3^n designs the observations in the standard order are regarded as consecutive sets of three (see Table 8G·1), and the method consists of performing three operations on each set:

(i) Form the sum $(y_1 + y_2 + y_3)$

(ii) Form the difference $(y_3 - y_1)$ (this corresponds to the slope)

(iii) Form the expression $(y_1 - 2y_2 + y_3)$ (this corresponds to the curvature)

where y_1, y_2, and y_3 correspond to the three observations of a set.

The method will now be illustrated on the data of Example 8·5. Column (1) of Table 8G·1 gives the treatment combinations in standard order, and column (2) gives the corresponding responses. Divide these into successive sets of three as shown. Column (3) is made up of three sets of entries derived from column (2), the first set being the sums of the consecutive sets of three of column (2). The first entry is thus $159 + 395 + 149 = 703$, the second is $25 + 255 + 251 = 531$, and so on. This process is continued until the first third (in this case nine) of the entries in column (3) is completed, covering all the sets of three in column (2). The second set of nine entries in column (3) is formed by taking the first observation from the third in each set of three in column (2). For example, the tenth entry is $149 - 159 = -10$, the eleventh is $251 - 25 = 226$, and so on. The last set of nine entries is formed by taking the sum of the first and third minus twice the second for each set of three in column (2). For example, the nineteenth entry is $159 + 149 - (2 \times 395) = -482$, the twentieth is $25 + 251 - (2 \times 255) = -234$, and so on. Column (4) is derived from column (3) in exactly the same way as column (3) is derived from column (2), that is, column (3) is divided into consecutive sets of three; the first set of nine entries in column (4) represents the sums of the sets of three in column (3); the second set of nine entries represents the differences between the first and the third in each set of column (3); and finally the last set of nine entries represents the sums of the first and last minus twice the middle observation in each set.

Column (5) is also derived from column (4) in the same way. This operation is repeated as many times as there are factors, in this case three, so that we end at column (5).

The first entry in column (5) (viz. 7145) is the sum of the 27 responses of column (2). Similarly all other entries correspond to the main effects and interactions, which are identified by substituting capital letters for the small letters in column (1), with suffix 1 corresponding to linear and suffix 2 to quadratic effects. For example, the entry in column (5) opposite $c_2v_2n_1$ in column (1) is the interaction quadratic C $\times$ quadratic V $\times$ linear N (or $C_2V_2N_1$ for short).

All the entries in column (5) are linear functions of the responses of column (2), and therefore to calculate the sum of squares for any main effect or interaction, the square of the appropriate entry in column (5) must be divided by the sum of squares of the coefficients of the responses contributing to the effect. It can be shown that this divisor is given by the formula

$$\text{Divisor} = 2^m \, 3^{n-p} \quad \dots\dots\dots\dots\dots\dots (8G\cdot3)$$

where m = order of interaction, e.g. for two-factor interactions $m = 2$,

$\quad p$ = number of linear terms in the interaction,

$\quad n$ = number of factors examined.

For the interaction linear C × quadratic V × linear N (i.e. $C_1 V_2 N_1$), $m = 3$, $p = 2$, and $n = 3$, and the divisor is $2^3 \times 3^{3-2} = 8 \times 3 = 24$.

These divisors are given in column (6) of Table 8G·1, and the sums of squares for the effects in column (7) are formed by taking the squares of the appropriate entries in column (5) and dividing by the divisors shown in column (6). As each of these sums of squares is based on one degree of freedom column (7) will also give the mean square.

Since the total corrected sum of squares of the original responses given in column (2) should agree with the total sum of squares of column (7), a check on the computations is readily available.

In this example:

Crude sum of squares of column (2) = 2,328,793

Correction = $7145^2/27$ = 1,890,779

Corrected sum of squares   =   438,014

Sum of column (7)   =   438,012

This agrees within rounding-off errors.

If an intermediate check is required for columns (2)–(5), then the following can be done quite simply:

For each column form the quantities S_1, S_2, S_3, X, and Y,

where S_1 = sum of the 1st, 4th, 7th, . . . entries,

$\quad S_2$ = sum of the 2nd, 5th, 8th, . . . entries,

$\quad S_3$ = sum of the 3rd, 6th, 9th, . . . entries,

$\quad X = S_1 + S_2 + S_3$,

$\quad Y = S_1 - S_2 + 3S_3$

Then Y in column $(k-1) = X$ in column (k), e.g. Y in column (3) $= X$ in column (4).

If the treatment combinations have been replicated r times, then the entries in column (2) will be the sums of the r observations for each set of conditions, and the method of analysis differs only in that the divisor for the sum of squares becomes

$$\text{Divisor} = 2^m \, 3^{n-p} r$$

where r is the number of replicates.

Table 8G·1

				Column				
(1)	(2)	(3)	(4)	(5)	Effect	(6)	(7)
(1)	159	703	2,159	7,145	(T)		
c_1	395	531	2,578	716	(C_1)	18	28,481
c_2	149	925	2,408	− 3,700	(C_2)	54	253,519
v_1	25	826	410	610	(V_1)	18	20,672
c_1v_1	255	790	150	557	(C_1V_1)	12	25,854
c_2v_1	251	962	156	757	(C_2V_1)	36	15,918
v_2	184	713	− 880	992	(V_2)	54	18,223
c_1v_2	363	730	− 1,136	− 685	(C_1V_2)	36	13,034
c_2v_2	378	965	− 1,684	335	(C_2V_2)	108	1,039
n_1	260	− 10	222	249	(N_1)	18	3,445
c_1n_1	454	226	136	− 254	(C_1N_1)	12	5,376
c_2n_1	112	194	252	− 804	(C_2N_1)	36	17,956
v_1n_1	98	− 148	204	30	(V_1N_1)	12	75
$c_1v_1n_1$	422	172	274	− 125	$(C_1V_1N_1)$	8	1,953
$c_2v_1n_1$	270	126	79	− 291	$(C_2V_1N_1)$	24	3,528
v_2n_1	237	4	318	− 348	(V_2N_1)	36	3,364
$c_1v_2n_1$	362	69	412	217	$(C_1V_2N_1)$	24	1,962
$c_2v_2n_1$	363	83	27	399	$(C_2V_2N_1)$	72	2,211
n_2	146	− 482	566	− 589	(N_2)	54	6,424
c_1n_2	417	− 234	208	266	(C_1N_2)	36	1,965
c_2n_2	150	− 164	218	− 292	(C_2N_2)	108	789
v_1n_2	103	− 536	− 268	202	(V_1N_2)	36	1,133
$c_1v_1n_2$	455	− 476	− 366	− 265	$(C_1V_1N_2)$	24	2,926
$c_2v_1n_2$	172	− 124	− 51	− 479	$(C_2V_1N_2)$	72	3,187
v_2n_2	195	− 538	− 178	368	(V_2N_2)	108	1,254
$c_1v_2n_2$	492	− 635	292	413	$(C_1V_2N_2)$	72	2,369
$c_2v_2n_2$	278	− 511	221	− 541	$(C_2V_2N_2)$	216	1,355
S_1	1,407	532	2,553	8,659			
S_2	3,615	1,173	2,548	840			
S_3	2,123	2,456	1,626	− 4,616			
X	7,145	4,161	6,727	4,883			
Y	4,161	6,727	4,883				

CHAPTER 9

CONFOUNDING IN FACTORIAL DESIGNS

FACTORIAL EXPERIMENTATION WHEN UNIFORM CONDITIONS CANNOT BE MAINTAINED THROUGHOUT THE EXPERIMENT

WHEN three or more factors are investigated simultaneously the appropriate factorial design may be larger than can be carried out under uniform conditions, say, on one homogeneous batch of raw material, or on one plant unit in a reasonably short time. This chapter describes the most efficient way of dealing with this situation, which is to divide the experimental data into smaller blocks in a particular manner, such that the main effects of the factors and their more important interactions are investigated under uniform conditions; while the heterogeneity introduced in consequence of the size of the experiment is allowed to affect only interactions which are likely to be unimportant. Experimental designs for achieving this object are explained for experiments in which the factors are to be investigated at two or at three levels, and a tabulated list of designs sufficient to cover most industrial requirements is given in an appendix.

Introduction

9·1. When a number of treatments are to be compared it is obvious that the comparisons should be carried out under conditions which are as nearly alike as practicable, because any extraneous variation will add to the experimental error. A plant-scale experiment designed to compare the effect of a number of changes in reaction conditions on the yield or quality of a chemical product may well consume a large quantity of materials representing several deliveries from different makes. Different deliveries or makes of raw materials are seldom of the same quality; variations arise which, although commercially unimportant, are nevertheless undesirable for experimental work, since they increase the experimental error and consequently decrease the discrimination of the experiment. Care must therefore be taken that variations in the deliveries of raw material do not vitiate the conclusions to be drawn.

Suppose four deliveries of raw materials are involved in the whole experiment and it is desired to assess the effect of four different temperatures on the yield of the product, then if all batches of product at one temperature are made from one delivery, all batches at another temperature are made from another delivery, and so on, the comparison between the yields at the four temperatures will be confused with the effects of the differing qualities of the raw

367

materials. An elementary precaution is to randomise completely the order of the batches with respect to deliveries; this at least will not vitiate the comparison between the factors examined but it has the disadvantage of inflating the experimental error due to the variation in quality of raw materials. There are however other and more efficient means of overcoming this kind of difficulty, particularly when the experiment involves a large number of comparisons some of which are more important than others; and if the experiment can be arranged in such a way as to ensure that only unimportant comparisons are confused with the variation between the deliveries of raw material, then the remaining more important comparisons, being freed from the error due to variations between the deliveries, may be assessed with greater precision.

Confounding

9·11. The process by which unimportant comparisons are deliberately confused for the purpose of assessing the more important comparisons with greater precision is called Confounding, and confounding is required in factorial experiments in which the number of observations capable of being carried out under strictly comparable conditions is less than the number required for the whole design. A similar situation has already been encountered in Chapter 6 in a varietal trial for which the size of block could not accommodate all the varieties to be compared; the solution there lay in the use of balanced or semi-balanced incomplete block designs. The method of incomplete blocks, although applicable in theory, is usually impracticable for factorial designs because it requires an excessive number of replicates. The solution for factorial designs consists in finding systematic methods of confounding particular unimportant comparisons with unavoidable differences between batches of raw material. Before explaining the general principles of confounding and describing the situations in which it is used, a simple illustration and a practical example will be given.

Simple illustration of confounding

9·111. A production department investigating a batch chemical process on the plant scale wishes to determine the effect on yield of certain changes in reaction conditions, for instance, specific departures from normal temperature, normal time of reaction, and normal rate of agitation. Denote these three factors in the usual way by A, B, and C, the normal condition by (1), and the new conditions by a, b, and c respectively. To examine all combinations of these factors would require the 2^3 factorial design of Table 9·1.

If the base material used in the chemical process is made by a batch process, the quality of that material will vary from one batch to the next, producing consequential variations in the yield and/or quality of the product. The variation may be reduced by blending several batches of the base material, and

Table 9·1

2³ FACTORIAL DESIGN

		Level of factor C			
		(1)		(c)	
		Level of factor B		Level of factor B	
		(1)	b	(1)	b
Level of	(1)	(1)	b	c	bc
factor					
A	a	a	ab	ac	abc

it will be effectively eliminated if the blend can be made large enough to supply sufficient base material of uniform quality for the whole experiment. However, blending on this scale may not be practicable. Assume it is convenient to obtain (by blending if necessary) the material in uniform lots, each sufficient to make four batches of the product, then the above factorial design based on eight batches will require two lots of base material. The problem is to determine the best arrangement for the experiment, that is, which particular four batches to make from each of the respective lots of raw material. If the four batches denoted in Table 9·1 by (1), a, c, and ac (at the lower level of factor B) are made from one lot, and the other four batches denoted by b, ab, bc, and abc (at the higher level of factor B) are made from the second lot, then the effect of factor B (time of reaction), measured by the difference between the mean of the four batches from lot 1 and the mean of the four batches from lot 2, will be confounded with the difference between the two lots. In other words, if the two lots differ in quality to such an extent as to produce an appreciable difference in yield, then this difference will be included in the effect of B, as shown below:

Lot 1	*Lot* 2
(1)	$b + X$
a	$ab + X$
c	$bc + X$
ac	$abc + X$

where the small letters denote the responses to the treatment combinations and X denotes the contribution due to the difference between the lots. The difference between the means of the four observations of lot 2 and the four observations of lot 1 then measures $B + X$; in other words, B is confounded with X. All the other effects, A, C, AB, AC, BC, and ABC, are clear of the difference between the lots. For instance, A is given by the difference between the mean of the observations containing a and the mean of the observations not containing a, viz.

$$\tfrac{1}{4}[(ab + X) + (abc + X) + a + ac] - \tfrac{1}{4}[(b + X) + (bc + X) + (1) + c]$$

in which the X's cancel and the expression reduces to the usual form for A [§ 7·44]. Similarly, the interaction AB is given by

$$\tfrac{1}{4}[(abc + X) + (ab + X) + (1) + c] - \tfrac{1}{4}[(bc + X) + (b + X) + ac + a]$$

where the X's again cancel and the expression reduces to the usual form for AB.

By suitable rearrangement any other effect may be confounded, and when any one effect is confounded all the other effects are clear of the difference between lots. The effect confounded with lots is either lost or determined with a lower degree of precision than the other effects, and since the experimenter is free to choose any one effect to confound he naturally chooses the least important, which in this case is likely to be the highest-order interaction ABC. All that remains then is to divide the eight treatments of the factorial design into two lots of four in such a manner that the comparison between lots corresponds to the three-factor interaction. One way of doing this is to express the interaction in algebraic form [§ 7·44], that is:

$$ABC = \tfrac{1}{4}(a - 1)(b - 1)(c - 1)$$

Expanding this expression, the interaction is obtained as a difference between two lots of four observations, viz.

$$\tfrac{1}{4}[(a + b + c + abc) - (ab + bc + ac + (1))]$$

In order therefore to confound the three-factor interaction, the four batches denoted by a, b, c, and abc must be made with one lot of base material, and the other four batches denoted by ab, bc, ac, and (1) with the other; the difference between lots then corresponds to the confounded three-factor interaction. The actual design is shown in Table 9·11.

Table 9·11

PARTITION OF THE 2^3 FACTORIAL DESIGN CONFOUNDING ABC

Made from lot 1 of base material		Made from lot 2 of base material	
(1)	ac	c	a
bc	ab	b	abc

It may be verified that with the exception of the three-factor interaction all effects are clear of the difference between the two lots, for, denoting as before the responses of the treatment combinations by the small letters and adding X to the elements from lot 2 to indicate the difference between the two lots, the quantity X will cancel in the expressions for the main effects and all two-factor interactions, e.g.

$$\text{Interaction } AB = \tfrac{1}{4}[\{(1) + ab + (c + X) + (abc + X)\} \\ - \{(a + X) + (b + X) + ac + bc\}]$$

where it is seen that X cancels.

9·12. The assumption involved in the design of Table 9·11 is that no appreciable interactions exist between the effects and the lots of base material; in other words, if a particular treatment combination produces a given improvement with one lot, then, apart from experimental error, it will produce an equivalent improvement with the other. The assumption is usually justified, first because the extent of variation in the quality of normal batches made by the same chemical process should not be large, and next because the nature of this variation in quality is not usually such as to involve interactions with the factors under investigation. Clearly each type of investigation has to be considered on its merits.

By confounding the three-factor interaction with the two lots of base material (called blocks) it has been possible to reduce the error in the assessment of the other and more important effects. When the three-factor interaction may be assumed negligible, the difference recorded between the blocks measures the effect of the difference in quality between the two lots of base material, and this information may well be important. If, for instance, the difference between lots shown by the experiment appeared large relative to the effects of the factors under investigation, it would indicate that a closer study of the effect of the quality of base material would be worth while, with the object of improving the quality and consistency of the product.

Analysis of variance

9·13. The analysis of variance table takes the form of Table 9·12.

If it is necessary to rely on the experiment to supply its own estimate of error the two-factor interactions must be combined for this purpose. In such circumstances it is clear that an experiment on this small scale will only be carried out when no interaction is likely to be appreciable and when the experimenter is interested only in relatively large main effects. In most plant-scale experiments relating to improvements in works processes an estimate of the variance due to experimental error, i.e. the variance due solely to the operation of the process, can usually be obtained from an examination of previous performance, since it should be possible from past records to

Table 9·12

ANALYSIS OF VARIANCE OF TABLE 9·11

Source of variation	Degrees of freedom
Main effects:	
A	1
B	1
C	1
Two-factor interactions:	
AB	1
AC	1
BC	1
Between lots 1 and 2 .. (= ABC interaction)	1
Total	7

pick out sufficient cases in which two or more batches of the product have been made from uniform qualities of base material. Alternatively, by means of the control-chart technique applied to the plant records [*S.M.*, Chapter 10] it is usually possible to obtain an estimate of the variation produced by the operation of the process alone, clear of variations imposed by different qualities of intermediates. A knowledge of this variance is very useful, and it is desirable to obtain such information for all works processes, especially since it can normally be obtained with little extra trouble. When an estimate of the experimental error variance within lots of base material is available from past records, a simple 2^3 design may enable the main effects and two-factor interactions to be estimated with sufficient precision. When an independent estimate of the error variance for the process is not available, or when greater precision is required in the estimates of the effects, it will be necessary to replicate the above 2^3 design using further lots of base materials.

Example 9·1. Yield of an organic chemical

9·14. This example is based on an investigation into the effect of the amount and quality of ammonium chloride on the yield of an organic chemical, the main interest lying in the comparison between the use of finely ground and coarse ammonium chloride. The normal process used the coarse quality, but it would be worth while using the finely ground quality if it resulted in an increase in yield of $2\frac{1}{2}\%$, or 4 lb. per batch. The first step in the investigation was to estimate the number of batches needed to detect an increase in yield of 4 lb. with a reasonable degree of probability. The value of the standard deviation from batch to batch, as estimated from past and current normal manufacture, was 2·5 lb., so that the Normal deviate corresponding to 4 lb. was $4/2·5 = 1·6$. The consequence of not detecting an improvement as small as 4 lb. was not serious, since the process would then remain unchanged; accordingly the chance of this error (the error of the second kind) was taken at $\beta = 0·10$. On the other hand, the consequence of making an error of the first kind, that is of concluding that an appreciable improvement had resulted when in fact it had not, was serious, because the process would then change over to using finely ground ammonium chloride, which would use up valuable grinding capacity and might possibly require additional plant; accordingly the chance of making such an error was taken at $\alpha = 0·025$. Since it could be inferred from chemical considerations that finely ground ammonium chloride could not produce a lower yield, and in any case a decrease in yield was of no interest, a single-sided test was appropriate. The number of observations required is obtained from Formula (*2·7*) and Table A, entering with $\alpha = 0·025$, $\beta = 0·10$, and $(a_2 - a_1)/\sigma = 1·6$, which on calculation gives n equal to 8. Eight batches are required for each quality of ammonium chloride, giving a total of 16, and the experiment should therefore be planned on sixteen batches or thereabouts. Fewer batches might suffice if the change resulted in more than a $2\frac{1}{2}\%$ improvement in yield, because this improvement would be detectable with fewer batches.

The base material used in the manufacture of the chemical is made by a batch process, and one batch of the base material is normally sufficient to make two batches of the product. A simple comparison of the two qualities of ammonium chloride can then be carried out by making a normal batch and a batch using a fine-grade ammonium chloride from the same quality or batch of base material, and repeating on seven further batches of base material.

9·15. Since in this experiment about sixteen batches are required to assess the effect of fine grade ammonium chloride it is worth while examining other (possibly less important) factors,* because, using the principles of the factorial design, additional factors may often be introduced without increasing the number of observations, so that more general conclusions can be drawn. If some interactions are large enough to be significant their presence will reduce the number of effective replicates available, but on the other hand a knowledge of the existence of these interactions may be of great value either for improving the yield or for specifying the operating conditions more

---

* If interest centred only in the comparison of the two grades of ammonium chloride it would be preferable to use the sequential method, assessing each pair of yields in succession (Chapter 3).

closely. In this case there were two other factors of particular interest, one being the effect of a 10% increase in the charge of ammonium chloride to the batch and the other a plant factor. The plant consists of two apparently identical units in which the actual conversion of base to product takes place. At this stage of the process the product is in a crude state and the remaining stages are mainly concerned with the extraction of the pure product. At the extraction stage the identity of the batches is largely lost owing to mixing of the crude material from the two units, it being uneconomic to extract the material separately for each batch. In order to assess the amount of pure product in the crude batch (and hence the efficiency of the extraction process) the crude material was weighed, sampled, and then tested in the laboratory for strength.*

Summary

9·16. In addition to comparing fine and coarse qualities of ammonium chloride, the investigation covered the effect of an increase of 10% in the amount of ammonium chloride used and a comparison of the efficiency of the two units. A complete factorial design for these three factors involves $2^3 = 8$ batches, and as 16 batches were required it was necessary to provide for a repeat. Each batch of the base material was sufficient to make only two batches of the product, and therefore blending of batches of base material and/or confounding was required. From chemical considerations there was unlikely to be any interaction between amount or quality of ammonium chloride and unit of plant; more explicitly, if fine grade ammonium chloride produced a given increase in yield in one unit it should also, apart from experimental error, produce an equivalent increase in yield in the other unit. The three-factor interaction between quality of ammonium chloride, amount of ammonium chloride, and plant unit, was still less likely to be appreciable, and could safely be confounded. It was sufficient, therefore, to blend the base material in lots of two batches, each lot sufficient to make four batches of the product. The same result could probably have been achieved using aliquot amounts from pairs of batches of base material, but this procedure is not usually so satisfactory in practice because of the amount of handling required.

The design, together with the observed yields of the product, is shown in Table 9·2.

---

* The investigation in its original form also included the assessment of the efficiency of sampling and testing following the lines already fully discussed in Chapter 4. In order to simplify this illustration these details are not included, but the point to note is that many investigations into the effect of various factors on yield and quality of a chemical product require also an investigation into sampling and testing techniques, either as a preliminary to, or as part of, the main investigation.

Table 9·2

YIELD IN LB. OF ORGANIC CHEMICAL FOR THE VARIOUS
TREATMENT COMBINATIONS

		Lot of base material							
		1		2		3		4	
Ammonium chloride		Unit		Unit		Unit		Unit	
Quality	Amount	1	2	1	2	1	2	1	2
Coarse	Normal	(1) 155			(c) 156		(c) 161	(1) 164	
	+ 10%		(bc) 152	(b) 168		(b) 175			(bc) 162
Fine	Normal		(ac) 150	(a) 162		(a) 171			(ac) 153
	+ 10%	(ab) 157			(abc) 161		(abc) 173	(ab) 171	
Total	.. ..	614		647		680		650	

Notation

(1) = coarse quality and normal amount of ammonium chloride in unit 1.

a = change to fine ammonium chloride.

b = increase of 10% in ammonium chloride.

c = change to unit 2.

The actual treatment combinations are indicated in the table.

Analysis

9·17. The statistical analysis of the 2^3 design in which the three-factor interaction is confounded follows the conventional procedure detailed in Chapter 7, with the exception that the three-factor interaction is identified with the variation between lots of base material. When there is replication the analysis is carried out in the first place ignoring confounding, and the effects confounded are then calculated separately. The analysis of Table 9·2 ignoring confounding takes the form given in Table 9·21. (See Appendix 9A for full calculations.)

Table 9·21

ANALYSIS OF VARIANCE OF TABLE 9·2, IGNORING CONFOUNDING

Source of variation	Sum of squares	Degrees of freedom	Mean square
Ammonium chloride:			
Quality	1·56	1	1·56
Amount	138·06	1	138·06
Between units	189·06	1	189·06
Two-factor interactions ..	9·68	3	3·23
Three-factor interaction ..	248·06	1	248·06
Replication	342·52	8	42·82
Total	928·94	15	

The two-factor interactions, shown separately in Table 9A·4, have been combined because none appeared significant. The only further step required is to calculate the corrected sum of squares between the four lots of base material and to derive the remainder sum of squares.

The three-factor interaction, although included in Table 9·21, has been confounded with variation between lots of base material. Regarding the latter in greater detail, it is apparent that [lots $(1 - 2)$] represents the three-factor interaction in the first replicate and [lots $(4 - 3)$] that in the second replicate. The three-factor interaction for the sum of the two replicates is denoted by [lots $(1 + 4)$ — lots $(2 + 3)$]. This absorbs only one of the three degrees of freedom between the four lots, the other two being [lots $(1 - 4)$ + lots $(2 - 3)$] and [lots $(1 - 4)$ — lots $(2 - 3)$]. Since the treatment combinations are similar for lots 1 and 4 and for lots 2 and 3, these two degrees of freedom represent differences between replicates, and the relevant comparisons are included in the replication sum of squares. To take due account of confounding, therefore, the corrected sum of squares between the four lots of base material must be calculated and subtracted from the combined total of the three-factor interaction and the replication sums of squares in Table 9·21. The remainder is the replication sum of squares included in Table 9·22, in which the three-factor interaction, originally assumed to be insignificant, is merged with the variation between lots of base material. There is no need to calculate the three-factor interaction separately, as is done in Table 9·21.

The variance of the process estimated from past performance is 6·25, based on a large number of degrees of freedom.

Full details of the analysis are given in Appendix 9A.

Table 9·22

ANALYSIS OF VARIANCE OF TABLE 9·2, CONFOUNDING THE
THREE-FACTOR INTERACTION

Source of variation	Sum of squares	Degrees of freedom	Mean square
Ammonium chloride:			
Quality	1·56	1	1·56
Amount	138·06	1	138·06
Between units	189·06	1	189·06
Two-factor interactions ..	9·68	3	3·23
Between lots of base material	546·19	3	182·06
Replication (= remainder) ..	44·39	6	7·40
Total	928·94	15	

Interpretation of Table 9·22

9·18. The replication mean square, although slightly larger than the variance of the process, does not differ significantly from it. The difference between the replication mean square and the normal process variation must be fortuitous, for on common-sense grounds the experimental error in a carefully supervised experiment is unlikely to be greater than the normal process variation.*

The conclusions as to the significance of the effects are the same, whether we use as the error mean square 7·40, the estimate provided by the experiment, or 6·25, the estimate provided from past experience. The question which mean square to use frequently arises in investigations of this kind. It is usually preferable to make the experiment self-contained, deriving an estimate of the error mean square from the results of the experiment itself, but making the experiment self-contained may not be practicable when only a few degrees of freedom are available for the estimate. Strictly, the decision which error mean square to use should be made before the results are analysed; for once we knew the figures we should tend to choose the smaller, so that in the long run the significance of the effects would be overestimated. In this example a fair number of degrees of freedom for error were available from the experiment itself, and it was practicable to use the replication mean square as error.

* There is, however, an additional source of error in this investigation, namely the sampling and testing error in estimating the yield of the batch, but the full details of the investigation (not included here) showed that these errors were small compared with the overall variation in yield and also smaller than the variation introduced at the purification of the material on the plant scale.

Again, the two-factor interactions were not expected to be appreciable, and their mean square could if desired be combined with the remainder variance, giving an error mean square of 6·01 based on a larger number (nine) of degrees of freedom.

The mean square between lots of base material is significant, and it is clear that confounding has removed a large source of variation from the experimental error and has thus made the experiment much more sensitive.

The only other significant effects are associated with the amount of ammonium chloride and the difference between the two units. Each of these two effects represents a difference between the means of eight results, and the 95% confidence limits to be attached to the effects (using the normal process variation as the error variance) are therefore $\pm 1{\cdot}96\sqrt{(6{\cdot}25 \times 2/8)} = \pm 2{\cdot}45$. The 95% confidence limits of the significant effects are:

Effect of a 10% increase in amount of ammonium chloride $= 5{\cdot}88 \pm 2{\cdot}45$
Unit 1 − unit 2 $= 6{\cdot}88 \pm 2{\cdot}45$

There is thus justification for increasing the amount of ammonium chloride. A 10% increase might not be the optimum, and therefore this experiment was followed by a further investigation of this particular factor. A close inspection revealed that unit 2 suffered from a slight mechanical fault, which accounted for its poor performance in relation to unit 1; this had not been observed previously because in the normal operation of the process the batches from units 1 and 2 are mixed at the extraction stage.

As to the effect of quality of ammonium chloride, there was clearly no justification for changing to the use of the fine grade.

Situations requiring the use of the principles of confounding

9·2. The practical example of the previous section was introduced in order to illustrate the main principles of confounding. The reason for confounding was based on the practical difficulty of obtaining sufficient raw materials of uniform quality for the whole experiment. By confounding an unimportant high-order interaction between lots of materials it was possible to eliminate the error due to variation in raw material quality from the estimates of the more important effects of the factors under investigation. The alternative to confounding when large-scale blending of the raw materials is impracticable is to treat the variation in quality of the raw materials as a component of experimental error. To do this it would be necessary to randomise the treatment combinations among the various lots of the raw material, and here it must be stressed that randomisation is essential in order to enable unbiased estimates of the effects to be obtained. Randomisation without confounding would provide a valid design, and all effects would be estimated with the same degree of precision, but the experimental error having been increased by the variation between the raw materials, the efficiency of the experiment would be less than that obtained when using confounding.

The principles of confounding for factorial designs may be used with advantage whenever there is difficulty in obtaining sufficient material of uniform quality for the whole experiment, or in general whenever there is a restriction on the number of preparations or observations which can be made under relatively uniform conditions. In laboratory work on the effects of various factors on yield of penicillin the number of preparations which can be made at any given time is limited, and is usually less than the number required for the whole experiment. The experiment must consequently be divided into two or more lots or blocks to be examined at different times, and it is necessary to eliminate the variation between blocks from the more important effects by confounding the unimportant higher-order interactions with the differences between the blocks.

When a factorial experiment is carried out on a multiple plant consisting of two or more parallel units it may happen that seemingly identical units differ in efficiency; thus when two or more units are used in the factorial experiment the factor combinations should be allocated to the units so that the differences between the units are identified with unimportant high-order interactions. For a 2^3 design in two units the combinations required will be those of Table 9·11, substituting "unit" for "lot." The units 1 and 2 are interchangeable in the table, and in practice the order is decided by tossing a coin.

In an investigation into the accuracy of chemical analytical methods the analyst may be interested in the comparison of two or more different methods for assessing the purity of a manufactured chemical. A variety of samples with different levels of purity is required, and because of the possibility of operator or apparatus bias it may be necessary to use two or more operators, laboratories, or sets of apparatus. The number of tests involved in a factorial combination is given by the product of the numbers of methods, operators, and samples, and this may well be greater than can be performed under one set of uniform conditions, e.g. on one day. In view of the possibility of day-to-day variation it is desirable to arrange the combinations carried out each day so that the comparisons between days correspond to high-order interactions, which are almost certain to be negligible. Yet another important application of the principles of confounding to experimental work carried out on the plant or on a semi-production scale remains to be considered. As pointed out [§ 5·13], the records for a large number of chemical products covering several years' production indicate that the yield and quality of many of the products tend to vary in an oscillatory manner, that is, to follow wavy trends, usually irregular in amplitude and period. These trends are sometimes related to variations in the quality of the materials used, but often their causes are a matter of speculation, and even if they could be determined they could not be controlled. The comparison of adjacent batches is less liable to this type of error than the comparison of batches separated by longer intervals of time, and so in a factorial experiment it is desirable to keep all the more important comparisons within relatively short intervals. This feature has already been considered in Chapter 5 in relation to randomised block experiments, and similar considerations apply to factorial experiments. In order to minimise the effect of the trends on the experimental error the treatment combinations are divided into two or more blocks, each block representing a number of consecutive observations in time, and unimportant high-order interactions are confounded between those time blocks so that the more important effects are measured by comparisons within blocks comprising relatively short intervals of time. It is clearly an advantage to keep the blocks as small as practicable without sacrificing important information, and in later sections of this chapter methods are given for dividing the design into more than two blocks. The importance of randomisation is again stressed, especially when time trends may exist, and attention is again drawn to the assumption involved that there are no appreciable interactions with blocks.

Before giving a general treatment of confounding we introduce the idea of partial confounding and give a simple illustration.

Partial confounding

9·21. When a 2^3 factorial design is replicated and the experiment has to be carried out in blocks of four observations, confounding one effect in each replicate, the experimenter is free to confound any effect in any replicate. There is no need to confound the same interaction in all replicates: with two replicates the interaction ABC may be confounded in the first and a different interaction, say AB, in the second. When this is done the first replicate gives an estimate of the interaction AB (since this is not confounded in that replicate), and the second gives an estimate of the other interaction ABC, while both replicates together give estimates of all the effects. Using two replicates it is thus possible to recover information on the interactions confounded in each. When an interaction is confounded in one replicate and not in another the experiment is said to be Partially Confounded. Since only a portion of the observations are used to estimate the partially confounded interactions the latter are determined with a lower degree of precision than the other effects, but since nothing is lost by partial confounding instead of confounding the same interaction in all replicates it is worth while using partially confounded designs in replicated experiments, so that some information is obtained concerning the interactions which are confounded. There is a slight increase in the complexity of the experimental design and in the analysis, but this is not serious. There are four interactions, AB, AC, BC, and ABC, in a 2^3 factorial design, and in order to obtain complete balance, partially confounding all interactions to the same extent, we require four replicates. The design is shown in Table 9·23.

Table 9·23

PARTIAL CONFOUNDING OF INTERACTIONS IN 2^3 FACTORIAL DESIGNS

Interaction confounded	ABC		AB		AC		BC	
Lot of base material = block	X_1	Y_1	X_2	Y_2	X_3	Y_3	X_4	Y_4
Treatment combinations	(1)	a	(1)	a	(1)	a	(1)	b
	ab	b	ab	b	b	ab	a	ab
	ac	c	c	ac	ac	c	bc	c
	bc	abc	abc	bc	abc	bc	abc	ac

The detailed analysis of the design is given in Appendix 9B. The analysis differs from that of an ordinary 2^3 factorial design replicated four times only in the calculation of the partially confounded interactions, each interaction being calculated from the three replicates in which the given interaction is not confounded.

Classified lists of designs for confounding 2^n factorial experiments

9·22. An extensive list of designs suitable for most industrial applications of confounding is given in Appendix 9E. It covers up to six factors in blocks of four, up to seven factors in blocks of eight, and also up to seven factors in blocks of 16 observations. While the reader may be willing to take the more complex designs for granted, it is essential for him to have a firm grasp of the principles involved and to satisfy himself that the system works, at least in the simpler cases.

General principles of confounding 2^n designs in two blocks. Rules for confounding a given interaction in a 2^n factorial design

9·3. Confounding any given interaction with two blocks amounts to dividing the treatment combinations into two sets so that the comparison between the sets corresponds to the effect which it is required to confound. There are several ways of determining which treatment combinations should appear in the same block; two of these are:

(i) Write the interaction which it is desired to confound in its algebraic form [§ 7·44] and expand the expression. The treatment combinations with a plus sign fall into one block and those with a minus sign fall into the other.

To confound the interaction ABC in a design with four factors, the fourth factor being denoted by D, the algebraic expression for ABC (apart from a constant multiplier) is

$$(a - 1)(b - 1)(c - 1)(d + 1)$$

Expanding and rearranging give

$$(a + b + c + abc + ad + bd + cd + abcd)$$
$$- (1 + ab + ac + bc + d + abd + acd + bcd)$$

The first bracket comprises the treatment combinations of one block and the second bracket comprises the treatment combinations of the other. When the number of factors is six or less, refer to Table M at the end of the volume, in which the appropriate signs in the expansion of any interaction are given. The appropriate treatment combination for the two blocks may then be read directly from this table, the pluses comprising one block and the minuses the other.

(ii) Apply the following rule: To confound any interaction, say ABC, assign all the treatment combinations comprising an even number (including zero) of the corresponding small letters a, b, c to one block and the remainder comprising an odd number of the letters a, b, c to the other.

9·31. This rule may be conveniently illustrated by reference to the designs of Table 9·23, in which the interactions ABC, AB, AC, and BC are confounded respectively in four replicates of a 2^3 factorial design. In the first replicate the interaction ABC is confounded. The corresponding small letters in this interaction are a, b, c. Applying the rule, one block will contain the following combination of a, b, c:

(i) None of a, b, c, that is, (1).

(ii) a, b, c two at a time, that is, $ab, ac,$ and bc. If there were more factors and higher-order interactions were confounded, then the letters four at a time, six at a time, etc., would also be included.

The other block comprises the remaining treatment combinations, viz. a, b, c one at a time and three at a time, that is $a, b, c,$ and abc.

In the second replicate of Table 9·23 the interaction AB is confounded. The corresponding small letters are a, b. Applying the rule, we obtain the following combinations for the first block:

(i) Treatment combinations not containing a or b, that is, $(1), c$.

(ii) Treatment combinations containing a, b, two at a time, that is, ab, abc. The first block is then $(1), c, ab, abc$. The other block contains the remaining treatment combinations, that is, combinations containing a or b but not ab together. These are a, ac, b, bc. The rule may similarly be illustrated for the other two replicates.

As a further illustration let us confound ABC in a four-factor experiment, the fourth factor being D. The small letters corresponding to the interaction to be confounded are a, b, c. Applying the rule, the first block consists of the following combinations:

(i) The letters a, b, and c absent, that is, (1), d.
(ii) The letters a, b, and c present two at a time, that is, ab, ac, bc, abd, acd, bcd.

The other block will consist of the remaining combinations containing an odd number of a, b, and c, that is, a, b, c, abc, ad, bd, cd, $abcd$.

The following is an example of a five-factor experiment.

Example 9·2. Confounding in a 2^5 factorial experiment

9·32. This example is taken from laboratory work on investigations into the effects of various factors on the yield of penicillin in surface culture experiments.* In such experiments the nutrient medium is placed in a conical flask, sterilised, inoculated with a spore suspension of *P. chrysogenum*, and then incubated. The spores of *P. chrysogenum* rise to the surface and during growth form a felt-like mycelium covering the surface. The growth of the mycelium is accompanied by the formation of penicillin. The medium is usually a complex one, and much experimental work was required to determine suitable ingredients in optimum concentration in relation to the rate of production of penicillin. Owing to the interdependence of various conditions, factorial designs were extensively used. In the work described below it was required to check the findings of other workers relating to the effects of small quantities of glucose, sodium nitrate, and a precursor, and different concentrations of lactose and corn steep liquor in the medium, on the yield of penicillin by surface culture. These five factors were each examined at two levels by means of a 2^5 factorial design. The levels of the factors were:

A: Corn steep liquor, strength 2% and 3%
B: Lactose, 2% and 3%
C: Precursor, 0 and 0·05%
D: Sodium nitrate, 0 and 0·3%
E: Glucose, 0 and 0·5%

The other ingredients in the medium were kept constant.

The complete design required 32 combinations, but as it was inconvenient to carry out all at one time it was decided to test 16 combinations in the first

---

* Surface culture experiments were carried out in the early stages of the development of penicillin; but this process has now been superseded by submerged culture work, in which the inoculated medium is agitated continuously and the mycelium is grown in suspension in the medium.

week and the remaining 16 in the second week. It is known that large week-to-week variations may occur, and this necessitated confounding one of the interactions, the obvious choice being the five-factor interaction as the one likely to be least important. Denoting the factors by *A*, *B*, *C*, *D*, and *E* respectively, the appropriate blocks are

(1): *a, b, c, d, e, abc, abd, abe, acd, ace, ade, bcd, bce, bde, cde, abcde*

(2): 1, *ab, ac, ad, ae, bc, bd, be, cd, ce, de, bcde, acde, abde, abce, abcd*

These blocks may be obtained by applying any of the above methods or by direct reference to the tabulated list of confounded designs in Appendix 9E [Design 9E·31].

The yields of penicillin for these combinations of factors are shown in Table 9·3.

Table 9·3

YIELDS OF PENICILLIN IN SURFACE CULTURE EXPERIMENT

			No glucose		0·5% glucose	
		CSL *	No sodium nitrate (1)	0·3% sodium nitrate *d*	No sodium nitrate *e*	0·3% sodium nitrate *de*
No precursor	2% lactose	2%	(1)	(1) 142	148 (d)	106 (e)	(de) 101
		3%	a	114 (a)	(ad) 108	(ae) 106	114 (ade)
	3% lactose	2%	b	129 (b)	(bd) 146	(be) 88	140 (bde)
		3%	ab	(ab) 109	95 (abd)	98 (abe)	(abde) 72
0·05% precursor	2% lactose	2%	c	185 (c)	(cd) 200	(ce) 113	130 (cde)
		3%	ac	(ac) 162	164 (acd)	88 (ace)	(acde) 83
	3% lactose	2%	bc	(bc) 200	215 (bcd)	166 (bce)	(bcde) 145
		3%	abc	172 (abc)	(abcd) 118	(abce) 79	110 (abcde)

* CSL = Strength of corn steep liquor.

The left-hand member of each cell belongs to one block and the right-hand member to the other block.

The logarithms of the yields are given in Table 9·31. The logarithmic transformation was used because the error was expected to be proportional to the result; in other words, the coefficient of variation rather than the standard deviation was expected to be constant.

Table 9·31

LOGARITHMS OF YIELDS OF TABLE 9·3

	(1)	d	e	de
(1)	(1) 2·152	2·170 (d)	2·025 (e)	(de) 2·004
a	2·057 (a)	(ad) 2·033	(ae) 2·025	2·057 (ade)
b	2·111 (b)	(bd) 2·164	(be) 1·944	2·146 (bde)
ab	(ab) 2·037	1·978 (abd)	1·991 (abe)	(abde) 1·857
c	2·267 (c)	(cd) 2·301	(ce) 2·053	2·114 (cde)
ac	(ac) 2·210	2·215 (acd)	1·944 (ace)	(acde) 1·919
bc	(bc) 2·301	2·332 (bcd)	2·220 (bce)	(bcde) 2·161
abc	2·236 (abc)	(abcd) 2·072	(abce) 1·898	2·041 (abcde)

The analysis follows the same procedure as for a 2^5 factorial design without confounding, the only difference in the final analysis being that the five-factor interaction is identified with the difference between the two blocks. The details of the analysis are given in Appendix 9C and the final analysis of variance table is as Table 9·32.

Table 9·32

ANALYSIS OF VARIANCE OF TABLE 9·31

Source of variation	Effect (if significant)	Degrees of freedom	Mean square
Main effects:			
A	(− 0·1184)	1	0·1122
B		1	0·0001
C	(+ 0·0958)	1	0·0734
D		1	0·0003
E	(− 0·1398)	1	0·1564
Two-factor interactions:			
CE	(− 0·0582)	1	0·0271
Remaining two-factor interactions, combined		9	0·0051
Three-factor interactions		10 ⎤	0·0029 ⎤
Four-factor interactions ..		5 ⎬ 15	0·0044 ⎬ 0·0034
Five-factor interaction = between weeks		1 ⎦	0·0187 ⎦
Total	.. .. ..	31	

The magnitudes of the significant effects are quoted in the table. Note that the interaction CE, which is the largest two-factor interaction, has been separated from the remainder. Caution must be exercised in assessing the significance of the largest interaction in a group, and the question is discussed in relation to this example in Appendix 9C.

Discussion of the results

9·33. The error variance is estimated from the three- and four-factor interaction mean squares. It is clear from Table 9·32 that the three-factor interaction cannot be appreciable, and the three- and four-factor interactions are combined to give an error variance of 0·0034 based on 15 degrees of freedom. A mean square of 4·54 times this error variance, viz. 0·0154, is required for each effect for significance at the 5% level. The variance ratios required for significance at the 10% and 1% levels are 3·07 and 8·68 respectively. The difference between blocks, although much smaller than that usually experienced, is significant, and a gain in efficiency has resulted from the use of confounding as compared with a design in which all the treatment combinations are allocated randomly between the two blocks. In other words, the error variance is reduced by using confounding.

The method of calculating the gain in efficiency is detailed in § 6·35 of Ref. [9·4].

The significant effects are A (3% v. 2% corn steep liquor), C (the presence of 0·05% precursor), E (the presence of 0·5% glucose), and the two-factor interaction CE. The actual magnitudes of the main effects in terms of logarithms of the observations and the antilogarithms of these effects are as follows:

$$A = -0·1184 \qquad \text{Antilog} = 0·76$$
$$C = +0·0958 \qquad \text{Antilog} = 1·25$$
$$E = -0·1398 \qquad \text{Antilog} = 0·72$$

The effect of A is to decrease the logarithm of the yield by 0·1184, which is equivalent to multiplying the actual yield by 0·76, representing a 24% decrease; and so on for the other effects.

To sum up, the increase in strength of the corn steep liquor (factor A) reduces the yield by 24% of its value, the presence of 0·05% precursor (factor C) increases the yield by 25%, and an increase in concentration of glucose from 2% to 3% (factor E) reduces the yield of penicillin by 28% of its value, while the different concentrations of lactose and sodium nitrate have no appreciable effects. The main effects are average effects, and since the interaction between C and E is significant it is necessary to consider the effect of C (or E) at the separate levels of E (or C). The interaction is negative, which means that the effect of precursor is reduced in the presence of glucose. The effect of glucose is negative, indicating that the best conditions are obtained with no glucose and 0·05% precursor.

These effects are shown in Table 9·321, a 2 × 2 table of means.

Table 9·321

TWO-WAY TABLE OF FACTORS C AND E BASED ON MEANS

| | | C = Precursor | | Mean |
		o	0·05%	
E (= Glucose)..	o	2·0878	2·2418	2·1648
	0·5%	2·0061	2·0438	2·0249
Mean		2·0469	2·1428	2·0948

This table is obtained by condensing the original table of the logarithms of the detailed results, and together with the effect of A it summarises the information from this experiment.

Higher degrees of confounding in 2^n factorial designs

9·4. In the previous sections only the simplest cases of confounding were considered, in which the treatment combinations were split up into two blocks confounding one interaction, usually that of the highest order. Higher degrees of confounding involve a larger number of blocks, which in a 2^n factorial design must be a power of 2. For two blocks one interaction is confounded, for four blocks three interactions are confounded, and so on. For more than two blocks there are certain restrictions on the choice of the interactions to be confounded. With four blocks any two interactions may be chosen, and the third is then determined, and so on.

The following simple illustration shows how such restrictions come about. Consider a 2^3 design with factors denoted by A, B, and C, and assume the treatment combinations are to be divided into four blocks confounding three effects. Let AB be one of the effects to be confounded and BC another. To confound AB between two blocks only it is necessary to use the design corresponding to the second replicate in Table 9·23, which with a slight rearrangement becomes Table 9·4.

It is also required to confound the interaction BC, and the design for confounding BC alone is represented by the fourth replicate in Table 9·23. In the arrangement of Table 9·4 the four treatment combinations $\begin{Bmatrix} (1), & abc \\ a, & bc \end{Bmatrix}$

Table 9·4

2³ FACTORIAL DESIGN CONFOUNDING *AB*

Block X ..	..	(1), *abc*, *c*, *ab*	
Block Y ..	..	*a*, *bc*, *b*, *ac*	

on the left-hand side of the table form one of the blocks for confounding *BC*, and the treatment combinations on the right-hand side $\begin{Bmatrix} c, \ ab \\ b, \ ac \end{Bmatrix}$ form the other block. If therefore Table 9·4 is written in the form of Table 9·41

Table 9·41

2³ FACTORIAL DESIGN CONFOUNDING *AB* AND *BC*

		Confounding *BC*			
		Column 1		Column 2	
Confounding *AB*	Row 1	(1)	*abc*	*c*	*ab*
	Row 2	*a*	*bc*	*ac*	*b*

the interaction *AB* is confounded between the two rows and the interaction *BC* between the two columns. Considering each cell of the above table as a block and numbering them $\begin{Bmatrix} 1, \ 2 \\ 3, \ 4 \end{Bmatrix}$ in that order, the comparison

$$(1 + 2) - (3 + 4) \text{ represents } AB$$
$$\text{and} \quad (1 + 3) - (2 + 4) \text{ represents } BC.$$

In other words, the above arrangement of four blocks gives the required design which confounds *AB* and *BC*, because these represent two of the comparisons between the four blocks. In a 2 × 2 table two of the effects are represented by the comparison between the rows and columns respectively, and the only other comparison is the interaction between the rows and columns. In Table 9·41 this is the comparison between the diagonal totals

$$(1 + 4) - (2 + 3)$$

To identify this comparison write down the corresponding treatment combinations; these are

$$[(1), abc, ac, b] - [a, bc, c, ab]$$

Referring to Table 9·23, it is seen that this separation corresponds to the interaction *AC*, showing that if *AB* and *BC* are confounded, *AC* is confounded in consequence.

An interesting observation is the following. An interaction is usually denoted by a symbolic product of terms, e.g. the interaction of A with B is AB, and extending the notation, the interaction of AB with BC is $ABBC$. The above shows that

$$(AB)(BC) = AC$$

or $\quad AB^2C \quad = AC$

that is $\quad B^2 \quad = 1$

These ideas will be considered in more general terms in the next section and in the appendices.

Multiplication law for two or more effects for factors at two levels—generalised interactions

9·41. A simple rule exists for identifying the third interaction which is confounded, but before giving this rule it is necessary to define a further concept, namely the Generalised Interaction between two effects. For two main effects A and B the interaction is denoted by AB; for two interactions AB and CD the interaction between them is denoted by $ABCD$. For two interactions with an effect in common, e.g. ABC and CDE, their product is $(ABC)(CDE)$. It can be shown that this product is the effect $ABDE$ (a simple illustration of this has been given in the previous section). This leads to the rule that when multiplying two effects the common letters are struck out, or, what is equivalent, the square of any effect is equated to unity, so that $A^2 = B^2 = C^2 = \ldots = 1$. For example, the product of $ABCD$ and $CDEF$ is $ABC^2D^2EF = ABEF$. When two or more effects are multiplied in this way the result may be termed the Generalised Interaction of the given effects.

The following rule, which has already been illustrated in § **9·4**, may now be stated:

When confounding a 2^n factorial design over four blocks, two interactions may be chosen at will, and the third is then determined by their product.

In the general case when a 2^n factorial design is divided into 2^p blocks it can be shown that p interactions may be chosen at will and the remaining $(2^p - p - 1)$ interactions confounded in consequence are represented by the products of the p chosen interactions in all possible ways, that is, two at a time, three at a time, four at a time, etc. These ideas are linked up with the theory of Finite Groups in Appendix 9D. Illustrations are given later.

Systems of confounding in four blocks*

9·42. When confounding over four blocks the interactions confounded may be chosen in several ways; obviously the experimenter will seek to sacrifice

* An adequate table of designs for six or fewer factors and with various degrees of confounding is given in Appendix 9E.

the least possible amount of information, and he will normally confound the lower-order interactions to the least possible extent. The lowest-order design which will permit confounding over four blocks is the design involving three factors, A, B, and C. Suppose ABC is chosen as one of the interactions and a two-factor interaction AB as the second. If this is done, then the third effect confounded will be represented by the product $(AB)(ABC) = A^2B^2C = C$. In other words, if ABC and AB are the two chosen interactions, then the main effect C must also be confounded. A design which confounds a main effect is of little value and must be rejected. If instead of choosing a three-factor and a two-factor interaction for confounding we choose two two-factor interactions, say AB and AC, then the third which must be confounded is $(AB)(AC) = BC$. This is clearly a more satisfactory arrangement and is in fact the best for the 2^3 design. The next step in confounding the interactions AB, AC, and BC is to determine the treatment combinations for each block. There are several methods of doing this, one of which, given in [9·1], will now be considered.

Table M at the end of the volume gives the appropriate signs for the various effects. The relevant part of the table for the 2^3 design, set out in a slightly different form, is given in Table 9·42 in order to simplify the explanation.

Table 9·42

SIGNS APPERTAINING TO TREATMENTS AND EFFECTS IN 2^3 FACTORIAL DESIGNS

	(1)	a	b	ab	c	ac	bc	abc
T	+	+	+	+	+	+	+	+
A	−	+	−	+	−	+	−	+
B	−	−	+	+	−	−	+	+
AB	+	−	−	+	+	−	−	+
C	−	−	−	−	+	+	+	+
AC	+	−	+	−	−	+	−	+
BC	+	+	−	−	−	−	+	+
ABC	−	+	+	−	+	−	−	+

The method is as follows. Consider the signs of the small letters in the rows corresponding to the two interactions proposed to be confounded. There are four distinct combinations of signs, namely: $(+)(+)$, $(+)(−)$, $(−)(+)$, and $(−)(−)$; the first sign appertaining to the upper row and the second sign to the lower row. These four products break up the small letters into the four blocks required.

Applying this method we derive the arrangement of Table 9·43.

Table 9·43

DESIGN FOR CONFOUNDING AB, AC, AND BC

Block 1	AB (+)	AC (+)	(1)	abc
Block 2	AB (+)	AC (−)	ab	c
Block 3	AB (−)	AC (+)	b	ac
Block 4	AB (−)	AC (−)	a	bc

The method just given is easy to apply to six and fewer factors but tends to be cumbersome for larger numbers. Further methods and rules suitable for more complex designs are given in Appendix 9D.

The larger the number of factors the greater is the choice between systems of confounding. To divide a 2^4 design into four blocks it is necessary to confound three degrees of freedom, two of which may be chosen at will. The two interactions least likely to be important are the four-factor interaction $ABCD$ and a three-factor interaction, say ABC. These are not suitable for confounding, since their product $(ABCD)(ABC) = D$ is a main effect. The next choice is two three-factor interactions ABC and BCD, which have a two-factor interaction AD as their product. Other possibilities are two two-factor interactions AB and CD and their product $ABCD$. These alternatives are tabulated as follows:

(1)	$ABCD$	ABC	D
(2)	ABC	BCD	AD
(3)	AB	CD	$ABCD$

Of these the second is usually the best because it involves the least number of low-order interactions. With four factors there are several possible arrangements involving a two-factor interaction and two three-factor interactions, but in practice the two factors least likely to interact are made to correspond with A and D respectively. The treatment combinations to be allocated to each block may be determined by the method given above, by one of the methods given in Appendix 9D, or by reference to the tabulated designs of Appendix 9E. To employ the first method, refer to Table M and note the signs for any two of the interactions confounded, say ABC and BCD. The division of the treatment combination into the blocks is as Table 9·44.

Table 9·44

2^4 FACTORIAL DESIGN CONFOUNDING ABC, BCD, AND AD

Block 1	ABC (+)	BCD (+)	b	c	ad	$abcd$
Block 2	ABC (+)	BCD (−)	a	abc	bd	cd
Block 3	ABC (−)	BCD (+)	ab	ac	d	bcd
Block 4	ABC (−)	BCD (−)	(1)	bc	abd	acd

9·421. If required, a still higher degree of confounding—over eight blocks—may be introduced into a 2^4 design. There are seven degrees of freedom between the eight blocks, and therefore seven effects will have to be confounded. Three of these may be chosen at will and the others derived by multiplying them in all possible ways. If in the three chosen one is a product of the other two, then another interaction may be chosen at will. We start then with three chosen interactions, none of which is a product of the other two, for instance, the three two-factor interactions AB, BC, and BD. The other interactions are products of these two at a time and all three together. The products two at a time are

$$(AB)(BC) = AC \qquad (AB)(BD) = AD \qquad (BC)(BD) = CD$$

and three at a time:

$$(AB)(BC)(BD) = (AC)(BD) = ABCD$$

The seven interactions confounded are then

$$AB, BC, BD, AC, AD, CD, ABCD$$

This represents the best system because, had a three-factor interaction been chosen, it would have been impossible to avoid having main effects in the products. For example, choosing ABC, CD, and AD, the products two at a time are

$$ABD, BCD, AC$$

and the product of all three is

$$(ABC)(CD)(AD) = (ABD)(AD) = B = \text{a main effect}$$

The method of allotting the treatment combinations to the eight blocks is an extension of the one used for four blocks. Write down the signs of the three chosen interactions, which must of course be independent, i.e. no interaction must denote the product of another two. The treatments are then allocated according to the possible sequence of signs, e.g. $(+)(+)(+)$ in one block, $(+)(+)(-)$ in another block, $(+)(-)(-)$ in a third block, and so on. For the above system of confounding, the signs of the treatment combinations for the chosen interactions, obtained from Table M, written horizontally, are as Table 9·45.

Table 9·45

DERIVATION OF DESIGN CONFOUNDING AB, BC, AND BD

	(1)	a	b	ab	c	ac	bc	abc	d	ad	bd	abd	cd	acd	bcd	abcd
AB	+	−	−	+	+	−	−	+	+	−	−	+	+	−	−	+
BC	+	+	−	−	−	−	+	+	+	+	−	−	−	−	+	+
BD	+	+	−	−	+	+	−	−	−	−	+	+	−	−	+	+

The blocks are as Table 9·451.

Table 9·451

DESIGN FOR FOUR FACTORS CONFOUNDING *AB*, *BC*, *BD*, *AC*, *AD*, *CD*, AND *ABCD*

Block 1	AB (+)	BC (+)	BD (+)	(1)	abcd
Block 2	AB (+)	BC (+)	BD (−)	abc	d
Block 3	AB (+)	BC (−)	BD (+)	c	abd
Block 4	AB (−)	BC (+)	BD (+)	a	bcd
Block 5	AB (+)	BC (−)	BD (−)	ab	cd
Block 6	AB (−)	BC (+)	BD (−)	bc	ad
Block 7	AB (−)	BC (−)	BD (+)	ac	bd
Block 8	AB (−)	BC (−)	BD (−)	b	acd

9·422. When it is required to confound over 16 blocks involving five or more factors, 15 interactions must be confounded. Four independent interactions may be chosen at will and the remainder may be derived by multiplying these two at a time, three at a time, and all four together. To allocate the treatments to the blocks we use a simple extension of the methods given earlier or the methods described in Appendix 9D.

Defining contrasts. Principal block

9·423. The interactions confounded in any system of confounding are called the Defining Contrasts. Multiplying any two of the defining contrasts using the rule given above, $A^2 = B^2 = C^2 = \ldots = 1$, yields another defining contrast, because when any two interactions are confounded their product is also confounded. It is usual to add the term unity to the set of defining contrasts, which are then referred to as the Group of Defining Contrasts. This group is closed to multiplication; in other words, when any two or more of the elements are multiplied together algebraically and the indices are reduced by the conditions $A^2 = B^2 = C^2 = \ldots = 1$, the product is also an element of the group. This is considered more fully in Appendix 9D.

The Principal Block in a system of confounding is the block which contains the treatment combination (1), where all the factors are at the lower level. When the treatment combinations are multiplied together subject to the condition $a^2 = b^2 = c^2 = \ldots = 1$, the following useful relations hold:

(i)   The elements of the principal block form a group closed to multiplication. If therefore some elements of the principal block are known, others may be derived by multiplication. This rule is useful also as a check on the members of the principal block.

(ii) Multiplying the principal block by a treatment combination not contained in the block generates another block in the same system. Multiplying the elements of any block by an element from the same block will generate the principal block. Therefore, given any block in a system of confounding, the whole system may be derived simply by multiplication.

These rules are considered more fully in Appendix 9D. The reader is recommended to apply the rules relating to the defining contrasts and the elements of the blocks on several of the systems of confounding listed in Appendix 9E.

Example 9·3. Confounding in a 2^5 factorial design in sets or blocks of eight

9·424. It is proposed to use Example 9·2 to illustrate a higher degree of confounding. Suppose the conditions were such that the observations could at most be carried out in sets of eight at a time. It would then have been necessary to confound three interactions between four sets. Confounding the five-factor interaction $ABCDE$ and a four-factor interaction, e.g. $ABCD$, involves confounding a main effect (in this case E). Confounding the five-factor interaction and a three-factor interaction, e.g. ABC, involves confounding a two-factor interaction, in this case DE. Normally the best arrangement is to confound a four-factor interaction and two three-factor interactions, e.g. $BCDE$, ABC, and ADE, and this is the design used for this example.

The appropriate design [§9E·22] is given in Appendix 9E by interchanging A and E and therefore a and e; it may also be derived by any of the methods referred to above. The treatment combinations for the whole design and also the logarithms of the penicillin yield are given in Tables 9·46 and 9·461 respectively.

Table 9·46

2^5 FACTORIAL DESIGN CONFOUNDING ABC, ADE, AND $BCDE$

Block 1 $(-)(-)$	Block 2 $(-)(+)$	Block 3 $(+)(-)$	Block 4 $(+)(+)$
(1)	e	b	a
de	d	bde	ade
bc	bce	c	abc
bcde	bcd	cde	abcde
abe	ab	ae	be
abd	abde	ad	bd
ace	ac	abce	ce
acd	acde	abcd	cd

Table 9·461

LOG YIELDS OF PENICILLIN

(Derived from Table 9·31)

2·152	2·025	2·111	2·057	
2·004	2·170	2·146	2·057	
2·301	2·220	2·267	2·236	
2·161	2·332	2·114	2·041	
1·991	2·037	2·025	1·944	
1·978	1·857	2·033	2·164	
1·944	2·210	1·898	2·053	
2·215	1·919	2·072	2·301	
Totals ..	16·746	16·770	16·666	16·853	67·035

Analysis

9·425. Initially the analysis is carried out as in the unconfounded 2^5 design. This has already been done in Appendix 9C. The three confounded degrees of freedom ABC, ADE, and $BCDE$ are then combined and identified with the three degrees of freedom between the four blocks. The summarised analysis of variance table then reads as Table 9·47.

Table 9·47

ANALYSIS OF VARIANCE OF TABLE 9·461

Source of variation	Sum of squares	Degrees of freedom	Mean square
Main effects	0·3424	5	0·0685
Interactions:			
Two-factor	0·0727	10	0·0073
Three-factor	0·0279	8	0·0035
(excl. ABC, ADE)			
Four-factor (excl. $BCDE$) ..	0·0211	4	0·0053
Five-factor	0·0187	1	0·0187
Blocks (ABC, ADE, $BCDE$)	0·0022	3	0·0007
Total	0·4850	31	

The corrected sum of squares of the four block totals in Table 9·461 after dividing by the number 8 in each block is 0·0022, agreeing with the sum for ABC, ADE, and $BCDE$. This furnishes a check. The mean square between blocks is in this case small because this arrangement was artificially super-imposed for illustrative purposes. Normally the higher-order interactions would be combined to give an estimate of the error variance. The five-factor interaction appears large because this was in fact the block effect in the original investigation; otherwise the interpretation is the same as that for the original example.

Double confounding

9·43. Double confounding may best be explained by means of an illustration. Consider the simple case of a 2^3 design carried out on a chemical process on the plant scale, and assume two intermediates are used in the process and the qualities of both may vary from one delivery to another. If each delivery is sufficient for four batches of the product, then it is possible to confound between two deliveries of one intermediate and also between two deliveries of the other. The design would be that of Table 9·41, where the two columns refer to the two deliveries of one intermediate, and the two rows to the deliveries of the second intermediate. This represents double confounding, one interaction being used to confound between lots of intermediate (1) and another interaction to confound between lots of intermediate (2). When this is done, another interaction, viz. the product of these two interactions, is also confounded. This is seen to be the familiar case of confounding between four blocks, and the appropriate design is that given in Table 9·41, with appropriate legends. No new principle is involved in double confounding, nor in triple, etc., confounding. All is covered by the treatment given in the previous sections for confounding in 2^p blocks.

Confounding in 3^n factorial designs

9·5. The basic principles of confounding in 3^n factorial designs are similar to those for the 2^n designs dealt with in the previous sections, subject to differences in procedure due to the larger number of levels per factor. Since each factor has three levels, the number of blocks, if of equal size, must be $3, 9, 27, \ldots$, or in general 3^p, where p is less than the number of factors. To the experimenter who does not wish to pursue the theoretical basis of confounding for 3^n designs but only to apply the method, classified lists of suitable designs are given in Appendix 9G to cover most likely industrial applications.

The simplest design in this class is based on two factors, denoted in the usual way by A and B, with levels 0, 1, and 2. Using the notation of Chapter 8, this design may be written as in Table 9·5, where the numerals $1, 2, \ldots, 9$ are used to identify the nine treatment combinations.

Assuming three deliveries of raw materials are available each sufficient to make three preparations, the nine observations must be divided into three sets of three. There are many ways of doing this, some of which correspond to definite effects of the two factors. If the three lots correspond to the three rows of Table 9·5, then the division corresponds to the main effect of A,

Table 9·5

3² FACTORIAL DESIGN

Level of factor A	Level of factor B		
	o	1	2
o	1	4	7
1	2	5	8
2	3	6	9

because the comparisons between the averages of the rows represent the main effect of A. Similarly, the division of the nine observations according to the three columns corresponds to the main effect of B. There are two other ways of dividing the nine observations into three sets of three, corresponding to effects which may be readily interpreted. All these arrangements are given in Table 9·51, in which the three lots are identified by Greek letters.

Table 9·51

WAYS OF PARTITIONING A 3² DESIGN INTO
THREE BLOCKS OF THREE

9·511

Level of factor A	Level of factor B		
	o	1	2
o	α	α	α
1	β	β	β
2	γ	γ	γ

9·512

Level of factor B		
o	1	2
α	β	γ
α	β	γ
α	β	γ

9·513

Level of factor A	Level of factor B		
	o	1	2
o	α	γ	β
1	β	α	γ
2	γ	β	α

9·514

Level of factor B		
o	1	2
α	β	γ
β	γ	α
γ	α	β

Arrangement 9·511 confuses the differences between lots with the differences between the levels of A, in other words, it confounds the main effect A, while arrangement 9·512 confounds the other main effect, B. Evidently both are unsatisfactory. In the third arrangement the three lots form a Latin

Square in relation to the factors A and B. The main effects A and B are now unaffected by the differences between the lots, the reason being that each of α, β, and γ is equally represented in each row (and each column), so that the α's, β's, and γ's are eliminated when taking the difference between the means of any two rows (or any two columns), provided there is no interaction between the factors and the lots. The same considerations hold for the other Latin Square given by design 9·514. If, therefore, the observations are divided among the three lots according to either arrangement 9·513 or 9·514, the two main effects are not confounded with lots. But two degrees of freedom must be so confounded in each design, and together must represent a pair out of the four degrees of freedom for the interaction between A and B. The designs 9·511–9·514 are all independent (or orthogonal) and the comparisons depicted represent the eight degrees of freedom for the 3^2 factorial design. YATES [9·1] calls the pair of interactions represented by Table 9·513 the I-interactions, and the pair represented by Table 9·514 the J-interactions, between A and B [§ 5·7]. The distinction between these two pairs of interactions is just a mathematical convenience for the purpose of confounding and has no other practical significance; in other words, the two interactions do not have independent interpretations. If A and B are interchanged, the comparisons giving the I- and J-interactions remain the same but appear in a different order.

9·51. These arrangements will now be examined in greater detail. For the I-interactions the lots α, β, and γ are denoted by i_0, i_1, and i_2, and for the J-interactions by j_0, j_1, and j_2 respectively. The factorial design may then be written in the form of Table 9·52.

Table 9·52

THE 3^2 FACTORIAL DESIGN SHOWING THE ORTHOGONAL
COMPONENTS

Level of factor A	Level of factor B		
	0	1	2
0	$i_0 j_0$	$i_2 j_1$	$i_1 j_2$
1	$i_1 j_1$	$i_0 j_2$	$i_2 j_0$
2	$i_2 j_2$	$i_1 j_0$	$i_0 j_1$

The i's form a Latin Square with respect to the factors A and B, and so also do the j's, and both the i's and j's together form a Graeco-Latin Square with respect to A and B. The analysis of the Graeco-Latin Square has already been given in Chapter 5, but it will simplify the presentation here to recall this analysis. The method is as follows.

Letting the numerals of Table 9·5 denote the actual observations, then the Main Effect of A is given by the two degrees of freedom corresponding to the variations between the row totals:

$$a_0 = 1 + 4 + 7 \quad \text{(The numerals refer to}$$
$$a_1 = 2 + 5 + 8 \quad \text{the combinations of}$$
$$a_2 = 3 + 6 + 9 \quad \text{Table 9·5.)}$$

The main effect of B is given by the two degrees of freedom corresponding to the variation between the column totals:

$$b_0 = 1 + 2 + 3$$
$$b_1 = 4 + 5 + 6$$
$$b_2 = 7 + 8 + 9$$

In a similar manner there are two degrees of freedom due to the variation between the I-totals. The I-totals are

$$i_0 = 1 + 5 + 9$$
$$i_1 = 2 + 6 + 7$$
$$i_2 = 3 + 4 + 8$$

Finally there are two degrees of freedom due to the variation between the J-totals. The J-totals are

$$j_0 = 1 + 6 + 8$$
$$j_1 = 2 + 4 + 9$$
$$j_2 = 3 + 5 + 7$$

The final analysis of variance then takes the form of Table 9·53.

Table 9·53

ANALYSIS OF VARIANCE OF 3^2 FACTORIAL DESIGN

Source of variation	Degrees of freedom
Main effect of A ..	2
Main effect of B ..	2
Between I-totals ..	2
Between J-totals ..	2
Total	8

Table 9·53 accounts for the eight degrees of freedom between the nine observations of the factorial design, and shows the four orthogonal pairs of degrees of freedom. The total sum of squares for the I- and J-interactions could be obtained by subtracting the sum of squares for A and B from the total in the usual way, but the above method shows how the interactions may be obtained directly, and reveals their structure. The reader is recommended to carry out the above analysis in detail, substituting actual figures for the symbols.

9·52. To summarise, suitable systems of confounding for 3^2 designs are given by either of Tables 9·513 or 9·514, where α, β, and γ denote the three lots, the former design confounding the I-interactions and the latter the J-interactions. The analysis is the same as that given in Table 9·53, but with one pair of interactions confounded with lots, and follows the usual analysis for a Latin Square considered in Chapter 5. Confounding in a 3^2 design is then simply a case of using a Latin Square with the blocks occupying the treatments positions and the two factors occupying the rows and columns respectively.

Confounding in a 3³ design

9·6. This is a more common case, and as before it is necessary to examine the structure of the designs before it is possible to derive suitable systems of confounding. The designs are tabulated for convenience in Appendix 9G [§§ **9G·12** and **9G·21**] and are derived as follows.

The 27 observations may be set out as Table 9·6.

Table 9·6

TABULATION OF 3³ FACTORIAL DESIGN

Level of factor A	Level of factor C								
	0			1			2		
	Level of factor B			Level of factor B			Level of factor B		
	0	1	2	0	1	2	0	1	2
0	000	010	020	001	011	021	002	012	022
1	100	110	120	101	111	121	102	112	122
2	200	210	220	201	211	221	202	212	222

The combinations of the levels of the three factors are entered in the table, the numerals in each triple-figure entry referring to the levels of the three factors A, B, and C in that order. The main effect of A corresponds to a division of the 27 observations into three sets of nine, one set with A at level 0, the second with A at level 1, and the third with A at level 2. Similarly the main effect of B corresponds to a division of the observations into three sets of nine, as seen from the columns of Table 9·6. The main effect of C corresponds to yet another division of the observations into three sets of nine.

To calculate the interaction between factors A and B we form the two-way table of A and B by summing over C. The interactions may be divided into two pairs, one corresponding to the I- and the other to the J-interactions. Each of these represents a division of the two-way table into three sets of three, and since each entry is the sum of three observations of Table 9·6, each of these interactions represents a division of the 27 observations into three sets of nine. Similarly the other two-factor interactions, $AC(I$ and $J)$ and $BC(I$ and $J)$, represent divisions of the 27 observations into three sets of nine.

The actual division of the observations into the three groups corresponding to each of these interactions is shown in Table 9·61.

Table 9·61

3^3 FACTORIAL DESIGN: *AB* INTERACTIONS

Level of first factor A	Levels of second and third factors B and C					
	i_0	i_1	i_2	j_0	j_1	j_2
0	00	20	10	00	10	20
0	01	21	11	01	11	21
0	02	22	12	02	12	22
1	10	00	20	20	00	10
1	11	01	21	21	01	11
1	12	02	22	22	02	12
2	20	10	00	10	20	00
2	21	11	01	11	21	01
2	22	12	02	12	22	02

Table 9·611

3^3 FACTORIAL DESIGN: *AC* INTERACTIONS

Level of first factor A	Levels of second and third factors B and C					
	i_0	i_1	i_2	j_0	j_1	j_2
0	00	02	01	00	01	02
0	10	12	11	10	11	12
0	20	22	21	20	21	22
1	01	00	02	02	00	01
1	11	10	12	12	10	11
1	21	20	22	22	20	21
2	02	01	00	01	02	00
2	12	11	10	11	12	10
2	22	21	20	21	22	20

Table 9·612

3³ FACTORIAL DESIGN: *BC* INTERACTIONS

Level of first factor A	Levels of second and third factors B and C					
	i_0	i_1	i_2	j_0	j_1	j_2
0	00	10	20	00	01	02
0	11	21	01	21	22	20
0	22	02	12	12	10	11
1	00	10	20	00	01	02
1	11	21	01	21	22	20
1	22	02	12	12	10	11
2	00	10	20	00	01	02
2	11	21	01	21	22	20
2	22	02	12	12	10	11

The main effects and two-factor interactions account for 18 degrees of freedom, two for each main effect and two pairs for each of the three two-factor interactions, leaving eight degrees of freedom for the three-factor interaction *ABC*. Just as the four degrees of freedom for each interaction may be divided into two pairs corresponding respectively to the *I*- and *J*-interactions, so the eight degrees of freedom for the three-factor interaction may be divided into four pairs of degrees of freedom all independent of one another, each pair corresponding to a division of the 27 observations into three sets of nine. These four pairs are identifiable and, following the notation of YATES, are referred to as the *W*-, *X*-, *Y*-, and *Z*-interactions. The actual divisions of the 27 observations corresponding to these interactions are given in Table 9·62.

Table 9·62

3³ FACTORIAL DESIGN: THE THREE-FACTOR INTERACTIONS

Combination of 1st and 2nd factors		W interactions			X interactions			Y interactions			Z interactions		
		w_0	w_1	w_2	x_0	x_1	x_2	y_0	y_1	y_2	z_0	z_1	z_2
1	00	0	2	1	0	1	2	0	2	1	0	1	2
2	10	1	0	2	2	0	1	1	0	2	2	0	1
3	20	2	1	0	1	2	0	2	1	0	1	2	0
4	01	2	1	0	1	2	0	1	0	2	2	0	1
5	11	0	2	1	0	1	2	2	1	0	1	2	0
6	21	1	0	2	2	0	1	0	2	1	0	1	2
7	02	1	0	2	2	0	1	2	1	0	1	2	0
8	12	2	1	0	1	2	0	0	2	1	0	1	2
9	22	0	2	1	0	1	2	1	0	2	2	0	1

This table may be taken as the definition of the W-, X-, Y-, and Z-interactions. The W-interaction is represented by the comparison between the sum of the observations in each of the columns w_0, w_1, and w_2, and so for the X-, Y-, and Z-interactions. It can readily be verified that the sum of the sums of squares for the W-, X-, Y-, and Z-interactions does in fact equal the three-factor interaction sum of squares calculated as a remainder in the ordinary way. This was done in Appendix 8F on a numerical example. The distinction between the W-, X-, Y-, and Z-interactions is a matter of convenience for confounding and does not have any other practical significance.

The complete analysis of a 3^3 design according to the main effects and the above interactions is given in Table 9·63.

Table 9·63

ANALYSIS OF 3^3 FACTORIAL DESIGN

Source of variation	Degrees of freedom
Main effects:	
A	2
B	2
C	2
Two-factor interactions:	
$AB\begin{cases} I\ .. \end{cases}$	2
$\begin{cases} \mathcal{J}\ .. \end{cases}$	2
$AC\begin{cases} I\ .. \end{cases}$	2
$\begin{cases} \mathcal{J}\ .. \end{cases}$	2
$BC\begin{cases} I\ .. \end{cases}$	2
$\begin{cases} \mathcal{J}\ .. \end{cases}$	2
Three-factor interactions:	
W	2
X	2
Y	2
Z	2
Total	26

For the W-, X-, Y-, and Z-interactions defined above it is necessary to specify the particular order A, B, C, D for the factors, for if the order is changed, then the W, X, Y are interchanged in a particular way, but Z remains invariant. There is therefore no essential difference between the W-, X-, and Y-interactions, but these interactions represent a convenient way of dividing the eight degrees of freedom for the three-factor interaction into four orthogonal pairs.

A 3^3 design in three blocks

9·7. The best arrangement for dividing a 3^3 design into three blocks is to confound a pair of three-factor interactions. We may use the W-, X-, Y-, or

Z-interactions for this purpose, and there is nothing to choose between them. To confound the W-interaction, refer to Table 9·62 and place the treatment combinations of column w_0 in one block, of w_1 in another, and of w_2 in the third block. Similar considerations apply if any other pair of three-factor interactions is chosen for confounding. The analysis confounding the W-interaction is simply as in Table 9·7.

Table 9·7

ANALYSIS OF 3^3 DESIGN CONFOUNDING THE W-INTERACTION

Source of variation	Degrees of freedom
Main effects:	
A	2
B	2
C	2
Two-factor interactions:	
AB	4
BC	4
AC	4
Blocks (W-interaction)	2
Remaining interactions.. ..	6
Total	26

When there is no replication the remainder interaction mean square may be used for the error variance. When any or all of A, B, C are quantitative factors, the linear and quadratic effects may be calculated for the main effects and two-factor interactions. It would not be possible, even if it were desirable, to analyse the remaining three-factor interactions in this way.

For some purposes it may be simpler to express the designs of Table 9·62 in the form of Tables 9·71–9·74.

Table 9·71

CONFOUNDING W-INTERACTIONS

Level of factor A	Level of factor C								
	0			1			2		
	Level of factor B			Level of factor B			Level of factor B		
	0	1	2	0	1	2	0	1	2
0	α	γ	β	γ	β	α	β	α	γ
1	β	α	γ	α	γ	β	γ	β	α
2	γ	β	α	β	α	γ	α	γ	β

Table 9·72

CONFOUNDING X-INTERACTIONS

Level of factor A	Level of factor C								
	0			1			2		
	Level of factor B			Level of factor B			Level of factor B		
	0	1	2	0	1	2	0	1	2
0	a	γ	β	β	a	γ	γ	β	a
1	β	a	γ	γ	β	a	a	γ	β
2	γ	β	a	a	γ	β	β	a	γ

Table 9·73

CONFOUNDING Y-INTERACTIONS

Level of factor A	Level of factor C								
	0			1			2		
	Level of factor B			Level of factor B			Level of factor B		
	0	1	2	0	1	2	0	1	2
0	a	β	γ	γ	a	β	β	γ	a
1	β	γ	a	a	β	γ	γ	a	β
2	γ	a	β	β	γ	a	a	β	γ

Table 9·74

CONFOUNDING Z-INTERACTIONS

Level of factor A	Level of factor C								
	0			1			2		
	Level of factor B			Level of factor B			Level of factor B		
	0	1	2	0	1	2	0	1	2
0	a	β	γ	β	γ	a	γ	a	β
1	β	γ	a	γ	a	β	a	β	γ
2	γ	a	β	a	β	γ	β	γ	a

An important property of the analysis of the 26 degrees of freedom given in Table 9·63 is that all the 13 pairs of degrees of freedom are independent, so that any pair may be confounded without affecting any of the other pairs, provided only that there is no interaction of effects with blocks. It will be instructive for the reader to verify this independence on numerical results, for example, by adding a constant quantity to the observations in w_0 and another constant quantity to the observations in w_1 and working out the analysis step by step as given in Appendix 9F. He will find the addition of these two constants has not affected the main effects, nor the two-factor interactions, nor the remaining three-factor interactions. This is a consequence of orthogonality. (See also the remarks in Appendix 9G on the 3^3 designs.)

Confounding 3^3 designs over nine blocks of three observations

9·8. To divide the observations among nine blocks it is necessary to use up four pairs of degrees of freedom. We cannot choose any four pairs at will. If two pairs of three-factor interactions are chosen, say W and X, two other pairs of degrees of freedom are automatically confounded, one of which is a main effect; the best system is one which confounds one pair of three-factor interactions and three pairs of two-factor interactions. Any pair of three-factor interactions may be chosen, but in order to derive a satisfactory design we are limited in the choice of two-factor interactions for the other pair of degrees of freedom. The best designs are any of the following:

(1) $W(ABC)$, $\mathcal{J}(AB)$, $\mathcal{J}(AC)$, $I(BC)$

(2) $X(ABC)$, $\mathcal{J}(AB)$, $I(AC)$, $\mathcal{J}(BC)$

(3) $Y(ABC)$, $I(AB)$, $\mathcal{J}(AC)$, $\mathcal{J}(BC)$

(4) $Z(ABC)$, $I(AB)$, $I(AC)$, $I(BC)$

where $W(ABC)$ represents the W-component of the three-factor interaction ABC, $\mathcal{J}(AB)$ the $\mathcal{J}$-component of the two-factor interaction AB, and so on. There is no difference in practice between the W-, X-, Y-, and Z-interactions or between the I- and $\mathcal{J}$-interactions, and no meaning can be attached to the separate parts of any interaction. There is nothing to choose between the four arrangements (1)–(4), all being equally suitable, and in practice the choice should be made at random. The corresponding designs are tabulated in Appendix 9G [§§ 9G·121–4], any of which will be suitable.

9·81. We shall now show how to construct the designs corresponding to the above four systems. Consider system (1). To confound $W(ABC)$ we simply refer to Table 9·62, in which the treatment combinations for the corresponding blocks w_0, w_1, and w_2 are given. To confound the second interaction

$\mathcal{J}(AB)$ it is necessary to divide each of the W columns into three parts, those belonging to i_0, to i_1, and to i_2, and this is done by referring to Table 9·61, in which the division for $\mathcal{J}(AB)$ is given. To divide the W column into three blocks we draw up a two-way table (as in Table 9·8 below) for w (0, 1, 2) and $j(AB)$ (0, 1, 2). For w_0 (Table 9·62) we note that the first observation 000 is a member of $j_0(AB)$ and it is therefore entered in the cell $w_0 j_0(AB)$ of Table 9·8. The second observation 101 of w_0 is a member of $j_1(AB)$, and this is then entered in cell $w_0 j_1(AB)$ of Table 9·8. Similarly, the third observation 202 of w_0 is a member of $j_2(AB)$, and so on. Doing this successively for all members of w_0, w_1, and w_2 gives Table 9·8.

Table 9·8

3^3 FACTORIAL DESIGN CONFOUNDING $W(ABC)$ AND $\mathcal{J}(AB)$

	w_0			w_1			w_2		
$j_0(AB)$	000	211	122	002	210	121	001	212	120
$j_1(AB)$	101	012	220	100	011	222	102	010	221
$j_2(AB)$	202	110	021	201	112	020	200	111	022

Table 9·8 gives the nine blocks which confound $W(ABC)$ and $\mathcal{J}(AB)$. It may be verified that the I- and $\mathcal{J}$-components of this design are in fact the remaining two pairs of interactions, $\mathcal{J}(AC)$ and $I(BC)$, which are confounded; this shows that if we confound $W(ABC)$ and $\mathcal{J}(AB)$ we must confound $\mathcal{J}(AC)$ and $I(BC)$ in consequence. It would be instructive for the reader to carry out the above procedure for any two other pairs of the interactions, e.g. $\mathcal{J}(AC)$ and $I(BC)$; he will find that the same design will be obtained but with the blocks in a different order. If the factors are quantitative, it is possible to analyse the main effects into linear and quadratic components, but a similar analysis for the interactions not confounded is not possible. The analysis of variance will have the form given in Table 9·81.

Example 9·4. Yield of cotton dyestuffs
9·82. The method of analysis for a 3^3 design involving confounding is illustrated in detail in Appendix 9F, using the observations of Example 8·5 of Chapter 8. This represents a 3^3 factorial design replicated twice, and although no mention was made of confounding in relation to this example in Chapter 8, the experiment was in fact divided into blocks of nine observations carried out in sequence as a safeguard against possible changes in technique and possible trends due to other causes, since several weeks were required to carry out the 54 preparations of product required by the design.

Table 9·81

ANALYSIS OF VARIANCE OF 3^3 FACTORIAL DESIGN CONFOUNDED
IN NINE BLOCKS

Source of variation	Degrees of freedom
Main effects:	
A	2
B	2
C	2
Two-factor interactions:	
$I(AB)$	2
$I(AC)$	2
$J(BC)$	2
Blocks	8
Remaining three-factor interactions..	6
Total	26

Confounding in 3^4 factorial experiments

9·9. In a 3^4 factorial design there are two degrees of freedom for each of the four main effects (denoted by A, B, C, and D), four degrees of freedom (consisting of two pairs, the I- and the J-) for each of the six two-factor interactions, eight degrees of freedom (consisting of four pairs, the W-, X-, Y-, and Z-) for each of the four three-factor interactions, and finally sixteen degrees of freedom for the four-factor interactions consisting of eight pairs. Any of these pairs may be confounded between three blocks, and by so doing, the other degrees of freedom are unaffected. Suitable designs may be readily derived from Table 9·62 by simple substitution. Consider, for example, the design confounding the W-interactions; in order to generate the blocks for a confounded design for four factors we replace each level of the third factor by three given combinations of the third and fourth factors as follows:

$$0 = 1, 5, 9 \quad (\text{i.e. } 00, 11, 22)$$
$$1 = 2, 6, 7 \quad (\text{i.e. } 10, 21, 02)$$
$$2 = 3, 4, 8 \quad (\text{i.e. } 20, 01, 12)$$

This gives Table 9·9.

The figures in brackets represent the levels of the third factor of the original 3^3 factorial design, which have been replaced by three combinations of

Table 9·9

CONFOUNDING 3^4 FACTORIAL DESIGN IN THREE BLOCKS

Combination of 1st and 2nd factors		Combination of 3rd and 4th factors								
		w_1				w_2				w_3			
1	00	(0)	00	11	22	(2)	20	01	12	(1)	10	21	02
2	10	(1)	10	21	02	(0)	00	11	22	(2)	20	01	12
3	20	(2)	20	01	12	(1)	10	21	02	(0)	00	11	22
4	01	(2)	20	01	12	(1)	10	21	02	(0)	00	11	22
5	11	(0)	00	11	22	(2)	20	01	12	(1)	10	21	02
6	21	(1)	10	21	02	(0)	00	11	22	(2)	20	01	12
7	02	(1)	10	21	02	(0)	00	11	22	(2)	20	01	12
8	12	(2)	20	01	12	(1)	10	21	02	(0)	00	11	22
9	22	(0)	00	11	22	(2)	20	01	12	(1)	10	21	02

the third and a fourth factor, to generate the design appropriate for four factors.

The above substitution set corresponds to the familiar I's, and for this reason it is known as the I-set. We could equally well have used the J-set:

$$0 = 1, 8, 6 \quad \text{(i.e. 00, 12, 21)}$$
$$1 = 4, 2, 9 \quad \text{(i.e. 01, 10, 22)}$$
$$2 = 7, 5, 3 \quad \text{(i.e. 02, 11, 20)}$$

Application of the I- and J-sets to each of the W, X, Y, and Z columns of Table 9·62 will generate eight designs, each confounding a pair of four-factor interactions corresponding to the eight pairs of degrees of freedom for the four-factor interactions. To confound a 3^4 factorial design in nine blocks it is necessary to use four of the three-factor interactions. These have been conveniently tabulated by YATES [9·1], and the designs are given in Appendix 9G. To extend, we apply again either the I- or the J-sets to step up to five factors.

Confounding in $2^m 3^n$ designs

9·91. Confounding in $2^m 3^n$ designs, that is, with some factors at two levels and others at three levels, is more complicated, and it is not proposed to consider such designs in this book. The reader is referred to [9·1] for their treatment. Apart from the complication, the scope for confounding is limited, and they should be avoided, particularly where the experimenter has some freedom in the choice of levels of the factors.

REFERENCES

[9·1] YATES, F. *The Design and Analysis of Factorial Experiments.* Imperial Bureau of Soil Science (Harpenden, 1937).

[9·2] FISHER, R. A. *The Design of Experiments.* 6th edition. Oliver & Boyd (London and Edinburgh, 1951).

[9·3] NAIR, K. R. "The Studentised Form of the Extreme Mean Square Test in the Analysis of Variance." *Biometrika*, 35 (1948), 16–31.

[9·4] COCHRAN, W. C., and COX, G. M. *Experimental Design.* Wiley (New York, 1950).

APPENDIX 9A

DETAILS OF THE STATISTICAL ANALYSIS OF EXAMPLE 9·1

9A·1. The data are given in Table 9·2. The computation is simplified by deducting a constant quantity (150 lb.) from all the yields.

Table 9A·1

YIELDS OF TABLE 9·2 LESS 150 LB.

Ammonium chloride		Lot of base material							
		|— 1 —|		|— 2 —|		|— 3 —|		|— 4 —|	
Quality	Amount	Unit 1	2	Unit 1	2	Unit 1	2	Unit 1	2
Coarse	Normal	5			6		11	14	
	+ 10%		2	18		25			12
Fine	Normal		0	12		21			3
	+ 10%	7			11		23	21	
Total		14		47		80		50	
								Grand total = 191	

This is a 2^3 factorial design replicated twice and confounded between four lots of base material. The preliminary analysis is carried out ignoring confounding, that is, regarding lots 1 and 2 as the first replicate and lots 3 and 4 as the second replicate. The steps in the analysis are as follows.

9A·2. Sum the results over the two replicates. This gives a 2^3 factorial table in which the factors are denoted by A, B, and C respectively, as shown in Table 9A·2.

Table 9A·2

DERIVED FROM TABLE 9A·1 BY SUMMING OVER LOTS OF BASE
MATERIAL

Ammonium chloride		Unit (C)	
Quality (A)	Amount (B)	1	2
Coarse (1)	Normal (1)	19	17
	+ 10% (b)	43	14
Fine (a)	Normal (1)	33	3
	+ 10% (b)	28	34

The results of the design are analysed in the usual way, that is, by arranging
the observations in standard order and computing the sums and differences
of pairs as shown in Table 9A·3.

Table 9A·3

ANALYSIS OF THE DATA OF TABLE 9A·2

Treatment combination	(1)	(2)	(3)	(4)	Effect = Col (4)/8*	Mean square = Col (4)²/16*
(1)	19	52	123	191	T	—
(a)	33	71	68	5	$A = 0·63$	1·56
(b)	43	20	− 1	47	$B = 5·88$	138·06
(ab)	28	48	6	5	$AB = 0·63$	1·56
(c)	17	14	19	− 55	$C = − 6·88$	189·06
(ac)	3	− 15	28	7	$AC = 0·88$	3·06
(bc)	14	− 14	− 29	9	$BC = 1·13$	5·06
(abc)	34	20	34	63	$ABC = 7·88$	248·06
					Total	586·42

* The divisors here denote twice the usual number, since the results of Table 9A·2
denote the sums of two replicates.

As a check, calculate the corrected sum of squares of the eight results of
column (1) and divide by 2 to allow for the fact that these observations are
each the sum of two yields. This gives $5733/2 − 2280·06 = 586·44$, which
agrees within rounding-off errors with the sum of the last column of Table
9A·3.

9A·3. Calculate the total sum of squares of the 16 observations of Table 9A·1 about their mean, viz. $(5^2 + 6^2 + \ldots + 23^2 + 21^2) - 191^2/16 = 3209 - 2280 \cdot 06 = 928 \cdot 94$.

9A·4. The analysis of variance then follows as Table 9A·4.

Table 9A·4

ANALYSIS OF VARIANCE OF TABLE 9A·1, IGNORING CONFOUNDING

Source of variation	Sum of squares	Degrees of freedom	Mean square
Ammonium chloride:			
Quality (A)	1·56	1	1·56
Amount (B)	138·06	1	138·06
Between units (C) ..	189·06	1	189·06
Interactions:			
AB	1·56	1	1·56
AC	3·06	1	3·06
BC	5·06	1	5·06
ABC	248·06	1	248·06
Remainder = error ..	342·52	8	42·82
Total	928·94	15	

The remainder sum of squares can also be obtained directly from the sum of squares of the differences between the duplicates of Table 9A·1. For example, in the first row of this table 14 is a duplicate of 5, 11 a duplicate of 6, and so on for the other rows. The actual differences in order are

$$9, 5, 10, 7, 3, 9, 14, 12$$

The sum of these is 69. The sum of squares of the eight differences is 685, which has to be divided by 2. This gives 342·50, agreeing within rounding-off errors with the remainder sum of squares of Table 9A·4.

9A·5. The next stage introduces confounding. Calculate the corrected sum of squares between the four lots. This is derived from the totals of each lot as follows:

$$(14^2 + 47^2 + 80^2 + 50^2)/4 - 191^2/16 = 2826 \cdot 25 - 2280 \cdot 06 = 546 \cdot 19$$

Since the three-factor interaction has been confounded between lots, the sum of squares due to this effect is merged in the sum of squares between the four lots. The three-factor interaction is seen to be the comparison between the sums of lots 1 and 4 and lots 2 and 3. The other two degrees of freedom are contained in the replication sum of squares, since lot 3 is a replicate of lot 2, and lot 4 a replicate of lot 1.

The final analysis of variance table can now be constructed as Table 9A·5.

Table 9A·5

FINAL ANALYSIS OF VARIANCE OF TABLE 9A·1

Source of variation	Sum of squares	Degrees of freedom	Mean square
Ammonium chloride:			
Quality (A)	1·56	1	1·56
Amount (B)	138·06	1	138·06
Between units (C) ..	189·06	1	189·06
Interactions:			
AB	1·56 ⎫	1 ⎫	1·56 ⎫
AC	3·06 ⎬ 9·68	1 ⎬ 3	3·06 ⎬ 3·23
BC	5·06 ⎭	1 ⎭	5·06 ⎭
Between lots of base material	546·19	3	182·06
Remainder (= error) ..	44·39	6	7·40
Total	928·94	15	
Process variation.. ..			6·25

The remainder sum of squares and degrees of freedom are obtained by subtraction from the total. The process variance (6·25) is that calculated from the records of previous manufacture.

Interpretation

9A·6. The remainder mean square does not differ significantly from the process variation. The mean squares for amount of ammonium chloride and for the difference between units are both highly significant, whether compared with the remainder or with the process variation. A discussion on the relative merits of these two as error variances is given in the text [§ 9·18]. The mean square between lots of base material is highly significant, showing that there is strong evidence of differences in quality between the lots of base material. None of the two-factor interactions is significant.

The magnitudes of the significant effects other than quality of base material are:

Mean unit 1 − mean unit 2   = 15·375 − 8·500
                                     = 6·875 lb.

Mean (+ 10%) − mean (Normal)   = 14·875 − 9·000
     ammonium chloride   = 5·875 lb.

In this example it turns out that the variation between the blends of base material is large, and that therefore a large increase in precision has been gained by confounding. In addition, valuable information has been gained on the variations in quality of base material, indicating that this is a source of variation which is worth while investigating.

Appendix 9B

PARTIAL CONFOUNDING IN A 2^3 FACTORIAL DESIGN

9B·1. When an interaction is confounded in one replicate and not in another, it is said to be Partially Confounded. There are four interactions, AB, AC, BC, and ABC, in a 2^3 factorial design, and in order to obtain a completely balanced design partially confounding all interactions to the same extent we require four replicates. The design is that of Table 9·23.

All the main effects are completely free of the block differences and consequently their sums of squares may be calculated in the usual way for replicated 2^3 factorial designs.

Writing $S(A) =$ (Sum of the 16 observations containing a — Sum of the 16 observations not containing a), then

Main effect of $A = S(A)/16$

Sum of squares $= [S(A)]^2/32$

$=$ mean square for one degree of freedom

The divisor for the squares of $S(A)$ is 32 because $S(A)$ is based on all the 32 observations. A similar computation is used for the other main effects B and C, and the corresponding sum of squares.

9B·2. The next step is to obtain an estimate of the magnitudes of the interactions which are partially confounded and calculate their mean squares. Referring to Table 9·23, it is seen that the three-factor interaction ABC is confounded in the first replicate and not in the other three; consequently ABC can be calculated from the second, third, and fourth replicates as follows:

$$ABC = \tfrac{1}{4}(a - 1)(b - 1)(c - 1)$$
$$= \tfrac{1}{4}[(abc + a + b + c) - (ab + ac + bc + (1))]$$
$$= \tfrac{1}{4}[S_1(ABC) - S_2(ABC)]$$

where $S_1(ABC)$ denotes the sum of the observations $(abc + a + b + c)$ and $S_2(ABC)$ the sum $(ab + ac + bc + (1))$ in any replicate. For each of the last three replicates calculate the quantities $S_1(ABC)$ and $S_2(ABC)$ and their difference. Denoting the sum of the differences by $D(ABC)$, then

$$ABC = D(ABC)/(3 \times 4)$$

$$\text{Sum of squares } (= \text{mean square}) = [D(ABC)]^2/24$$

The estimate of the interaction is of course the average of the estimates from each of the three replicates. The divisor of the sum of squares is 24, which is equal to the number of observations involved in the expression $D(ABC)$. The other three interactions are calculated similarly.

AB is calculated from the first, third, and fourth replicates, AC from the first, second, and fourth, and BC from the first, second, and third.

9B·3. All that is now required to complete the analysis of variance is the total sum of squares of the 32 observations and the sums of squares between the eight blocks; the analysis of variance table will then take the form of Table 9B·1.

Table 9B·1

ANALYSIS OF VARIANCE

Source of variation	Degrees of freedom
Main effects:	
A	1
B	1
C	1
Two-factor interactions:	
AB	1
AC	1
BC	1
Three-factor interaction:	
ABC	1
Between blocks	7
Remainder (= error)	17
Total	31

The remainder mean square may be used as error variance in the usual way to assess the significance of the effects.

It is interesting to note that when calculating the main effects all the 32 observations are utilised, while the calculation of the various interactions involves only 24 observations, i.e. three-quarters of the total, so that the main effects are determined with higher precision than the interactions, the ratio being 4 : 3. No correction is required for this in the analysis of variance, as these points have already been taken into consideration when using the appropriate divisor for the sum of squares.

Relation between partial confounding and balanced incomplete blocks
9B·4. Table 9·23 is completely balanced as far as the interactions are concerned, that is, all interactions are replicated to the same extent. The main effects are replicated to a greater extent, and the design is therefore not balanced with respect to all the effects. Complete balance can be attained by the addition of three further replicates in which the main effects $A, B,$ and C are confounded in turn. These seven replicates then give a balanced incomplete block design of eight treatments in 14 blocks of four observations each [§ **6A·44**].

APPENDIX 9C
DETAILS OF STATISTICAL ANALYSIS OF EXAMPLE 9·2

9C·1. This is a 2^5 experiment in which the five-factor interaction is confounded between two blocks. The analysis is that appropriate to any 2^5 factorial experiment, with the difference that the five-factor interaction is equated to blocks, that is, to the difference between the two weeks. The formal analysis is given in Table 9C·1.

9C·2. The next step is to obtain a suitable error variance, and this is normally supplied by the higher-order interactions. A summarised form of the analysis of variance derived from Table 9C·1 is given in Table 9C·2.

The five-factor interaction has been confounded between blocks, and the first choice for the error variance is the combined four-factor interactions. It is clear in this example that both the three- and the four-factor interactions may be combined to form the error variance because there is no appreciable difference between them. Further, when the experiment was planned the three- and four-factor interactions were not expected to be appreciable, and it was the intention to use these as the error variance based on 15 degrees of freedom if the observations did not contradict this hypothesis. The error variance is then $(0·0293 + 0·0219)/15 = 0·0034$. Compared with this a mean square of $4·54 \times 0·0034 = 0·0154$ is required for any single effect to be significant at the 5% level (4·54 is the value of F for 1 and 15 degrees of freedom). Referring to Table 9C·1, the effects $A, C, E, CE,$ and blocks, are thus found to be significant.

The final analysis of variance takes the form of Table 9·32.

9C·3. On the usual F-test one of the two-factor interactions appears significant. It may be argued that since the combined two-factor interactions are

PENICILLIN YIELD. 2^5 FACTORIAL EXPERIMENT

Factor combination	Yield	Log yield	1	2	3	4	5		Effect = (Col. 5)/16	Variance = (Col. 5)²/32
(1)	142	2·152	4·209	8·357	17·371	34·636	67·035			
a	114	2·057	4·148	9·014	17·265	32·399	−1·895	A	−0·1184	0·1122
b	129	2·111	4·477	8·345	16·100	−0·960	0·057	B	−0·0036	0·0001
ab	109	2·037	4·537	8·920	16·299	−0·935	0·643	AB	−0·0402	0·0129
c	185	2·267	4·203	7·985	−0·291	0·174	1·533	C	0·0958	0·0734
ac	162	2·210	4·142	8·115	−0·669	0·117	0·533	AC	−0·0333	0·0089
bc	200	2·301	4·516	8·064	−0·384	0·210	0·533	BC	−0·0333	0·0089
abc	172	2·236	4·404	8·235	−0·551	0·433	0·003	ABC	0·0002	0·0000
d	148	2·170	4·050	−0·169	0·001	1·232	0·093	D	0·0058	0·0003
ad	108	2·033	3·935	−0·122	0·173	0·301	0·545	AD	−0·0341	0·0093
bd	146	2·164	3·997	−0·323	0·006	0·024	0·067	BD	0·0042	0·0001
abd	95	1·978	4·118	−0·346	0·111	0·557	0·337	ABD	−0·0211	0·0035
cd	200	2·301	4·061	0·047	0·013	0·070	0·041	CD	0·0026	0·0000
acd	164	2·215	4·003	−0·431	0·223	0·463	0·329	ACD	0·0206	0·0034
bcd	215	2·332	4·033	0·236	0·166	0·154	0·181	BCD	−0·0113	0·0010
abcd	118	2·072	4·202	0·315	0·267	0·157	0·581	ABCD	0·0363	0·0105
e	106	2·025	−0·095	−0·061	0·657	−0·106	2·237	E	0·1398	0·1564
ae	106	2·025	−0·074	0·060	0·575	0·199	0·025	AE	0·0016	0·0000
be	88	1·944	−0·057	0·061	0·130	0·378	0·291	BE	0·0182	0·0026
abe	98	1·991	−0·065	0·112	0·171	0·167	0·223	ABE	0·0139	0·0016
ce	113	2·053	−0·137	0·115	0·047	0·172	0·931	CE	0·0582	0·0271
ace	88	1·944	−0·186	0·121	0·023	0·105	0·581	ACE	0·0363	0·0106
bce	166	2·220	−0·086	0·058	0·478	0·236	0·393	BCE	0·0246	0·0048
abce	79	1·898	0·260	0·169	0·079	0·101	0·311	ABCE	0·0194	0·0030
de	101	2·004	0	0·021	0·121	0·082	0·305	DE	0·0191	0·0029
ade	114	2·057	0·047	0·008	0·051	0·041	0·211	ADE	0·0132	0·0014
bde	140	2·146	0·109	0·049	0·236	0·070	0·277	BDE	0·0173	0·0024
abde	72	1·857	0·322	0·174	0·227	0·399	0·135	ABDE	0·0084	0·0006
cde	130	2·114	0·053	0·047	0·029	0·172	0·123	CDE	0·0077	0·0005
acde	83	1·919	0·289	0·213	0·125	0·009	0·469	ACDE	0·0293	0·0069
bcde	145	2·161	0·195	0·342	0·260	0·096	0·163	BCDE	0·0102	0·0008
abcde	110	2·041	0·120	0·075	0·417	0·677	0·773	(ABCDE = blocks)	0·0483	0·0187
Total	4,146	67·035						Total	..	0·4848

Check: Corrected sum of squares of log titres = 0·4849, which agrees within rounding-off errors.

E2

Table 9C·2

EXAMPLE 9·2. SUMMARY OF ANALYSIS OF VARIANCE

Source of variation	Sum of squares	Degrees of freedom	Mean square
Main effects	0·3424	5	0·0685
Interactions:			
Two-factor	0·0727	10	0·0073
Three-factor	0·0293	10	0·0029
Four-factor	0·0219	5	0·0044
Five-factor (= blocks)	0·0187	1	0·0187
Total	0·4850	31	

not significant, a more stringent test should be used to assess the significance of CE (see Appendix 7D). It can be verified that the interaction CE does not reach the 5% level and its significance on the basis of this test alone would remain in doubt. However, information existed from earlier work that interaction CE was likely to be appreciable. To examine the nature of this interaction we construct the two-way table of C and E (that is, precursor and glucose) by averaging over the other factors, as shown in Table 9·321.

Ignoring for the moment the possibility of interaction, the effect of glucose is negative and that of precursor positive, from which we conclude that the best conditions are given by the presence of precursor and absence of glucose. The interaction is negative, which means that the effect of precursor is greater in the absence of glucose than in its presence, and this effect enhances the superiority of the condition: 0·05% precursor and no glucose.

9C·4. In this example it happens that the same conclusion as to the best treatment combination is arrived at whether or not the interaction CE is regarded as significant. On strictly logical grounds we should have to conclude on the evidence of this experiment alone that the interaction CE was not significant. It could be regarded as significant only when (as in this case) there was some prior information which indicated that interaction CE was likely to be greater than the other interactions.

APPENDIX 9D

CONFOUNDING FROM THE STANDPOINT OF FINITE GROUPS

THE subject of confounding may be usefully approached from the standpoint of finite groups.

Groups

9D·1. A group is a set of objects or elements with which is associated a definite law of composition so that the sum, product, or other resultant of any two elements is also an element of the group. In other words, the group is closed to addition, multiplication, or some other law of composition.

The numerals on an ordinary clock dial form a finite group, the law of composition being addition followed by reduction modulo 12 (division by 12 and taking the remainder). Thus II + III = V, IV + VII = XI, V + VII = midday, VI + IX = III, and so on.

The fourth roots of unity form a finite multiplication group, viz.

$$1, i, -1, -i \qquad (i = \sqrt{(-1)})$$

for $(i)(-1) = -i, (-1)(-i) = i$, and so on.

Confounding in 2^n factorial design
Main effects and interactions

9D·2. The set of main effects and interactions may be treated as a finite multiplication group. For a 2^n design we require n generators, which may be identified with the main effects $A, B, C, \ldots$. The law of composition then consists in forming all possible products of $A, B, C, \ldots$ subject to the condition that $A^2 = B^2 = C^2 = \ldots = 1$. Applying these ideas to a 2^3 factorial experiment we have:

	Elements of group	Number of elements
Unity	I	I
Main effects	A, B, C	3
Two-factor interactions..	AB, AC, BC	3
Three-factor interaction..	ABC	I
		8

in which every element of order higher than the first is derived as a product of elements of lower order. With the condition $A^2 = B^2 = \ldots = 1$ the product of any two or more elements is itself an element of the group, e.g., $ABC \times AB = A^2B^2C = C, AB \times AC = A^2BC = BC$; and so on.

Although it is convenient to use A, B, and C as generators there is no need to do so. Any set of three elements may be so used provided they are independent. Thus, taking A, B, and BC as generators we have:

	Elements of group	How obtained	Number of elements
Generators	A, B, BC		3
Products two at a time	AB, ABC, C	$A \times B\ \ = AB$ $A \times BC = ABC$ $B \times BC = B^2C = C$	3
Product three at a time	AC	$A \times B \times BC$ $= AB^2C = AC$	1
Product of any element with itself ($=$ unity)	1	$A \times A = A^2 = 1$	1
			8

We have now accounted for all eight elements, and it is easy to show that any further multiplications only lead to repetitions of results already obtained. Writing down the results in standard order, the group is

$$1, A, B, AB, C, AC, BC, ABC$$

in agreement with the previous result. Note that we could not have used A, BC, and ABC as generators, because these three elements are not independent; any one may be derived from the other two.

By this device we have invested the set of main effects and interactions with the properties of a finite multiplication group, viz. that the product of any two elements yields another element, and the group is closed to multiplication. The method may obviously be extended to a 2^n factorial experiment. Excluding the identity, the group comprises $2^n - 1$ elements, of which n may be treated as independent and the rest as consequential.

Defining contrasts

9D·3. The set of effects confounded in any system of confounding is known as the set of Defining Contrasts, and the defining contrasts plus the identity (1) form a finite multiplication group, or more explicitly a sub-group of the main group of effects. The utility of this proposition is immediately apparent. Given that a 2^n factorial design is to be confounded in 2^p blocks, we have to write down a set of $2^p - 1$ defining contrasts, of which p may be chosen arbitrarily (provided they are independent) and the remaining $2^p - p - 1$ are determined in consequence. Let us apply these ideas to a 2^5 factorial design proposed to be confounded in eight blocks of four observations. Since $8 = 2^3$ the group of defining contrasts will comprise seven elements, excluding the identity, of which three may be taken as generators. Taking CDE, ACE, and $ABDE$, which are obviously independent, we have:

	Element of group	How obtained	Number of elements
Generators	CDE, ACE, ABDE		3
Products two at a time	AD, ABC, BCD	$\begin{cases} CDE \times ACE \\ \quad = AC^2DE^2 = AD \\ CDE \times ABDE \\ \quad = ABCD^2E^2 \\ \quad = ABC \\ ACE \times ABDE \\ \quad = A^2BCDE^2 \\ \quad = BCD \end{cases}$	3
Product of all three	BE	$CDE \times ACE \times ABDE$ $= A^2BC^2D^2E^3 = BE$	I
Unity	I	$(CDE)^2 = C^2D^2E^2 = $ I	I
			8

Writing out the results in a form suitable for checking, we have for the group of defining contrasts:

$$1, AD, BE, ABDE, ABC, ACE, BCD, CDE$$

which agrees with § 9E·13.

The check is readily applied, for $AD \times BE = ABDE$, and the last four terms represent the products of the first four terms with ABC. This group confounds no main effects and is generally the most efficient. Had we tried to confound one five-factor and two four-factor interactions we could not have avoided confounding main effects. Using $ABCD$, $ACDE$, and $ABCDE$ as generators we have:

	Elements of group	Number of elements
Generators	ABCD, ACDE, ABCDE	3
Products two at a time ..	BE, E, B	3
Product of all three	ACD	I
Unity	I	I
		8

Therefore the group of defining contrasts is

$$1, B, E, BE, ACD, ABCD, ACDE, ABCDE$$

which contains B and E, and is therefore unsuitable.

Treatment combinations

9D·4. Treatment combinations are denoted by small letters. Obviously a set of treatment combinations forms a group under the condition that the square of any element is unity, for it is generated by the multiplication of the elements in all possible ways, e.g. (a, b, c), (ab, ac, bc), abc, 1, generated by (a, b, c), is a set of eight elements having group properties.

It is worth noting:

(i) That we could have generated the group equally well from a, bc, ac, and in many similar ways.

(ii) That the result of multiplying the elements of a group by an element of the group is to regenerate the group in a different order. Thus $(abc)(1, a, b, ab, c, ac, bc, abc) = abc, bc, ac, c, ab, b, a, 1$.

Principal block

9D·5. The Principal Block is the block in a system of confounding containing the identity (1). Once this block has been found, the remaining blocks may be determined by multiplying its contents successively by elements not in the block nor in any previous block so formed. This principal block forms a subgroup closed to multiplication, and when a number of elements of the principal block are known, others may be obtained by multiplication, provided the known elements are independent.

The orthogonality rule

9D·6. Given the group of defining contrasts, it remains to be shown how the principal block may be derived. Once this has been done, the whole system of confounding may be constructed. There are various ways of doing this, of which the following is one. Any effect may be written in the form:

$$A^p B^q C^r D^s$$

in which the exponents are restricted to the values 0 and 1. Similarly any treatment combination may be written in the form

$$a^w b^x c^y d^z$$

with the same restrictions. For the present purpose we say that a treatment combination is orthogonal to an effect when the product-sum of the two sets of exponents, taken each to each, yields zero or a multiple of 2. More specifically, the treatment combination $a^w b^x c^y d^z$ is said to be orthogonal to the effect $A^p B^q C^r D^s$ if the set of equations given by

$$pw + qx + ry + sz = 0 \ (\text{mod } 2)$$

is satisfied.

Consider the effect BC and the treatment combination abd in a 2^4 factorial design. Written in full those are

$$A^0B^1C^1D^0 \qquad a^1b^1c^0d^1$$

so that $\qquad pw = 0, qx = 1, ry = 0, sz = 0$ and $\Sigma pw = 1$

This expression is not equal to 0 (mod 2) and therefore the treatment combination is not orthogonal to the effect. Consider $A^1B^1C^1D^0$ (i.e. ABC) and the treatment combination $a^1b^1c^0d^0$ (i.e. ab). We have $pw = 1$, $qx = 1$, $ry = sz = 0$, and the sum is $2 = 0$ (mod 2). ABC and ab are then orthogonal to each other. In words, a treatment combination is orthogonal to a given effect when it contains an even number (including zero) of the small letters corresponding to the capital letters in the effect.

9D·61. The principal block contains only those treatment combinations which are orthogonal to the effects confounded, i.e. to the defining contrasts. In other words, the principal block consists of those treatment combinations containing an even number (including zero) of letters from each of the defining contrasts. This may be observed to be true on trial, or may be taken as the definition of the principal block. Consider a 2^4 experiment confounding AD, ABC, and BCD. The element $1 = a^0b^0c^0d^0$ is clearly orthogonal to all these defining contrasts. The element ad is orthogonal to the first but not to the second and third. The element abd, however, is orthogonal to all three; so are acd and bc, and the principal block is

$$1, \; abd, \; acd, \; bc$$

Rules

9D·62. The foregoing may be summarised in the following four rules.

1. In any system of confounding the defining contrasts together with the identity (1) form a group closed to multiplication, i.e. the product of any two or more effects which are confounded is also confounded.
2. The principal block forms a group closed to multiplication, i.e. the product of two or more elements of the principal block is also a member of the principal block.
3. If the elements of the principal block are multiplied by a treatment combination not contained in the block, then another block of the same system of confounding is generated. The whole system may be generated in this way.
4. The treatment combinations of the principal block are all orthogonal to the defining contrasts, i.e. each of the treatment combinations contains an even number (including zero) of small letters corresponding to the large letters in each of the defining contrasts.

These rules will be found useful for constructing systems of confounding not tabulated in Appendix 9E.

Confounding in 3^n factorial designs

9D·7. The ideas discussed in the previous section may be extended to 3^n factorial designs. Each factor is denoted by a capital letter, and its level by the small letter with the index 0, 1, or 2. The three levels of factor A are thus denoted by a^0, a^1, and a^2. The expression $a^1 b^0 c^2 d^1$ in a four-factor experiment represents the middle levels of A and D, the lowest level of B, and the highest level of C. It is sometimes convenient to replace b^0 by 1 and b^1 by b, etc., in which case the above treatment combination may be written $ac^2 d$. In general, a treatment combination is expressed as $a^\alpha b^\beta c^\gamma d^\delta \ldots$. We may introduce a multiplication rule for these treatment combinations in much the same way as for 2^n factorial designs, but in this case the indices are reduced to 0, 1, or 2 (mod 3), that is, the remainder after dividing by 3. Thus $a^3 = a^0 = 1$ and consequently $(a^2 bc^2 e) \times (a^2 ce^2) = a^4 bc^3 e^3 = ab$, since $a^4 = a^1$ and $c^3 = e^3 = 1$. The expression $a^\alpha b^\beta c^\gamma d^\delta \ldots$ generates all the 3^n treatment combinations of the factorial design when α, β, γ, δ, $\ldots$ assume the values 0, 1, 2 in all possible combinations. Using the multiplication rule, the product of any two or more treatment combinations yields another treatment combination of the group.

A similar rule may be introduced for the capital letters, thus, $A^3 = B^3 = C^3 = 1$, and $(A^2 BC^2 E) \times (A^2 CE^2) = AB$.

The meaning of the expression $A^\alpha B^\beta C^\gamma D^\delta \ldots$ is a little more complicated than for 2^n designs. If α, β, γ, δ, $\ldots$ assume the values 0, 1, 2 in all combinations, then 3^n terms similar in form to the treatment combinations defined above in which the small letters are replaced by capitals are generated, and one of these is $A^0 B^0 C^0 D^0 \ldots$, that is, unity, which is denoted by the capital letter I. For a 3^3 factorial design the 27 terms are I, A, B, C, A^2, B^2, C^2, AB, AC, BC, A^2B, AB^2, $\ldots$, AB^2C, ABC^2, $A^2B^2C^2$. These 27 terms form a group closed to multiplication under the conditions $A^3 = B^3 = C^3 = I$. There exists a correspondence between these 27 terms and the effects, that is, the main effects, two-factor interactions, etc., but before establishing this correspondence it is necessary to interpret the term orthogonality as applied to 3^n factorial designs.

Orthogonality: 3^n designs

9D·71. Two elements $a^\alpha b^\beta c^\gamma \ldots$ and $a^r b^s c^t \ldots$ of a 3^n design are said to be orthogonal if

$$\alpha r + \beta s + \gamma t + \ldots = 0 \ (\text{mod } 3) \quad \ldots \ldots \ldots \ldots (1)$$

In a similar way $a^\alpha b^\beta c^\gamma \ldots$ and $A^r B^s C^t \ldots$ are orthogonal, or $A^\alpha B^\beta C^\gamma \ldots$ and $A^r B^s C^t \ldots$ are orthogonal, when condition (1) is satisfied.

It is possible to choose several sub-groups from the 27 terms of the form $A^\alpha B^\beta C^\gamma$ where α, β, and γ take the values 0, 1, 2; for instance, I, A, A^2 is a sub-group of order three, since it has three members and is closed to multiplication. Another sub-group is I, AB, A^2B^2, and yet another is I, A^2BC,

AB^2C^2. Considering the first group (I, A, A^2), it is possible to find a group of nine treatment combinations which are orthogonal to (I, A, A^2). These are the treatment combinations in which a has an index of 0, that is:

$$a^0b^0c^0 \qquad a^0b^0c^1 \qquad a^0b^0c^2$$
$$a^0b^1c^0 \qquad a^0b^1c^1 \qquad a^0b^1c^2$$
$$a^0b^2c^0 \qquad a^0b^2c^1 \qquad a^0b^2c^2$$

This can readily be verified, because the sum of products of the indices of each of these nine terms with the corresponding indices of each of $(A^0B^0C^0, A^1B^0C^0, A^2B^0C^0)$ is zero, e.g. for $a^0b^2c^2$ and $A^2B^0C^0$ we obtain

$$\Sigma ar = 0 \times 2 + 2 \times 0 + 2 \times 0 = 0$$

The above nine treatment combinations are those for the zero level of A. Multiplying successively by a and a^2, we generate the treatment combinations corresponding to the other levels of A. The sub-group (I, A, A^2) is thus seen to correspond to the main effect A. The treatment combinations which are orthogonal to the group are termed the Completely Orthogonal Sub-group. We then say that (I, A, A^2) corresponds to the main effect A, because the completely orthogonal sub-group represents the terms containing a_0 in the division of the 27 observations into three sets of nine corresponding to the main effect A. In a similar way (I, B, B^2) and (I, C, C^2) correspond to the main effects B and C respectively.

It is interesting to note that the other two sets of blocks of treatment combinations may be obtained from the completely orthogonal sub-group by multiplying throughout successively by treatment combinations not contained in the sub-group, e.g. a, a^2, for the sub-group of $(1, A, A^2)$. This resembles Rule 3 for 2^n factorial designs.

Another sub-group from the 27 effects is

$$(I, A^2B, AB^2)$$

The treatment combinations for which $\Sigma ar = 0 \pmod 3$ with respect to this group are the treatment combinations containing a^0b^0, a^1b^1, and a^2b^2, viz.

$$a^0b^0c^0 \qquad a^0b^0c^1 \qquad a^0b^0c^2$$
$$a^1b^1c^0 \qquad a^1b^1c^1 \qquad a^1b^1c^2$$
$$a^2b^2c^0 \qquad a^2b^2c^1 \qquad a^2b^2c^2$$

The completely orthogonal sub-group thus represents the set i_0 when the 27 observations are divided into three groups corresponding to the interaction $I(AB)$. The other two sets, i_1 and i_2, may be obtained by multiplication successively by a and a^2 or b and b^2 respectively. The group (I, A^2B, AB^2) thus corresponds to the interaction $I(AB)$. Similarly (I, A^2C, AC^2) corresponds to $I(AC)$. It can also be shown that (I, AB, A^2B^2) corresponds to $J(AB)$.

Thirteen sub-groups of order 3 may be obtained from the 27 members, and these can be shown to correspond to the 13 pairs of degrees of freedom in the 3^3 factorial design. The complete list is:

$$
\begin{array}{lll}
I, A, A^2 & \text{corresponds to the main effect} & A \\
I, B, B^2 & \text{,,} \quad \text{,, ,,} \quad \text{,,} \quad \text{,,} & B \\
I, C, C^2 & \text{,,} \quad \text{,, ,,} \quad \text{,,} \quad \text{,,} & C \\
I, A^2B, AB^2 & \text{,,} \quad \text{,, ,,} \quad \text{interaction} & I(AB) \\
I, AB, A^2B^2 & \text{,,} \quad \text{,, ,,} \quad \text{,,} & \mathcal{J}(AB) \\
I, A^2C, AC^2 & \text{,,} \quad \text{,, ,,} \quad \text{,,} & I(AC) \\
I, AC, A^2C^2 & \text{,,} \quad \text{,, ,,} \quad \text{,,} & \mathcal{J}(AC) \\
I, B^2C, BC^2 & \text{,,} \quad \text{,, ,,} \quad \text{,,} & I(BC) \\
I, BC, B^2C^2 & \text{,,} \quad \text{,, ,,} \quad \text{,,} & \mathcal{J}(BC) \\
I, A^2BC, AB^2C^2 & \text{,,} \quad \text{,, ,,} \quad \text{,,} & W(ABC) \\
I, AB^2C, A^2BC^2 & \text{,,} \quad \text{,, ,,} \quad \text{,,} & X(ABC) \\
I, ABC^2, A^2B^2C & \text{,,} \quad \text{,, ,,} \quad \text{,,} & Y(ABC) \\
I, ABC, A^2B^2C^2 & \text{,,} \quad \text{,, ,,} \quad \text{,,} & Z(ABC)
\end{array}
$$

This scheme can be extended to any 3^n design.

Note that the product of the second and third elements of every group is unity, so that the elements are reciprocal. These groups give the defining contrasts.

9D·72. The reasoning may be extended to confounding four pairs of degrees of freedom between nine blocks, each of 3^{n-2} combinations. For this we choose a sub-group of nine which must contain I. Two pairs of degrees of freedom may be chosen at will, e.g.

$$I, AB, A^2B^2 \text{ (corresponding to } \mathcal{J}(AB))$$
$$I, BC, B^2C^2 \text{ (corresponding to } \mathcal{J}(BC))$$

The group must then contain $I, AB, A^2B^2, BC, B^2C^2$, and all effects derivable by multiplication, e.g.

$$
\begin{array}{ll}
(AB)(BC) = AB^2C & (A^2B^2)(BC) = A^2C \\
(AB)(B^2C^2) = AC^2 & (A^2B^2)(B^2C^2) = A^2BC^2
\end{array}
$$

This gives the sub-group

$$I, AB, A^2B^2; BC, B^2C^2; AC^2, A^2C; AB^2C, A^2BC^2$$

which is seen to embrace the sub-groups

$$
\begin{array}{l}
I, AB, A^2B^2 \text{ (i.e. } \mathcal{J}(AB)) \\
I, BC, B^2C^2 \text{ (i.e. } \mathcal{J}(BC)) \\
I, AC^2, A^2C \text{ (i.e } I(AC)) \\
I, AB^2C, A^2BC^2 \text{ (i.e. } X(ABC))
\end{array}
$$

The above are then the eight degrees of freedom corresponding to the group of nine defining contrasts. It is easy to divide the defining contrasts into the corresponding pairs of degrees of freedom because the product of the first and second letter combinations in any such pair gives unity.

Similar reasoning may be used for 3^4 and higher designs. For example, in a 3^4 design confounding eight effects in blocks of nine we may choose any two pairs of degrees of freedom at will, e.g.

$$I, A^2BC, AB^2C^2 \text{ (corresponding to } W(ABC))$$
$$I, ABD^2, A^2B^2D \text{ (corresponding to } Y(ABD))$$

The complete group will be

$$I, A^2BC, AB^2C^2, ABD^2, A^2B^2D, B^2CD^2, BC^2D, A^2C^2D^2, ACD$$

The two further pairs of degrees of freedom confounded are then

$$I, B^2CD^2, BC^2D \text{ (corresponding to } X(BCD))$$
and $$I, ACD, A^2C^2D^2 \text{ (corresponding to } Z(ACD))$$

This may be readily extended to a higher degree of confounding, e.g. 3^5 in 27 blocks of 9, etc.

As in the 2^n designs, it can be shown that the combinations obtained by multiplying any two or more elements of the completely orthogonal sub-group will give another element of the group.

9D·73. It is shown above that, given the defining contrasts, the completely orthogonal sub-group may be determined and that similarly, given a completely orthogonal sub-group, the defining contrasts may be derived.

The completely orthogonal sub-group must contain the element $a^0b^0c^0$, i.e. 1. Given any block in a confounded design, the completely orthogonal sub-group may be derived by multiplication throughout by the reciprocal of any one of the elements. The other blocks in the confounded design may be derived by multiplication by suitable treatment combinations, that is, by expressions which will not result in combinations already present in earlier blocks.

APPENDIX 9E

SYSTEMS OF CONFOUNDING IN 2^n FACTORIAL DESIGNS

9E·1. Four observations per block

9E·11. *Three factors. Confound ABC*

Block 1 ..	..	(1), ab, ac, bc
Block 2 ..	..	a, b, c, abc

9E·12. *Four factors. Confound AD, ABC, BCD*

NOTE. Choose the two-factor interaction least likely to be appreciable and denote this by *AD*. Then we must confound *ABC* and *BCD*. The design is:

Block 1 ..	.. (1), *bc, abd, acd*
Block 2 ..	.. *a, abc, bd, cd*
Block 3 ..	.. *b, c, ad, abcd*
Block 4 ..	.. *d, bcd, ab, ac*

9E·13. *Five factors. Confound AD, BE, ABC, BCD, CDE, ACE, ABDE*

NOTE. Choose two two-factor interactions (with no letters common) which are least likely to be appreciable. Denote these by *AD* and *BE*. Then the other interactions confounded are as shown. The design is:

Block 1 ..	.. (1), *bce, acd, abde*
Block 2 ..	.. *a, abce, cd, bde*
Block 3 ..	.. *b, ce, abcd, ade*
Block 4 ..	.. *c, be, ad, abcde*
Block 5 ..	.. *d, bcde, ac, abe*
Block 6 ..	.. *e, bc, acde, abd*
Block 7 ..	.. *ab, ace, bcd, de*
Block 8 ..	.. *ae, abc, cde, bd*

9E·14. *Six factors. Confound AD, BE, CF, ABC, BCD, CDE, ACE, DEF, AEF, ABF, BDF, ABDE, BCEF, ACDF, ABCDEF*

NOTE. Arrange the six factors in three pairs, avoiding the interactions which are likely to be appreciable. Denote these by *AD, BE, CF*. Then the other interactions which must be confounded are as shown. The design is:

Block 1 ..	.. (1), *bcef, acdf, abde*
Block 2 ..	.. *a, abcef, cdf, bde*
Block 3 ..	.. *b, cef, abcdf, ade*
Block 4 ..	.. *c, bef, adf, abcde*
Block 5 ..	.. *d, bcdef, acf, abe*
Block 6 ..	.. *e, bcf, acdef, abd*
Block 7 ..	.. *f, bce, acd, abdef*
Block 8 ..	.. *ab, acef, bcdf, de*
Block 9 ..	.. *ac, abef, df, bcde*
Block 10 ..	.. *ad, abcdef, cf, be*
Block 11 ..	.. *ae, abcf, cdef, bd*
Block 12 ..	.. *af, abce, cd, bdef*
Block 13 ..	.. *bc, ef, abdf, acde*
Block 14 ..	.. *bf, ce, abcd, adef*
Block 15 ..	.. *abc, aef, bdf, cde*
Block 16 ..	.. *abf, ace, bcd, def*

9E·2. Eight observations per block

9E·21. *Four factors. Confound the four-factor interaction ABCD*
The design is:

>   Block 1 .. .. (1), ab, ac, bc, ad, bd, cd, abcd
>   Block 2 .. .. a, b, c, abc, d, abd, acd, bcd

9E·22. *Five factors. Confound BCE, ADE, ABCD*
NOTE. Choose two three-factor interactions with one factor in common, and choose that arrangement for which the interactions are least likely to be appreciable.

Denote the common factor by E and the interactions by BCE and ADE. Then we must also confound $ABCD$.

The design is:

>   Block 1 .. .. (1), ad, bc, abcd, abe, bde, ace, cde
>   Block 2 .. .. a, d, abc, bcd, be, abde, ce, acde
>   Block 3 .. .. b, abd, c, acd, ae, de, abce, bcde
>   Block 4 .. .. e, ade, bce, abcde, ab, bd, ac, cd

9E·23. *Six factors. Confound ADE, BCE, ACF, BDF, ABCD, ABEF, CDEF*
NOTE. Choose four three-factor interactions with one, and only one, letter common to each pair, to correspond to the set which is least likely to involve appreciable interactions. Denote these by ADE, BCE, ACF, and BDF; the other interactions confounded are then as shown. One of the three-factor interactions will be the product of the other three.

The design is:

>   Block 1 .. .. (1), ace, bde, abcd, adf, cdef, abef, bcf
>   Block 2 .. .. a, ce, abde, bcd, df, acdef, bef, abcf
>   Block 3 .. .. b, abce, de, acd, abdf, bcdef, aef, cf
>   Block 4 .. .. c, ae, bcde, abd, acdf, def, abcef, bf
>   Block 5 .. .. d, acde, be, abc, af, cef, abdef, bcdf
>   Block 6 .. .. e, ac, bd, abcde, adef, cdf, abf, bcef
>   Block 7 .. .. f, acef, bdef, abcdf, ad, cde, abe, bc
>   Block 8 .. .. ab, bce, ade, cd, bdf, abcdef, ef, acf

9E·24. *Seven factors. Interaction confounded: ACF, ADE, BCE, BDF, CDG ABG, EFG, ABEF, CDEF, ABCD, BDEG, ACEG, ADFG, BCFG ABCDEFG*
NOTE. Choose seven three-factor interactions with one, and only one, letter in common with each pair (only four of these will be independent) and choose that set involving to the least extent those interactions which are likely to be appreciable. Denote these by ACF, ADE, BCE, BDF, CDG, ABG, EFG; the other interactions confounded are then as shown.

The design is:

Block 1 ..	.. (1), *aceg, bdeg, abcd, adfg, cdef, abef, bcfg*
Block 2 ..	.. *a, ceg, abdeg, bcd, dfg, acdef, bef, abcfg*
Block 3 ..	.. *b, abceg, deg, acd, abdfg, bcdef, aef, cfg*
Block 4 ..	.. *c, aeg, bcdeg, abd, acdfg, def, abcef, bfg*
Block 5 ..	.. *d, acdeg, beg, abc, afg, cef, abdef, bcdfg*
Block 6 ..	.. *e, acg, bdg, abcde, adefg, cdf, abf, bcefg*
Block 7 ..	.. *f, acefg, bdefg, abcdf, adg, cde, abe, bcg*
Block 8 ..	.. *g, ace, bde, abcdg, adf, cdefg, abefg, bcf*
Block 9 ..	.. *ab, bceg, adeg, cd, bdfg, abcdef, ef, acfg*
Block 10 ..	.. *ac, eg, abcdeg, bd, cdfg, adef, bcef, abfg*
Block 11 ..	.. *ad, cdeg, abeg, bc, fg, acef, bdef, abcdfg*
Block 12 ..	.. *ae, cg, abdg, bcde, defg, acdf, bf, abcefg*
Block 13 ..	.. *af, cefg, abdefg, bcdf, dg, acde, be, abcg*
Block 14 ..	.. *ag, ce, abde, bcdg, df, acdefg, befg, abcf*
Block 15 ..	.. *bg, abce, de, acdg, abdf, bcdefg, aefg, cf*
Block 16 ..	.. *abg, bce, ade, cdg, bdf, abcdefg, efg, acf*

9E·3. Sixteen observations per block

9E·31. *Five factors. Confound ABCDE*

The design is:

Block 1 .. (1), *ab, ac, bc, ad, bd, cd, abcd, ae, be, ce, abce, de, abde, acde, bcde*

Block 2 .. *a, b, c, abc, d, abd, acd, bcd, e, abe, ace, bce, ade, bde, cde, abcde*

9E·32. *Six factors: Confound ABCD, BCEF, ADEF*

NOTE. The best design is given by three four-factor interactions chosen in the above way.

The design is:

Block 1 .. (1), *bc, ad, abcd, ef, bcef, adef, abcdef, bde, cde, abe, ace, bdf, cdf, abf, acf*

Block 2 .. *a, abc, d, bcd, aef, abcef, def, bcdef, abde, acde, be, ce, abdf, acdf, bf, cf*

Block 3 .. *b, c, abd, acd, bef, cef, abdef, acdef, de, bcde, ae, abce, df, bcdf, af, abcf*

Block 4 .. *e, bce, ade, abcde, f, bcf, adf, abcdf, bd, cd, ab, ac, bdef, cdef, abef, acef*

9E·33. *Seven factors. Confound seven four-factor interactions, ABCD, BCEF, ADEF, ACFG, BDFG, ABEG, CDEG*

The design is:

Block 1 .. (1), *bde, adg, abeg, bcg, cdeg, abcd, ace, efg, bdfg, adef, abf, bcef, cdf, abcdefg, acfg*

Block 2 .. *a, abde, dg, beg, abcg, acdeg, bcd, ce, aefg, abdfg, def, bf, abcef, acdf, bcdefg, cfg*

Block 3 .. *b, de, abdg, aeg, cg, bcdeg, acd, abce, befg, dfg, abdef, af, cef, bcdf, acdefg, abcfg*

Block 4 .. *c, bcde, acdg, abceg, bg, deg, abd, ae, cefg, bcdfg, acdef, abcf, bef, df, abdefg, afg*

Block 5 .. *d, be, ag, abdeg, bcdg, ceg, abc, acde, defg, bfg, aef, abdf, bcdef, cf, abcefg, acdfg*

Block 6 .. *e, bd, adeg, abg, bceg, cdg, abcde, ac, fg, bdefg, adf, abef, bcf, cdef, abcdfg, acefg*

Block 7 .. *f, bdef, adfg, abefg, bcfg, cdefg, abcdf, acef, eg, bdg, ade, ab, bce, cd, abcdeg, acg*

Block 8 .. *g, bdeg, ad, abe, bc, cde, abcdg, aceg, ef, bdf, adefg, abfg,bcefg, cdfg, abcdef, acf*

APPENDIX 9F

EXAMPLE OF A 3^3 DESIGN CONFOUNDED IN THREE BLOCKS
AND DETAILS OF ANALYSIS

9F·1. The details of the analysis of a 3^3 factorial design confounded in three blocks will be illustrated on Example 8·5. The example as given in Chapter 8 represented a 3^3 factorial design replicated twice, and although no mention was made there of confounding, the experiment was actually divided into blocks of nine, and these were examined in sequence. The whole experiment involved 54 preparations of the product, and a relatively long period of time was required to complete the investigation. Although the conditions were capable of accurate laboratory control, the experiment was carried out in blocks of nine, confounding certain three-factor interactions between the blocks as an additional safeguard against possible time trends. Since there were two replicates, some advantage was gained by confounding different pairs of three-factor interactions in the two replicates, because this made information available on all interactions. This is therefore a case of partial confounding. The W-interactions were confounded in the first replicate and the Y in the second, these two being chosen randomly from the full set W, X, Y, and Z. The design used was based on Design 1 and Design 3 in § 9·G2, or the W and Y of Table 9·62.

Statistical analysis

9F·2. In the following we give a full analysis of all the interactions, separating those which are confounded from those which are not. In practice this is frequently unnecessary to evaluate the three-factor interactions separately, because in a well-designed experiment they will rarely be important. In most cases the three-factor interactions can be combined with the error variance and the whole determined by subtraction from the total. In the present example it is sufficient to calculate the main effects, the two-factor interactions, and the variations between blocks. The error term would then comprise the remainder from the total, being the replication sum of squares plus the sum of squares of the three-factor interactions not confounded.

The first step is to analyse the whole experiment ignoring confounding. This has already been done in Chapter 8, and the final analysis of variance is given in Table 8F·8. The next step is to allow for confounding. We know that when confounding a pair of three-factor interactions between three blocks all the main effects and two-factor interactions are completely unaffected. The analysis of the main effects and two-factor interactions is therefore the same as that given in Table 8F·8. The only modification that needs to be introduced is in the three-factor interaction and the remainder variance. Let C (concentration of material A) be the first factor, V (volume of free water) the second factor, and N (amount of material B) the third factor. One way of calculating the interaction which is confounded is to arrange the observations into the three blocks as in Table 9·62. The first replicate corresponds to the design confounding W, for which the first block contains the observations 000, 101, 202, etc. Inserting the actual observations we obtain Table 9F·1.

Table 9F·1

THE W- AND Y-INTERACTIONS OF C, V, AND N

(Derived from Table 8·61)

	First replicate (W confounded)			Second replicate (Y confounded)		
	w_0	w_1	w_2	y_0	y_1	y_2
	74	71	112	85	75	148
	166	211	201	288	184	216
	90	47	74	60	65	75
	56	46	13	52	12	47
	110	216	218	239	204	145
	146	147	102	104	70	124
	130	69	125	70	107	115
	227	220	199	164	265	142
	195	164	198	165	183	114
Sum	1,194	1,191	1,242	1,227	1,165	1,126
Grand sum ..	3,627			3,518		

The treatment combinations comprising w_0, w_1, and w_2 are indicated by a_1, β_1, and γ_1 respectively and y_0, y_1, and y_2 by a_2, β_2, and γ_2 respectively in Table 8·61. These sums could be obtained directly from Tables 9·71 and 9·73, as shown below for the calculation of the X- and Z-interactions.

If we were concerned only with the first replicate, then the sum of squares due to the confounded interaction would be

$$(1194^2 + 1191^2 + 1242^2)/9 - 3627^2/27 = 182$$

and this would be equated to blocks. The remaining three-factor interactions could then be obtained as a difference, or if required they could be calculated direct by a method similar to that used below for X- and Z-interactions. With both replicates there are six blocks, and the sum of squares due to blocks is

$$(1194^2 + 1191^2 + 1242^2 + 1227^2 + 1165^2 + 1126^2)/9 - (3627 + 3518)^2/54$$
$$= 946{,}368 - 945{,}389 = 979$$

This sum of squares is based on five degrees of freedom. Now these five degrees of freedom consist of two in the first replicate due to confounding W, two in the second replicate due to confounding Y, and one further degree of freedom due to replication. The X- and Z-interactions are not confounded, and these are calculated from the table formed by the sum of the two replicates (Table 8F·1). One method of deriving the X-interaction is to form the (x_0, x_1, x_2) totals by reference to Table 9·62, or more simply by reference to Table 9·72, where the x_0 terms are indicated by a, the x_1 terms by β, and the x_2 terms by γ. We therefore form the three sub-totals by summing the terms of Table 8F·1, which occupy respectively the a, β, and γ positions of Table 9·72. These sub-totals are:

$$a(= x_0) = 159 + 255 + 378 + 112 + \ \ 98 + 362 + 417 + 172 + 195 = 2148$$
$$\beta(= x_1) = 395 + 251 + 184 + 260 + 422 + 363 + 150 + 103 + 492 = 2620$$
$$\gamma(= x_2) = 149 + \ \ 25 + 363 + 454 + 270 + 237 + 146 + 455 + 278 = 2377$$
$$\text{Grand total} = 7145$$

Similarly for the Z-interaction referring to Tables 8F·1 and 9·74:

$$a(= z_0) = 159 + 251 + 363 + 112 + 422 + 237 + 417 + 103 + 278 = 2342$$
$$\beta(= z_1) = 395 + \ \ 25 + 378 + 260 + 270 + 362 + 150 + 455 + 195 = 2490$$
$$\gamma(= z_2) = 149 + 255 + 184 + 454 + \ \ 98 + 363 + 146 + 172 + 492 = 2313$$
$$\text{Grand total} = 7145$$

The sums of squares for the X- and Z-interactions are respectively:

$$X = [2148^2 + 2620^2 + 2377^2]/18 - 7145^2/54$$
$$= 951{,}580 - 945{,}389 = 6191$$
$$Z = [2342^2 + 2490^2 + 2313^2]/18 - 7145^2/54$$
$$= 946{,}391 - 945{,}389 = 1002$$

F2

These refer to the sums over the two replicates, and so the divisors of the sums of squares are 18 and 54 respectively and not 9 and 27, which would be the appropriate divisors for a single replicate.

NOTE. For three observations, or three sums each based on the same number of observations, the corrected sum of squares is equal to the sum of squares of differences in pairs divided by the total number of observations. For example, for the X-interaction the differences of the pairs are

$$(2377 - 2148) = 229 \quad (2377 - 2620) = -243 \quad (2620 - 2148) = 472$$
Sum of squares of the differences $= 334,274$
Total number of observations $= 54$

$\therefore$ Corrected sum of squares due to $X = 334,274/54 = 6190$
This agrees within rounding-off errors with the previous result.

Now W is confounded in the first replicate but not in the second. W is therefore calculated from the second replicate only. This gives, using Table 8·61:

$$w_0 = 85 + 145 + 183 + 288 + 124 + 107 + 60 + 47 + 265 = 1304$$
$$w_1 = 184 + 104 + 115 + 65 + 52 + 142 + 75 + 239 + 114 = 1090$$
$$w_2 = 75 + 12 + 164 + 148 + 204 + 165 + 216 + 70 + 70 = 1124$$

w_0, w_1, w_2 are the responses in the second replicate of Table 8·61 corresponding to the positions a_1, β_1, γ_1 respectively given for the first replicate, i.e. as in Table 9·71.

Similarly Y is confounded in the second replicate but not in the first; Y is therefore calculated from the first replicate, using Table 8·61:

$$y_0 = 74 + 147 + 199 + 166 + 46 + 198 + 90 + 216 + 125 = 1261$$
$$y_1 = 211 + 13 + 195 + 47 + 218 + 130 + 71 + 102 + 227 = 1214$$
$$y_2 = 74 + 110 + 69 + 112 + 146 + 220 + 201 + 56 + 164 = 1152$$

y_0, y_1, and y_2 are the responses in the first replicate of Table 8·61 corresponding to the positions a_2, β_2, γ_2 respectively given for the second replicate, i.e. as in Table 9·73.

The sums of squares due to W and Y each based on two degrees of freedom and calculated from the differences of pairs are respectively:

$$(180^2 + 214^2 + 34^2)/27 = 2939 \quad (47^2 + 109^2 + 62^2)/27 = 664$$

The total due to the unconfounded three-factor interactions is therefore based on eight degrees of freedom. The analysis of variance will then read as Table 9F·2.

In practice we would normally calculate only the main effects, two-factor interactions, blocks, and remainder, the latter comprising the error term. The remainder would consist of the replication sum of squares plus the total sum of squares for the three-factor interactions not confounded. The sum of squares for this remainder is 29,803, based on 30 degrees of freedom, giving a

Table 9F·2

ANALYSIS OF VARIANCE OF EXAMPLE 8·5, ALLOWING FOR CONFOUNDING

Source of variation	Sum of squares	Degrees of freedom	Mean square
Main effects..	165,383	6	
Two-factor interactions ..	43,881	12	
Unconfounded three-factor interactions	(X) 6,191 (Z) 1,002 (W) 2,939 (Y) 664 $\Big\} = 10,796$	8	1,350
Blocks	979	5	196
Remainder (= error) ..	19,007	22	864
Total	240,046	53	

mean square of 993. In this case the mean square due to blocks is not significant. Nothing was lost however by carrying out the experiment in this way, and had there been appreciable time trends a worthwhile gain in accuracy would have been achieved.

APPENDIX 9G

CONFOUNDED 3^n FACTORIAL DESIGNS*

SUITABLE confounded 3^n designs are given in this appendix, classified first according to the number of observations per block, and next according to the number of factors. The particular interactions confounded and the identities of the blocks in relation to those interactions are shown, thus assisting in the analysis and understanding of these designs. Practically, the design need only be considered as so many blocks, each consisting of the treatment combinations shown.

9G·1. Three observations per block

9G·11. *Two factors in three blocks of three*

There are two sets to choose from, one confounding $I(AB)$ and the other confounding $J(AB)$. The designs are:

* There are two or more designs to choose from when confounding 3^n designs. Any design is suitable, and the one to use should be chosen at random. The blocks have all been identified in order to indicate which particular interactions are confounded, but this is not necessary for practical application.

Design 1
CONFOUNDING $I(AB)$

Block 1 (i_0)	00	11	22
Block 2 (i_1)	10	21	02
Block 3 (i_2)	20	01	12

Design 2
CONFOUNDING $\mathcal{J}(AB)$

Block 1 (j_0)	00	21	12
Block 2 (j_1)	10	01	22
Block 3 (j_2)	20	11	02

9G·12. *Three factors in nine blocks of three*

There are four basic designs to choose from, confounding in turn $W(ABC)$, $X(ABC)$, $Y(ABC)$, and $Z(ABC)$, together with the corresponding two-factor interactions, the factors always being taken in the order A, B, C. In any application choose one of the designs at random, allocate A, B, and C to the factors at random, and randomise the order of the blocks.

The four basic designs are:

9G·121. *Design* 1. *Confound* $W(ABC), \mathcal{J}(AB), I(BC), \mathcal{J}(AC)$

	$i_0(BC)$	$i_1(BC)$	$i_2(BC)$
$j_0(AB)$	Block 1 000 122 211	Block 2 002 121 210	Block 3 001 120 212
$j_1(AB)$	Block 4 011 100 222	Block 5 010 102 221	Block 6 012 101 220
$j_2(AB)$	Block 7 022 111 200	Block 8 021 110 202	Block 9 020 112 201

The nine blocks are as shown. The columns confound the interaction $I(BC)$ and the rows the interaction $\mathcal{J}(AB)$; and regarding the nine blocks as a 3×3 table, the I- and $\mathcal{J}$-diagonals confound the interactions $\mathcal{J}(AC)$ and $W(ABC)$ respectively. In fact:

$$
\begin{aligned}
i_0 \text{ (of table)} &= j_0(AC) & j_0 \text{ (of table)} &= w_0(ABC) \\
i_1 &= j_1(AC) & j_1 &= w_1(ABC) \\
i_2 &= j_2(AC) & j_2 &= w_2(ABC)
\end{aligned}
$$

9G·122. *Design* 2. *Confound* $X(ABC)$, $J(AB)$, $J(BC)$, $I(AC)$

	$j_0(BC)$	$j_1(BC)$	$j_2(BC)$
$j_0 (AB)$	Block 1 000 121 212	Block 2 001 122 210	Block 3 002 120 211
$j_1(AB)$	Block 4 012 100 221	Block 5 010 101 222	Block 6 011 102 220
$j_2(AB)$	Block 7 021 112 200	Block 8 022 110 201	Block 9 020 111 202

The rows confound $J(AB)$
The columns confound $J(BC)$
The I-diagonals confound $I(AC)$
The J-diagonals confound $X(ABC)$

9G·123. *Design* 3. *Confound* $Y(ABC)$, $I(AB)$, $J(BC)$, $J(AC)$

	$j_0(BC)$	$j_1(BC)$	$j_2(BC)$
$i_0(AB)$	Block 1 000 112 221	Block 2 001 110 222	Block 3 002 111 220
$i_1(AB)$	Block 4 021 100 212	Block 5 022 101 210	Block 6 020 102 211
$i_2(AB)$	Block 7 012 121 200	Block 8 010 122 201	Block 9 011 120 202

The rows confound $I(AB)$
The columns confound $J(BC)$
The I-diagonals confound $Y(ABC)$
The J-diagonals confound $J(AC)$

9G·124. *Design* 4. *Confound* $Z(ABC)$, $I(AB)$, $I(BC)$, $I(AC)$

	$i_0(BC)$	$i_1(BC)$	$i_2(BC)$
$i_0(AB)$	Block 1 000 111 222	Block 2 002 110 221	Block 3 001 112 220
$i_1(AB)$	Block 4 022 100 211	Block 5 021 102 210	Block 6 020 101 212
$i_2(AB)$	Block 7 011 122 200	Block 8 010 121 202	Block 9 012 120 201

The rows confound $I(AB)$
The columns confound $I(BC)$
The I-diagonals confound $Z(ABC)$
The J-diagonals confound $I(AC)$

9G·2. Nine observations per block

Three factors in three blocks of nine.

9G·21. $N = 3$. Choose any one of the following four designs which confound in turn $W(ABC)$, $X(ABC)$, $Y(ABC)$, and $Z(ABC)$.

Level of factor A	Level of factor B	Effect confounded											
		Design 1 $W(ABC)$			Design 2 $X(ABC)$			Design 3 $Y(ABC)$			Design 4 $Z(ABC)$		
		Block 1(w_0)	Block 2(w_1)	Block 3(w_2)	Block 1(x_0)	Block 2(x_1)	Block 3(x_2)	Block 1(y_1)	Block 2(y_2)	Block 3(y_3)	Block 1(z_1)	Block 2(z_2)	Block 3(z_3)
		Level of factor C											
0	0	0	2	1	0	1	2	0	2	1	0	1	2
1	0	1	0	2	2	0	1	1	0	2	2	0	1
2	0	2	1	0	1	2	0	2	1	0	1	2	0
0	1	2	1	0	1	2	0	1	0	2	2	0	1
1	1	0	2	1	0	1	2	2	1	0	1	2	0
2	1	1	0	2	2	0	1	0	2	1	0	1	2
0	2	1	0	2	2	0	1	2	1	0	1	2	0
1	2	2	1	0	1	2	0	0	2	1	0	1	2
2	2	0	2	1	0	1	2	1	0	2	2	0	1

9G·22. *Four factors in nine blocks of nine*

Choose any of the following four designs.

Level of factor A	Level of factor B	Design 1 Effects confounded W(ABC) Y(ABD) Z(ACD) X(BCD)									Design 2 Effects confounded X(ABC) Z(ABD) W(ACD) Y(BCD)								
		Block 1	Block 2	Block 3	Block 4	Block 5	Block 6	Block 7	Block 8	Block 9	Block 1	Block 2	Block 3	Block 4	Block 5	Block 6	Block 7	Block 8	Block 9
		Combinations of factors C and D																	
0	0	1	5	9	8	3	4	6	7	2	1	9	5	6	2	7	8	4	3
1	0	5	9	1	3	4	8	7	2	6	9	5	1	2	7	6	4	3	8
2	0	9	1	5	4	8	3	2	6	7	5	1	9	7	6	2	3	8	4
0	1	6	7	2	1	5	9	8	3	4	8	4	3	1	9	5	6	2	7
1	1	7	2	6	5	9	1	3	4	8	4	3	8	9	5	1	2	7	6
2	1	2	6	7	9	1	5	4	8	3	3	8	4	5	1	9	7	6	2
0	2	8	3	4	6	7	2	1	5	9	6	2	7	8	4	3	1	9	5
1	2	3	4	8	7	2	6	5	9	1	2	7	6	4	3	8	9	5	1
2	2	4	8	3	2	6	7	9	1	5	7	6	2	3	8	4	5	1	9

Level of factor A	Level of factor B	Design 3 Effects confounded Z(ABC) W(ABD) X(ACD) W(BCD)									Design 4 Effects confounded Y(ABC) X(ABD) Y(ACD) Z(BCD)								
		Block 1	Block 2	Block 3	Block 4	Block 5	Block 6	Block 7	Block 8	Block 9	Block 1	Block 2	Block 3	Block 4	Block 5	Block 6	Block 7	Block 8	Block 9
		Combinations of factors C and D																	
0	0	1	6	8	9	2	4	5	7	3	1	8	6	5	3	7	9	4	2
1	0	6	8	1	2	4	9	7	3	5	8	6	1	3	7	5	4	2	9
2	0	8	1	6	4	9	2	3	5	7	6	1	8	7	5	3	2	9	4
0	1	9	2	4	5	7	3	1	6	8	5	3	7	9	4	2	1	8	6
1	1	2	4	9	7	3	5	6	8	1	3	7	5	4	2	9	8	6	1
2	1	4	9	2	3	5	7	8	1	6	7	5	3	2	9	4	6	1	8
0	2	5	7	3	1	6	8	9	2	4	9	4	2	1	8	6	5	3	7
1	2	7	3	5	6	8	1	2	4	9	4	2	9	8	6	1	3	7	5
2	2	3	5	7	8	1	6	4	9	2	2	9	4	6	1	8	7	5	3

CHAPTER 10

FRACTIONAL FACTORIAL EXPERIMENTS

A COMPLETE factorial experiment, in which all possible combinations of all the levels of the different factors are investigated, will involve a large number of tests when the number of factors is five or more. It is shown that it is possible to investigate the main effects of the factors and their more important interactions in a fraction of the number of tests required for the complete factorial experiment. The appropriate experimental designs (which must be followed closely) are given, together with examples showing the methods of analysis. These designs are closely related to the designs of the preceding chapter, a fractional factorial design being in fact equivalent to one block in a system of confounding.

Introduction

10·1. The experimental arrangements discussed in the three preceding chapters are complete factorial designs, that is, designs entailing all combinations of all the levels of all the factors considered. It has been pointed out that within the scale of the experiment and within the limits set by the experimental error, these designs:

(i) enable the main effects of every factor to be estimated independently of one another;

(ii) enable the dependence of the effect of every factor upon the levels of the others (the interactions) to be determined;

(iii) enable the effects to be determined with maximum precision;

(iv) supply an estimate of the experimental error for the purpose of assessing the significance of the effects, and enable confidence limits to be determined.

When the number of factors is large the number of trials required may become prohibitive. Thus an investigation of five factors each at two levels will entail $2^5 = 32$ observations, each under a different set of experimental conditions. An experimenter might well consider 32 observations excessive, even after consideration of the advantages of the factorial design given above. In any case the experimenter may not require the high degree of accuracy in the estimates of the effects given by the complete factorial design, and he may be satisfied from prior knowledge of the process or similar processes that many of the interactions, particularly the higher-order ones, are not appreciable, and moreover he may already have a sufficiently reliable estimate of the experimental error. Even when an experiment of this magnitude may eventually be required he would prefer to carry out the work as a series of smaller experiments.

The classical field, in which the theory of factorial designs has been evolved, is that of agricultural experimentation. Experiments on such subjects as the action of different combinations of fertilisers require in general at least one growing season to yield their results. In order then that any problem may be solved in reasonably short time all the treatment combinations which may be of interest must be investigated within one season. Further, the experimental error in agricultural trials is generally considerable, so that experiments have to be planned on a fairly large scale in order to allow definite conclusions to be reached, and the number of replicates needed can profitably be used to afford information on additional factors.

In physical or chemical work similar considerations may sometimes apply (for example in storage trials or extended weathering tests). Often, however, the trials are carried out one at a time in succession and the results of a trial may be available within a few days or even a few hours. Also the experimental error in physical or chemical tests may be relatively small, so that it is not usually necessary to have a large experiment to control it. Such conditions enable a sequential approach to be made, with considerable economy of effort.

The industrial research worker requires a method of designing experiments which will enable him to proceed in a series of short steps each involving relatively few observations, each step being as efficient as possible and such that he can whenever necessary obtain information on interactions hitherto neglected or test additional factors. He tends to think in terms of comparatively small experiments, following one another in series, and leaving him free at any stage to pursue the most promising lines of enquiry, rather than in terms of large experiments intended to cover an extensive field in all its details and entailing rigid adherence to a preformed plan. Since the fullest possible information would be obtained from a complete factorial design, the experimenter is led to consider the economies resulting from the investigation of a portion only of the complete design. If later the situation appears to require more elaborate investigation it will always be practicable to perform further portions, or the remainder in its entirety. In this chapter we shall therefore be concerned with Fractional Factorial Designs, sometimes called Fractional Replicates.

The object of these designs is to obtain information on the main effects and as many of the interactions as seems necessary with a smaller number of observations than is required by the complete design. Careful consideration of the best combinations of experimental treatments is needed, and the theory brings out in detail what becomes of the interactions neglected in any particular design, and what are the results if, unexpectedly, they are not negligible in reality.

There are two approaches to the problem of obtaining a suitable design in any particular case. We may begin with the full factorial design appropriate to the number of factors to be investigated, and by confounding interactions which are likely to be small or unimportant with one another and with other interactions considered worth measuring we can arrive at a design in which all (or almost all) of the comparisons are made between effects likely to be important. The number of observations needed will clearly depend on the number of such comparisons. Alternatively, we may begin with the full factorial design corresponding to a number of factors smaller than is actually under investigation and substitute the remaining factors for those comparisons which measure effects considered unlikely to be appreciable. We shall show how both methods of obtaining fractional factorial designs are used. Naturally, since they provide two routes to one objective, they lead to identical designs, and in practice we may use whichever appears more natural in any particular case. Later in the chapter it will be indicated how such designs may be used in a sequence of experiments.

The types of investigations considered in this chapter are those in which the experimenter requires to know the behaviour of several factors over a defined range for each, beginning with two levels only. There are many investigations in which we wish to compare two conditions only of each of a number of factors, e.g. two different qualities (crude and purified) of one or more of the materials used in a process; high and low agitation rates, these rates being restricted by the design of the plant; two different designs of filter presses or filter cloths; two different units of a plant; slow and vigorous reflux conditions; two different solvents; and so on. Several examples of these are considered in the earlier parts of this chapter and in the previous chapters on factorial designs and confounding. Fractional replication of 3^n factorial designs is considered in a section at the end of this chapter.

10·11. The basic principles and methods of construction of fractional factorial designs can be explained very simply by means of a 2^2 design. Denoting the factors by A and B, the lower level of each factor by — and the upper level by +, the four combinations of the factor levels constituting the complete design may be represented as in Table 10·1.

Table 10·1

NOTATION FOR 2^2 FACTORIAL DESIGNS

Observation	Level of factor A	Level of factor B	(AB)	Treatment combination
y_1	—	—	+	(1)
y_2	+	—	—	a
y_3	—	+	—	b
y_4	+	+	+	ab

The fourth column is added for a purpose shown later. The first observation, denoted by $- \; -$, involves the lower levels of both A and B; the second observation, denoted by $+ \; -$, involves the higher level of A and the lower level of B; and so on for the other two observations. In the other notation used in previous chapters, the treatment combinations, i.e. the combinations of the factor levels, are denoted respectively by (1), a, b, and ab. The sign notation for indicating levels of factors and treatment combinations is a convenient one, and it will be used extensively in this chapter. As shown earlier [§ **7·441**], the signs are also those appropriate to apply to the corresponding observations to calculate the main effects.
Thus

$$A = \tfrac{1}{2}(- y_1 + y_2 - y_3 + y_4)$$
$$B = \tfrac{1}{2}(- y_1 - y_2 + y_3 + y_4)$$

Using the treatment combinations to indicate the observations, we obtain the equivalent expressions

$$A = \tfrac{1}{2}[- (1) + a - b + ab]$$
$$B = \tfrac{1}{2}[- (1) - a + b + ab]$$

These represent two of the comparisons between the four observations; the third comparison yields the interaction AB; and the signs given in the fourth column of Table 10·1 are simply the products of the signs for A and B, so that

$$AB = \tfrac{1}{2}[(1) - a - b + ab]$$

Assuming the two factors A and B do not interact, the comparison represented by AB will be zero, apart from experimental error. It is then possible to utilise the AB comparison to measure the effect of a third factor (provided, as shown later, that the third factor does not interact with A or B). Denoting the additional factor by C, we "equate" C to AB in Table 10·1, and the signs then give the levels of factor C. This results in the design of Table 10·11 for measuring three factors in four observations.

Table 10·11

DESIGN FOR THREE FACTORS IN FOUR OBSERVATIONS

Observation	A	B	$C \, (= AB)$	Treatment combination
y_1	$-$	$-$	$+$	c
y_2	$+$	$-$	$-$	a
y_3	$-$	$+$	$-$	b
y_4	$+$	$+$	$+$	abc

The main effect of C is

$$\tfrac{1}{2}[c - a - b + abc]$$

Using the comparison representing interaction AB to measure a main effect C is referred to as "equating" C to AB.

Another design exists for three factors in four observations, obtained by equating C to $- AB$. The design is similar to that of Table 10·11, but with the signs of column C reversed. Both are half-factorial designs and the two together comprise the complete factorial design of three factors at two levels. The treatment combinations for the two designs are:

Design 1 ($C = AB$):	c	a	b	abc
Design 2 ($C = - AB$):	(1)	ac	bc	ab

It is interesting to note that the difference between the two designs represents the three-factor interaction ABC [§ 9·111], so that either design represents a block in the system confounding the interaction ABC. We shall return to this point later.

In both designs all four observations are used to estimate the three effects, the precision being that of the difference between two means each of two observations. The precision with which each effect is estimated is equal to that which would be obtained if the four observations measured one effect only. A half-factorial design thus retains the advantages associated with the complete factorial design in that each effect is measured with the maximum precision possible for the number of observations.

Important relationships are apparent upon inspection of Table 10·11: the fact that C has been equated to AB is shown by the signs of column C being the products of the signs of A and B, so that the comparison measures C when AB is zero. We see also that the signs of A are the products of B and C, while the signs of B are the products of those of A and C. It follows, therefore, that:

The four treatment combinations of Table 10·11 may be used to estimate three main effects provided all interactions between them are zero, or may be assumed negligible.

In general the factors A, B, and C may or may not interact; it is clear from the design of Table 10·11 that since there can only be three independent comparisons between four observations, all three comparisons are taken up in estimating A, B, and C, and any interaction which may exist between them will be confused in some way with these estimates. In particular, the comparison represented by AB has been used to measure C upon the assumption that $AB = 0$, and if AB is not zero, then the comparison measures $C + AB$. To sum up:

After equating C to AB in a 2^2 design, the comparison measures $C + AB$, and the other comparisons measure $A + BC$ and $B + AC$ respectively. Similarly, after equating C to $- AB$, the comparison measures $C - AB$, and the other comparisons measure $A - BC$ and $B - AC$ respectively.

Simple illustration

The weighing problem

10·12. A fractional factorial design can be simply illustrated by the operation of weighing a number of objects on a spring balance.* Suppose there are three objects, A, B, and C, to weigh, and the balance has a zero error. By the ordinary method the zero error is determined first and then each object is weighed separately, the estimated weight of each object being obtained as a difference between two readings, that for the given object and that for the zero error. If σ^2 is the variance of each reading, the variance of the estimated weight of each object will then be $2\sigma^2$.

Writing a $+$ when a given object to be weighed is on the balance and a $-$ when it is not, the arrangement for weighing each object separately may be represented by the following design.

Table 10·12

WEIGHING DESIGN: THREE OBJECTS WEIGHED SEPARATELY

Observation	Object			
	A	B	C	
y_1	$-$	$-$	$-$	Zero error
y_2	$+$	$-$	$-$	A only
y_3	$-$	$+$	$-$	B only
y_4	$-$	$-$	$+$	C only

An analogy exists between weighing an object and measuring the main effect of a factor, the objects A, B, and C being regarded as factors and the reading of the dial as the response. We know there cannot be any interaction between weighings of objects, for the effect of A (that is the increase in weight due to A) must be the same whatever combination of other objects is present. The conditions are then appropriate for the application of the design of Table 10·11; since $+$ indicates that the corresponding object is on the balance and $-$ that it is not, the interpretation of the design is:

* The choice of this illustration must not be taken as a recommendation for weighing objects. The example is only introduced because it represents one of the few cases in which there obviously can be no interactions.

$y_1' =$ reading of balance with object C

$y_2' =$ reading of balance with object A

$y_3' =$ reading of balance with object B

$y_4' =$ reading of balance with all three objects together

Note that this design does not require a zero error determination. The weight of A is the main effect of A, which is

$$\tfrac{1}{2}(-y_1' + y_2' - y_3' + y_4') = \tfrac{1}{2}(y_2' + y_4') - \tfrac{1}{2}(y_1' + y_3')$$

In other words, we apply the signs of column A to the observations. The above expression denotes a difference between two means each based on two observations, and since the variance of each reading is σ^2, the variance of the estimated weight is $2\sigma^2/2 = \sigma^2$. Comparing this variance with the variance of $2\sigma^2$ obtained when each object is weighed separately we see that the design of Table 10·11 is twice as efficient as that of Table 10·12. Table 10·11 represents one half of a complete design with three factors at two levels, the remaining four treatment combinations being (1), ac, bc, and ab. The second half of the factorial design, written in the $+$ and $-$ notation, is as Table 10·13.

Table 10·13

ALTERNATIVE WEIGHING DESIGN FOR THREE OBJECTS

Observation	A	B	C	
y_1''	$-$	$-$	$-$	Zero error
y_2''	$+$	$-$	$+$	Objects A and C
y_3''	$-$	$+$	$+$	Objects B and C
y_4''	$+$	$+$	$-$	Objects A and B

From this it is seen that:

$$\text{Weight of A} = \tfrac{1}{2}(-y_1'' + y_2'' - y_3'' + y_4'')$$
$$\text{Weight of B} = \tfrac{1}{2}(-y_1'' - y_2'' + y_3'' + y_4'')$$
$$\text{Weight of C} = \tfrac{1}{2}(-y_1'' + y_2'' + y_3'' - y_4'')$$

The design resembles that of Table 10·11 but with the signs of column C reversed; it may be derived directly from Table 10·1 by equating C to $-AB$, and it has similar properties. These are the two weighing designs for three objects which have maximum efficiency.

Designs of eight observations, all factors at two levels

10·2. In this section we extend the above method to designs involving four, five, six, and seven factors in eight observations. A more detailed treatment will be given later, but it is desirable to discuss the simpler aspects of the problem here in order that the subsequent discussion can be more readily appreciated.

Designs of four observations cannot cope with more than three factors, because three factors exhaust all the independent comparisons between the four observations. The next larger fractional factorial design of the kind discussed in this chapter is one of eight observations. A design of this size can usually be carried out without serious practical difficulties, even with complex industrial processes.

Eight observations are sufficient to supply estimates of all main effects and all interactions for a complete factorial design with three factors each at two levels. The + and − scheme is as Table 10·2.

Table 10·2
2³ FACTORIAL DESIGNS

Observation	A	B	C	AB	AC	BC	ABC	I	Treatment combination
y_1	−	−	−	+	+	+	−	+	(1)
y_2	+	−	−	−	−	+	+	+	a
y_3	−	+	−	−	+	−	+	+	b
y_4	+	+	−	+	−	−	−	+	ab
y_5	−	−	+	+	−	−	+	+	c
y_6	+	−	+	−	+	−	−	+	ac
y_7	−	+	+	−	−	+	−	+	bc
y_8	+	+	+	+	+	+	+	+	abc

This table falls into two parts: columns A, B, and C show the levels of the factors in each treatment combination and the signs for A, B, and C when applied to the corresponding observations give, apart from the divisor 4, the estimates of the main effects. The second part of the table—columns AB, AC, ... , I gives the appropriate signs to apply to the observations in order to estimate these effects.

If the three-factor interaction ABC may be assumed zero or negligible, the relevant comparison may be used to examine another factor D by "equating" D to ABC of Table 10·2. The + and − signs of this column then give the levels of the factor D in each treatment combination. The design is as Table 10·21.

Table 10·21

DESIGN FOR FOUR FACTORS IN EIGHT OBSERVATIONS

Observation	A	B	C	D	Treatment combination
y_1	−	−	−	−	(1)
y_2	+	−	−	+	ad
y_3	−	+	−	+	bd
y_4	+	+	−	−	ab
y_5	−	−	+	+	cd
y_6	+	−	+	−	ac
y_7	−	+	+	−	bc
y_8	+	+	+	+	abcd

This table represents one half of a 2^4 factorial design, and it is therefore a half-replicate. It can be verified that the products of the corresponding signs in the columns A, B, and C give those of D, that is $ABC = D$. We also note that the products of the signs of any three columns give those of the fourth, and the products of the signs of any two columns are the same as the products for the other two. Therefore $ABD = C$, $ACD = B$, $BCD = A$ and $AB = CD$, $AC = BD$, $AD = BC$. When two effects have the same signs, the interpretation is that the comparison obtained by applying the signs to the corresponding observations measures the sum of the effects. It follows that if all three-factor interactions and all interactions of D with A, B, and C are zero, the design of Table 10·21 measures A, B, C, D, AB, AC, and BC.

By equating D to $- ABC$ we obtain a design which is similar to that of Table 10·21 but with the signs changed in column D. The treatment combinations are respectively

$$d, a, b, abd, c, acd, bcd, abc$$

These combinations represent the other half of the complete factorial design, and the two halves form the two blocks in the design confounding the four-factor interaction $ABCD$. The comparisons in the second half of the design measure respectively $A − BCD$, $B − ACD$, $C − ABD$, $D − ABC$, $AB − CD$, $AC − BD$, $BC − AD$.

Additional factors may be introduced into Table 10·2 if in addition to D having no interaction with A, B, and C, certain other two-factor interactions may be assumed zero. For example, if BC is zero the corresponding comparison may be equated to an additional factor E provided no interaction exists between E and the remaining factors. The levels of E in the treatment combinations are then given by the signs in the corresponding column. The design is given in Table 10·22.

Table 10·22

DESIGN FOR FIVE FACTORS IN EIGHT OBSERVATIONS

Observation	A	B	C	E	D	Treatment combination
I	−	−	−	+	−	e
2	+	−	−	+	+	ade
3	−	+	−	−	+	bd
4	+	+	−	−	−	ab
5	−	−	+	−	+	cd
6	+	−	+	−	−	ac
7	−	+	+	+	−	bce
8	+	+	+	+	+	$abcde$

This represents one quarter of a 2^5 factorial design (i.e. a quarter-replicate)

There are three other designs having similar properties, and these are obtained by changing the sign of D, or E, or both. The four possibilities are

$$D = \pm ABC$$
$$E = \pm BC$$

taking the + and − signs in all combinations. When the treatment combinations for every design are written in full it will be seen that they form the four blocks in the design confounding $ABCD$, BCE, and ADE, as shown in Appendix 9E·22.

From the method of construction of Table 10·22 we know that $ABC = D$, and this can be checked by multiplying the columns A, B, and C. We see also by multiplication of the columns that $AE = D$ and $BCDE = D$. The effect D is thus confused with AE, ABC, and $BCDE$. The method may be used to determine the effects confused in each comparison, but it is rather cumbersome when applied in this way, particularly to small fractions of larger factorial designs. The method may be made systematic and simpler, and this will be done in greater detail in § **10·4**. We may note, however, at this stage that another factor, F, may be introduced into the design of Table 10·2 by equating the comparisons $\pm AC$ to F, provided interaction AC and all interactions with F are negligible. If also AB is negligible, yet another factor, G, may be introduced by equating $\pm AB$ to G. A design of eight observations may therefore be used:

(i) To estimate the effects of three factors and all interactions between them. This constitutes a complete factorial design for three factors.

(ii) To estimate the effects of four factors and the two-factor interactions between three of them, all other interactions being assumed zero or negligible.

(iii) To estimate the effects of five factors and an interaction of one factor with each of two others, all other interactions assumed zero or negligible.

(iv) To estimate the effects of six factors and one two-factor interaction, all other interactions assumed zero or negligible.

(v) To estimate the effects of seven factors, all interactions assumed zero or negligible.

Relation between fractional factorial designs and confounding

10·3. It was shown that there were two possible half-replicates of a 2^3 and a 2^4 factorial design, and that the two half-replicates constituted the two blocks in the complete factorial design confounding the highest-order interaction. There are four possible quarter-replicates of a 2^5 factorial design, and these represent four blocks in a confounded design. These simple examples illustrate the general principle that any fractional design of the kind considered in this chapter represents a block in a confounded design.

When the design is confounded in four blocks, any block constitutes a quarter-replicate. Similarly for designs confounded over 8, 16, etc., blocks, any block constitutes a one-eighth, a one-sixteenth, etc., replicate respectively. In confounding, the best designs are those which involve the least sacrifice of useful information, and are usually the designs which confound the lower-order interactions to the least possible extent. The same designs supply the best fractional replicates, in the sense that they provide the maximum amount of information of value. A fractional factorial design can thus be obtained by selecting a block in the appropriate confounded design. In theory, all the blocks are equally suitable and the selection should be made at random, but sometimes it is desirable to include a given treatment combination, e.g. one in which all the factors are at normal level, or one in which all the factors are changed together. Any of the methods given in Chapter 9 for constructing the principal block or the system of confounding may be used to derive a suitable fractional design, and conversely any method for deriving a fractional design may be used to construct the whole system of confounding; for, as shown in Appendix 9D, when one block of the system is known, the other blocks may be derived. The method introduced in § **10·2** for constructing a fractional design is, however, probably the most convenient and direct.

As shown in Chapter 9, a system of confounding is specified by the defining contrasts. When a fractional design has been obtained by equating a factor to an interaction in a complete factorial design, e.g. by putting $D = ABC$, the defining contrast is obtained by multiplying (with the rule of § **9·41**) both sides of this equation by the symbol representing the new factor, giving in this case $D^2 = ABCD$, or $I = ABCD$, since $D^2 = I$. When an additional factor has been introduced in this way, e.g. $E = BC$, another defining contrast is obtained by repeating the procedure, giving in this case $E^2 = I = BCE$. Multiplying together these two defining contrasts gives the remaining member of the set, thus $I = ABCD$ and $I = BCE$ when multiplied together give $I = ADE$, so that the defining contrast group is I, $ABCD$, BCE, ADE.

A similar procedure is applicable if still further factors are equated to other interactions, the rule being to multiply together all equations of the type $I = \ldots$ until all the defining contrasts have been identified.

When a factor is equated to the negative of the interaction, e.g. $D = - ABC$, minus signs will appear in the defining contrasts; in this case $I = - ABCD$. For the quarter-replicates defined by $D = \pm ABC$, $E = \pm BC$ we obtain the four sets of defining contrasts:

(i) I, $ABCD$, BCE, ADE
(ii) I, $- ABCD$, BCE, $- ADE$
(iii) I, $ABCD$, $- BCE$, $- ADE$
(iv) I, $- ABCD$, $- BCE$, ADE

These define respectively the four blocks in the system confounding $ABCD$, BCE, and ADE. The principal block is the one which contains the treatment combination (1), that is with all factors $-$. In order to obtain this combination, i.e. a row of negative signs, it is clear by reference to Table 10·2 that when equating an additional factor to an even interaction, i.e. one with an even number of letters, the minus sign should be used, and when equating to an odd interaction the plus sign should be used. The set of defining contrasts corresponding to the principal block is therefore the set in which all even interactions are positive and all odd interactions are negative. In the above system this corresponds to (iii).

The other blocks can readily be identified; for instance (i) may be derived from (iii) by changing the sign of E, and it therefore corresponds to the block which contains the treatment combination e; (ii) is derived from (iii) by changing the sign of B or C, and it therefore corresponds to the block containing the treatment combination b and c, and so on. By changing the signs of two or more letters it may be seen that there are many ways of deriving one set of defining contrasts from another.

Confusion of effects in a fractional design. Aliases

10·4. Assuming that interactions of all orders are real, it follows that in a half-replicate each effect is confused with another effect, that is, the effects occur in pairs; in a quarter-replicate the effects occur in sets of four and each effect is confused with three others; in an eighth-replicate the effects occur in sets of eight, and so on. The effects which are confused in this way are termed Aliases [10·1, 10·2]. It is clearly imperative to determine the aliases for any proposed fractional design in order to avoid confusion of important effects. As mentioned above [§ **10·2**], these aliases may be found from the design by multiplying the columns of signs in all possible ways and grouping the effects measured by the same comparison, that is, which have the same signs or have all the signs reversed. (Two comparisons which differ in sign only clearly measure the same effects apart from sign.) Applying these considerations to Table 10·22 shows that the following columns and products of columns have the same signs:

(i) $A, BCD, ABCE, DE$

(ii) $B, ACD, CE, ABDE$

(iii) $C, ABD, BE, ACDE$

(iv) AB, CD, ACE, BDE, and so on

It is possible to systematise the method of obtaining the aliases because all the sets may be obtained from the defining contrasts. For instance, the defining contrasts for the design of Table 10·22 are

$$I, ABCD, BCE, ADE$$

Multiplying successively by A, B, C, etc., yields the above aliases. This result is perfectly general for all fractional designs, and leads to the rule:

The effects confused with any given effect in a fractional design are derived by multiplying the defining contrasts by the given effect. The whole set of comparisons is derived by multiplying the defining contrasts successively by the main effects, two-factor interactions, etc., until all the effects have been accounted for.

The comparisons measure the sums and differences of the aliases, the appropriate signs being those given by the defining contrasts. For the above alias sets, the signs will all be positive, the comparisons measuring respectively

$$A + BCD + ABCE + DE$$
$$B + ACD + CE + ABDE, \text{ and so on}$$

The quarter-replicate obtained by equating D to $- ABC$ and E to BC has the defining contrasts I, $- ABCD, BCE$, and $- ADE$, and the comparisons measure

$$A - BCD + ABCE - DE$$
$$B - ACD + CE - ABDE, \text{ and so on}$$

A more detailed discussion of the actual signs of the aliases will be given later; for present purposes it is sufficient to know what effects are confused in the design. It is interesting to note that in the above quarter-replicate of a 2^5 factorial design, two-factor interactions are confused with main effects.

A summary of the natures of the aliases in fractional designs is given in Appendix 10A.

Notes on the general methods of constructing fractional factorial designs

10·41. We have seen that there are two general methods of constructing fractional factorial designs. The first is to select a block from the corresponding confounded design. If it is required to examine five factors in eight observations, then we require a quarter-replicate of a 2^5 factorial design, and the corresponding confounded design is that for a 2^5 factorial design divided into blocks of eight observations, i.e. confounding three interactions. Suitable designs are given in Appendix 9E·22, which cover most practical requirements. Sometimes it may be necessary to use a design not given in this table, e.g. a quarter-replicate of a 2^7 factorial design. The first task is to choose suitable defining contrasts involving the lower-order interactions to the least extent and corresponding to the least amount of confusion of important effects. For this we must use all the letters and derive the defining contrasts by trial. For example, we could take

$$ABCD, EFG, ABCDEFG$$

which involves a three-factor interaction. The following is better:

$$ABCDE, DEFG, ABCFG$$

as it does not involve a three-factor interaction. It is clear that we cannot, do better than this, because if a letter is added to the four-factor interaction the product with one of the others will be a four-factor interaction. Having derived the defining contrasts, the confounded design may be constructed using YATES'S method [§ **9·42**] or the method of Appendix 9D.

The second general method is the one introduced in § **10·2**. In relation to the above illustration of five factors in eight observations we select three of the factors which are most likely to interact, say A, B, and C, and equate the other two factors to the interactions between A, B, and C least likely to be appreciable, e.g. to ABC and BC, so that $D = ABC$ and $E = BC$. As shown earlier, there are two ways of equating D to ABC, viz. $D = + ABC$ and $D = - ABC$, and similarly there are two ways of equating E to BC viz. $E = \pm BC$. This gives the four schemes:

$(D = + ABC)$	$(D = - ABC)$	$(D = - ABC)$	$(D = + ABC)$
$(E = + BC)$	$(E = + BC)$	$(E = - BC)$	$(E = - BC)$

which define the four blocks in the system confounding $ABCD$, BCE, and ADE. The process is in effect the reverse of YATES'S method. The latter breaks down the full factorial design using the combinations $+$ and $-$ for two of the defining contrasts, and the above method builds up the complete factorial design by a reverse process. This is a further illustration of the relation between fractional factorial designs and confounding.

Other designs for five factors in eight observations are obtained by equating the additional factors D and E to other pairs of interactions, e.g. $D = \pm AB$, $E = \pm BC$. A convenient way of comparing these designs is by means of the defining contrasts. Multiplying $D = \pm ABC$ by D gives $I = \pm ABCD$, and multiplying $E = \pm BC$ by E gives $I = \pm BCE$. Dropping the signs, this leads to the defining contrasts

$$I, ABCD, BCE, ADE \quad \dots\dots\dots\dots\dots\dots(10·1)$$

Similarly equating D to $\pm AB$ and E to $+ BC$ gives

$$I, ABD, BCE, ACDE \quad \dots\dots\dots\dots\dots\dots(10·2)$$

The two sets of designs are equivalent* because interchanging B and E in $(10·1)$ gives $(10·2)$.

We will now show how the second general method may be used to construct a fractional factorial design from the defining contrasts. Let the defining contrasts be $I, -ABC, CDE, -ABDE$. The corresponding design is a quarter-replicate of a 2^5 factorial design and consists of $2^3 = 8$ observations. A complete design of eight observations requires three factors; let these be chosen out of $ABCDE$ so that when multiplied together they do not represent or include any of the interactions in the defining contrasts. Evidently A, B, D satisfies this requirement. The problem now is to introduce the additional factors C and E into this design. From $I = -ABC$ and $I = -ABDE$ we see that this can be done by equating C to $-AB$ and E to $-ABD$. When the signs of the defining contrasts are not specified, there are the four possibilities, viz. $C = \pm AB$ and $E = \pm ABD$.

Statistical analysis of fractional factorial designs

10·42. All fractional designs of the kind considered in this chapter contain 2^p observations, where p is less than n, the number of factors. For the purpose of the initial stages of the analysis such designs may be considered as complete factorial designs in any p of the factors if the remaining $n - p$ factors are assumed not to exist. In this form we may apply YATES's systematic method of analysis, which is fully described in § 7·45. The other factors are introduced at the final stage to identify the combinations of effects measured by each comparison. The method is applied in detail in Appendix 10C to all the examples of this chapter.

For designs of eight or fewer observations it may be found more convenient to calculate the effects by applying the signs directly to the observations.

Example 10·2. Four factors in eight observations

10·421. In an investigation of the conditions of filtration during the preparation of a dyestuff the object was to improve the quality of the product. Four factors were examined:

---

* Such equivalence does not generally occur for larger designs, and for these more consideration must be given to the choice of interactions to equate to additional factors. The point is dealt with later in § 10·6.

A. Concentration of liquor when filtered (concentrated v. dilute).

B. Effect of keeping (fresh v. old). The liquor was either filtered immediately or was kept a week before filtration.

C. Presence or absence of butanol. Butanol is used to prevent frothing.

D. Temperature of filtration (high v. low).

It was considered unlikely that there would be large interactions between these factors, and as a first step it was decided to examine them in eight observations, i.e. by means of a half-replicate of a 2^4 factorial design. The design is derived from the 2^3 factorial design for A, B, C, by equating D to $+ ABC$ as in Table 10·21; details are given in Table 10·23.

Table 10·23

DESIGN AND OBSERVATIONS FOR FILTRATION EXPERIMENT

No of prepara-tion	Level of factor				Observation (purity)
	A Dil. = − Conc. = +	B Old = − Fresh = +	C No butanol = − Butanol = +	D Low temp. = − High temp. = +	
1	−	−	−	−	107
2	+	−	−	+	114
3	−	+	−	+	122
4	+	+	−	−	130
5	−	−	+	+	106
6	+	−	+	−	121
7	−	+	+	−	120
8	+	+	+	+	132

The purity of the product was measured by means of a photoelectric instrument, giving the results recorded in the above table. The higher the value the purer the product, but the scale is not necessarily linearly correlated with actual purity measured as per cent of chemically pure material present.

Since this is a half-replicate, each comparison measures a pair of effects the pairs being

(A, BCD); (B, ACD); (C, ABD); (D, ABC); (AB, CD); (AC, BD); (AD, BC),

The three-factor interactions could be safely ignored. The magnitudes of the effects obtained by applying the signs of Table 10·23 to the observations are

Total $A = - 107 + 114 - 122 + 130 - 106 + 121 - 120 + 132 = 42$

Main Effect $A = \frac{1}{4} \times 42 = 10·5$

and so on for the other main effects.

The comparison (AB, CD) using the signs given by the products of A and B, or C and D, is

$$\text{Total } (AB, CD) = 107 - 114 - 122 + 130 + 106 - 121 - 120 + 132$$
$$= -2$$

Effect $(AB, CD) = -0.5$

The other interactions are obtained in the same way. This leads to the analysis given in Table 10·24.

Table 10·24

EFFECTS AND ANALYSIS OF VARIANCE

(1) Comparison	(2) Total	(3) Effect = (Col. 2)/4	(4) Degrees of freedom	(5) Sum of squares = (Col. 2)²/8
A	42	10·5	1	220·5
B	56	14·0	1	392·0
C	6	1·5	1	4·5
D	− 4	− 1·0	1	2·0
(AB, CD)	− 2	− 0·5	1	0·5
(AC, BD)	12	3·0	1	18·0
(AD, BC)	− 6	− 1·5	1	4·5
Total.. ..	—	—	7	642·0

The total sum of squares for the eight observations is $107^2 + 114^2 + \ldots + 132^2 - 952^2/8 = 642$, and this agrees with the sum of the last column, thus supplying an arithmetical check. Since every effect is based on one degree of freedom, the sums of squares also denote the mean squares.

The error variance was known from past experiments to be about 4·0, and on this basis A, B, and (AC, BD) are significant. The interaction (AC, BD) is thus probably real, and from chemical considerations we may conclude the significant interaction is almost certainly that between A and C. The form of the interaction AC is seen from the two-way table of totals for A and C (Table 10·25).

Table 10·25

INTERACTION OF A AND C

	C	
	No butanol (−)	Butanol (+)
A Dilute (−)	114·5	113·0
Concentrated (+) ..	122·0	126·5

This indicates that in dilute liquor butanol has no effect, while in concentrated liquor there is a slight advantage in using butanol. Clearly there is an advantage in using concentrated liquor, whether butanol is present or not.

It is concluded that the quality measured in this way is

(i) markedly better when the liquor is filtered immediately,

(ii) further improved by using concentrated liquors,

(iii) slightly further improved by using butanol,

(iv) not affected by temperature (within the limits used).

Example 10·3. Five factors in eight observations. Yield of a medicinal product

10·43. This experiment represented part of a laboratory investigation of the conditions affecting the yield of a medicinal product, the five factors investigated and their levels being as follows:

A	Amount of reactant	..	..	..	4 mols.	5 mols.
B	Concentration of acid	..	..	..	Concentrated	Dilute
C	Amount of acid ..	..	..	..	2 mols.	2·5 mols.
D	Time of reaction ..	..	..	..	2 hours	4 hours
E	Temperature of reaction..		..	..	Low	High

Denoting the levels of the factors by − and + in the order given above, the design of the experiment, obtained by equating D to $-AC$ and E to $+AB$ in Table 10·2, is shown in Table 10·31.

Table 10·31

DESIGN OF EXPERIMENT AND YIELD OF PRODUCT

Treatment combination	A	B	C	D	E	Per cent yield
e	−	−	−	−	+	59·1
ad	+	−	−	+	−	57·0
b	−	+	−	−	−	58·6
abde	+	+	−	+	+	63·9
cde	−	−	+	+	+	67·2
ac	+	−	+	−	−	71·6
bcd	−	+	+	+	−	79·2
abce	+	+	+	−	+	76·9

This particular design was chosen at random from the four possibilities $D = \pm AC, E = \pm AB$. It is the same design as that obtained by equating E to $-BCD$ and A to $-CD$, and has the following defining contrasts

$$I, -BCDE, -ACD, ABE$$

derived in the usual way. From these we obtain the aliases given in Table 10·32, omitting three-factor and higher-order interactions, which are assumed to be zero.

Carrying out the analysis, we obtain Table 10·32.

Table 10·32

ANALYSIS OF VARIANCE OF TABLE 10·31

(1) Total	(2) Effect (Col. 1)/4	(3) Degrees of freedom	(4) Mean square (Col. 1)²/8	(5) Effects and aliases
5·3	1·3	1	3·51	$A, -CD, BE$
23·7	5·9	1	70·21	B, AE
56·3	14·1	1	396·21	$C, -AD$
1·1	0·3	1	0·15	$D, -AC$
0·7	0·2	1	0·06	E, AB
10·9	2·7	1	14·85	$BC, -DE$
14·1	3·5	1	24·85	$BD, -CE$
	Total ..	7	509·84	

The total sum of squares agrees within rounding-off errors with the sum of squares of the eight observations about their mean.

The standard error for this type of reaction was known to be about 1%, giving a variance of 1·00. Even if the variance is taken to be 2·00, the effects denoted by the leading terms B, C, BC, and BD are highly significant. The largest is C (amount of acid) and the next largest is B (concentration of acid). The two significant interactions are the next in order of magnitude. The comparisons measure the sums of the effects given in the last column of Table 10·32, and since some two-factor interactions have been shown to be appreciable and two-factor interactions are aliases of main effects, it is possible that the sums of squares corresponding to B and C are influenced by appreciable interactions. The effects attributed to B and C are, however, very large, and on technical grounds it appears unlikely that the aliases can be responsible for much of these effects.

The effects $(BC, -DE)$, and $(BD, -CE)$ are significant. One way of examining these interactions is to set up two-way tables of means for the pairs of interactions. For the first pair we have Tables 10·33 and 10·331.

Table 10·33
INTERACTION *BC*

Factor C Amount of acid	Factor B	
	Conc. acid	Dilute acid
2 mols. ..	58·1	61·3
2·5 mols. ..	69·4	78·1

Table 10·331
INTERACTION *DE*

Factor E Temperature of reaction	Factor D Time of reaction	
	2 hrs.	4 hrs.
Low ..	65·1	68·1
High ..	68·0	65·6

It is easy to confirm that these interactions are (apart from sign) numerically equivalent within rounding-off errors, for:

$$2 \times BC = (78\cdot1 - 61\cdot3) - (69\cdot4 - 58\cdot1) = 16\cdot8 - 11\cdot3 = + 5\cdot5$$
$$2 \times DE = (65\cdot6 - 68\cdot1) - (68\cdot0 - 65\cdot1) = - 2\cdot5 - 2\cdot9 = - 5\cdot4$$

From Table 10·33 it appears that the best combination is 2·5 mols. of dilute acid. From Table 10·331 the best combination is either a long time at low temperature or a short time at high temperature.

The corresponding tables for the interactions (*BD, CE*) are Tables 10·34 and 10·341.

Table 10·34
INTERACTION *BD*

Factor D	Factor B	
	Conc.	Dilute
2 hours ..	65·4	67·8
4 hours ..	62·1	71·6

Table 10·341
INTERACTION *CE*

Factor E	Factor C	
	2 mols.	2·5 mols.
Low temp.	57·8	75·4
High temp.	61·5	72·1

Table 10·34 suggests that dilute acid should be used with a reaction time of 4 hours, and Table 10·341 that a low temperature should be used with 2·5 mols. of acid. Considering all four tables we reach the unambiguous conclusion that the best conditions are 2·5 mols. of dilute acid, with a reaction time of 4 hours at the lower temperature.

It is fortunate that the conclusions reached from the four tables are not contradictory. It might well have happened that Table 10·33 would have suggested concentrated acid and Table 10·34 dilute acid. In the absence of any technical reason for supposing one interaction to be non-existent it would have been necessary to carry out further trials to decide which concentration to use.

Designs of sixteen observations

10·5. The method of constructing fractional factorial designs of eight observations may readily be extended to designs of 16 observations. Sixteen observations are sufficient for a complete factorial design for four factors each at two levels. Denoting the factors by A, B, C, and D, then the complete factorial design in the $+$ and $-$ notation is given in columns A, B, C and D of Table 10·4 and alternatively by the small letters in the first column of the table.

Table 10·4

2^4 FACTORIAL DESIGN

Treatment combination	A	B	C	D	AB	AC	AD	BC	BD	CD	ABC	ABD	ACD	BCD	ABCD	I
(1)	−	−	−	−	+	+	+	+	+	+	−	−	−	−	+	+
a	+	−	−	−	−	−	−	+	+	+	+	+	+	−	−	+
b	−	+	−	−	−	+	+	−	−	+	+	+	−	+	−	+
ab	+	+	−	−	+	−	−	−	−	+	−	−	+	+	+	+
c	−	−	+	−	+	−	+	−	+	−	+	−	+	+	−	+
ac	+	−	+	−	−	+	−	−	+	−	−	+	−	+	+	+
bc	−	+	+	−	−	−	+	+	−	−	−	+	+	−	+	+
abc	+	+	+	−	+	+	−	+	−	−	+	−	−	−	−	+
d	−	−	−	+	+	+	−	+	−	−	−	+	+	+	−	+
ad	+	−	−	+	−	−	+	+	−	−	+	−	−	+	+	+
bd	−	+	−	+	−	+	−	−	+	−	+	−	+	−	+	+
abd	+	+	−	+	+	−	+	−	+	−	−	+	−	−	−	+
cd	−	−	+	+	+	−	−	−	−	+	+	+	−	−	+	+
acd	+	−	+	+	−	+	+	−	−	+	−	−	+	−	−	+
bcd	−	+	+	+	−	−	−	+	+	+	−	−	−	+	−	+
abcd	+	+	+	+	+	+	+	+	+	+	+	+	+	+	+	+

The signs have the same interpretation as in Table 10·2.

Additional factors may be introduced as before by equating them to interactions on the assumption that the interactions involved are zero. Equating E to $ABCD$ involves the assumption that $ABCD$ is zero, and from the corresponding defining contrasts I, $ABCDE$, it is evident that the other main effects are also aliases of four-factor interactions, and the assumption is involved that all other four-factor interactions are zero. It can readily be seen that a design of 16 observations may be used for the following purposes:

(i) *To estimate four factors and all interactions between them.*
This constitutes a full 2^4 factorial design.

(ii) *To estimate five factors and all two-factor interactions on the assumption that all three-factor and higher-order interactions are zero or negligible.*

This is a half-replicate of a 2^5 design with the defining contrasts $I, ABCDE$.

(iii) *To estimate six factors and not more than nine two-factor interactions, no two of which fall in the same alias group.*

This design is a quarter-replicate of a 2^6 factorial design. A quarter-replicate is particularly suitable for six factors when two of the factors do not interact with each other or any of the other four factors. The "best" quarter-replicates have the defining contrasts $I, BCDE, ACDF, ABEF$, obtained by equating E to $\pm BCD$ and F to $\pm ACD$.

(iv) *To estimate seven factors and not more than eight two-factor interactions, no two of which fall in the same alias group.*

This is a one-eighth replicate of a 2^7 factorial design. A one-eighth replicate is particularly suitable for seven factors when three of the factors do not interact with one another or with the other four factors. The "best" one-eighth replicates of a 2^7 design have the defining contrasts $I, BCDE, ACDF, ABDG, ABEF, ACEG, DEFG, BCFG$, obtained by equating E to $\pm BCD$, F to $\pm ACD$ and G to $\pm ABD$.

(v) *To estimate eight or more factors with appropriate restrictions on the allowable two-factor interactions.*

Even with eight factors it is possible to estimate all the two-factor interactions from four of the factors provided all other interactions are negligible. It is unlikely that more than eight factors will be required to be examined in a single chemical experiment.

The method may readily be extended to designs of 32 observations, but usually when such large designs are required it is necessary to introduce confounding. This will be dealt with in § **10·6**.

It was shown that for designs of eight observations there were several ways of introducing two additional factors into the complete factorial design for three factors A, B, and C. One was to equate the factor D to the highest-order interaction ABC, and the factor E to the next highest, that is a two-factor interaction. Essentially the same result is obtained by equating both D and E to two-factor interactions. For designs of 16 observations a fifth factor, E, is introduced into the complete factorial design for $A, B, C,$ and D by equating E to the four-factor interaction $ABCD$. Again there are several ways of introducing two factors, e.g.

$$E = ABCD \qquad F = ABC$$

or $\qquad\qquad\qquad E = BCD \qquad F = ACD, \text{ and so on}$

These do not give equivalent fractional replicates; the first has the defining contrasts

$$I, ABCDE, ABCF, DEF$$

and the second

$$I, BCDE, ACDF, ABEF$$

Provided all interactions involving E or F are negligible, both designs are satisfactory. The second design, however, requires less stringent conditions than the first; in the first, D, E, and F have two-factor interactions as aliases, but in the second, all main effects are clear of two-factor interactions. This leads to the rule:

> To introduce one additional factor we equate it to the highest-order interaction. To introduce two additional factors we equate them to interactions of order one lower than the highest. Further factors are equated to the same order interactions and, when these are exhausted, to the highest-order interactions available.

Example 10·4. Five factors in sixteen observations. Quality of a basic dyestuff

10·51. This investigation was carried out under manufacturing conditions with the object of improving the quality of a basic dyestuff. The process was one of long standing, and although at one time it consistently gave product of standard quality, the quality became more variable for a period prior to this investigation. Several conditions had necessarily changed because of increased output required of the plant. Although on chemical grounds none of these changes was expected to affect quality, they could be regarded as possible causes of the deterioration in quality. Various theories were held as to the factors responsible. It was unlikely that many of the factors were responsible, and it appeared worth while examining all the theories in a compact fractional replicate design in the expectation that only a few of the factors and interactions would have appreciable effects. Three stages in the process were examined, and the factors were as follows.

Stage 1   Oxidation

   A Temperature ..   .. Low ($-$)   High ($+$)

   B Two qualities of starting materials .. $-$ $+$

Stage 2   Reduction

   C Reduction pressure   .. Atmospheric ($-$) Increased pressure ($+$)

Stage 3 Oven drying under pressure

| D | Pressure | .. | .. | .. | .. | Low (−) | High (+) |
| E | Vacuum leak | .. | .. | .. | .. | Low (−) | High (+) |

Technical considerations suggested that A and B might interact and so might C, D, and E, but it was less likely that there would be interactions between A and B on one hand and C, D, and E on the other. Suitable designs are obtained by equating the factor E to the interaction $\pm ABCD$, and the minus sign was chosen for this investigation. This involves reversing the signs in column $ABCD$ of Table 10·4 and gives a half-replicate of a 2^5 design, with the defining contrasts I, $- ABCDE$.

One measure of the quality of the product is based on an assessment of the shade by a recording photoelectric spectrometer, the lower the value recorded the better being the quality. The design and the quality assessed in this way are shown in Table 10·51.

Table 10·51

DESIGN AND OBSERVATIONS OF EXAMPLE 10·4

| Treatment combination | Level of factor | | | | | Quality |
	A	B	C	D	E	
(1)	−	−	−	−	−	201·5
ae	+	−	−	−	+	178·0
be	−	+	−	−	+	183·5
ab	+	+	−	−	−	176·0
ce	−	−	+	−	+	188·5
ac	+	−	+	−	−	178·5
bc	−	+	+	−	−	174·5
abce	+	+	+	−	+	196·5
de	−	−	−	+	+	255·5
ad	+	−	−	+	−	240·5
bd	−	+	−	+	−	208·5
abde	+	+	−	+	+	244·0
cd	−	−	+	+	−	274·0
acde	+	−	+	+	+	257·5
bcde	−	+	+	+	+	256·0
abcd	+	+	+	+	−	274·5

The results are arranged in standard order with respect to the factors A, B, C, and D, which facilitates the application of the systematic method of analysis, details of which are given in Appendix 10·C. The analysis is given in Table 10·52.

Table 10·52

ANALYSIS OF VARIANCE OF TABLE 10·51

Effect*	Total	Effect	Degrees of freedom	Mean square
A	+ 3·5	0·4	I	0·77
B	− 60·5	− 7·6	I	228·77
C	+ 112·5	14·1	I	791·02
D	+ 533·5	66·7	I	17,788·89
E	+ 31·5	3·9	I	62·02
AB	+ 133·5	16·7	I	1,113·89
CE	− 37·5	− 4·7	I	87·89
CD	+ 114·5	14·3	I	819·39
DE	− 0·5	− 0·1	I	0·02
AC	+ 24·5	3·1	I ⎫	37·52 ⎫
AD	+ 41·5	5·2	I ⎪	107·64 ⎪
AE	− 18·5	− 2·3	I ⎬ 6	21·39 ⎬ 121·68
BC	+ 66·5	8·3	I ⎪	276·39 ⎪
BD	− 28·5	− 3·6	I ⎪	50·77 ⎪
BE	+ 61·5	7·7	I ⎭	236·39 ⎭
Total ..			15	21,622·76

* The aliases of the main effects and two-factor interactions are respectively four-factor and three-factor interactions which are regarded as negligible.

Since A and B were not expected to interact with C, D, and E, and in fact none of the two-factor interactions of this kind was large, the six interactions were combined to give an estimate of error variance of 121·68 based on six degrees of freedom. The significant effects in order of magnitude are D, AB, CD, and C. Clearly factors A and B on the one hand and C and D on the other require to be examined together. The corresponding two-way table of means for factors C and D is shown in Table 10·53.

Table 10·53

INTERACTION CD

Factor D Drying pressure	Factor C Reduction pressure	
	Low	High
Low	184·8	184·5
High	237·1	265·5

The higher drying pressure is unfavourable, and this is particularly so at high reduction pressure. At low drying pressure the change in reduction pressure appears to have no effect.

Interaction AB is illustrated by the two-way Table 10·54.

Table 10·54

INTERACTION *AB*

Factor A Temperature of oxidation	Factor B Oxidation condition	
	−	+
Low	229·9	205·6
High	213·6	222·8

It is seen that low oxidation temperature should be coupled with the higher level of *B* and high oxidation temperature with the lower level of *B*, the first alternative being preferable. The conclusions are that low drying pressure should be used and that under these conditions the reduction pressure is not important. It is preferable to change the oxidation condition, denoted by factor B, to the higher level, and when this is done it is necessary to use the lower temperature of oxidation. However, the normal oxidation condition coupled with a high temperature is almost as good. The vacuum leak, either high or low, makes no material difference.

Confounding in fractional factorial designs

10·6. It is sometimes necessary to introduce confounding into a fractional factorial design. The type of situation requiring confounding has already been considered at length in the previous chapter [§ **9·2**]. The smallest fractional factorial design which permits a degree of confounding is one of eight observations. These eight observations can be divided into two sets and any of the interactions not likely to be appreciable may be confounded. In the design of Table 10·21 four of the seven degrees of freedom are taken up by the main effects *A*, *B*, *C*, and *D*, while the remaining three degrees of freedom represent two-factor interactions estimating respectively $AB + CD$, $AC + BD$, $AD + BC$.

As mentioned earlier, this half-replicate would be used only when all three-factor interactions were negligible, and at most one interaction out of each of the three pairs of two-factor interactions given above was likely to be appreciable. This requirement is satisfied if the three-factor interaction between *A*, *B*, and *C*, and all interactions of the fourth factor, *D*, with *A*, *B*, and *C* are negligible. If in addition another two-factor interaction, say *AB*, may be assumed negligible, then the comparison represented by (*AB*, *CD*) may be confounded between two blocks. One block should contain the treatment combinations marked plus in this comparison and the other block should contain the treatment combinations marked minus, that is:

Block 1	(1)	*ab*	*cd*	*abcd*
Block 2	*ad*	*bd*	*ac*	*bc*

Confounding in a fractional factorial design is thus a simple extension of confounding in complete factorial designs; the only difference is that in the latter the effects confounded are simple ones, whereas in the former the effects confounded are combinations of simple effects. In Example 10·4 any of the interactions between A, B, and C, D, E could be confounded.

The following example of confounding in a half-replicate of a 2^5 design over four blocks gives a further illustration of the principles involved.

Example 10·5. Yield of penicillin

10·61. There are three main stages in the production of penicillin, namely the production of the inoculum, the fermentation stage, and the chemical extraction of the penicillin, and this investigation was concerned only with the first two stages of the process. The inoculum produced at the first stage is used in the second stage for the production of the penicillin.

There were several factors considered likely to affect the efficiency of the process, and the following four were chosen for investigation:

Stage 1	*Preparation of inoculum*
A	Concentration of corn steep liquor
B	Amount of sugars
C	Quality of sugars
Stage 2	*Fermentation*
D	Concentration of corn steep liquor

There was insufficient corn steep liquor from one delivery for the whole design, and it was decided to use two deliveries, each to be used in one half of the design. This necessitated adding the factor

E Quality of corn steep liquor

There were four similar fermenters available, introducing another factor:

F Fermenters 1, 2, 3, and 4

No large differences were expected between these fermenters or between the deliveries of corn steep liquor; consequently no interactions were likely between these two factors and the remainder.

The investigation was confined to one change in each of the factors, the change being made in the direction considered more likely to improve the yield. The changes in any factor were relatively small, so that no large interactions were likely to arise. As a safeguard it was decided to retain as many as possible of the interactions between A, B, C, and D.

A design of 16 batches was considered the minimum of any practical value, because of the relatively large variation known to arise in the biological process; this number is sufficient for a complete factorial design involving four factors. A, B, C, and D are the more important factors, and since these are the only ones that are likely to interact we construct a basic factorial design with them. This enables the following 15 effects to be estimated.

Main effects	A, B, C, D
Two-factor interactions	AB, AC, AD, BC, BD, CD
Three-factor interactions	ABC, ABD, ACD, BCD
Four-factor interaction	$ABCD$

To introduce the two qualities of corn steep liquor, factor E, we equate E to the interaction $ABCD$. There are four fermenters, and to introduce these it is necessary to use up three degrees of freedom. This is really the problem of confounding the fractional factorial design for the five factors A–E into four blocks, each block corresponding to one fermenter [§ **9·42**]. Two of the degrees of freedom may be chosen at will, but the third will be determined by their product. The best arrangement is based on two three-factor interactions and their product, which unfortunately must be a two-factor interaction. BC is the interaction least likely to be appreciable and therefore we choose ABD, ACD and BC to represent the comparisons between the fermenters. The general method of dividing the observations into four blocks has been given in § **9·42**. Considering the signs of ABD and ACD (see corresponding columns in Table 10·4), it is evident that those observations which are + for both ABD and ACD should be allocated to one fermenter, those which are + for ABD and − for ACD to another, and so on.

The resulting design and the observations obtained are given in Table 10·6.

Table 10·6
DESIGN FOR EXAMPLE 10·5

A	B	C	D	E	Fermenter	Observation
−	−	−	−	+	4	775
+	−	−	−	−	1	625
−	+	−	−	−	2	756
+	+	−	−	+	3	666
−	−	+	−	−	3	593
+	−	+	−	+	2	625
−	+	+	−	+	1	785
+	+	+	−	−	4	628
−	−	−	+	−	1	819
+	−	−	+	+	4	735
−	+	−	+	+	3	745
+	+	−	+	−	2	841
−	−	+	+	+	2	878
+	−	+	+	−	3	656
−	+	+	+	−	4	851
+	+	+	+	+	1	732

This design is arranged in standard order with respect to factors A, B, C, and D.

The design may also be written in the form of Table 10·61.

Table 10·61

ALTERNATIVE METHOD OF SETTING OUT THE DESIGN OF TABLE 10·6

	Fermenter		
1	2	3	4
a	b	c	e
d	cde	bde	ade
bce	ace	abe	abc
abcde	abd	acd	bcd

This is the half-factorial design *ABCDE* confounded between four fermenters.

Analysis of results

10·62. The analysis is given in Table 10·7 and the details of the calculation in Appendix 10C.

Table 10·7

ANALYSIS OF RESULTS OF TABLE 10·6

Factor	Totals	Means	Sum of squares	Degrees of freedom	Mean square
A	− 694	− 87	30,102	1	30,102
B	298	37	5,550	1	5,550
C	− 214	− 27	2,862	1	2,862
D	804	101	40,401	1	40,401
E	172	22	1,849	1	1,849
Interaction					
AB ..	154	19	1,482	1	
AC ..	− 238	− 30	3,540	1	
BD ..	− 136	− 17	1,156	1	
CD ..	168	21	1,764	1 ⎬7	2,312
DE ..	− 326	− 41	6,642	1	
AD ..	36	5	81	1	
AE ..	− 156	− 20	1,521	1	
Fermenter					
1	2,961	740			
2	3,100	775	26,554	3	8,851
3	2,660	665			
4	2,989	747			

The process variance calculated from plant records was 2500, from which it is seen that factors A, D, and fermenters have significant effects. If the experiment is to be regarded as self-contained the interactions have to be combined to give an estimate of error, yielding a mean square of 2312 based on 7 degrees of freedom. On this basis A and D are significant and fermenters possibly significant. From the prior knowledge of the process variation, however, there is little doubt of the significance of the variation between fermenters, which is seen to be due to fermenter 3 giving a low yield.

The conclusions are that:

(i) Increase in concentration of corn steep liquor in stage 1 (factor A) reduces the yield.

(ii) Increase in concentration of corn steep liquor in stage 2 (factor D) increases the yield.

(iii) Fermenter 3 gives a lower yield than the other fermenters.

Discussion on the application of fractional factorial designs

10·7. In the chemical industry it is frequently required to examine the effect on the yield or quality of a chemical product of varying a number of reaction conditions. One requirement for the satisfactory use of fractional factorial designs is that some at least of the interactions are small compared to the main effects or interactions of a lower order. In any given investigation the chemist may know from theoretical considerations or from previous experience that certain of the interactions are not likely to be appreciable or that certain interactions are more likely to arise than others. For instance, in most chemical reactions he would expect an interaction between the time of reaction and the temperature of reaction: it is not unusual for the optimum time of reaction to change with the temperature of reaction. He would, therefore, in fractional factorial designs involving these two factors keep this particular interaction free of all main effects. There may be other interactions which require to be kept free of serious entanglement.

The magnitude of an interaction depends upon the ranges of the variables examined; as the ranges are decreased the interactions become smaller compared with the main effects, and when the region to be examined is sufficiently small the interactions with few exceptions become negligible.

As the range becomes narrower the magnitudes of the effects become smaller, and the more likely are they to be masked by the experimental error. The range chosen must be such as to produce effects which are measurable but not so large as to give rise to appreciable interactions. The choice of range requires careful consideration and detailed examination of past experimental work and plant records. If the effect corresponding to the given range of the factor chosen for investigation is small compared to the experimental error of each observation, a fairly large number of observations or runs will be required, and a complete factorial design may be needed.

Fractional designs are most successful in investigations involving several possible factors of which only a few have an appreciable effect. This is particularly true in investigations of a process giving trouble on the plant [Example 10·4]. The trouble may be due to many possible factors and a number of theories or possible explanations may be presented. One technician might regard the trouble as due to filtration or drying temperatures but not to rate of addition or other causes; another might consider the cause to be inadequate agitation and not filtration, nor rate of addition, and so on. In such circumstances it is worth while examining as many factors as possible in a fractional design because it is unlikely that more than two of them have large effects, and even more unlikely that appreciable interactions exist except between the factors that have large main effects. If the results are contrary to expectation and more than two factors have large effects, then important results have emerged, and it would be worth while carrying out further experimental work in order to examine the factors and their interactions more closely.

Experimental error

10·71. In the fractional factorial designs likely to be required in chemical work most of the degrees of freedom are used up in estimating main effects and certain two-factor interactions, and often few degrees of freedom are left for obtaining an independent estimate of the error variance. When no prior information exists on the experimental error it is necessary to use the variance supplied by the experiment itself in order to assess the significance of the effects. With so few degrees of freedom available for error the test of significance will not be sensitive. The first fractional design does not usually constitute the whole experiment but is used as a guide to further experimental work; as the experiment proceeds, more and more information is accumulated on the experimental error. It is usually desirable for the experiment to supply its own estimate of error variance because of the possibility of the error varying from one experiment to the next. However, a vast amount of information exists on chemical and physical experimentation, both in the laboratory and on the plant, and for most processes fairly reliable information already exists on the magnitude of the experimental error. It is not necessary, therefore, to design the experiment on a large scale merely to supply reliable estimates of this quantity; the prime consideration is to design the experiment either as a whole or as a series of fractional replicates large enough to give the required precision in the estimation of the effects. When this is done there may or may not be sufficient degrees of freedom available in the experiment itself to give a reliable estimate of the error variance. Even when only a few degrees of freedom are available in any given experiment the variance should be calculated, noted for use in further experimental work, and compared with previous estimates of error obtained for the same or similar processes in the past. Caution should be exercised when the error variance obtained from the experiment differs appreciably from the value expected.

The use of fractional factorial designs in sequence

10·711. An important feature of most industrial experiments is that the observations are made in sequence, either singly or in sets of a few at a time, so that the results of one set become available before the next need be started. The time interval between successive sets of observations is usually short—often a matter of days or even hours—in contrast to agricultural field experiments, for which a whole year must elapse between successive trials.

A high degree of flexibility is possible in most industrial work because the situation may be reviewed during the course of the experiment after each set of results comes to hand. It is not necessary to set up a design for the whole experiment at the beginning; but the design of the first part may be added to as the result of information gained from the earlier observations.

A complete investigation of unfavourable levels of one or more factors is not of practical interest. Assume a complete factorial design has been carried out and the change in one or more of the factors adversely affects the yield of a certain product. Even when only one of the factors is involved half of the observations will be affected by an unfavourable level; if the work has been on the plant it may represent a large financial loss, and even in the laboratory where the material costs are usually small, a certain proportion of the experimenter's time will be virtually wasted, because when one factor produces a large effect, adverse or otherwise, appreciable interactions are practically certain to arise between this and the other factors, so that only one-half of the design is available for assessing the effects of the other factors. If instead of carrying out a full design only a half-replicate had been carried out the loss would have been reduced to one-half, and for a quarter-replicate to a quarter, and so on. If, on the other hand, no single factor produces a large effect, nothing is lost by carrying out a fractional factorial design because if the design does not give sufficient information we can follow up with other fractional designs of the same system until sufficient precision is attained.

The procedure to be followed when investigating a number of factors even when a full factorial design may ultimately be required is to divide the factorial design into blocks confounding higher-order interactions, and deal with these blocks in succession, examining each as soon as it is completed. It may happen that the first block will give all information required, in which case the other blocks need not be examined. Again one or more of the factors may give a large effect, in which case all further work will be confined to the more favourable levels of such factors. The experiment is then redesigned with fewer factors or, if required, with other factors to replace the ones dropped as the result of the first trial.

It is here assumed that when a factor has a large effect that effect is present, although to a variable extent, in all conditions of the other factors; in other words, that interactions are not likely to arise of such a magnitude as to obscure the large effect of the factor obtained in the initial fractional factorial design. While this is usually a safe assumption to make, the experimenter is advised to seek supporting evidence based on theoretical grounds or on earlier experience with the same or similar processes. Risks of this sort must frequently be taken, for otherwise the experimenter may be involved in a prohibitive amount of work; but we know that such risks are small and worth taking when we consider the large saving in experimental work resulting in the long run.

The considerations which decide the continuation of the experiment after carrying out one, two, or more of the fractional replicates are:

   (i) The main effects are not given with sufficient precision.

   (ii) Certain main effects are confused with two-factor interactions and may require to be separated.

   (iii) Certain sets of two-factor interactions may require to be separated.

   (iv) Additional factors may require to be introduced.

More precision can be obtained by repeating the fractional replicate, or equally efficiently, by performing another fractional replicate belonging to the same system of confounding. As will be shown in detail in § **10·72**, the latter procedure has the added advantage of separating the aliases to a certain extent, and therefore, as a general rule, it should be adopted.

Separation of aliases

10·72. In a quarter-factorial design each degree of freedom represents a group of four effects, that is to say, each effect is confused with three other effects. Now, two quarter-factorial designs together form a half-factorial design for which each effect is confused with only one other effect. The second fractional factorial design has thus produced a degree of separation of the effects, and twice the number of effects may be independently estimated. There is usually a choice of design for the second set, and different pairs of fractional factorial designs in the same system produce different types of separation. Consider a design of eight observations covering five factors A, B, C, D, and E derived by equating D and E to the interactions ABC and BC respectively. As shown earlier [§ **10·41**], there are four possible designs of this type, namely:

(i) $(D = ABC)$ Defining contrasts $= I, ABCD, BCE, ADE$
  $(E = BC)$
(ii) $(D = -ABC)$ Defining contrasts $= I, -ABCD, -BCE, ADE$
  $(E = -BC)$
(iii) $(D = -ABC)$ Defining contrasts $= I, -ABCD, BCE, -ADE$
  $(E = BC)$
(iv) $(D = ABC)$ Defining contrasts $= I, ABCD, -BCE, -ADE$
  $(E = -BC)$

The groups of effects or alias sets measured by each of the above factorial designs may be derived, as shown above, by multiplication.

The main effect A and its aliases with their appropriate signs for the above four fractional designs are respectively:

(i) $A + BCD + ABCE + DE$ $(= x_1)$
(ii) $A - BCD - ABCE + DE$ $(= x_2)$
(iii) $A - BCD + ABCE - DE$ $(= x_3)$
(iv) $A + BCD - ABCE - DE$ $(= x_4)$

Using any one of these fractional designs it is necessary to assume that most of the two-factor interactions and all the higher-order interactions are zero in order to estimate the main effects. Assume that we have carried out the fractional replicate corresponding to (i) or (ii) and that it is necessary to carry out a further fractional replicate in order (*a*) to obtain a higher degree of precision and/or (*b*) to separate the main effects from the two-factor interactions. If a higher degree of precision is required it is possible at the same time to separate the effects. Referring to the alias sets, we see that in order to separate the main effects and two-factor interactions we must follow either of blocks (i) or (ii) with block (iii) or (iv), or vice versa. Denoting the actual magnitude of the comparisons containing A in the first and third blocks by x_1 and x_3 respectively, then adding and subtracting the two expressions yields

$$A + ABCE = \tfrac{1}{2}(x_1 + x_3)$$
$$BCD + DE = \tfrac{1}{2}(x_1 - x_3)$$

Similar expressions exist for the other main effects. The two fractional designs together have thus separated the main effects and two-factor interactions, and provided three-factor and higher-order interactions may be assumed zero, all main effects and two-factor interactions may then be estimated.

One of the other combinations of two fractional designs which will separate the main effects and two-factor interactions, for instance the first and fourth blocks, gives

$$A + BCD = \tfrac{1}{2}(x_1 + x_4)$$
$$ABCE + DE = \tfrac{1}{2}(x_1 - x_4)$$

This, however, is not quite as good as the first set, because the main effect is confused with a lower-order interaction.

When a further fractional factorial design is carried out in addition to the first two a still further separation of the effects is achieved. Assume the designs represented by the first three blocks have been carried out. Considering the same effect group as previously, we see that the three effects A, DE, and BCD can be separated, each now being confused with the four-factor interaction $ABCE$. Thus, from the first and third we obtain by addition $(A + ABCE)$, from the first and second by subtraction $(BCD + ABCE)$, and from the second and third by subtraction $(DE - ABCE)$. When $ABCE$ is assumed zero we obtain estimates of the main effect, a two-, and a three-factor interaction. We must note that only two-thirds of the observations are used for each of these estimates. The conclusion then is that the separate estimates of A, DE, and BCD can only be obtained from the three-quarter replicate with an efficiency of $66\frac{2}{3}\%$. When the experimental error is not large this loss of efficiency is more than offset by the information gained on the separated interactions. If, however, the three- and four-factor interactions can be assumed zero and we wish only to estimate A and DE from the three-quarter factorial design, then putting $BCD = ABCE = 0$ we obtain the expressions

$$\text{(i)} \quad A + DE = x_1$$
$$\text{(ii)} \quad A + DE = x_2$$
$$\text{(iii)} \quad A - DE = x_3$$

Averaging the first and second expressions we obtain

$$A + DE = \tfrac{1}{2}(x_1 + x_2)$$

and combining with the third expression:

$$A = \tfrac{1}{4}x_1 + \tfrac{1}{4}x_2 + \tfrac{1}{2}x_3$$
$$DE = \tfrac{1}{4}x_1 + \tfrac{1}{4}x_2 - \tfrac{1}{2}x_3$$

Since each x denotes a difference between two means of four observations each, the variance of these estimates is $\frac{1}{2}[\tfrac{1}{4}^2 + \tfrac{1}{4}^2 + \tfrac{1}{2}^2]\sigma^2 = 3\sigma^2/16$. The smallest possible variance for an estimate of one effect from 24 observations is $\sigma^2(\tfrac{1}{12} + \tfrac{1}{12}) = \sigma^2/6$, and therefore the efficiency of the estimates of A and DE in the three-quarter factorial design, assuming that all three- and four-factor interactions are zero, is $88\frac{8}{9}\%$. When all interactions other than those between A, B, and C can be assumed negligible, then of course, all main effects and the two-factor interactions between A, B, and C can be estimated with 100% efficiency in the three-quarter factorial design. When the fourth set is carried out the factorial design is complete, and all effects can be separated and estimated with 100% efficiency. The above considerations may be readily extended to all the other main effects and certain interactions (in this case AB and AC), and similar considerations may be applied to any sequence of fractional factorial designs.

Fractional replication in 3^n factorial designs

10·8. Factorial experiments used in the chemical industry can frequently be reduced to the investigation of the factors at two levels; this does not necessarily restrict the range over which the factors are examined, because an experiment may consist of a series of fractional replicates in each of which the factors are examined at two levels, but not necessarily at the same two levels in the whole series. Sometimes, however, it is required to examine the factors at three levels in one experiment, and we may require fractional replicates of 3^n designs. The basic principles of fractional replicates of 3^n designs are similar to those of 2^n designs, but the construction of the designs and their interpretation is naturally more complicated. Once the basic principles are understood there should, however, be no difficulty.

In the first place, fractional replication in 3^n designs may be related to confounding just as in 2^n designs. For instance, any one of the blocks in a design confounded in three blocks gives a one-third replicate, in nine blocks a one-ninth replicate, and so on. As in 2^n designs, the best fractional replicates belong to systems which confound the lower-order interactions to the least extent. An enumeration has already been given of all useful confounded 3^n designs for n up to 4, together with a method of extension for n greater than 4; and the same methods yield suitable fractional replicates. A more detailed examination, however, will be given in this chapter.

A one-third replicate of a 3^3 design will consist of nine observations, capable of measuring eight independent effects. In the complete design divided into three blocks, one of which is the given one-third replicate, there are 26 degrees of freedom, two of which are confounded with blocks. The one-third replicate clearly contains no information on the two effects confounded between blocks, and the remaining 24 effects are represented by the eight degrees of freedom of the fractional replicate. Each degree of freedom must therefore represent a combination of three effects. Therefore in a one-third replicate each effect has two aliases or belongs to a group of three aliases. In order to determine the exact nature of these aliases it is necessary to have a full understanding of the subject matter of Appendix 9D, dealing with the algebraic theory of confounding in 3^n designs. This, however, is not essential for practical application.

In all one-third replicates each effect belongs to a group of three aliases which cannot be separately estimated. Similarly in all one-ninth replicates each effect belongs to a group of nine aliases, and so on for higher fractional replicates.

Fractional replication is not as satisfactory in 3^n design as in 2^n design; relatively large experiments are required to free the two-factor interactions even when dealing with as few as four factors. For five factors as many as 81 observations are required to give separate estimates of all main effects and two-factor interactions. Although it is possible in theory to examine a larger number of factors provided the interactions between three only of the factors are likely to exist, in practice a high or even moderate degree of fractional replication should be undertaken only when most, if not all, of the interactions may be assumed negligible, so that only main effects and a very limited number of two-factor interactions are of interest. In a 2^n design the interactions have a clear practical interpretation, but for fractional replication in 3^n designs the interactions have to be expressed as I, J, W, X, Y, Z, and although I and J are mathematically distinct their physical interpretations are not, so that the exact meaning of the aliases from a practical point of view is uncertain.

In practice, fractional replication for three levels is best avoided whenever there is any likelihood of several appreciable two-factor interactions and whenever the experimenter has sufficient freedom of choice in the levels to be examined. When the factors are quantitative, two levels per factor should be the rule when fractional replication is contemplated. For qualitative factors it may sometimes be necessary to use three levels. When examining the effect of various factors on a testing method, e.g. different observers, sampling variation, different positions in a testing machine, small modifications of the testing method, etc., the assumption of negligible interaction is usually valid, and fractional replication with factors at three or more levels may then be profitable.

10·81. It is convenient to introduce at this stage a summary of what follows in the form of Table 10·81.

Table 10·81

FRACTIONAL REPLICATES IN 3^n DESIGNS

No. of observations	No. of factors	Confusion of effects
9	2	All effects clear, this being a complete 3^2 factorial design.
	3	Two-factor interactions are confused with one another and main effects. May be used only when all interactions are negligible, to estimate main effects. Two degrees of freedom are left over for error.

Table 10·81 (*continued*)

No. of observations	No. of factors	Confusion of effects
	4	Two-factor interactions are confused with one another and main effects. May be used only when all interactions are negligible, to estimate the main effects. No degrees of freedom are left over for error.
27	3	All effects are clear, this being a complete 3^3 factorial design.
	4	Main effects are clear of two-factor interactions, but there is some confusion between the two-factor interactions. May be used to estimate main effects and the two-factor interactions between three of the factors provided these do not interact with the fourth.
	5	Only two main effects are clear of two-factor interactions. May be used to estimate main effects and two-factor interactions between three of them provided all other interactions are negligible.
	6 or 7	May be used to estimate main effects and two-factor interactions between three of them provided all other interactions are negligible.
	8 or more	Main effects with diminishing number of two-factor interactions.
81	4	All effects are clear, this being a complete 3^4 factorial design.
	5	All main effects and all two-factor interactions are clear of one another. May thus be used to estimate main effects and two-factor interactions provided higher-order interactions are negligible.
	6	Main effects are all clear of two-factor interactions, but some confusion in the latter. May be used to estimate the main effects and some two-factor interactions (at least between four of the factors) on the assumption that the remainder are negligible.
	7–28	May be used to estimate main effects and two-factor interactions between four of them provided all other interactions are negligible.

If in any investigation it is required to estimate certain specific two-factor interactions in addition to the main effects when all other interactions can be assumed negligible it is necessary to follow very carefully the method of construction given in the next section. If the number of observations in the factorial design is 3^p and there are n factors, we must select p factors out of the n so that the only likely two-factor interactions arise between these factors; the remaining $(n - p)$ factors are then equated to the higher-order interactions between the p factors so selected.

Analysis of results

10·82. The analysis of fractional designs with factors at three levels follows the general methods already given in Chapter 8 for complete factorial designs. The analysis is restricted to main effects and those two-factor interactions which are free of main effects and for which a separate estimate is required. For these two-factor interactions we form the two-factor tables by summing over the remaining factors and analyse in the usual way by the methods appropriate for qualitative or quantitative factors according to the nature of the factors. All the remaining degrees of freedom representing interactions and their aliases, assumed to be negligible, are derived as a remainder and if required used as an error variance.

Designs of nine observations

10·83. Nine observations are sufficient for a complete factorial design with two factors each at three levels. This design may be represented in standard form as Table 10·82 [§ **9·5**].

Table 10·82

STANDARD FORM FOR 3^2 DESIGNS

Levels of factor A	Levels of factor B		
	b_0	b_1	b_2
a_0	1	4	7
a_1	2	5	8
a_2	3	6	9

The structure of these 3×3 designs has already been examined [§ **9·5**]; to recapitulate, there are four degrees of freedom for interactions which can be represented by the comparisons within two sets of diagonal totals, the i set and the j set as follows:

$$\begin{pmatrix} i_0 = 1 + 5 + 9 \\ i_1 = 2 + 6 + 7 \\ i_2 = 3 + 4 + 8 \end{pmatrix} \quad \begin{pmatrix} j_0 = 1 + 6 + 8 \\ j_1 = 2 + 4 + 9 \\ j_2 = 3 + 5 + 7 \end{pmatrix}$$

There are two degrees of freedom within the i set and two within the j set, these two pairs being orthogonal to each other and to the main effects A and B. Assuming that interactions do not exist, then the comparisons within the i and j sets will furnish a measure of the experimental error.

Consider now a third factor, C, with levels of c_0, c_1, and c_2 and let the three observations of i_0, that is 1, 5, and 9, be carried out at zero level of C, i_1 (i.e. 2, 6, 7) at the middle level and i_2 (i.e. 3, 4, 8) at the highest level.* This will result in the design of Table 10·83.

Table 10·83

DESIGN FOR THREE FACTORS

	b_0	b_1	b_2
a_0	c_0	c_2	c_1
a_1	c_1	c_0	c_2
a_2	c_2	c_1	c_0

i.e. $\begin{pmatrix} a_0 b_0 c_0 & a_0 b_1 c_2 & a_0 b_2 c_1 \\ a_1 b_0 c_1 & a_1 b_1 c_0 & a_1 b_2 c_2 \\ a_2 b_0 c_2 & a_2 b_1 c_1 & a_2 b_2 c_0 \end{pmatrix}$

This is of course a Latin Square (Chapter 5); it is also a one-third replicate of a 3^3 design. Note that we have made the comparisons between i_0, i_1, and i_2 coincide with the main effect C, and have thus equated the interaction $I(AB)$ to C, so that the main effect C is confused with the interaction $I(AB.)$ Table 10·83 may now be rearranged as Table 10·84.

Table 10·84

REARRANGEMENT OF TABLE 10·83

	c_0	c_1	c_2
a_0	b_0	b_2	b_1
a_1	b_1	b_0	b_2
a_2	b_2	b_1	b_0

From this we see that the comparisons between the i-diagonals coincide with the comparisons between b_0, b_1, and b_2, that is $I(AC) = B$. Similarly it can be shown that $I(BC) = A$.

The complete set of aliases and the method of deriving them are given in Appendix 10B, but the foregoing is sufficient to show that in a one-third replicate of a 3^3 design the main effects are confused with two-factor

---

* This is equivalent to confounding the interaction $I(AB)$ in the 3^2 design between three blocks and equating the blocks to the three levels of the additional factor C.

interactions. Such a design can be used to obtain estimates of the main effects only when the two-factor interactions can be assumed negligible.

We have accounted for six of the degrees of freedom of the design; there are two remaining degrees of freedom corresponding to the j-totals. It is shown in Appendix 10B that these j-interactions are free of main effects but are confused with other interactions; in fact

$$\mathcal{J}(AB) = \mathcal{J}(AC) = \mathcal{J}(BC)$$

This is not the only third replicate; we could have equated

$$j_0 = c_0, \quad j_1 = c_1, \quad j_2 = c_2$$

or

$$i_0 = c_2, \quad i_1 = c_0, \quad i_2 = c_1$$

or

$$i_0 = c_1, \quad i_1 = c_2, \quad i_2 = c_0, \text{ etc.}$$

These different schemes would generate as many as twelve Latin Squares and are, in fact, the same as the four sets of three blocks of Table 9·62, in which the three-factor interactions W, X, Y, and Z are separately confounded between blocks. Any of these blocks provides a suitable one-third replicate.

In the nine observations of Table 10·82 it is possible to introduce a fourth factor, D, by equating the j-diagonals to the three levels d_0, d_1, and d_2, e.g.

$$j_0 \,(= 1, 6, 8) = d_0$$
$$j_1 \,(= 2, 4, 9) = d_1$$
$$j_2 \,(= 3, 5, 7) = d_2$$

This gives the design of Table 10·85.

Table 10·85

DESIGN FOR FOUR FACTORS

	b_0	b_1	b_2
a_0	$c_0 d_0$	$c_2 d_1$	$c_1 d_2$
a_1	$c_1 d_1$	$c_0 d_2$	$c_2 d_0$
a_2	$c_2 d_2$	$c_1 d_0$	$c_0 d_1$

that is

$$\begin{pmatrix} a_0 b_0 c_0 d_0 & a_0 b_1 c_2 d_1 & a_0 b_2 c_1 d_2 \\ a_1 b_0 c_1 d_1 & a_1 b_1 c_0 d_2 & a_1 b_2 c_2 d_0 \\ a_2 b_0 c_2 d_2 & a_2 b_1 c_1 d_0 & a_2 b_2 c_0 d_1 \end{pmatrix}$$

This design is a one-ninth replicate of a 3^4 design; it is also a Graeco-Latin Square (Chapter 5). There are many such Graeco-Latin Squares, any one of which would provide a one-ninth replicate. Note that all the degrees of freedom are now taken up by main effects and that two-factor interactions are aliases of main effects. The full set of aliases is given in Appendix 10B. Such a design can only be used when all the two-factor interactions can be assumed negligible. The analysis of these designs has already been considered (Chapter 5).

Designs of 27 observations

10·84. Twenty-seven observations are sufficient for a full factorial design with three factors each at three levels. The structure of these designs has already been considered in § 9·6, where it was shown that the 26 degrees of freedom consist of:

(i) Two for each of the three main effects, giving a total of 6.

(ii) Two for each of the I and J components of the three two-factor interactions, giving a total of 12.

(iii) Two for each of the W, X, Y, and Z components of the three-factor interactions, giving a total of 8.

Each of the three-factor interactions W, X, Y, and Z corresponds to a division of the 27 observations into three lots of nine, and these divisions are given in Table 9·62. This table is reproduced for the present purpose as Table 10·86.

Table 10·86

THREE-FACTOR INTERACTIONS IN 3^3 DESIGN

Combination of 1st and 2nd factors		(1) W Interactions			(2) X Interactions			(3) Y Interactions			(4) Z Interactions		
		w_0	w_1	w_2	x_0	x_1	x_2	y_0	y_1	y_2	z_0	z_1	z_2
1	00	0	2	1	0	1	2	0	2	1	0	1	2
2	10	1	0	2	2	0	1	1	0	2	2	0	1
3	20	2	1	0	1	2	0	2	1	0	1	2	0
4	01	2	1	0	1	2	0	1	0	2	2	0	1
5	11	0	2	1	0	1	2	2	1	0	1	2	0
6	21	1	0	2	2	0	1	0	2	1	0	1	2
7	02	1	0	2	2	0	1	2	1	0	1	2	0
8	12	2	1	0	1	2	0	0	2	1	0	1	2
9	22	0	2	1	0	1	2	1	0	2	2	0	1

The two degrees of freedom of the W-interaction are the comparisons between w_0, w_1, and w_2. We can introduce another factor, D, by equating w_0 to d_0, w_1 to d_1, and w_2 to d_2. This gives the design of Table 10·87.

Table 10·87

0000	1010	2020	0120	1100	2110	0210	1220	2200	(w_0)
0021	1001	2011	0111	1121	2101	0201	1211	2221	(w_1)
0012	1022	2002	0102	1112	2122	0222	1202	2212	(w_2)

where in each treatment combination the four numbers indicate the levels of factors A, B, C, and D respectively.

12

This design is a one-third replicate of a 3^4 design in which we have equated $W(ABC)$ to D. In the same way we could have equated D to X or Y or Z and obtained an equally suitable one-third replicate. Moreover, the order of equating the levels of D could be changed, e.g. $w_0 = d_1$, $w_1 = d_0$, $w_2 = d_2$, or in other ways, and all these yield suitable one-third replicates in which three-factor interactions are aliases of main effects and certain two-factor interactions. The complete set of aliases for Table 10·87 is derived in Appendix 10B. If factor D does not interact with factors A, B, and C, then this design will estimate all main effects and all two-factor interactions between $A, B,$ and C without confusion. Factor D would then be equivalent to blocks, and the problem consists of confounding the 3^3 design with factors A, B, and C over three blocks and identifying these blocks with the levels of D.

In addition to introducing a fourth factor, D, we may introduce another factor E, by equating E to the interaction X, e.g. by making $x_0 = e_0$, $x_1 = e_1$, and $x_2 = e_2$. The method of doing this is straightforward; we add e_0 to all those elements of the design of Table 10·87 for which the levels of the first three factors correspond to x_0 of Table 10·86, and similarly for e_1 and e_2. Thus, the first element of Table 10·87 is 0000 and the levels of the first three factors are 000. Referring to Table 10·86, we see that 000 is the first element in x_0. We therefore add 0 to 0000, giving 00000 for the levels of the five factors A–E respectively. The second element of Table 10·87 is 1010, for which the levels of the first three factors are 101. This is the second element of x_2, and therefore we add e_2 to 1010, making 10102. Again for the third element, 2020 of Table 10·87, the first three factors have the levels 202, which is an element in x_1. We therefore add e_1 to this, making 20201, and so on. In this way we obtain the design of Table 10·88.

Table 10·88

00000	10102	20201	01201	11000	21102	02102	12201	22000
00212	10011	20110	01110	11212	21011	02011	12110	22212
00121	10220	20022	01022	11121	21220	02220	12022	22121

and this is a one-ninth replicate of a 3^5 design. There is naturally more confusion of effects than in the one-third replicate. The aliases are derived in Appendix 10B, where it is shown that main effects have two-factor interactions as aliases. In general, these one-ninth replicates are of practical value when two-factor interactions can be assumed negligible, or at most when all except a certain specified few can be assumed negligible. It can be seen from the above method of construction of the design that if D and E do not interact with each other and with A, B, and C, the design will estimate all main effects and all two-factor interactions between A, B, and C without con-fusion. Two further factors, F and G, may be introduced by equating them respectively to the Y- and Z-interactions; and provided A, B, and C are the only factors which interact, the design will estimate all seven main effects and the two-factor interactions between A, B, and C without confusion, and so on. The same principle may be used for confounding between three blocks. Occasionally it is desirable to include a factor with nine levels or to confound between nine blocks, e.g. different units of plant, slightly different qualities of intermediate, different periods of time, etc.

With nine levels for one factor we use up eight degrees of freedom. These eight degrees of freedom cannot represent any four pairs; only two pairs may be chosen at will, the other two pairs being then specified according to the rules of confounding.

REFERENCES

[10·1] FINNEY, D. J. "The Fractional Replication of Factorial Arrangements." *Annals of Eugenics*, **12** (1945), 4, 291–301.

[10·2] *Idem.* "Recent Developments in the Design of Field Experiments. III. Fractional Replication." *Journal of Agricultural Science*, **36** (1946), 3, 184–91.

[10·3] DAVIES, O. L., and HAY, W. A. "The Construction and Uses of Fractional Factorial Designs in Industrial Research." *Biometrics*, **6** (1950), 3, 233–49.

APPENDIX 10A

FRACTIONAL REPLICATES UP TO EIGHT FACTORS IN SIXTEEN OBSERVATIONS

Notes on Table

Only the fractional replicate corresponding to the principal block is given in Table 10A·1; the other fractional replicates of the same system are deriv-able by multiplication of the principal block by treatment combinations not contained in the principal block or in the blocks already formed in this way. For any fractional replicate derived from the principal block by multi-plication by a given treatment combination the corresponding defining con-trasts are derived from those of the principal block by changing to minus the signs of the capital letters corresponding to the given treatment combination. It will probably be found more convenient in practice to derive the design directly by means of column 5. Unless the design is specified by practical requirements, the fractional replicate should be chosen at random.

Table 10A·1

FRACTIONAL REPLICATES UP TO EIGHT FACTORS IN SIXTEEN OBSERVATIONS

(1) No. of observations	(2) No. of factors	(3) Fraction of complete factorial design	(4) Defining contrast of principal block	(5) Derivation of design	(6) Confusion of main effects and two-factor interactions	(7) Principal block
4	2	Full	—	—	All main effects and interactions are clear.	—
	3	$\frac{1}{2}$	$I, -ABC$	Equate C to $-AB$	All main effects are confused with two-factor interactions; gives main effects when all interactions are assumed negligible.	$(1), ab, ac, bc$
8	3	Full	—	—	All main effects and interactions are clear.	—
	4	$\frac{1}{2}$	$I, +ABCD$	Equate D to $+ABC$	All main effects are clear of two-factor interactions, but two-factor interactions are confused with one another; gives main effects and at most three two-factor interactions of one factor with each of the others or between any three of the factors, all other interactions assumed negligible.	$(1), ab, ac, bc, ad, bd, cd, abcd$
	5	$\frac{1}{4}$	$I, -BCE, -ADE, ABCD$	Equate D to ABC and E to $-BC$	All main effects are confused with two-factor interactions. The remaining two-factor interactions are confused with one another; gives main effects and the interactions of one factor with each of two others, all remaining interactions assumed negligible.	$(1), ad, bc, abcd, abe, bde, ace, cde$

Table 10A·1 (continued)

(1) No. of observations	(2) No. of factors	(3) Fraction of complete factorial design	(4) Defining contrast of principal block	(5) Derivation of design	(6) Confusion of main effects and two-factor interactions	(7) Principal block
8	6	$\frac{1}{8}$	$I, -ADE, -BCE,$ $-ACF, -BDF,$ $ABCD, ABEF,$ $CDEF$	Equate D to ABC, E to $-BC$, and F to $-AC$	All main effects are confused with two-factor interactions. The remaining two-factor interactions are confused with one another; gives main effects and one two-factor interaction, all other interactions assumed negligible.	$(1), ace, bde,$ $abcd, adf,$ $cdef, abef,$ bef
	7	$\frac{1}{16}$	$I, -ACF, -ADE,$ $-BCE, -BDF,$ $-CDG, -ABG,$ $-EFG, ABEF,$ $CDEF, ABCD,$ $BDEG, ACEG,$ $ADFG, BCFG,$ $-ABCDEFG$	Equate D to ABC, E to $-BC$, F to $-AC$ and G to $-AB$	All main effects are confused with two-factor interactions; gives main effects only, all interactions assumed negligible.	$(1), abcd,$ $abef, aceg,$ $adfg, bcfg,$ $bdeg, cdef$
16	4	Full	—	—	All main effects and interactions are clear.	$(1), ab, ac,$ $bc, ad, bd,$ $cd, abcd, ae,$ $be, ce, abce,$ $de, abde,$ $acde, bcde$
	5	$\frac{1}{2}$	$I, -ABCDE$	Equate E to $-ABCD$	All main effects and two-factor interactions are clear of one another; gives main effects and two-factor interactions when three-factor and higher-order interactions assumed negligible.	

Table 10A·1 (*continued*)

(1) No. of observations	(2) No. of factors	(3) Fraction of complete factorial design	(4) Defining contrast of principal block	(5) Derivation of design	(6) Confusion of main effects and two-factor interactions	(7) Principal block
16	6	$\frac{1}{4}$	*I, ABCE, BCDF, ADEF*	Equate *E* to *ABC* and *F* to *BCD*	All main effects are clear of two-factor interactions, but two-factor interactions are confused with one another; gives main effects and at most seven (not any seven) two-factor interactions, all other interactions assumed negligible. Satisfactory if the only interactions that exist are two-factor interactions between four of the factors.	(1), *bc, ae, abce, df, bcdf, adef, abcdef, abd, acd, bde, cde, abf, acf, bef, cef*
	7	$\frac{1}{8}$	*I, ABCE, BCDF, ADEF, BEFG, ACFG, CDEG, ABDG*	Equate *E* to *ABC, F* to *BCD,* and *G* to *ABD*	All main effects are clear of two-factor interactions, but two-factor interactions are confused with one another; gives all main effects and at most seven (not any seven) two-factor interactions, all other interactions assumed negligible. Satisfactory if the only interactions that exist are two-factor interactions between four of the factors.	(1), *bcg, aeg, abce, dfg, bcdf, adef, abcdefg, abdg, acd, bde, cdeg, abf, acfg, befg, cef*
	8	$\frac{1}{16}$	*I, ABCE, BCDF, ADEF, BEFG, ABFH, CDEG, ABDG, ACDH, BDEH, ACFG, CEFH, ABCDEFGH, DFGH, AEGH, BCGH*	Equate *E* to *ABC, F* to *BCD, G* to *ABD,* and *H* to *ACD*	All main effects are clear of two-factor interactions, but two-factor interactions are confused with one another; gives main effects and at most seven (not any seven) two-factor interactions, all other interactions assumed negligible.	(1), *bcgh, aegh, abce, dfgh, cbdf, adef, abcdefgh, abdg, acdh, bdeh, cdeg, abfh, acfg, befg, cefh*

The fractional replicates given in Table 10A·1 involve the least amount of confusion of the main effects and two-factor interactions. Other fractional replicates may be equally suitable for any given investigation, e.g. for six factors in sixteen observations an alternative design may be obtained by equating E to $-ABCD$ and F to ABC, giving the defining contrasts I, $-ABCDE$, $ABCF$, $-DEF$, and the principal block:

(1), ab, bc, ac, de, $abde$, $bcde$, $acde$, cdf, $abcdf$, bdf, adf, cef, $abcef$, bef, aef

If all interactions of F with A, B, C, D and E, and of D with E are known to be zero, the design will estimate all the main effects, all the six two-factor interactions between A, B, C and D, and the three interactions of E with A, B, and C, a total of nine compared with seven for the design given in Table 10A·1. In the alternative design the main effects D, E, and F are confused respectively with the two-factor interactions EF, DF, and DE, taken to be zero. In the design of Table 10A·1 all main effects are clear of two-factor interactions, but not more than seven two-factor interactions can be estimated separately. This design however is normally safer to use in practice. The remaining two degrees of freedom correspond to three-factor interactions.

For seven factors in sixteen observations it is possible to estimate an additional interaction from the alternative design obtained by equating E to $-ABCD$, F to BCD, and G to ABD, giving the defining contrasts I, $-ABCDE$, $BCDF$, $ABDG$, $-AEF$, $-CEG$, $ACFG$, and $-BDEFG$. This design estimates all main effects, all two-factor interactions between A, B, C, and D, and the additional two-factor interactions DE and BE, provided all other interactions are zero. In this design main effects A, C, E, F, and G are confused with the two-factor interactions, and it is necessary that these two-factor interactions should be negligible. In practice it is usually safer to use the design given in Table 10A·1.

APPENDIX 10B

ALIASES IN FRACTIONAL REPLICATES OF 3^n DESIGNS

One-third replicates of 3^3 designs

10B·1. A one-third replicate is a block in the design confounded in three blocks. The best fractional replicates are produced when the highest-order interactions are confounded; by best fractional replicates we mean those which involve the least confusion of the main effects and lower-order interactions.

In a 3^3 design there are four pairs of three-factor interactions $W(ABC)$, $X(ABC)$, $Y(ABC)$, and $Z(ABC)$. A suitable one-third replicate may be obtained by dividing any of these interactions, and the method is illustrated on $W(ABC)$. This interaction corresponds to (I, A^2BC, AB^2C^2) see Appendix 9D·71), which gives the defining contrasts sub-group

$$I, A^2BC, AB^2C^2 \quad \ldots\ldots\ldots\ldots\ldots\ldots(10B\cdot1)$$

As in 2^n designs, the aliases of each effect are obtained by multiplying the defining relation by the given effect. Thus, the aliases of A and A^2 are respectively

$$A = A^3BC = A^2B^2C^2$$
$$A^2 = A^4BC = A^3B^2C^2$$

Now $A^3 = 1$; therefore

$$A = BC \ \ = A^2B^2C^2 \quad \ldots\ldots\ldots\ldots\ldots(10B\cdot2)$$
$$A^2 = ABC = B^2C^2 \quad \ldots\ldots\ldots\ldots\ldots(10B\cdot3)$$

By rearrangement it follows from $(10B\cdot1)$, $(10B\cdot2)$, and $(10B\cdot3)$ that the three groups

$$(I, A, A^2); \ (I, BC, B^2C^2); \ (I, A^2B^2C^2, ABC)$$

are equivalent. These groups correspond respectively to the following pairs of degrees of freedom (see Appendix 9D):

$$A; \ \mathcal{J}(BC); \ Z(ABC)$$

These three effects are therefore aliases of one another. In a similar way it can be shown that the other sets of aliases are:

$$B = I(AC) = Y(ABC)$$
$$C = I(AB) = X(ABC)$$
$$\mathcal{J}(AB) = I(BC) = \mathcal{J}(AC)$$

In this particular one-third replicate, and in fact in all one-third replicates of 3^3 design with three-factor interactions as defining contrasts, two-factor interactions are aliases of main effects. Such a design is of value on its own account when two-factor interactions are negligible compared with main effects, but not otherwise.

One-third replicates of 3^4 designs

10B·2. The best one-third replicate of a 3^4 design is obtained by using a pair of four-factor interactions as defining contrasts. There are eight such pairs to choose from. These correspond to

I	$ABCD$	$A^2B^2C^2D^2$
I	$ABCD^2$	$A^2B^2C^2D$
I	ABC^2D	$A^2B^2CD^2$
I	AB^2CD	$A^2BC^2D^2$
I	A^2BCD	$AB^2C^2D^2$
I	A^2B^2CD	ABC^2D^2
I	A^2BC^2D	AB^2CD^2
I	A^2BCD^2	AB^2C^2D

In order to examine the general nature of aliases in these designs we may choose any of the above pairs of degrees of freedom. Choose the sixth one and form the defining contrast group:

$$I = A^2B^2CD = ABC^2D^2 \quad\ldots\ldots\ldots\ldots\ldots(10B\cdot4)$$

To determine the aliases for the main effect A we multiply by A and A^2 and obtain

$$A = B^2CD \quad = A^2BC^2D^2$$

and

$$A^2 = AB^2CD = BC^2D^2$$

The following three groups are then equivalent:

$$(I, A, A^2);\ (I, B^2CD, BC^2D^2);\ (I, AB^2CD, A^2BC^2D^2)$$

The first corresponds to a main effect, the second to a three-factor interaction, and the third to a four-factor interaction. The main effect A is thus clear of two-factor interactions. In a similar way it can be shown that all main effects are clear of two-factor interactions, and this applies whichever pair of four-factor interactions is used as defining contrasts.

Consider now a two-factor interaction, say $I(AB)$, i.e. (I, A^2B, AB^2). The aliases are

$$A^2B = ACD = B^2C^2D^2$$
$$AB^2 = BCD = A^2C^2D^2$$

The three groups (I, A^2B, AB^2), $(I, ACD, A^2C^2D^2)$, and $(I, BCD, B^2C^2D^2)$ are then equivalent, whence

$$I(AB) = Z(ACD) = Z(BCD)$$

$I(AB)$ is thus clear of other two-factor interactions. All two-factor interactions, however, are not clear of one another, e.g. consider the aliases of $\mathcal{J}(AB)$, which corresponds to the group (I, AB, A^2B^2). Multiplying the defining contrast sub-group $(10B\cdot4)$ we obtain

$$AB = CD \quad\ \ = A^2B^2C^2D^2$$
$$A^2B^2 = ABCD = C^2D^2$$

The groups (I, AB, A^2B^2), (I, CD, C^2D^2), and $(I, ABCD, A^2B^2C^2D^2)$ are then equivalent, whence $\mathcal{J}(AB) = \mathcal{J}(CD) =$ a four-factor interaction.

In a one-third replicate of a 3^4 design all main effects are clear of two-factor interactions, but there is some confusion between two-factor interactions. The method given in § **10·84** for constructing a one-third replicate of a 3^4 design will allow certain specific interactions to be kept clear of one another.

One-ninth replicates of 3^4 and 3^5 designs

10B·3. In a one-ninth replicate of a 3^4 design there are eight degrees of freedom, and since there are also eight degrees of freedom for main effects the latter will each have several two-factor interactions as aliases. Provided the method given in § **10·83** is used to construct these designs, i.e. provided the designs used are Graeco-Latin Squares, the main effects will be clear of one another.

It is of interest to examine the aliases in a one-ninth replicate of a 3^5 design in greater detail. Now there are two degrees of freedom for each main effect and four for each two-factor interaction; there are five factors and consequently $5 \times 4/2 = 10$ sets of two-factor interactions, so that 10 degrees of freedom are required to estimate the main effects and 40 for the two-factor interactions, giving a total of 50 degrees of freedom. In order to be able to estimate all main effects and two-factor interactions it would be necessary to carry out more than 50 observations and the smallest possible design of the 3^n class would consist of 81 observations, i.e. would be a one-third replicate of a 3^5 design. In a one-ninth replicate consisting of 27 observations we cannot expect to keep all two-factor interactions clear of one another, and the most that can possibly be hoped for is to keep the main effects clear of two-factor interactions. As shown below, even this is impossible.

When a 3^5 design is split into nine blocks of 27 observations each, eight degrees of freedom are confounded between blocks. Two pairs may be chosen at will, but the other two pairs are then specified and correspond to the products of the two chosen pairs. We must choose two pairs of interactions which with their products contain the fewest possible number of the lower-order interactions. Unfortunately it is impossible to avoid three factor interactions, because a product of two four-factor interactions contains a three-factor interaction, while a product of two five-factor interactions contains a two-factor interaction. We therefore choose two four-factor interactions, e.g. (I, BC^2DE^2, B^2CD^2E) and $(I, A^2B^2DE^2, ABD^2E)$. The defining contrast group will include the products of all these terms and will be

$$I, A^2BC, AB^2C^2, BC^2DE^2, B^2CD^2E, A^2B^2DE^2, ABD^2E, A^2C^2D^2E, ACDE^2$$

The aliases, ignoring four- and five-factor interactions, can readily be derived. They are:

$A = \mathcal{J}(BC) = Z(ABC) = Y(CDE) = X(BDE)$
$B = I(AC) = Y(ABC) = X(CDE) = X(ADE)$
$C = I(AB) = X(ABC) = Y(BDE) = Y(ADE)$
$D = W(BCE) = Z(ABE) = Y(ACE)$
$E = X(BCD) = Y(ABD) = Z(ACD)$
$I(AD) = \mathcal{J}(BE) = Y(BCD) = W(CDE) = X(ACE)$
$I(AE) = \mathcal{J}(CD) = Y(BCE) = W(BDE) = X(ABD)$
$I(BC) = \mathcal{J}(AB) = \mathcal{J}(AC) = I(DE)$
$I(BD) = \mathcal{J}(AE) = W(ACD) = Z(BCE) = Z(CDE)$
$I(BE) = I(CD) = W(ACE) = W(ADE) = W(ABD)$
$I(CE) = \mathcal{J}(AD) = W(ABE) = Z(BDE) = Z(BCD)$
$\mathcal{J}(BD) = \mathcal{J}(CE) = X(ACD) = Z(ADE) = X(ABE)$
$\mathcal{J}(DE) = W(BCD) = X(BCE) = Z(ABD) = Y(ABE) = Z(ACE) = Y(ACD)$

Appendix 10C

SYSTEMATIC ANALYSIS OF RESULTS OF FRACTIONAL FACTORIAL DESIGNS

THE first requirement is to see that the results are arranged in standard form. If the number of treatment combinations is 2^p, we choose p out of the n factors and arrange the treatment combinations in standard order with respect to these p factors as though they were the only factors investigated. The standard order with respect to factors A, B, C, etc., is given by the following signs.

A $-$ and $+$ alternating, starting with $-$
B $- -$ and $+ +$ alternating, starting with $- -$
C $- - - -$ and $+ + + +$ alternating, starting with $- - - -$
D $(-) \times 8$ and $(+) \times 8$ alternating, starting with $(-) \times 8$
E $(-) \times 16$ and $(+) \times 16$ alternating, starting with $(-) \times 16$, etc.

The systematic analysis is carried out as for a complete factorial design with only p of the factors. The remaining factors are introduced when each effect is associated with its appropriate aliases.

Example 10·2

The results are written in standard order with respect to factors A, B, and C in Table 10·23. The systematic analysis is given in Table 10C·1. The effects on the basis of factors A, B, and C and their aliases are given in the final column.

Table 10C·1

ANALYSIS OF EXAMPLE 10·2

Factor combina- tion	Observation (= purity)	(1)	(2)	(3)	Mean effect = (Col. 3)/4	Sum of squares = (Col. 3)²/8	Effects measured: Aliases
(1) ..	107	221	473	952	—	—	—
a(d) ..	114	252	479	42	10·50	220·50	A, BCD
b(d) ..	122	227	15	56	14·00	392·00	B, ACD
ab ..	130	252	27	− 2	− 0·50	0·50	AB, CD
c(d) ..	106	7	31	6	1·50	4·50	C, ABD
ac ..	121	8	25	12	3·00	18·00	AC, BD
bc ..	120	15	1	− 6	− 1·50	4·50	BC, AD
abc(d) ..	132	12	− 3	− 4	− 1·00	2·00	ABC, D

Total sum of squares   .. 642·00

This design is obtained by equating D to ABC, giving the defining contrasts I, $ABCD$.

Example 10·3

The results are written in standard order with respect to factors A, B, and C in Table 10·41. The analysis is given in Table 10C·2. The design is a quarter-replicate, so that each effect has three aliases. These are given in the last column of Table 10C·2, where the leading term is the effect on the basis of factors A, B, and C.

Table 10C·2

ANALYSIS OF EXAMPLE 10·3

Factor combination	Observation	(1)	(2)	(3)	Mean effect = (Col. 3)/4	Sum of squares = (Col. 3)²/8	Effects measured: Aliases
(1)(e) ..	59·1	116·1	238·6	533·5	—	—	—
a(d) ..	57·0	122·5	294·9	5·3	1·33	3·51	$A, - CD, BE, - ABCDE$
b ..	58·6	138·8	3·2	23·7	5·93	70·21	$B, - ABCD, AE, - CDE$
ab(de)..	63·9	156·1	2·1	0·7	0·18	0·06	$AB, - BCD, E, - ACDE$
c(de) ..	67·2	− 2·1	6·4	56·3	14·08	396·21	$C, - AD, ABCE, - BDE$
ac ..	71·6	5·3	17·3	− 1·1	− 0·28	0·15	$AC, - D, BCE, - ABDE$
bc(d) ..	79·2	4·4	7·4	10·9	2·73	14·85	$BC, - ABD, ACE, - DE$
ab(e) ..	76·9	− 2·3	− 6·7	−14·1	− 3·53	24·85	$ABC, - BD, CE, - ADE$

Total sum of squares .. .. 509·84

This design is obtained by equating D to $- AC$ and E to AB, giving the defining contrasts $I, - ACD, + ABE, - BCDE$.

We see that the main effect E is given by comparison AB, and D by $- AC$.

Example 10·4

The results are written in standard order with respect to factors A, B, C, and D in Table 10·51. The analysis is given in Table 10C·3. The design is a half-replicate, so that each effect has one alias. Note again the signs of the aliases; in particular that the main effect E is given by $-ABCD$.

Table 10C·3

ANALYSIS OF EXAMPLE 10·4

Treatment combination	Observation	(1)	(2)	(3)	(4)	Mean effect = (Col. 4)/8	Sum of squares = (Col. 4)²/16	Effects measured: Aliases
(1) ..	201·5	379·5	739·0	1,477·0	3,487·5	—	—	—
a(e) ..	178·0	359·5	738·0	2,010·5	3·5	0·44	0·77	$A, -BCDE$
b(e) ..	183·5	367·0	948·5	− 19·0	− 60·5	− 7·56	228·77	$B, -ACDE$
ab ..	176·0	371·0	1,062·0	22·5	133·5	16·69	1,113·89	$AB, -CDE$
c(e) ..	188·5	496·0	− 31·0	− 16·0	112·5	14·06	791·02	$C, -ABDE$
ac ..	178·5	452·5	12·0	− 44·5	24·5	3·06	37·52	$AC, -BDE$
bc ..	174·5	531·5	20·5	48·0	66·5	8·31	276·39	$BC, -ADE$
abc(e) ..	196·5	530·5	2·0	85·5	0·5	0·06	0·02	$ABC, -DE$
d(e) ..	255·5	− 23·5	− 20·0	− 1·0	533·5	66·69	17,788·89	$D, -ABCE$
ad ..	240·5	− 7·5	4·0	113·5	41·5	5·19	107·64	$AD, -BCE$
bd ..	208·5	− 10·0	− 43·5	43·0	− 28·5	− 3·56	50·77	$BD, -ACE$
abd(e) ..	244·0	22·0	− 1·0	− 18·5	37·5	4·69	87·89	$ABD, -CE$
cd ..	274·0	− 15·0	16·0	24·0	114·5	14·31	819·39	$CD, -ABE$
acd(e) ..	257·5	35·5	32·0	42·5	− 61·5	− 7·69	236·39	$ACD, -BE$
bcd(e) ..	256·0	− 16·5	50·5	16·0	18·5	2·31	21·39	$BCD, -AE$
abcd ..	274·5	18·5	35·0	− 15·5	− 31·5	− 3·94	62·02	$ABCD, -E$
Total sum of squares							21,622·76	

This design is obtained by equating E to $-ABCD$, giving the defining contrasts $I, -ABCDE$.

Example 10·5

The results written in standard order with respect to factors A, B, C and D are given in Table 10·6, and the systematic analysis is given in Table 10C·4.

Table 10C·4

ANALYSIS OF EXAMPLE 10·5

Treatment combination	Observation	(1)	(2)	(3)	(4)	Mean effect = (Col. 4)/8	Sum of squares = (Col. 4)²/16	Effects measured
(1)(e) ..	775	1,400	2,822	5,453	11,710	—	—	—
a ..	625	1,422	2,631	6,257	− 694	− 86·75	30,102	A, BCDE
b ..	756	1,218	3,140	− 365	298	37·25	5,550	B, ACDE
ab(e) ..	666	1,413	3,117	− 329	154	19·25	1,482	AB, CDE
c ..	593	1,554	− 240	217	− 214	− 26·75	2,862	C, ABDE
ac(e) ..	625	1,586	− 125	81	− 238	− 29·75	3,540	AC, BDE
bc ..	785	1,534	12	− 129	190	23·75	2,256	BC, ADE (Fermenters)
abc ..	628	1,583	− 341	283	− 326	− 40·75	6,642	ABC, DE
d ..	819	− 150	22	− 191	804	100·50	40,401	D, ABCE
ad(e) ..	735	− 90	195	− 23	36	4·50	81	AD, BCE
bd(e) ..	745	32	32	115	− 136	− 17·00	1,156	BD, ACE
abd ..	841	− 157	49	− 353	412	51·50	10·609	ABD, CE (Fermenters)
cd(e) ..	878	− 84	60	173	168	21·00	1,764	CD, ABE
acd ..	656	96	− 189	− 17	− 468	− 58·50	13,689	ACD, BE (Fermenters)
bcd ..	851	− 222	180	− 249	− 156	− 19·50	1,521	BCD, AE
abcd(e) ..	732	− 119	103	− 77	172	21·50	1,849	ABCD, E
Total sum of squares							123,504	

This design is obtained by equating E to $ABCD$, giving the defining contrasts I, $ABCDE$. In addition, interactions BC, ABD, and ACD are confounded between four fermenters. The aliases with respect to the four factors A–E are given in the last column. This example is more complicated than the previous one because of the confounding with respect to fermenters.

The sum of squares for the three degrees of freedom between fermenters is the sum of BC, ABD, and ACD, i.e. 26,554, which agrees with the sum of squares calculated directly as follows.

In all the above tables the total of the sum of squares column agrees with the corrected sum of squares of the observations, and this provides an arithmetical check.

The totals for each of the four fermenters given in Table 10·7 are respectively 2961, 3100, 2660, and 2989. Each of these is based on four observations, and the grand total is 11,710. The corrected sum of squares between the four fermenters is then $[2961^2 + 3100^2 + 2660^2 + 2989^2]/4 − 11,710^2/16$ $= 26,554$.

CHAPTER 11

THE DETERMINATION OF OPTIMUM
CONDITIONS

THIS chapter deals with the problem of finding the best operating conditions for a process by maximising some feature such as the yield or purity of the product, or minimising the cost. When initially the conditions are far removed from those giving an optimum result a method is given for determining new levels which approach more nearly to the optimum ones by following a Path of Steepest Ascent. As the optimum is approached the technique of Local Exploration is used so that the optimum can be specified more precisely and the conditions most suitable for practical use determined. New experimental designs are described which enable this to be done efficiently and economically. This new approach to a problem of great importance in industry has been applied successfully to a number of chemical processes, and the examples cited for illustrative purposes are taken from these investigations.

Introduction

11·1. The problem studied in this chapter is that of determining by experiment conditions giving an optimum result. The problem stated in this way is a very general one. In the chemical industry it arises when a particular route for manufacture has been decided upon but the conditions of such factors as temperature, concentration, proportion of the reactants, etc., which give highest yield or purity or least cost are not known. This problem has recently been discussed by BOX and WILSON [11·1]. What follows is a practical exposition; the reader seeking more detailed knowledge of the theoretical background is referred to the original paper.

Theoretically, the behaviour of chemical reactions, or for that matter the behaviour of any system, is governed by ascertainable laws, and it should be possible to determine optimum conditions by applying such laws. In practice, however, the underlying mechanisms of the system are frequently so complicated that an empirical approach is necessary. It is with the strategy of this approach that this chapter is concerned. The opening sections give an explanation of the notation and terminology to be used.

Factors

11·11. In previous chapters the designs have been of the factorial type involving combinations of certain specific factor levels. In this chapter the designs used are of a more general type, and it will be convenient to denote the levels of k factors or process variables such as temperature, time of reaction, concentration, or proportion of reactant by x_1, x_2, . . . , x_k: thus x_1 might refer to the level of temperature, x_2 to the time of reaction, and so on.

Response

11·12. The object of the methods discussed is to find the levels of the factors which give an optimum response. In a particular investigation the response might be the yield or purity of the product or its cost, and the object would be to maximise the yield or purity or minimise the cost. The true level of response corresponding to any particular combination of factor levels is denoted by η, and the problem is to maximise η. Where the problem is one of minimisation it can always be converted to one of maximisation; for example, by considering the savings as compared with some standard process instead of the cost. By the true response η is meant the hypothetical value which would be obtained in the absence of experimental error. Because of experimental error, which is supposed to have variance σ^2, the response actually observed for the particular combination of factor levels differs from η and is denoted by y.

The response function

11·13. To say that the level of the true response η depends on the levels x_1, x_2, . . . , x_k of k quantitative factors is equivalent to saying that there exists some mathematical function of x_1, x_2, . . . , x_k, the value of which for any given combination of factor levels supplies the corresponding value of η:

$$\eta = \phi(x_1, x_2, \ldots, x_k)$$

This function ϕ is called the Response Function.

The response surface

11·14. It is convenient to visualise the relation between response and the factor levels geometrically. Just as the relation $\eta = \phi(x_1)$ between η and the levels of a single factor x_1 may be represented by a curve, so the relation between η and two factors x_1 and x_2 may be represented by a surface called the Response Surface. A model of such a surface, in which x_1 is the reaction time, x_2 the concentration of one of the reactants, and η the yield, is shown in Figure 11·1.

A section of the solid bounded by the surface at any particular level of time shows the corresponding curve of yield against concentration for that time; similarly a section for any particular concentration shows the curve of yield against time. The surface thus incorporates all such curves.

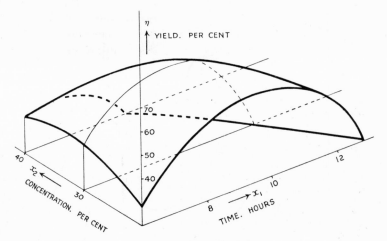

Fig. 11·1. A yield surface

Representation of the response surface by contours

11·15. An alternative and very useful representation of the surface is obtained by drawing lines of equal response on a graph whose co-ordinates denote the levels of the factors; these lines are the response contours and are shown for the surface of Figure 11·1 in Figure 11·11. This type of representation is commonly used in maps to show rise and fall of land, and in weather charts to show the distribution of atmospheric pressure. To appreciate the relation between the surface represented in Figure 11·1 and the contour graph of Figure 11·11 the reader might imagine a solid model of the surface in Figure 11·1 enclosed in a tank. If water is poured up to the level 50% it will reach a line shown by the 50% contour in Figure 11·11.

If the experimenter performed a series of trials with various combinations of time and concentration, the sets of conditions used would correspond to points on a time-concentration space diagram like Figure 11·11. These will be called the Experimental Points. For example, the four experimental points shown in the figure correspond to a 2^2 factorial design in which the levels of time are 9·8 hours and 10·8 hours, and the levels of concentration 38·5% and 43·5%. The great advantage of the contour representation is that it focuses attention on the levels of the factors. The experimenter may imagine the response contours on the same diagram without the distraction of representing the response in a further dimension.

Geometrical representation of the response surface in the three-factor case. Contour surfaces

11·16. A further advantage of the contour representation is that the situation may be visualised geometrically with as many as three factors. The third

K2

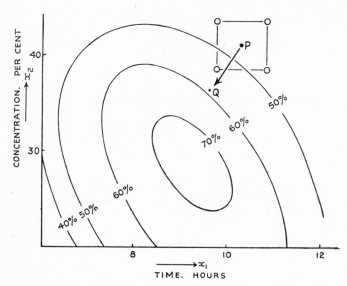

Fig. 11·11. Yield contours for the surface of Figure 11·1 with 2^2 factorial design

dimension is no longer required for the representation of the response and it may be used to accommodate an extra factor. The methods developed are in no way limited by the fact that geometrical illustration is only possible up to three dimensions; however, a familiarity with the geometrical representation for two and three factors enables the general situation for k factors, which cannot be visualised geometrically, to be more readily understood. Suppose then that in addition to the time of reaction x_1 and concentration x_2 a third factor, the temperature of reaction x_3, was studied, then contour surfaces of equal yield could be imagined in the three-dimensional factor space as illustrated in Figure 11·12. To avoid confusion only the contour surfaces for 60% and 70% yield have been drawn. Contour surfaces for other levels of yield may be visualised outside those shown, like a series of shells.

As before, combinations of factor levels correspond to points in the space. The levels used in any set of trials are represented by a cluster of such points, the configuration of which may be called the Experimental Design. In Figure 11·12 a collection of eight points is shown in the space, corresponding to a 2^3 factorial design.

The experimental region

11·17. At the outset of an investigation the experimenter could usually define, at least approximately, that region of the factor space corresponding to factor combinations of potential interest. This will be called the Experimental

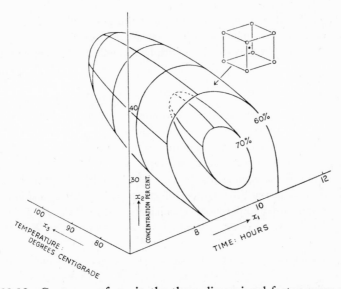

Fig. 11·12. Contour surfaces in the three-dimensional factor space with 2^3 factorial design

Region, and the problem stated geometrically is to find the point or points of maximum response in this region of the factor space.

Polynomial representation of the response surface

11·18. Assume at first that the experimenter is studying the effect on the response η of changing the level x_1 of a single variable, for example the time of reaction. Provided the functional relation $\eta = \phi(x_1)$ between the response η and time of reaction x_1 is smooth, it is possible to represent it to any required degree of approximation by taking a sufficient number of terms in the following series, suitably choosing the constants β_0, β_1, β_{11}, etc.

$$\eta = \beta_0 + \beta_1 x_1 + \beta_{11} x_1^2 + \beta_{111} x_1^3 + \cdots \qquad \cdots \cdots (11\cdot1)$$

The right-hand side of this expression is called a polynomial in x_1, and the successive terms are said to be of degree 0, 1, 2, and so on. Taking terms up to degree 1 the expression is the equation of a straight line; taking terms up to degree 2 it is the equation of a parabola. The wider the range of values of x_1 the more terms will be necessary to obtain an adequate fit. In particular, over a sufficiently narrow range not including a turning point of the curve a good approximation is supplied by the straight line $\eta = \beta_0 + \beta_1 x_1$.

The polynomial equation of $(11\cdot1)$ is for one factor or x_1 only; for two factors x_1, x_2 the corresponding polynomial equation is

$$\eta = \beta_0 + \beta_1 x_1 + \beta_2 x_2 + \beta_{11} x_1^2 + \beta_{22} x_2^2 + \beta_{12} x_1 x_2 + \beta_{111} x_1^3 + \cdots \qquad (11\cdot11)$$

The method of formation of the terms of the polynomial in the general case and the scheme of notation will be apparent. The degree of a term is defined by the number of variables multiplied together. Thus β_0 multiplies 1, which is of degree 0; β_1 and β_2 multiply x_1 and x_2 respectively, which are of degree 1; β_{11}, β_{22}, and β_{12} multiply x_1^2, x_2^2, and $x_1 x_2$, which are of degree 2, and so on. The corresponding coefficients β_0, (β_1, β_2), $(\beta_{11}, \beta_{22}, \beta_{12})$ are said to be of orders 0, 1, and 2. Suppose the origin of the variables is taken at some point 0 in the region in which the approximation is required. Then if the polynomial (11·11) exactly represents the response function ϕ (x_1, x_2) in this region, β_0 is the level of response at the origin, β_1 and β_2 are the values of the first order differential coefficients $\partial\phi/\partial x_1$, $\partial\phi/\partial x_2$ at the origin and may be referred to briefly as the First Order Effects, β_{11}, β_{22}, and β_{12} are multiples of the second order differential coefficients, i.e. $\frac{1}{2}\partial^2\phi/\partial x_1^2$, $\frac{1}{2}\partial^2\phi/\partial x_2^2$, $\partial^2\phi/\partial x_1 \partial x_2$ and may be referred to briefly as the Second Order Effects, and so on.

The constants β_0, β_1, etc., are sometimes called Regression Coefficients and the polynomial a Regression Function. x_1, x_2, x_1^2, x_2^2, $x_1 x_2$, x_1^3, etc., would then be called the Independent Variables in the regression equation. In the terminology of Appendix 8C, β_1 and β_2 in Equation (11·11) measure the Linear Effects, β_{11} and β_{22} the Quadratic Effects, β_{12} the Linear $\times$ Linear Interaction, and so on.

The series will normally supply a closer approximation to the response surface as terms of higher degree are added. Thus, if terms of degree 2 and over are ignored in (11·11), the function is approximated by

$$\eta = \beta_0 + \beta_1 x_1 + \beta_2 x_2$$

This is the equation of a plane, β_1 representing the slope of the plane in the direction of the first variable and β_2 the slope of the plane in the direction of the second variable. To approximate a response surface like that of Figure 11·1 such an expression might be adequate if it was required to represent only a small sub-region of the surface not near a turning point. If a larger region of the space was to be covered or if the region was near a turning point it would be necessary to include terms of higher degree, which would take into account curvature of the surface. As larger regions of the factor space were considered, so polynomials of higher degree would be needed to provide a reasonable approximation to the response surface.

Methods for finding a maximum response

11·2. For a single variable, say the reaction time, the problem of finding the level giving the best response (e.g. the highest yield) could be solved by performing a series of trials using different reaction times covering the whole experimental region, that is, the whole range of reaction times of practical interest. The observed yield y could be plotted against the reaction time x_1 and a smooth curve drawn between the points by eye. The value of x_1 corresponding to the highest yield would provide an estimate of the optimum reaction time. Instead of drawing the curve by eye, a polynomial like (*11·1*) could be fitted to the experimental points by the method of Least Squares (Appendix 11B).

The position of a true maximum occurring within the range considered could then be estimated by differentiating the fitted expression and equating the derivative to zero. For example, if terms up to third degree were included and b_0, b_1, b_{11}, and b_{111} were the Least Squares estimates of β_0, β_1, β_{11}, and β_{111}, the fitted equation would be

$$Y = b_0 + b_1 x_1 + b_{11} x_1{}^2 + b_{111} x_1{}^3$$

where the notation Y means the value calculated from the fitted equation, to distinguish it from η the true value, and from y the observed value, of the response. Differentiating both sides of this equation and equating the derivative to zero we have

$$\mathrm{d}Y/\mathrm{d}x_1 = b_1 + 2b_{11}x_1 + 3b_{111}x_1{}^2 = 0$$

On solving this quadratic equation and taking the appropriate root, the value of x_1 corresponding to a maximum on the fitted curve would be found.

When this procedure is generalised for k factors we have what may be called the grid method. That is to say, trials are performed at a grid of points throughout the experimental region and a yield surface is plotted through these points. The set of levels for the factors corresponding to the highest point on this surface provides an estimate of the optimum combination. In k dimensions, plotting by eye is not possible, but the method of differentiating a fitted surface can still be used.

With more than two factors the number of trials required for such a scheme might be very large. For example, if a factorial grid were employed with five factors and four levels for each factor, $4^5 = 1024$ trials would be required. This number could be reduced somewhat by employing other types of experimental arrangement (e.g. by fractional replication), but in practice a minimum number of experimental points would be required to fill the space adequately and this number would often be too large to merit consideration.

Now if the whole investigation had to be planned at one time or if, because of large experimental error, a large number of trials were necessary to obtain adequate precision, the exploration of the whole surface could be justified. In chemical experimentation however the making of observations is usually expensive and time-absorbing and the number of trials required for explora-on of the whole region is impracticably large. Fortunately however, in this field, the whole investigation usually need not be planned at one time since the result of each trial or small group of trials is known before the next is performed and the experimental error is fairly small, allowing accurate information to be gained from a comparatively small set of trials. This allows the work to be planned sequentially as a series of small sets of trials, each set being planned using the knowledge gained in previous sets.

Exploration of limited experimental sub-regions

11·21. When the experimental error is small, a small sub-region of the factor space may be explored with only a few experimental points, for in these circumstances fairly small changes in response can be distinguished, and within such a sub-region a low-degree polynomial containing only a few constants will adequately represent the local response surface. Further, since the trials are conducted sequentially, a technique may be developed by means of which the results obtained by examining a small sub-region may be used to deduce which region should next be studied, or in some cases what further trials are required in the present region.

In practice the procedure of locating optimum conditions involves two distinct phases. The procedure will be described in the first place by considering two factors, x_1 and x_2.

Method of steepest ascent to approach a stationary point

11·22. If the response contours are as shown in Figure 11·11, where the initial conditions represented by the point P are remote from the maximum, the surface can be represented locally by a sloping plane. The experimenter estimates the slopes b_1, b_2 of this plane by performing a suitably arranged set of trails in a small sub-region about P, and from the relative magnitudes and signs of these slopes calculates the direction of Steepest Ascent or greatest slope up the plane. This is the direction at right angles to the contour lines and shows the relative amounts by which the factors must be varied to give a maximum increase in response. He then proceeds to a point Q in this direction, where the slopes are redetermined, and the process is repeated. In this way, by a step-by-step procedure, points of higher and higher response are reached.

Now this procedure eventually defeats itself, for usually the higher up the response surface the experimenter moves the more gradual do the slopes b_1, b_2 become and the more difficult it is to estimate them in further sets of trials. Moreover the plane approximation becomes less satisfactory, because constants of higher order, particularly those of second order, become relatively more important. Therefore this technique alone will not accurately locate a maximum but will rapidly bring the experimenter to what may be called a near-stationary region, that is, a region where the surface slopes are small compared with the errors of estimation. Once such a region has been reached its nature and the location of an adjacent maximum (if such exists) can be determined without an excessively large number of trials, but a new technique becomes necessary.

This method aims at climbing up the response surface rather than exploring the whole region, and its success depends on the assumption that the ultimate maximum can be reached by a rising path. The method may break down if the surface has more than one peak. In such cases the particular peak scaled would depend on the starting point for the investigation. The possibility of more than one peak must be kept in mind, but so far no cases have been met in practice where this was suspected. It seems likely that surfaces having more than one peak would indicate a fundamental change in the mechanism of the reaction.

Method of local exploration of a near-stationary point

11·23. The fact that a region is near-stationary, i.e. that the response surface is locally nearly flat, does not mean necessarily that the experimenter is in the neighbourhood of a maximum like that in Figure 11·2a. If the region has been reached by the process of ascent described above the experimenter cannot, of course, be near a minimum, but it frequently happens that the surface contains a ridge which may be stationary, as in Figure 11·2b or slowly rising, as in Figure 11·2c. Another possibility is that the point reached is near a Minimax (sometimes called a Col or Saddle-point) at which the response is a minimum for one direction and a maximum for another, as in Figure 11·2d. This would imply the existence of two distinct regions of maximum yield, and might provide a useful warning of a two-peaked system. A real minimax is probably uncommon in chemical work; on the other hand, oblique ridges are common, and indicate interdependence between the factors. Thus in Figure 11·2b, if x_1 denoted the temperature and x_2 the time of reaction, then it would be implied that the reaction would produce a yield of just over 80% at a variety of different combinations of temperature and time, and that a long time at a low temperature or a short time at a high temperature would be equally satisfactory. Figure 11·2c would indicate a similar effect, except that low temperatures and long times of reaction would be slightly better than high temperatures and short times.*

The discovery of the existence and the nature of surface ridges is of great practical importance, not only because in examples such as Figure 11·2c it is

---

* This diagram shows clearly the weakness of the one-factor-at-a-time method of experimentation. A series of trials made along the line AB, at varying levels of x_1, holding x_2 constant, and a similar set made along the line DC, would lead to the wrong conclusion that E was a maximum.

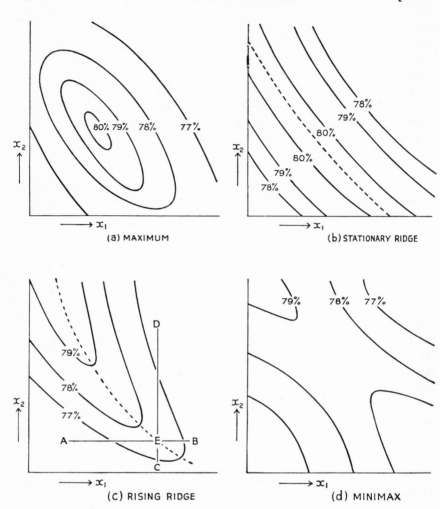

Fig. 11·2. Types of surface in a near-stationary region shown by yield
contours

possible to follow the rising ridge to conditions of higher response, but also
because when a stationary ridge like that in Figure 11·2b occurs there is not a
unique optimum process but a whole series of processes producing nearly
equal responses. If the position of the ridge, or more specifically the equation
of the maximum contour line, can be determined, the best level of x_1 for any
desired level of x_2 in the region will be known. In a system showing a
marked dependence between time and temperature of the sort described

above, the direction of the ridge indicates the amount by which the temperature should be increased to compensate for a given decrease in time of reaction. When a ridge maximum occurs for the most important response, conditions may be chosen which bring auxiliary responses to most satisfactory levels. For example, the particular point on a stationary yield ridge might be chosen which gave the product having greatest purity.

When the experimenter has reached a near-stationary region he will require to know whether he is in the neighbourhood of:

(i) A true maximum like Figure 11·2a, in which case he will wish to estimate its position.

(ii) A ridge like Figure 11·2b or 11·2c, in which case he will wish to determine its direction and slope, if any.

(iii) A minimax like Figure 11·2d, when he will wish to know in which direction "to climb out of it."

A set of trials is performed in the near-stationary region so arranged that a polynomial of degree higher than the first may be fitted to the response surface in the region. If the region is not too large, an equation of second degree should provide a sufficiently close fit. A study of the coefficients of the fitted equation shows the nature of the region and provides answers to the questions posed. The discussion has so far been illustrated in the two-factor case; the number of possible types of near-stationary regions is considerably increased when more than two factors are considered. The methods developed are, however, equally effective for a larger number of factors. A general treatment is discussed later.

Summary of the methods for locating a stationary point

11·24. In the first phase a near-stationary region is found by eliminating large first-order effects by the method of steepest ascent. In the second phase the nature of the near-stationary region is examined by determining effects up to second order* in the region. The relative importance of the two phases varies in different investigations. When the problem is to improve still further a process which has already received attention it may be found that the region already reached is near-stationary and only the second phase is necessary.

In §§ 11·3 and 11·4 which follow, the application of the steepest ascent method of moving to a near-stationary region is dealt with, and in §§ 11·5 and 11·6 the exploration of a near-stationary region is discussed.

---

* Occasionally it might be necessary to determine effects up to third order.

Application of steepest ascent method of moving to a near-stationary region

11·3. Suppose the point O is in a region in the factor space which may be locally approximated by a plane, and that it is desired to move from O to a point P distant r from O so that the gain in response shall be as large as possible. It can be shown that the required direction will be followed by making changes in the variables which are proportional to the surface slopes $\beta_1, \beta_2, \ldots, \beta_k$. This direction is at right angles to the contour lines or surfaces and is called the Direction of Steepest Ascent. This has been illustrated in Figures 11·11 and 11·12 for two and for three dimensions.

The first-order approximation to the response surface implies that locally the contours can be approximated by equidistant straight lines or planes; this would be a reasonable approximation in the regions illustrated.

Choice of scales of measurement

11·31. When a graph is drawn its appearance will depend to some extent on the relative scales chosen to represent the variables. To talk about moving a distance r in the space or of moving at right angles to the contour planes has no meaning unless the relative scales of measurement are specified. In practice these relative scales are fixed by the judgment of the experimenter when he decides the relative amounts by which the factors will be varied in the experimental design. Thus, in a particular example, he might decide to change the temperature by ten degrees and to match this by a change of 50% in the concentration of a catalyst. The direction of steepest ascent calculated will be the direction at right angles to contours drawn according to these relative scales of measurement. In judging the amount by which the factors should be varied in the experimental design the experimenter is subconsciously attempting to get as near as possible to a representation in which the function is symmetrical with respect to the factors. Skilful choice of the amounts by which the factors should be varied may considerably reduce the amount of subsequent work necessary. In § **11·42** it is shown how an unsuitable choice of units may be rectified.

Experimental designs to determine first-order effects

11·32. If it may be assumed that within a given region the response surface may be approximated by a plane, estimates of the surface slopes ($b_1, b_2, \ldots, b_k$ for k variables) may be obtained by fitting the equation

$$\eta = \beta_0 x_0 + \beta_1 x_1 + \beta_2 x_2 + \ldots + \beta_k x_k \quad \ldots\ldots\ldots\ldots(11·2)$$

to the suitably chosen set of experimental points. In Equation $(11·2)$ a dummy variable x_0 is introduced which is always equal to unity; β_0 and $\beta_0 x_0$ are then of course equivalent, but the latter form is more convenient for the present purpose.

Designs suitable for determining the constants in this equation are the two-level factorial designs and fractional factorial designs described in Chapters 7 and 10 respectively. The response surface is assumed to be plotted in a k-dimensional space in which the units are chosen so that the levels of the

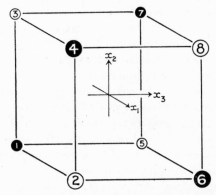

Fig. 11·3. A 2^3 factorial design showing the division
into two half-replicate designs

factors are -1 and $+1$, that is, the origin 0 for the variables is taken at the mid-point of the design, and the co-ordinates of the experimental points consist of -1's and $+1$'s. Thus in a complete 2^3 factorial design the experimental points would be located at the vertices of a cube as illustrated in Figure 11·3. Table 11·1 shows the factor levels at the eight experimental points.

Table 11·1

A 2^3 FACTORIAL DESIGN

Trial	Factor level		
	x_1	x_2	x_3
I	-1	-1	-1
2*	1	-1	-1
3*	-1	1	-1
4	1	1	-1
5*	-1	-1	1
6	1	-1	1
7	-1	1	1
8*	1	1	1

If the factors are assumed not to interact with one another, then as explained in Chapter 10 it is unnecessary to perform the complete set of eight trials. Instead, a half-replicate of the complete 2^3 factorial design can be carried out. For example, one such half-replicate would consist of the trials 2, 3, 5, and 8 denoted by asterisks in Table 11·1; these experimental points are shown in Figure 11·3 by white circles and fall at the vertices of a regular tetrahedron. The experimental points for the other half-replicate are shown in Figure 11·3 by black circles and form a second regular tetrahedron. For a discussion of the geometrical aspect of these designs the reader is referred to [11·2]. The manner in which such designs may be found has already been fully described in Chapter 10; the only difference here is the notation, x_1, x_2, x_3, etc., being used as a general symbol to denote the factor levels.

It has been shown in previous chapters that, using factorial designs, the effects can be determined very simply. The reason for this is that the Least Squares estimates of the constants are orthogonal linear functions of the observations. An account of the method of Least Squares and of the simplifications arising from orthogonality is given in Appendix 11B. Briefly, because of orthogonality each coefficient b may be calculated separately as though this constant were the only one estimated from the data. Each estimate b is then given by the sum of the products of the observations (the y's) with the elements of the appropriate independent variable x divided by the sum of squares of the elements of this independent variable. Also if σ^2 is the experimental error variance, the variance of b is given by σ^2 divided by the sum of squares of the elements of the independent variable, i.e.

$$b = \Sigma yx/\Sigma x^2 \quad\dots\dots\dots\dots\dots\dots(11\cdot3)$$
$$V(b) = \sigma^2/\Sigma x^2 \quad\dots\dots\dots\dots\dots\dots(11\cdot31)$$

Thus if an estimate s^2 of σ^2 is available an estimate of $V(b)$ is $s^2/\Sigma x^2$.

For example, suppose the half-replicate design mentioned above involving the four experimental points 2, 3, 5, and 8 of Table 11·1 was utilised in a region in which the surface could be approximated by the plane:

$$\eta = \beta_0 x_0 + \beta_1 x_1 + \beta_2 x_2 + \beta_3 x_3 \quad\dots\dots\dots\dots\dots(11\cdot4)$$

If the observed responses were y_2, y_3, y_5, and y_8, a table of the values of the independent variables and of the responses could be written down in the form of Table 11·11.

Table 11·11

VALUES OF THE INDEPENDENT VARIABLES CORRESPONDING TO EQUATION (11·4) AND THE RESPONSES OBTAINED

| Independent variable | | | | Response |
x_0	x_1	x_2	x_3	y
1	1	− 1	− 1	y_2
1	− 1	1	− 1	y_3
1	− 1	− 1	1	y_5
1	1	1	1	y_8

Thus applying formulae (*11·3*) and (*11·31*):

$$b_0 = (1.y_2 + 1.y_3 + 1.y_5 + 1.y_8)/4 = \bar{y}$$
$$b_1 = (1.y_2 - 1.y_3 - 1.y_5 + 1.y_8)/4$$

etc.

$$V(b_0) = V(b_1) = V(b_2) = V(b_3) = \sigma^2/4$$

b_1 estimates β_1, the slope of the plane (*11·4*) in the direction x_1, that is the change in y per unit change in x_1. Since the convention has been adopted that the variable is changed from a level of -1 unit to a level of $+1$ unit, b_1 denotes half the average change in response on changing from the lower to the upper level of the factor, i.e. it is half the effect defined in Chapters 7 and 10.

The nature of possible bias in an estimate

11·33. Suppose that in the above example it is suspected that the first-degree approximation represented by Equation (*11·4*) is not adequate, and instead an equation represented by (*11·41*) including all terms up to second degree is necessary:

$$\eta = \beta_0 x_0 + \beta_1 x_1 + \beta_2 x_2 + \beta_3 x_3 + \beta_{11} x_1^2 + \beta_{22} x_2^2$$
$$+ \beta_{33} x_3^2 + \beta_{12} x_1 x_2 + \beta_{13} x_1 x_3 + \beta_{23} x_2 x_3 \quad \ldots\ldots(11·41)$$

then the estimates of the constants of Equation (*11·4*) will be biased owing to the existence of the higher terms. Because of special properties of these designs the nature of these biases* is easily seen.

The values of the independent variables corresponding to Equation (*11·41*) and the responses obtained are given in Table 11·12.

Table 11·12

VALUES OF THE INDEPENDENT VARIABLES CORRESPONDING TO
EQUATION (*11·41*) AND THE RESPONSES OBTAINED

			Independent variable							Response
x_0	x_1	x_2	x_3	x_1^2	x_2^2	x_3^2	$x_1 x_2$	$x_1 x_3$	$x_2 x_3$	y
I	I	$-$I	$-$I	I	I	I	$-$I	$-$I	I	y_2
I	$-$I	I	$-$I	I	I	I	$-$I	I	$-$I	y_3
I	$-$I	$-$I	I	I	I	I	I	$-$I	$-$I	y_5
I	I	I	I	I	I	I	I	I	I	y_8

* To conform with normal practice these biases in fractional factorial designs were called aliases in Chapter 10. The word alias is less appropriate for the more general situations considered in this chapter.

Since only four experiments have been carried out, not more than four quantities can be estimated, but it will be noticed that each column from the fifth to the tenth of Table 11·12 is a repetition of one or another of the first four. For example, the fifth, sixth, and seventh columns are identical with the first column, so that

$$b_0 \to \beta_0 + \beta_{11} + \beta_{22} + \beta_{33}$$

where the arrow notation means that the quantity on the left is an estimate of the quantity on the right. Also

$$b_1 \to \beta_1 + \beta_{23}$$
$$b_2 \to \beta_2 + \beta_{13}$$
$$b_3 \to \beta_3 + \beta_{12}$$

The meaning to be attributed to the first expression is: if the surface is plane, then b_0, that is $\bar{y}$, will be an unbiased estimate of β_0, the value of the response at the centre of the design; but if the surface is curved the mean $\bar{y}$ will be a biased estimate of the response at this point. For example, if the situation is visualised when the design straddles a maximum it is seen that $\bar{y}$ will be an underestimate of β_0, the response at the centre of the design. This same result is obtained from the formula, for β_{11}, β_{22}, and β_{33} would all have negative values, and b_0 would therefore be an estimate of a quantity less than β_0. Similarly, if the interaction effects β_{12}, β_{13}, and β_{23} are not zero, b_1, b_2, and b_3 will be biased.

As explained in the previous chapter, it is not necessary to proceed in this cumbrous way in order to decide the nature of the biases. For every row of the complete design given in Table 11·1 it is true that

$$x_1^2 = x_2^2 = x_3^2 = 1$$

In addition, the half-replicate has been chosen for which

$$x_1 x_2 x_3 = 1$$

From these two relations the identities between the columns of Table 11·12 follow, as do the expressions for b_0, b_1, b_2, and b_3 above, in the same way as in Chapter 10.

It is true not only of these experimental arrangements but of all experimental arrangements that the estimates of the b's may be biased if the assumptions concerning the degree of the polynomial necessary to ensure an adequate fit are not justified. To keep the nature of possible bias in mind it is a wise precaution to work out the expected values of the estimates on the assumption that the degree of the polynomial necessary to produce an adequate fit is one higher than that assumed. This is done in the example of § 11·4. A general formula for calculating bias coefficients is given in [11·1].

In what follows the change in level of a factor corresponding with a change from 0 to 1 in the design will be called the Unit, and the level associated with the value zero will be called the Base Level. Thus if the experimenter decided to test the reaction at the levels 60° and 65° C., associating the lower level with -1 and the upper level with $+1$ in a two-level factorial design, the unit for temperature would be $+2\cdot5$° C. and the base level would be 62·5° C.

An example of steepest ascent

11·4. To illustrate the steepest ascent procedure the following example is given. The investigation was on a laboratory scale and concerned a chemical reaction of the type

$$A + B + C \to D + \text{other products}$$

the reaction taking place in the presence of a solvent E. The object of the experiment was to maximise the yield of the product D for a given amount of A, which was the most expensive of the three starting materials and the amount of which was kept constant throughout. Conditions were known which gave about 45% of the theoretical yield (i.e. the yield which would be obtained if all of A were changed to D), but for a reaction of this type a 75% yield was thought to be possible. The experimental error of a single preparation was expected to be about 1% or less. Five factors were varied: the amount x_1 of E, the amount x_2 of C, the concentration x_3 of C, the time of reaction x_4, and the amount x_5 of B.

First experiment

11·41. The levels for x_1, x_2, x_3, x_4, and x_5 investigated in the first experiment are given in Table 11·2. The base levels were close to those which were known to give about 45% of the theoretical yield.

Table 11·2

FACTOR LEVELS FOR THE FIRST EXPERIMENT

Factor			Factor level -1	$+1$
x_1	Amount of solvent E	c.c.	200	250
x_2	Amount of C	mol. per mol. of A	4·0	4·5
x_3	Concentration of C	%	90	93
x_4	Time of reaction	hour	1	2
x_5	Amount of B	mol. per mol. of A	3·0	3·5

In view of the large gain believed possible (and consequently the probable remoteness of the starting conditions from their optimum levels), it was thought that first-order effects would be dominant and that higher-order effects could be ignored in the first stages of the investigation. An experiment consisting of a set of eight trials arranged as a quarter-replicate of a full factorial was therefore carried out. From consideration of the theoretical background of the reaction it was thought that the effects most likely to interact would be x_1 and x_3, and provision was made, therefore, in the design for the isolation of any interaction between these variables, that is to say, no extra factor was associated with the comparison measuring the interaction between x_1 and x_3. The design chosen and the yields obtained when the trials were performed in random order are set out below in Table 11·21.

Table 11·21

THE FIRST EXPERIMENT

| Trial | Factor level | | | | | Yield (%) |
	x_1	x_2	x_3	x_4	x_5	y
1	− 1	− 1	− 1	− 1	− 1	34·4
2	− 1	− 1	1	1	1	51·6
3	− 1	1	− 1	1	1	31·2
4	− 1	1	1	− 1	− 1	45·1
5	1	− 1	− 1	1	− 1	54·1
6	1	− 1	1	− 1	1	62·4
7	1	1	− 1	− 1	1	50·2
8	1	1	1	1	− 1	58·6

The method of construction of this design will be clear from Chapter 10. The defining relations are

$$x_4 = x_1 x_2 x_3 \quad \text{and} \quad x_5 = - x_2 x_3$$

whence $1 = x_1{}^2 = x_2{}^2 = x_3{}^2 = x_4{}^2 = x_5{}^2 = x_1 x_2 x_3 x_4 = -x_2 x_3 x_5 = -x_1 x_4 x_5$.

The following estimates were then obtained, using Formula $(11·3)$.

$$
\begin{aligned}
b_0 &\rightarrow + \beta_0 (+ \beta_{11}{}^* + \beta_{22} + \beta_{33}{}^* + \beta_{44} + \beta_{55}) = & 48\cdot5 \\
b_1 &\rightarrow + \beta_1 (- \beta_{45}) &= & 7\cdot9 \\
b_2 &\rightarrow + \beta_2 (- \beta_{35}) &= & - 2\cdot2 \\
b_3 &\rightarrow + \beta_3 (- \beta_{25}) &= & 6\cdot0 \\
b_{123} &\rightarrow + \beta_4 (- \beta_{15}) &= & 0\cdot4 \\
b_{23} &\rightarrow - \beta_5 (+ \beta_{14} + \beta_{23}) &= & - 0\cdot4 \\
b_{13} &\rightarrow \quad 0 \ (+ \beta_{13}{}^* + \beta_{24}) &= & - 1\cdot8 \\
b_{12} &\rightarrow \quad 0 \ (+ \beta_{12} + \beta_{34}) &= & 0\cdot2
\end{aligned}
$$

(Approximate standard error of estimates is 0·4, assuming $\sigma = 1$)

In the above equations the expected values of the calculated estimates are shown with second-order terms bracketed. The terms β_{11}, β_{33}, and β_{13} are marked by asterisks, since appreciable second-order effects corresponding to these constants are not unexpected from chemical considerations. The estimate b_{13} probably corresponds to a real effect which is most likely due to β_{13}. This effect, however, is not large compared with those of first order, and the steepest ascent formula was applied, ignoring second-order effects. The calculation of the direction in which maximum gain would be expected, the response surface being drawn in the scale of the design, is given in Table 11·22.

Table 11·22

CALCULATION OF PATH OF STEEPEST ASCENT AND SUBSEQUENT TRIALS ON THE PATH

	x_1 c.c.	x_2 mol.	x_3 %	x_4 hour	x_5 mol.
(1) Base level	225	4·25	91·5	1·5	3·25
(2) Unit	25	0·25	1·5	0·5	0·25
(3) Estimated slope b (change in yield per unit)	7·9	− 2·2	6·0	0·4	0·4
(4) Unit × b	197·5	− 0·55	9·0	0·2	0·1
(5) Change in level per 10 c.c. change in x_1	10	− 0·028	0·456	0·010	0·005
(6) The path of steepest	225	4·25	91·5	1·5	3·25
ascent represented	235	4·22	92·0	1·5	3·25
by a series of pos-	245	4·19	92·4	1·5	3·26
sible trials on it	255	4·17	92·9	1·5	3·26
	265	4·14	93·3	1·5	3·27
Trial (9)	275	4·11	93·8	1·6	3·27
	285	4·08	94·2	1·6	3·28
Trial (10)	295	4·06	94·7	1·6	3·28
	305	4·03	95·1	1·6	3·29

In this calculation line (1) shows the base levels for the factors, line (2) shows the unit, i.e. the change in level for the variable corresponding to the change from 0 to 1 in the design space, and line (3) shows the estimated slopes calculated on the assumption that second and higher order effects are small enough to be ignored. The factors must then be varied in proportion to these slopes; this is to be done in the units of the design. Thus for every 7·9 units by which x_1 is increased, x_2 should be decreased by 2·2 units, x_3 increased by 6·0 units, and so on. Thus, in terms of the original units of measurement, for each 25 × 7·9 c.c. that x_1 is varied, x_2 should be changed by 0·25 × (− 2·2) mol.

L2

These changes are shown in line (4) and define the direction of steepest ascent at the point given by the base levels in line (1) when the surface is scaled in the units of the design. The path leading from O in this direction can be set out by taking a convenient increment in one of the variables (10 c.c. in x_1 in the present case), and calculating the proportionate changes to be made in the other variables. These are given in line (5). These quantities may then be successively added to the average level to give the path (6). Because of the large gain theoretically possible, trial (9) was performed a fair distance along the path from the starting conditions. This gave a yield of 80% compared with a mean yield for the first eight trials of 48·5%, and trial (10) was therefore carried out still farther along the path. A yield of 79·4% was obtained in this trial. Although the second value was apparently somewhat lower than the first, no real significance could be attributed to this, and a second set of trials was carried out using the conditions corresponding to trial (10) as base point.

Before discussing this second series the logic of the procedure so far adopted will be reviewed. It should first be noted that the course of the investigation was decided by the results of the experiments. The tentative prior assumption concerning the dominance of first-order effects tended to be confirmed; the experimenter was therefore justified in continuing on this assumption. Had the analysis of the first experiment shown first-order effects which were small in magnitude compared with those aggregates of second-ordereffects which it was possible to estimate, then the method of attack would have been changed to that described in §§ 11·5 and 11·6, in which second-order effects are taken into account.

It is, of course, possible when fairly high order fractional factorial designs are being used that the experimenter will be completely misled. Thus a major part of the effects attributed to first-order derivatives could have been due to the second-order derivatives β_{45}, β_{35}, etc. If this were so, the estimates of first-order effects would have been so badly biased as to be worthless. On the basis of the prior evidence available such an explanation would seem unlikely, but the final safeguard was that if the assumptions were so far from the truth as to be valueless, then when trials were performed in the direction calculated the expected increase would not in fact have occurred. In the above experiment, as a result of following the path of steepest ascent a large increase in yield was obtained. If this had not been so it would have been concluded either that the estimates were heavily biased by effects which had been ignored or that the error of the observations was much greater than had at first been supposed. In these circumstances the group of observations already made would be augmented by further observations. As is shown later, the extra points could be added so that all first and second order effects were estimated, and the methods of §§ 11·5 and 11·6 could then be used.

Procedure when some factors produce only small effects

11·42. When a second experiment is carried out the experimenter is free to alter the units for the variables if he thinks this desirable. In particular, if the effect corresponding to a particular factor is small compared with the other effects, then it may be that:

(i) The base level chosen for this factor is near a conditional maximum. (A maximum for this particular factor when the other factors are held constant, but not a maximum in all the variables.)

(ii) The unit adopted for the factor is disproportionately small.

(iii) The system is independent of the level of this variable.

To clarify the situation therefore the base level for the factor is changed away from the calculated path and a larger unit is used in the next experiment. Then if (iii) is true the factor will again be found to be without effect, while if (i) or (ii) is true a real effect should be found.

In the first experiment neither of the variables x_4, x_5 gave appreciable effects. In the next experiment, therefore, base levels for both of these factors were moved away from the calculated direction of steepest ascent and larger units were used.

Second experiment

11·43. In considering suitable units for the factors x_1, x_2, x_3 in the second experiment it was necessary to bear in mind that as a stationary point was approached the first-order effects would become smaller and progress by this method would become more and more difficult because:

(i) The estimates of first-order effects would be relatively more in error.

(ii) The estimates of the first-order effects would be relatively more biased by second-order aliases.

If the units were increased to reduce the first difficulty the second would be aggravated. In the first experiment there was some evidence of the existence of appreciable second-order effects, probably due to β_{13}. But the estimated effects for x_1, x_2, and x_3 were all large compared with their probable standard errors. In view of this it seemed that if further progress was possible without taking effects of second order into account the best chance of success lay in making a small reduction of step lengths for these three factors. The ranges chosen for these variables were therefore somewhat narrower in the second experiment, although the relation between the units was kept about the same. It must be emphasised that the choice of ranges is by no means governed by rule of thumb, and judgment must play an important part in this procedure.

Levels for the factors in the second experiment are given in Table 11·3.

Table 11·3
FACTOR LEVELS FOR THE SECOND EXPERIMENT

Factor				Factor level	
				− I	+ I
x_1 Amount of solvent E	..	..	c.c.	280	310
x_2 Amount of C	..	..	mol. per mol. of A	3·85	4·15
x_3 Concentration of C	..	..	%	94	96
x_4 Time of reaction	..	..	hours	2	4
x_5 Amount of B	..	..	mol. per mol. of A	3·5	5·5

The design chosen and the yields obtained when the trials were performed are given in Table 11·31.

Table 11·31
THE DESIGN USED FOR THE SECOND EXPERIMENT AND THE YIELDS OBTAINED

Trial	Factor level					Yield (%)
	x_1	x_2	x_3	x_4	x_5	y
11	− I	− I	− I	− I	I	77·1
12	− I	− I	I	I	I	69·0
13	− I	I	− I	I	− I	75·5
14	− I	I	I	− I	− I	72·6
15	I	− I	− I	I	− I	67·9
16	I	− I	I	− I	− I	68·4
17	I	I	− I	− I	I	71·5
18	I	I	I	I	I	63·4

This design is similar to that used in the first experiment, but the defining relations are

$$x_4 = x_1 x_2 x_3 \quad \text{and} \quad x_5 = x_1 x_2$$

whence

$$1 = x_1^2 = x_2^2 = x_3^2 = x_4^2 = x_5^2 = x_1 x_2 x_3 x_4 = x_1 x_2 x_5 = x_3 x_4 x_5 *$$

* It was worth while taking the opportunity of changing the arrangement of the aliases, since this allowed some light to be shed on possible interactions previously associated with main effects. In the second experiment the comparison corresponding to b_{13} was not used for the estimation of any first-order constant, since an appreciable effect was found associated with this comparison in the first experiment. The estimate b_{12}, however, appeared to correspond to no real effect (although β_{12} and β_{34} might, of course, have cancelled each other out). In the second experiment, therefore, the comparison corresponding to this estimate was used for the estimation of β_5.

The following estimates were then obtained, using Formula (11·3):

$$b_0 \rightarrow \beta_0 \, (+ \, \beta_{11} + \beta_{22} + \beta_{33} + \beta_{44} + \beta_{55}) = 70\cdot7$$
$$b_1 \rightarrow \beta_1 \, (+ \, \beta_{25}) = -\,2\cdot9$$
$$b_2 \rightarrow \beta_2 \, (+ \, \beta_{15}) = \,0\cdot1$$
$$b_3 \rightarrow \beta_3 \, (+ \, \beta_{45}) = -\,2\cdot3$$
$$b_{123} \rightarrow \beta_4 \, (+ \, \beta_{35}) = -\,1\cdot7$$
$$b_{12} \rightarrow \beta_5 \, (+ \, \beta_{12} + \beta_{34}) = -\,0\cdot4$$
$$b_{13} \rightarrow 0 \, (+ \, \beta_{13} + \beta_{24}) = \,0\cdot4$$
$$b_{23} \rightarrow 0 \, (+ \, \beta_{23} + \beta_{14}) = -\,0\cdot4$$

(Approximate standard error of estimates is 0·4, assuming $\sigma = 1$)

These estimates are now compared with those found in the first experiment and given in § **11·41**. The average yield b_0 is higher than in the first experiment. That it is not so high as the value, 79·4%, of trial (10) is accounted for by curvature of the surface; for the measures of curvature β_{11}, β_{22}, etc., would all be negative near a maximum and b_0, the mean, would therefore be a negatively biased estimate of β_0, the yield at the centre of the design. The slopes b_1, b_2, and b_3 for the first three factors have all changed signs; this suggests that these factor levels have been moved too far from the first base and that it is necessary to move back. As already explained, the average level for x_4 was deliberately varied away from that used in trial (10), and the fairly large negative value now found for the estimate of β_4 indicates that the small value previously associated with the factor x_4 was probably due, not to its being without effect, but to its nearness to a conditional maximum. The sign of this estimate indicates that the level for this factor should also be changed back. Finally, in spite of the larger unit and different average level used for the fifth factor, the value found for the estimate of β_5 is still small, therefore the factor x_5 does not seem to be important in this region of the factor space.

In terms of the new units, the path of steepest ascent calculated as in § **11·41** was:

Table 11·32

PATH OF STEEPEST ASCENT: SECOND EXPERIMENT

	x_1 c.c.	x_2 mol.	x_3 %	x_4 hour	x_5 mol.
	295	4·0	95·0	3·0	4·5
Trial (19)	285	4·0	94·5	2·6	4·4
	275	4·0	93·9	2·2	4·3
Trial (20)	265	4·0	93·4	1·8	4·2
Trial (21)	255	4·0	92·8	1·4	4·1

Trials (19), (20), and (21) performed along the path gave yields of 80·8%, 84·0%, and 81·5% respectively. Four further trials were carried out around the conditions in (20), in which x_1 and x_2 only were varied and the calculated slopes were little different from zero. It was concluded that trial (20) defined conditions at which the yield was nearly stationary. It was clear that little further progress would be possible by this method, and that in further work higher-order effects should be taken into account. It was accordingly decided not to carry out further laboratory experiments but to take the process to the pilot plant stage and make further adjustments there.

Discussion

11·44. The technique described here has been used in a number of investigations, most of them similar in nature to the example given in detail above. One investigation of particular interest was on a reaction of the type

$$A + B + C \to D + E \text{ and other products}$$

The original object was to maximise the yield of D and minimise that of E (if more than a small amount of E were present in the product it would not be satisfactory). In this investigation the yields for both D and E were examined and the path followed was a compromise between one of steepest ascent for D and one of steepest descent for E. As might have been expected, similar paths were indicated on either basis for most of the variables. Starting from a yield of 64% of D and 15% of E, 92% was obtained for D after two cycles of the procedure, the product containing less than $\frac{1}{2}$% of E. At this stage it was suggested that the same reaction might be used for obtaining E, and a second investigation was begun, in this case maximising E. Three cycles of the technique led to conditions which gave a yield of about 70% for E.

Exploration of the yield surface in a near-stationary region. An example with two variables

11·5. Having reached a near-stationary region the experimenter will wish to determine its nature; in particular he will wish to ascertain whether he has reached a true maximum, a ridge, or possibly a col. To do this a polynomial of at least second degree must be fitted to a suitably arranged set of points in the region. The equation of second degree is the equation of a surface which may take a variety of forms, depending on the relative values of the coefficients. In particular, for two variables, surfaces of all the types in Figure 11·2 may be obtained.

Two problems arise: first, experimental arrangements are required which will supply efficient estimates of all effects of first and second order; next, methods are required which make it possible to recognise the nature and characteristics of the fitted surface.

In order that the essential principles should not be obscured by technical details an example in which only two factors x_1 and x_2 were the subject of study will first be considered. In this the effects of first and second order were determined by carrying out a 3^2 factorial experiment. Writing the levels for the factors as -1, 0, 1, the design matrix and the yields obtained are given in Table 11·4.

Table 11·4

A 3^2 FACTORIAL EXPERIMENT AND THE YIELDS OBTAINED

| Trial | Factor level | | Yield (%) |
	x_1	x_2	y
1	-1	-1	71·7
2	0	-1	79·2
3	1	-1	80·1
4	-1	0	75·2
5	0	0	81·5
6	1	0	79·1
7	-1	1	76·3
8	0	1	80·2
9	1	1	75·8

Estimation of the coefficients of the second-degree equation

11·51. It was assumed that in the neighbourhood considered the following second-degree equation would supply an adequate fit.

$$\eta = \beta_0 x_0 + \beta_1 x_1 + \beta_2 x_2 + \beta_{11} x_1^2 + \beta_{22} x_2^2 + \beta_{12} x_1 x_2 \quad ....(11.5)$$

The calculation can be made most conveniently by fitting an equation equivalent to (11.5) but expressed in a slightly different form, obtained as follows. The design given in Table 11·4 has the properties that

$$\Sigma x_1/n = \Sigma x_2/n = \Sigma x_1 x_2/n = 0$$

and
$$\Sigma x_1^2/n = \Sigma x_2^2/n = \tfrac{2}{3}$$

Using Equation (11.5), the mean of the η's, denoted by η_0, for this design is consequently given by

$$\eta_0 = \beta_0 + \tfrac{2}{3}\beta_{11} + \tfrac{2}{3}\beta_{22} \quad ....(11.51)$$

Subtracting this equation from (11.5), then

$$\eta = \eta_0 x_0 + \beta_1 x_1 + \beta_2 x_2 + \beta_{11}(x_1^2 - \tfrac{2}{3}) + \beta_{22}(x_2^2 - \tfrac{2}{3}) + \beta_{12} x_1 x_2 ..(11.52)$$

This is the alternative form of Equation ($11\cdot5$), which was fitted. The estimates obtained are the same whichever equation is fitted except that an estimate $\bar{y}$ of η_0 replaces an estimate b_0 of β_0; however, an estimate b_0 of β_0 can easily be obtained from the relation

$$b_0 = \bar{y} - \tfrac{2}{3}b_{11} - \tfrac{2}{3}b_{22} \quad \ldots\ldots\ldots\ldots\ldots(11\cdot53)$$

The values of the independent variables corresponding to Equation ($11\cdot52$) and the yields obtained are given in Table 11·41.

Table 11·41

VALUES OF THE INDEPENDENT VARIABLES CORRESPONDING TO
EQUATION ($11\cdot52$) AND THE YIELDS OBTAINED

Trial	Independent variable						Yield (%)
	x_0	x_1	x_2	$x_1{}^2 - \tfrac{2}{3}$	$x_2{}^2 - \tfrac{2}{3}$	$x_1 x_2$	y
1	1	-1	-1	$\tfrac{1}{3}$	$\tfrac{1}{3}$	1	71·7
2	1	0	-1	$-\tfrac{2}{3}$	$\tfrac{1}{3}$	0	79·2
3	1	1	-1	$\tfrac{1}{3}$	$\tfrac{1}{3}$	-1	80·1
4	1	-1	0	$\tfrac{1}{3}$	$-\tfrac{2}{3}$	0	75·2
5	1	0	0	$-\tfrac{2}{3}$	$-\tfrac{2}{3}$	0	81·5
6	1	1	0	$\tfrac{1}{3}$	$-\tfrac{2}{3}$	0	79·1
7	1	-1	1	$\tfrac{1}{3}$	$\tfrac{1}{3}$	-1	76·3
8	1	0	1	$-\tfrac{2}{3}$	$\tfrac{1}{3}$	0	80·2
9	1	1	1	$\tfrac{1}{3}$	$\tfrac{1}{3}$	1	75·8

It is found that for Equation ($11\cdot52$) the sum of products for any two columns in the table of independent variables is zero; because of this orthogonality the effects may be estimated simply by taking sums of products of the observations (the y's) with the elements of the appropriate independent variable and dividing by the sum of squares of the elements of the independent variable. This is the same result as given in § **11·32**, namely

$$b = \Sigma yx / \Sigma x^2$$

and the variance of b is given as before by

$$V(b) = \sigma^2 / \Sigma x^2$$

where σ^2 is the experimental error variance. Also the sum of squares in the analysis of variance due to b is $(\Sigma yx)^2 / \Sigma x^2$.

11·511. The calculations are given in Table 11·411.

Table 11·411

THE ESTIMATES OF THE CONSTANTS AND REGRESSION ANALYSIS
FOR EQUATION (*11·52*)

Constant estimated (1)	Σx^2 (2)	Σyx (3)	Estimate = (3)/(2) (4)	Component s. of s. = (3)²/(2) (5)
η_0	9	699·1	77·68	(1) 54,304·53
β_1	6	11·8	1·97	(1) 23·21 ⎫
β_2	6	1·3	0·22	(1) 0·28 ⎪
β_{11}	2	− 7·87	− 3·93	(1) 30·97 ⎬ 78·10
β_{22}	2	− 2·77	− 1·38	(1) 3·84 ⎪
β_{12}	4	− 8·9	− 2·22	(1) 19·80 ⎭

Deviations from regression .. (3)   0·38

Total ..   .. (9) 54,383·01

The analysis of variance is shown in column (5) of the table. The number in brackets before each sum of squares shows the appropriate degrees of freedom.

The first six elements of column (5) are the sums of squares due to each term of the fitted equation, and their sum is equal to the sum of squares of the values predicted by the regression equation.* At the foot of the column is written the total sum of squares of the observed values, and this has as many degrees of freedom as there are observations. The difference provides the sum of squares about regression, that is, the sum of squares of the discrepancies between the observed values and those values predicted by the regression equation. If it is possible to represent the true responses η by some equation of second degree within the region of the design, then this residual sum of squares divided by the number of its degrees of freedom provides an estimate of σ^2, the experimental error variance. If an equation of higher degree were necessary to fit the surface within the region considered, then this residual sum of squares would be inflated by terms involving these extra constants. If some prior estimate of σ^2 is available, therefore, a comparison of this prior estimate with the residual mean square provides a test for the existence of the higher-order terms, that is to say, it provides a test of goodness of fit of the second-degree equation. In this example previous experiments had suggested thot the value of σ^2 was about 0·6; this value is

* This additive property arises from the orthogonal nature of the design and is not true when the effects are not orthogonal [Appendix 11B].

larger than the residual estimate of 0·13, therefore there is no evidence to suggest that a second-degree approximation was not adequate within the regions considered.

The estimate b_0 using Equation $(11·53)$ is

$$b_0 = 77·68 + (3·93 \times 0·67) + (1·38 \times 0·67) = 81·22$$

Also, since the estimates are uncorrelated,

$$V(b_0) = V(\bar{y}) + (\tfrac{2}{3})^2 V(b_{11}) + (\tfrac{2}{3})^2 V(b_{22}) = 0·5555\sigma^2$$

This procedure leads to the following estimates:

$$
\begin{aligned}
b_0 &= 81·22 \pm 0·58 \\
b_1 &= 1·97 \pm 0·32 \\
b_2 &= 0·22 \pm 0·32 \\
b_{11} &= -3·93 \pm 0·55 \\
b_{22} &= -1·38 \pm 0·55 \\
b_{12} &= -2·22 \pm 0·39
\end{aligned}
$$

The estimates are followed by their approximate standard errors calculated on the assumption that $\sigma^2 = 0·6$.

Unless the regression equation accounts for a large and significant part of the variation it will be a valueless representation of the data to which it has been fitted. In the example given, a large proportion of the total sum of squares, after the fitting of the mean is allowed for, is ascribable to the regression equation, and therefore it is confirmed that an adequate fit has been made. A confirmation is also given by the magnitudes of the estimates in relation to their standard errors.

When an overall test of this kind has confirmed the adequate fit of an equation of a particular degree, the fact that an individual coefficient is or is not significantly different from zero has no particular relevance. For example, b_2 is not significantly different from zero, and it might be thought that this constant should have been dismissed as unnecessary in the regression equation, that is to say, it should have been replaced by the value zero. However, since there was no reason for making the hypothesis that $\beta_2 = 0$ such a procedure would be inappropriate. The value 0·22 is the best estimate for this constant, and it is therefore used in the equation.

Analysis of the fitted surface

11·52. From the calculations in the last section it was ascertained that an equation of second degree was probably adequate to describe the response surface in the region of the design and that an estimate of this equation was

$$Y = 81·22 + 1·97x_1 + 0·22x_2 - 3·93x_1{}^2 - 1·38x_2{}^2 - 2·22x_1x_2 \quad ....(11·6)$$

In this form the equation does not convey a great deal. One way of showing the nature of the fitted surface is to plot it. This can be done most conveniently by plotting a contour diagram.

The 80% yield contour, for example, is the locus of all points which satisfy the equation

$$80 = 81 \cdot 22 + 1 \cdot 97 x_1 + 0 \cdot 22 x_2 - 3 \cdot 93 x_1{}^2 - 1 \cdot 38 x_2{}^2 - 2 \cdot 22 x_1 x_2$$

Substituting any given value of x_1, a quadratic equation in x_2 would be obtained which could be solved in the usual way and the corresponding values of x_2 found. If this somewhat tedious calculation were carried through for a sufficiently large number of points the 80% contour and other contours could be drawn as in Figure 11·4. It will be noticed that the fitted expression has a true maximum to the right of and below the centre of the design, the

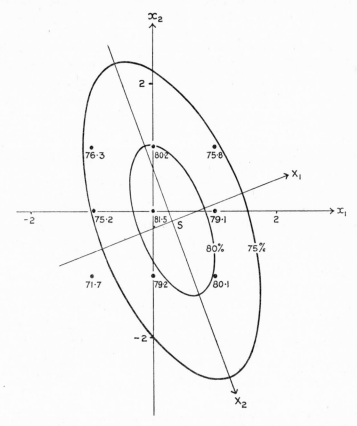

Fig. 11·4. Contours of fitted surface and observed yields at experimental points

axes of the contour system are inclined at an angle to the axes of the variables, and the surface is slightly elongated along the X_2-axis. It should be remembered that because of experimental error and possible lack of fit between the second-degree equation and the true surface the above interpretation is not necessarily correct for the true surface; therefore it must not be implied immediately that the true surface has a maximum or that it is at the point indicated. In practice further confirmatory trials would be performed about the maximum of the fitted surface, preferably in the directions of the axes of the fitted surface, and then followed by recalculation of the equation to include the extra information. (The methods of recalculation are given in [11·3] and [11·1].) Before such confirmatory trials can be planned the nature of the fitted surface must be appreciated, and it is with this that the present section is concerned.

A geometrical illustration of the fitted surfaces is also possible when there are three factors. Points on the contour surfaces can be obtained by methods analogous to that described, and if required these surfaces can be plotted by means of wire in a three-dimensional model, e.g. a wire cage. Another method is to plot sections in colour on *Perspex* sheets and layer these to form a series of shelves. For more than three factors geometrical illustration is not possible, and even with two or three factors location of the contours by the method outlined above could be exceedingly laborious. Fortunately it is not necessary to attempt this, for the second-degree equation can be reduced to a standard form (sometimes called the Canonical Form), which makes it possible to appreciate readily the nature of the fitted second-degree surface however many factors are involved, and to plot the contour lines or surfaces very easily in the two- and three-dimensional cases.

Consider Equation (*11·6*) and its representation in Figure 11·4. Suppose that instead of measuring the variables from O as origin a new origin is taken at the centre of the system at S, i.e. at the stationary point, and suppose also that instead of measuring the variables in the directions x_1 and x_2 they are measured in the directions of the principal axes denoted by X_1 and X_2. Then in these new co-ordinates the equation of the surface is of the form

$$Y - Y_S = B_{11}X_1{}^2 + B_{22}X_2{}^2 \dots\dots\dots\dots(11\cdot61)$$

where Y_S denotes the yield at the stationary point S. It is shown in § **11·53** that Equation (*11·6*) written in the form of Equation (*11·61*) is

$$Y - 81\cdot49 = -4\cdot35X_1{}^2 - 0\cdot96X_2{}^2 \dots\dots(11\cdot611)$$

and the centre of the system is at $x_1 = 0\cdot30$, $x_2 = -0\cdot16$.

Equation (*11·61*) may be interpreted as follows. The change in yield on moving away from the centre of the system S to some point whose co-ordinates are X_1 and X_2 is given by the expression on the right-hand side of the equation. In the example represented by Equation (*11·611*) the coefficients B_{11} and B_{22}

are both negative, and therefore there will always be a loss in yield whichever direction is taken from S; B_{11} measures the fall off in yield in the direction X_1, and B_{22} that in the direction X_2. Therefore for this example S is a true maximum of the fitted surfaces. In Figure 11·5 are shown examples of contour systems which are generated by second-degree equations in two variables and which might be found in a near stationary region. Four types of system can be distinguished, which may be used to represent a maximum, a stationary ridge, a rising ridge and a minimax.

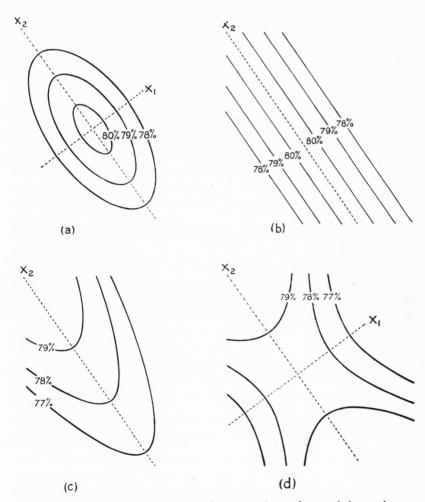

Fig. 11·5. Contour systems generated by equations of second degree in two variables

Type (a) is that discussed above; the coefficients B_{11} and B_{22} are both negative and the fitted contours are ellipses. When B_{22} is smaller in absolute value than B_{11} the contours will be elongated along the X_2-axis, as in the illustration.

Type (d) illustrates the system obtained when B_{11} is negative and B_{22} is positive; the fitted contours are hyperbolas. As in the previous case the relative magnitudes of these constants show the degree of elongation of the contours; in the example illustrated B_{22} would be smaller in absolute value than B_{11}.

Type (b) illustrates the system obtained when B_{11} is negative and B_{22} is zero, and it can be regarded as the limit of either type (a) or type (d) when the elongation in the direction of the X_2-axis is infinite. It really represents, mathematically, a transition stage between (a) and (d). There is no unique centre but a line of centres on the X_2-axis. The equation is of the form

$$Y - Y_S = B_{11}X_1{}^2$$

where Y_S is the response at any point on the X_2-axis.

Type (c) illustrates the system obtained when the centre is on the X_2-axis at infinity and B_{11} is negative; the fitted contours are parabolas. Taking as origin some convenient point on the X_2-axis, the equation is of the form

$$Y - Y_S = B_{11}X_1{}^2 + B_2X_2$$

The coefficient B_2 measures the rate of increase in the yield, i.e., the slope along the X_2-axis. This type can be regarded as a limiting case of either type (a) or type (d) when the centre is at infinity.

In experimental work, it is very unlikely that a fitted equation on reduction would be exactly either of type (b) or of type (c). Thus instead of finding that the coefficient B_{22} was exactly zero, indicating type (b), it would probably have some small positive or negative value. The resulting contours would be examples of either type (a) or type (d) elongated along the X_2-axis. Locally to the design the contours would appear to be of type (b) but with the lines slightly curved. Similarly, examples of type (c) would not occur; instead of the centre of the system being found to be at infinity, when the contours would be parabolas, the contours would be either of type (a) or of type (d), with the centre well outside the region of the design. It should be noted that the existence of a ridge, whether of type (b) or of type (c), is indicated when one of the coefficients B_{11} or B_{22} is found to have a small value.

It is important to remember that the fitted equation can be expected to supply an adequate approximation to the response surface only in the immediate neighbourhood of the design. The fitted equation is of no interest in other regions, where it may bear no resemblance to the response surface which is being approximated. For example, it is common to find, on analysis of the fitted second-degree equation, that a maximum is indicated remote from the region of the design but that the surface is elongated along an axis which passes close to the design. This indicates that the previous experimentation has brought the experimenter not to a maximum but close to a rising ridge. No conclusion about the position or even the existence of the remote maximum should be drawn, but attention should be focused on the local ridge and further experiments should be carried out along it.

When the axes of the fitted surface are inclined to the original co-ordinate axes and the surface is elongated along one of its axes, dependence is indicated between the variables; in other words, the point at which a maximum is obtained when x_1 is varied is not independent of the level of x_2. Where the interaction effect b_{12} is zero, X_1 and X_2 will be along the directions x_1 and x_2 and there will be no dependence between the variables. A non-zero value for b_{12}, although signifying that some dependence exists between the variables, does not indicate the extent of the dependence. To discover this it is necessary to estimate b_{11} and b_{22} also, and to reduce the resulting equation to canonical form.

Calculation of the canonical form

11·53. Having demonstrated for two factors the usefulness of the analysis of the fitted equation, the calculations involved in arriving at this form of the equation will be given in detail. A method of calculation will be used which can easily be generalised to the case where more factors are involved. The procedure is to calculate

(i) The position of S, the centre of the system of contours, and the value. Y_S of the response predicted at this point.

(ii) The values of B_{11} and B_{22}.

(iii) The directions of the axes X_1 and X_2.

11·531. The first step is then to find S, which is the point at which the response is stationary, that is to say, at which $\partial Y/\partial x_1$ and $\partial Y/\partial x_2$ are both zero. Thus for the example of § **11·52**, differentiating Equation (*11·6*) with respect to first x_1, then x_2, and equating the results to zero, the two equations to determine the point S are

$$7 \cdot 86x_1 + 2 \cdot 22x_2 = 1 \cdot 97$$
$$2 \cdot 22x_1 + 2 \cdot 76x_2 = 0 \cdot 22$$

The solution of these equations is $x_{1S} = 0 \cdot 30$, $x_{2S} = -0 \cdot 16$, which are the co-ordinates of S. Substitution of these values in Equation (*11·6*) gives $Y_S = 81 \cdot 49$.

11·532. The second step is to determine the values of the coefficients B_{11} and B_{22}. Consider the determinant

$$\begin{vmatrix} b_{11} - B & \tfrac{1}{2}b_{12} \\ \tfrac{1}{2}b_{12} & b_{22} - B \end{vmatrix} = \begin{vmatrix} -3 \cdot 93 - B & -1 \cdot 11 \\ -1 \cdot 11 & -1 \cdot 38 - B \end{vmatrix} \quad ..(11 \cdot 62)$$

The upper left-hand corner and the lower right-hand corner terms are $b_{11} - B$ and $b_{22} - B$ respectively, where b_{11} and b_{22} are the quadratic effects of the fitted equation and B is an unknown quantity. These are called the diagonal terms of the determinant, and the remaining terms the non-diagonal terms; the latter are equal to half the interaction effects. Multiplying out the right-hand determinant and equating the result to zero, what is called the Characteristic Equation is obtained. For this example this is given by

$$B^2 + 5 \cdot 31B + 4 \cdot 1913 = 0 \quad \dots \dots \dots \dots (11 \cdot 621)$$

The roots of this equation are $B = -4 \cdot 35$ and $-0 \cdot 96$. These are the values of the coefficients $B_{11} = -4 \cdot 35$ and $B_{22} = -0 \cdot 96$. The other alternative $B_{11} = -0 \cdot 96$ and $B_{22} = -4 \cdot 35$ could equally well have been taken. The result would only be to change the notation (the X_1-axis would have been called the X_2-axis, and vice versa).

The canonical form of the fitted second-degree Equation $(11 \cdot 6)$ is then

$$Y - 81 \cdot 49 = -4 \cdot 35X_1{}^2 - 0 \cdot 96X_2{}^2 \quad \dots \dots \dots \dots (11 \cdot 63)$$

At this stage of the calculation it is known that for some set of rectangular axes through S, Equation $(11 \cdot 6)$ can be expressed in the form $(11 \cdot 63)$. From the sign and relative magnitude of the coefficients B_{11} and B_{22}, and from the position of S, the type of surface to be dealt with will now be clear. It remains to determine the directions of the new axes X_1 and X_2.

11·533. Suppose the change of variables is given by the equations

$$\begin{aligned} X_1 &= m_{11}(x_1 - x_{1S}) + m_{12}(x_2 - x_{2S}) \\ X_2 &= m_{21}(x_1 - x_{1S}) + m_{22}(x_2 - x_{2S}) \end{aligned} \Bigg\} \quad \dots \dots (11 \cdot 64)$$

where the m's are to be determined. The transformation to be made is an orthogonal one, that is to say, the axes are to be rotated but they are to be kept at right angles.

The array of coefficients of Equations $(11 \cdot 64)$ is

$$\begin{matrix} m_{11} & m_{12} \\ m_{21} & m_{22} \end{matrix}$$

It can be shown that the transformation will only be orthogonal if for the above array of coefficients the sum of squares of the m's in any row or column is equal to unity and the sum of products of the m's in different rows or columns is zero. The m's are found for each equation of $(11 \cdot 64)$ in turn; m_{11} and m_{12} are solutions of the equations

$$\begin{aligned} 0 \cdot 42m_{11} - 1 \cdot 11m_{12} &= 0 \\ -1 \cdot 11m_{11} + 2 \cdot 97m_{12} &= 0 \end{aligned} \Bigg\} \quad \dots \dots \dots \dots (11 \cdot 641)$$

and m_{21} and m_{22} are solutions of the equations

$$\begin{aligned} -2 \cdot 97m_{21} - 1 \cdot 11m_{22} &= 0 \\ -1 \cdot 11m_{21} - 0 \cdot 42m_{22} &= 0 \end{aligned} \Bigg\} \quad \dots \dots \dots \dots (11 \cdot 642)$$

The coefficients of Equations (*11·641*) are the elements of the second determinant of (*11·62*) with $B_{11} = -4·35$ substituted for B, for example, $0·42 = -3·93 - (-4·35)$. In Equations (*11·642*) the coefficients are the elements of the determinant, but with $B_{22} = -0·96$ substituted for B. These equations do not allow the m's to be found explicitly, but numbers can be found to which they are proportional, as follows. In the first equation of (*11·641*) put $m_{11} = 1$, then $m_{12} = 0·42/1·11 = 0·378$; in the second equation put $m_{11} = 1$, then $m_{12} = 1·11/2·97 = 0·374$. To the degree of accuracy with which the calculations are made these values agree, as they should, and this provides a check on the accuracy of the calculated B's. Then m_{11} and m_{12} are proportional to the numbers 1 and 0·376 respectively. Their absolute values are found from the fact that for orthogonality $m_{11}{}^2 + m_{12}{}^2 = 1$. To ensure that this is so,

$$m_{11} = 1/\sqrt{(1^2 + 0·376^2)} = 0·936 \qquad m_{12} = 0·376/\sqrt{(1^2 + 0·376^2)} = 0·352$$

In a similar way it is found that $m_{21} = 0·352$ and $m_{22} = -0·936$.

Therefore the change of variables reducing Equation (*11·6*) to its canonical form (*11·63*) is given by

$$X_1 = 0·936(x_1 - 0·30) + 0·352(x_2 + 0·16)$$
$$X_2 = 0·352(x_1 - 0·30) - 0·936(x_2 + 0·16)$$

On the X_1-axis X_2 is zero, hence

$$0·352 (x_1 - 0·30) - 0·936(x_2 + 0·16) = 0$$

is the equation of the X_1-axis; likewise

$$0·936(x_1 - 0·30) + 0·352(x_2 + 0·16) = 0$$

is the equation of the X_2-axis. As already pointed out, these equations of the axes would be specially important when analysis of the fitted equation showed that a ridge occurred in the surface. The equation of the axis corresponding to the smaller B would be the equation of the ridge. For k variables the equations of the X_t-axis will be $X_1 = 0$, $X_2 = 0$, ..., $X_{t-1} = 0$, $X_{t+1} = 0$, ..., $X_k = 0$, since any point constrained by these equations can only move along the X_t-axis. Similarly the equations of the plane through the X_s and X_t axes will be $X_1 = 0$, $X_2 = 0$, ..., $X_k = 0$, where $X_s = 0$ and $X_t = 0$ are omitted.

An example showing a rising ridge

11·54. Before the general problem in several variables is discussed, a second example for two variables is described. In this example the centre of the fitted system is remote from the design.

Consider the fitted second-degree equation

$$Y - 60·64 = -3·672x_1 + 11·661x_2 - 3·514x_1{}^2 - 0·924x_2{}^2 + 2·220x_1x_2$$
$$\dots\dots\dots(11·7)$$

The co-ordinates of S and the predicted yield at this point are

$$x_{1S} = 2\cdot370, \; x_{2S} = 9\cdot157, \; Y_S = 109\cdot68\% \quad \ldots\ldots(11\cdot71)$$

The canonical form of equation $(11\cdot7)$ is

$$Y - 109\cdot68 = -3\cdot925X_1{}^2 - 0\cdot513X_2{}^2 \quad \ldots\ldots\ldots(11\cdot72)$$

and the transformation to X co-ordinates is given by

$$\left.\begin{array}{l} X_1 = 0\cdot938(x_1 - 2\cdot370) - 0\cdot348(x_2 - 9\cdot157) \\ X_2 = 0\cdot348(x_1 - 2\cdot370) + 0\cdot938(x_2 - 9\cdot157) \end{array}\right\} \quad \ldots\ldots(11\cdot73)$$

From Equation $(11\cdot72)$ the fitted contour surfaces are ellipses elongated along the X_2-axis and the stationary point S is a maximum. From the co-ordinates of the centre given in $(11\cdot71)$, however, S is remote from the centre of the design at O, and no conclusions about the nature of the surface in the neighbourhood of S can be drawn, since it is very unlikely that at such a remote point the fitted equation would have any relevance. In particular the predicted yield at this point is nearly 110%—obviously an impossible value. However the part of the fitted equation which is near to the design should provide a satisfactory approximation to the local surface, and it is this part of the surface that is of interest. Considering the problem now in terms of the co-ordinates X_1 and X_2 instead of x_1 and x_2, and substituting the values $x_1 = 0$, $x_2 = 0$, in $(11\cdot73)$, the centre O of the design is found to be at

$$X_1 = 0\cdot964 \qquad X_2 = -9\cdot414$$

Thus 0·964 and − 9·414 are the shortest distances of O from the X_2 and X_1 axes respectively, and it is seen that the X_2-axis passes close to O. Now because of the relatively small size of B_{22} it is known that the contours are drawn out along this axis. It is concluded, therefore, that the design has been performed close to a rising ridge, the direction of which is along the X_2-axis. The canonical form of the equation $(11\cdot72)$ is referred to a local origin on this nearby ridge, and this can be conveniently taken at

$$X_1 = 0 \qquad X_2 = -9\cdot414$$

the nearest point to O on the ridge, which is denoted by S'. Writing then

$$X_1{}' = X_1 \qquad X_2{}' = X_2 + 9\cdot414$$

and substituting in $(11\cdot72)$, the equation taking the origin at S' is

$$Y - 64\cdot22 = -3\cdot925X_1{}'^2 - 0\cdot513X_2{}'^2 + 9\cdot659X_2{}'$$

where 9·659 measures the slope up the ridge. The ridge is seen to be steeply rising, and the next experiment must explore the axis of this ridge $X_2{}'$ in the direction of increasing yield. The example approximates to type (c) in Figure 11·5.

The situation is illustrated in Figure 11·6. It should be noticed, however, that the nature of the system can be fully appreciated without resort to geometrical illustration. This is important because geometrical illustration is not possible in the general multi-variable case. Canonical reduction can, however, be undertaken however many variables exist and will often make it possible to understand the nature of complex systems.

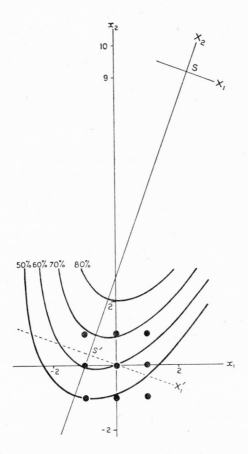

Fig. 11·6. Canonical reduction in the neighbourhood of a rising ridge in two variables

Exploration of the yield surface with several variables

11·6. The principles discussed for two variables may be applied equally well to three or more variables. Consideration is first given to designs suitable for determining the effects up to second order when there are k factors.

Designs to determine effects up to second order*

11·61. When effects up to second order are to be estimated for k factors, the complete three-level factorial designs (3^k) may be employed. Unfortunately, when k is greater than 2 the number of trials which such designs require often greatly exceeds the number of constants which it is desired to estimate. Consequently, when the experimental error is small and maximum economy in experiment is essential, 3^k designs are unsatisfactory. With four factors, for example, the factorial design involves $3^4 = 81$ trials, but the number of constants of second and lower order is only fifteen. These are:

Symbol	Interpretation	Order	Number
β_0	Response at the centre of the design	o	I
$\beta_1, \ldots, \beta_4$ ..	Linear effects	I	4
$\beta_{11}, \ldots, \beta_{44}$ ..	Quadratic effects	2	4
$\beta_{12}, \beta_{13}, \ldots, \beta_{34}$ ..	Interaction effects	2	6

Although the number of trials to be performed may be reduced by fractional replication, this device is much less effective in producing suitable arrangements with designs at three levels than with designs at two levels. For example, no satisfactory fractional replicate exists for four factors. For this reason alternative designs have been sought which will give estimates of all effects up to second order without necessitating a number of trials greatly in excess of the number of constants to be estimated. Designs of this sort which are particularly valuable for sequential experimentation are called Composite Designs, and their construction will now be discussed.

Composite designs

11·611. Composite designs to determine effects up to second order are built up from complete two-level factorials or fractional factorials. The procedure is first to choose a two-level design so that all effects of first order and all interaction effects of second order can be estimated. This design is then supplemented with further points which allow the estimation of the quadratic effects.

As an example, consider three factors. Here the 2^3 factorial provides the nucleus for the second-order design. If it can be assumed when using this two-level design that effects of order higher than the second can be ignored, then b_0 provides an estimate of $\beta_0 + \beta_{11} + \beta_{22} + \beta_{33}$; $b_1, b_2, b_3, b_{12}, b_{13}$, and b_{23} provide estimates of the corresponding β's, and b_{123} provides an estimate of experimental error. One effective arrangement to allow the separate estimation of β_{11}, β_{22}, and β_{33} is obtained by adding seven further points to

* A fuller discussion of the general problem for designs of order higher than the first will be found in [11·4] and [11·5].

the design, one at the centre and the remaining six in pairs along the co-ordinate axes at $\pm a_1$, $\pm a_2$, and $\pm a_3$ respectively. The design matrix is then given in Table 11·5.

Table 11·5

A THREE-FACTOR COMPOSITE DESIGN

Trial	Factor level		
	x_1	x_2	x_3
1	− 1	− 1	− 1
2	1	− 1	− 1
3	− 1	1	− 1
4	1	1	− 1
5	− 1	− 1	1
6	1	− 1	1
7	− 1	1	1
8	1	1	1
9	− a_1	0	0
10	a_1	0	0
11	0	− a_2	0
12	0	a_2	0
13	0	0	− a_3
14	0	0	a_3
15	0	0	0

The first eight points correspond to the 2^3 factorial, the next six are the axial points, while the last is the point at the centre. The resulting arrange-ment of experimental points is shown in Figure 11·7.

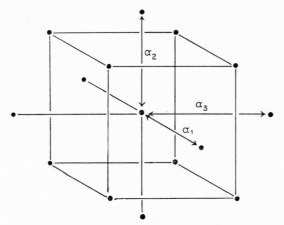

Fig. 11·7. A three-factor composite design

This way of constructing a composite design demonstrated for three factors may be applied for k factors. To the appropriate complete two-level factorial or fractional factorial are added $(2k + 1)$ supplementary points; one at the centre and the remaining $2k$ in pairs along the co-ordinate axes at $\pm a_1$, $\pm a_2, \ldots, \pm a_k$ respectively. Other types of composite design are described in [11·1].

One advantage of composite designs is that they allow the work to proceed naturally in stages. The first-order design can first be completed, then if it is found that the first-order effects are fairly large and the interaction effects of second order are small, the experimenter may proceed to a new base by means of the steepest ascent method. If on the other hand it appears from the relative magnitude of the effects of first order and the interaction effects of second order that it will be necessary to determine all second-order effects, then the extra points may be added to complete the composite design.

Orthogonal composite designs

11·612. In the composite designs constructed in § **11·611** for k factors, by taking $a_1 = a_2 = \ldots = a_k = a$ and suitably choosing a, an orthogonal design can be obtained. The manner in which these orthogonal composite designs are built up when the number of factors (k) is equal to 2, 3, 4, and 5 is outlined in Table 11·6.

Table 11·6

ORTHOGONAL COMPOSITE DESIGNS

Number of factors (k) ..	2	3	4	5
Basic two-level design ..	2^2	2^3	2^4	$\frac{1}{2}2^5$ $(x_1x_2x_3x_4x_5 = 1)$
Number of extra points $(2k + 1)$	5	7	9	11
Distance of axial points from centre (a)	1·000	1·215	1·414	1·547

In the second row of the table are shown the basic two-level designs forming the nuclei of the composite designs. These two-level designs are all complete factorials except the design for five factors, which is a half replicate of the complete 2^5 design having the defining relation $x_1x_2x_3x_4x_5 = 1$; this latter design can be written down by adding to the complete 2^4 factorial a new column $x_5 = x_1x_2x_3x_4$. In the fourth row the values of a are given which make the corresponding composite designs orthogonal. It will be noted that the orthogonal composite design for $k = 2$ is the same as the complete 3^2 factorial.

When the reduced number of trials required is allowed for, orthogonal composite designs compare favourably with the corresponding complete three-level factorials or fractional factorials.

Non-integral values for a do not give rise to any difficulty in practice. For example, suppose the three-factor orthogonal composite design given in Table 11·6 was used and one of the factors was temperature, and suppose that the levels corresponding to -1 and $+1$ in the design were 6.5° and 75° C. Then in the trial corresponding to the point $(a, 0, 0)$ of the design, where $a = -1·215$, the temperature would be adjusted to $70 - (5 \times 1·215)$, that is 63·9° C. to the nearest tenth, and the base levels would be used for the other two factors. It might be argued that the factors could not be controlled to the fine limits that appear to be required by the design. However, to the extent that it is possible to control the temperature at 70° C. it should be possible to control it at a level like 63·9° C.

Estimation of the coefficients of the second-degree equation

11·62. The following discussion is in terms of three factors when the second-degree equation to be fitted is

$$\eta = \beta_0 x_0 + \beta_1 x_1 + \beta_2 x_2 + \beta_3 x_3 + \beta_{11} x_1{}^2 + \beta_{22} x_2{}^2$$
$$+ \beta_{33} x_3{}^2 + \beta_{12} x_1 x_2 + \beta_{13} x_1 x_3 + \beta_{23} x_2 x_3 \quad \ldots . (11·8)$$

The procedure is perfectly general, and may be applied to designs with different numbers of factors.

Use of orthogonal composite designs

11·621. Each of the independent variables x_1, x_2, x_3, $x_1 x_2$, $x_1 x_3$, and $x_2 x_3$ of Equation $(11·8)$ when summed over the points of the design in Table 11·6 gives zero. Consequently, by the same argument as that employed in § 11·51 a slightly different form of the equation may be fitted which is more convenient for the present purpose. This is

$$\eta = \eta_0 x_0 + \beta_1 x_1 + \beta_2 x_2 + \beta_3 x_3 + \beta_{11} x_{11} + \beta_{22} x_{22}$$
$$+ \beta_{33} x_{33} + \beta_{12} x_1 x_2 + \beta_{13} x_1 x_3 + \beta_{23} x_2 x_3 \ldots . (11·81)$$

where $x_{11} = x_1{}^2 - \Sigma x_1{}^2 / n$, etc.

The estimates obtained by fitting Equation $(11·81)$ are the same as those which would be obtained by fitting Equation $(11·8)$, except that β_0 is estimated not directly, but from the relation

$$b_0 = \bar{y} - b_{11} \Sigma x_1{}^2 / n - b_{22} \Sigma x_2{}^2 / n - b_{33} \Sigma x_3{}^2 / n \quad \ldots \ldots (11·82)$$

In the table of independent variables corresponding to Equation $(11·81)$ and the design given in Table 11·6, the sum of products between any two columns is zero. Consequently the effects may be estimated as before simply by taking sums of products of the responses (the y's) with the elements of the appropriate independent variable and dividing by the sum of squares of the elements of the independent variable.

Use of non-orthogonal symmetrical composite designs

11·622. In the composite design described in § **11·611** it is not essential to choose the a's to fulfil the conditions for orthogonality or to have the a's all equal. By increasing the a's the variances of the estimates of the quadratic effects are reduced, but the estimates are correlated and the danger of possible bias from higher-order effects is increased. In order to get greater precision for the estimates of the quadratic effects larger values for the a's may be taken, but it would be unwise to take them as large as 3, since the magnitude of possible bias would then become serious.

In the general case, when the a's are not chosen to give orthogonality, the Least Square estimates of the β's and the standard errors are not found quite so readily. However, a degree of orthogonality still remains, and the estimates are obtained with no great difficulty. An account of the method of Least Squares and the simplifications which result from partial or complete orthogonality will be found in Appendix 11B. The procedure to be adopted in the present case will be outlined without a separate explanation of the theoretical background. It is convenient in the non-orthogonal designs to work with the original form of the second-degree equation, that is the form given in (*11·8*). If the table of independent variables corresponding to this form of the equation is written down, it will be found that whatever values are chosen for a_1, a_2, and a_3, sums of products between pairs of independent variables are all zero except those between x_0, x_1^2, x_2^2, and x_3^2. For this reason estimates of first-order effects and interaction effects and their variances may be obtained using Formulae (*11·3*) and (*11·31*) as before. For the remaining effects a set of four equations is obtained, the solutions of which give the estimates b_0, b_{11}, b_{22}, and b_{33}. (Correspondingly for k factors a set of $k+1$ equations will be obtained, the solutions of which give the estimates b_0, b_{11}, . . . , b_{kk}.) These may be written

$$\left. \begin{array}{l} C_{00}b_0 + C_{011}b_{11} + C_{022}b_{22} + C_{033}b_{33} = C_{y0} \\ C_{011}b_0 + C_{1111}b_{11} + C_{1122}b_{22} + C_{1133}b_{33} = C_{y11} \\ C_{022}b_0 + C_{1122}b_{11} + C_{2222}b_{22} + C_{2233}b_{33} = C_{y22} \\ C_{033}b_0 + C_{1133}b_{11} + C_{2233}b_{22} + C_{3333}b_{33} = C_{y33} \end{array} \right\} \dots (11\cdot83)$$

The coefficients in Equations (*11·83*) are the sums of products between pairs of the independent variables x_0, x_1^2, x_2^2, and x_3^2 and the response y. Thus, for example, C_{1122} is the sum of products between the variables x_1^2 and x_2^2; C_{y11} is the sum of products between the response y and the independent variable x_1^2, and so on.

The array of coefficients of Equations (*11·83*)

$$
\begin{array}{cccc}
C_{00} & C_{011} & C_{022} & C_{033} \\
C_{011} & C_{1111} & C_{1122} & C_{1133} \\
C_{022} & C_{1122} & C_{2222} & C_{2233} \\
C_{033} & C_{1133} & C_{2233} & C_{3333}
\end{array}
$$

is called the C-matrix. Equations (*11·83*) could be solved by straightforward elimination (or, for three or more equations, the method set out in § **11A·2** is more rapid and convenient, and possesses the great advantage that it is self-checking). It would be preferable in this case, however, not to solve the equations directly but to obtain what is called the Reciprocal of the C-matrix, denoted by C^{-1}.

This is an array of coefficients of the form

$$
\begin{array}{cccc}
C^{00} & C^{011} & C^{022} & C^{033} \\
C^{011} & C^{1111} & C^{1122} & C^{1133} \\
C^{022} & C^{1122} & C^{2222} & C^{2233} \\
C^{033} & C^{1133} & C^{2233} & C^{3333}
\end{array}
$$

The element of the reciprocal matrix C^{-1} in the position corresponding to the element C_{00} of the C-matrix is written C^{00}, and so on. The method for finding the Reciprocal of a Matrix is given in § **11A·3**. Once the reciprocal matrix has been calculated the solutions b_0, b_{11}, b_{22}, and b_{33} of Equations (*11·83*) are quickly found by taking the sum of products between the elements of the four columns of the reciprocal matrix C^{-1} and the elements of the column formed by the right-hand side terms of Equations (*11·83*). Thus

$$
b_0 = C^{00}C_{y0} + C^{011}C_{y11} + C^{022}C_{y22} + C^{033}C_{y33}
$$
$$
b_1 = C^{011}C_{y0} + C^{1111}C_{y11} + C^{1122}C_{y22} + C^{1133}C_{y33}
$$
$$
\text{etc.}
$$

The advantage of this method of calculation is that the reciprocal matrix, beside giving the b's, provides estimates of their standard errors. Quantities which multiply σ^2 to give the variance of the b's corresponding to the multipliers $1/\Sigma x^2$ in the orthogonal case are supplied by the diagonal elements of C^{-1}, while the non-diagonal elements yield the multipliers for the covariances. For example, $V(b_0) = C^{00}\sigma^2$, $V(b_{11}) = C^{1111}\sigma^2$, and $\text{Cov}(b_0 b_{11}) = C^{011}\sigma^2$.

A second advantage of solving Equations (*11·83*) using the reciprocal matrix is that when there are a number of responses to consider (for example, yield and purity) and it is desired to fit an equation to each response, C^{-1}, which is independent of y, may be calculated once for all, and from it the b's and $V(b)$'s for any number of responses may be obtained with very little labour.

The analysis of the fitted second-degree equation in k variables

11·63. When the second-degree equation has been fitted it is necessary to interpret it. As has been pointed out, by merely inspecting the coefficients in the second-degree equation it is not generally possible to obtain any clear idea of the nature of the surface it represents. Further, when the number of variables is greater than three, geometrical illustration is not possible. Canonical reduction will, however, in all cases make it possible to appreciate the meaning of the fitted equation and to indicate what further trials are required.

The relationship between the possible three-dimensional contour systems arising from second-degree equations and their corresponding canonical analysis repays careful study, for it makes it possible to interpret more readily the canonical analysis when the number of variables is greater than three.

Three-dimensional contour systems

11·64. Three-dimensional contour systems may be regarded as being generated from those in two dimensions. Conversely, systems in two dimensions are cross-sections of those in three dimensions. For example, the two-dimensional systems represented by (a), (b), (c), and (d) of Figure 11·5 and which are generated by second-degree equations in two variables are cross-sections of three-dimensional systems generated by second-degree equations in three variables. Some of the three-dimensional systems generated by second-degree equations are shown in Figure 11·8.

Point, line, and plane maxima. Stationary ridges

11·641. Figure 11·8 (A) shows a surface in which B_{11}, B_{22}, and B_{33} are all negative, the contour systems are ellipsoids, and there is a point maximum in the three variables.

In (B), B_{11} and B_{22} are negative and B_{33} is zero, the contour surfaces are elliptic cylinders, and the X_3-axis is a line maximum (i.e. a stationary or level ridge in one dimension). On this line a maximal response would be obtained, and departure from it in any direction would result in decreased response. There would thus be a range of alternative optimum processes, the various sets of optimum conditions being given by the equations defining the X_3-axis. In other words, the direction of the X_3-axis would define the changes to be made in the other variables if any single variable was changed in order that maximal response might be maintained.

In (C), B_{22} and B_{33} are both zero, the surface contains a plane maximum and the contour surfaces are planes running parallel to the plane containing the X_2- and X_3-axes. On this latter plane the response is maximal and falls off on either side. There is thus a very wide range of alternative optimum processes defined by the equation of the plane, which might be called a stationary ridge in two dimensions. In the canonical form of the equation B_{22} and B_{33} are both zero and B_{11} is negative. Both practical experience and theoretical considerations indicate that ridges of greater or less complexity are to be expected as a common feature of response surfaces in chemical work.

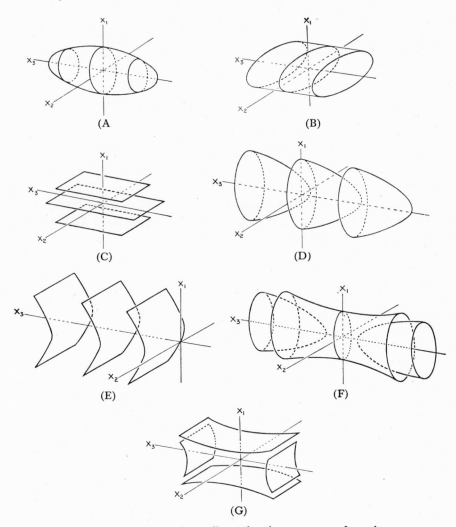

Fig. 11·8. Some possible three-dimensional contour surfaces in a near-stationary region

When a stationary ridge occurred, the experimenter using either the one-factor-at-a-time method or the steepest ascent technique alone would almost certainly arrive at some point on the ridge; the precise location of this point would depend chiefly on the starting point of his experiment. He would usually mistake this point for a unique maximum (since a change in level of any single variable from the conditions which he had found would be accompanied by a drop in response). It is unlikely that the point he reached would correspond to the most satisfactory or economical process, however, and in some cases great trouble might be taken to construct special apparatus to reproduce on a plant scale the conditions he had found when other much more easily attained conditions existed giving the same result.

When a line, plane, or space of near-optimum processes exists in the main response such as yield, the variation of other auxiliary responses such as purity may be examined on this maximum line, plane, or space, and that process chosen from among the alternative optimum processes which maximises the auxiliary response.

Rising ridges

11·642. In Figure 11·8 (D) the contour surfaces are elliptic paraboloids. The centre is at infinity and B_{33} is zero. Taking the origin on the X_3-axis, the second-degree equation can be reduced to the form

$$Y - Y_S = B_{11}X_1^2 + B_{22}X_2^2 + B_3X_3$$

where B_{11} and B_{22} are both negative, B_{33} is zero, and B_3 measures the slope up the X_3-axis. The system is a line ridge like (B), but the ridge is rising instead of stationary.

The system corresponding to (C), but representing a rising instead of a stationary ridge, is shown in (E).

The reader may examine for himself the remaining examples illustrated and may invent others for himself. He should consider what the practical implications of such surfaces would be with real variables like temperature, time, concentration, etc. He should also consider what characteristics the canonical form of the equation would have corresponding to each possibility.

Fitted surfaces met in practice

11·65. In general when one or more of the coefficients $B_{11}, B_{22}, \ldots, B_{kk}$ in the canonical form of the fitted second-degree equation are small compared with the others, some form of ridge system is indicated. If the centre of the system is in the immediate neighbourhood of the design the ridge system will be approximately stationary. When the centre of the system is remote from the neighbourhood of the design however it will normally be found (since first-order effects will already have been rendered small by application of the method of steepest ascent) that a rising ridge passes close to the neighbourhood of the design, and to determine its nature a new origin is chosen on the ridge. For example, if the coefficient B_{tt} is small compared with the others, then the X_t-axis defines a line ridge which for the reason given above will normally pass close to the neighbourhood of the design. A new origin is taken on the X_t-axis close to the design, and then the corresponding equation will contain a coefficient B_t which, if the centre is remote from the design, measures the slope up the ridge.

When two coefficients B_{tt} and B_{ss} are small compared with the others, the plane containing the axes X_t and X_s defines a plane ridge which will normally pass close to the design. A new origin is taken on this plane close to the design, and then the corresponding equation will contain coefficients B_t and B_s. If these coefficients are not small a rising ridge is indicated, the direction of greatest increase on it being found by the steepest ascent method.

An example of the exploration of a yield surface with three variables

11·7. The following example concerns a reaction of the type

$$A + B \rightarrow C + D$$

where two reactants, A and B, formed a mixture of C and D. The final product contained a mixture of C and D and unchanged A and B. The object was to obtain the maximum yield of C, subject to the condition that the amount of D should not exceed 20% (more than 20% of D would cause difficulties in purification).

A 2³ factorial design

11·71. The factors varied were temperature (T), initial concentration of A (c), and time of reaction (t), the starting quantity of B being kept constant throughout. Some previous work on the reaction had been carried out, and interactions between the factors were expected. Therefore a 2^3 factorial experiment was first performed, the levels chosen for the factors being those given in Table 11·7.

Table 11·7

FACTOR LEVELS FOR THE 2³ FACTORIAL EXPERIMENT

Factor		Factor level − 1	+ 1	Base level	Unit
T Temperature	° C.	142	152	147	5
c Concentration of A ..	%	35	40	37·5	2·5
t Time of reaction ..	hours	7	10	8·5	1·5

Thus, denoting the variables measured in units of the design by x_1, x_2, and x_3 respectively, then

$$x_1 = (T - 147)/5 \quad x_2 = (c - 37·5)/2·5 \quad x_3 = (t - 8·5)/1·5 \quad ..(11·9)$$

The 2^3 factorial design used in the experiment and the yields obtained are given in Table 11·71.

Table 11·71

THE 2^3 FACTORIAL DESIGN USED IN THE EXPERIMENT AND THE
YIELDS OBTAINED

Trial	Factor level			Yield of C (%)
	x_1	x_2	x_3	y
1	-1	-1	-1	55·9
2	-1	-1	1	63·3
3	-1	1	-1	67·5
4	-1	1	1	68·8
5	1	-1	-1	70·6
6	1	-1	1	68·0
7	1	1	-1	68·6
8	1	1	1	62·4

Applying Formulae (*11·3*) and (*11·31*), the following estimates were obtained:

$$b_0 \rightarrow \beta_0 + \beta_{11} + \beta_{22} + \beta_{33} = \quad 65·64 \pm 0·4$$
$$b_1 \rightarrow \beta_1 \quad\quad\quad\quad\quad = \quad 1·76 \pm 0·4$$
$$b_2 \rightarrow \beta_2 \quad\quad\quad\quad\quad = \quad 1·19 \pm 0·4$$
$$b_3 \rightarrow \beta_3 \quad\quad\quad\quad\quad = -0·01 \pm 0·4$$
$$b_{12} \rightarrow \beta_{12} \quad\quad\quad\quad = -3·09 \pm 0·4$$
$$b_{13} \rightarrow \beta_{13} \quad\quad\quad\quad = -2·19 \pm 0·4$$
$$b_{23} \rightarrow \beta_{23} \quad\quad\quad\quad = -1·21 \pm 0·4$$
$$b_{123} \rightarrow 0 \quad\quad\quad\quad\quad = \quad 0·31 \pm 0·4$$

The approximate standard errors of the b's are calculated on the assumption that the standard deviation of experimental error was about 1%, for which there was prior evidence. The three interaction effects are large compared with the first-order effects, and it is clear that little progress would be possible by the steepest ascent method. A further set of trials was performed, therefore, which in conjunction with the above design allowed all effects of first and second orders to be estimated, the assumption being made that effects of higher orders could be ignored.

Extra points to form a second-order composite design

11·72. The 2^3 factorial design was supplemented with extra points to complete a composite design. The procedure described in § **11·611** was adopted and seven further trials were performed, one at the centre of the design and the other six in pairs along the three co-ordinate axes all at a distance $a = 2$ from the centre. The levels for the factors employed in these extra trials are given in Table 11·72.

Table 11·72

FACTOR LEVELS FOR THE EXTRA TRIALS

Factor			Factor level		
			− 2	o	2
T Temperature	..	.. ° C.	137	147	157
c Concentration of A	..	%	32·5	37·5	42·5
t Time of Reaction	..	hours	5·5	8·5	11·5

The additional rows of the design are given in Table 11·73.

Table 11·73

THE EXTRA TRIALS FORMING A COMPOSITE DESIGN WITH THOSE
GIVEN IN TABLE 11·71 AND THE YIELDS OBTAINED

Trial	Factor level			Yield of C (%)
	x_1	x_2	x_3	y
9	o	o	o	66·9
10	2	o	o	65·4
11	− 2	o	o	56·9
12	o	2	o	67·5
13	o	− 2	o	65·0
14	o	o	2	68·9
15	o	o	− 2	60·3

In this composite design a was not chosen so that the design was completely orthogonal. However, as pointed out in § **11·622**, the estimates of the first-order effects and interaction effects are orthogonal to each other and also to the remaining estimates, and may therefore be obtained individually by the simple Formula (*11·3*). Also estimates of the variances of these b's are given by Formula (*11·31*).

The remaining estimates, b_0, b_{11}, b_{22}, and b_{33}, were obtained as solutions of the following set of equations, which corresponds to (*11·83*)

$$15b_0 + 16b_{11} + 16b_{22} + 16b_{33} = 976\cdot0$$
$$16b_0 + 40b_{11} + 8b_{22} + 8b_{33} = 1014\cdot3$$
$$16b_0 + 8b_{11} + 40b_{22} + 8b_{33} = 1055\cdot1$$
$$16b_0 + 8b_{11} + 8b_{22} + 40b_{33} = 1041\cdot9$$

For the reasons given in § **11·622**, these equations were best solved by finding the reciprocal C^{-1} of the matrix of coefficients C. This reciprocal matrix, found by the method described in § **11A·3**, is the following array of numbers:

$$\frac{1}{288} \begin{bmatrix} 224 & -64 & -64 & -64 \\ -64 & 26 & 17 & 17 \\ -64 & 17 & 26 & 17 \\ -64 & 17 & 17 & 26 \end{bmatrix}$$

The estimates of b_0, b_{11}, b_{22}, and b_{33} and their variances may now be easily obtained by the method given in § **11·622**, for example

$$b_0 = \frac{1}{288} \left[(976 \times 224) - (64 \times 1014\cdot3) - (64 \times 1055\cdot1) - (64 \times 1041\cdot9) \right]$$

and $V(b_0) = (224/288)\sigma^2$.

Taking σ^2 as equal to 1 unit, the standard error of b_0, which is the square root of $V(b_0)$, is equal to about 0·9.

Thus finally a complete set of estimates with their standard errors was obtained as follows:

$$
\begin{aligned}
b_0 &= 67\cdot711 \pm 0\cdot9 \\
b_1 &= 1\cdot944 \pm 0\cdot3 \\
b_2 &= 0\cdot906 \pm 0\cdot3 \\
b_3 &= 1\cdot069 \pm 0\cdot3 \\
b_{11} &= -1\cdot539 \pm 0\cdot3 \\
b_{22} &= -0\cdot264 \pm 0\cdot3 \\
b_{33} &= -0\cdot676 \pm 0\cdot3 \\
b_{12} &= -3\cdot088 \pm 0\cdot4 \\
b_{13} &= -2\cdot188 \pm 0\cdot4 \\
b_{23} &= -1\cdot212 \pm 0\cdot4
\end{aligned}
$$

The estimate of the residual mean square based on five degrees of freedom was 4·85; this was somewhat larger than would be expected if the fit were perfect, but not so large as to suggest that the second-degree approximation was seriously in error. If the fit were assumed perfect an estimate of the experimental error variance would be 4·85, and if this value were used instead of the value of 1 then the estimates of the standard deviations of the b's given above would each be multiplied by $\sqrt{4\cdot85} = 2\cdot20$.

Canonical analysis of the fitted equation

11·73. The fitted equation

$$Y = 67\cdot711 + 1\cdot944x_1 + 0\cdot906x_2 + 1\cdot069x_3 - 1\cdot539x_1{}^2 - 0\cdot264x_2{}^2$$
$$- 0\cdot676x_3{}^2 - 3\cdot088x_1x_2 - 2\cdot188x_1x_3 - 1\cdot212x_2x_3 \quad\ldots\ldots(11\cdot91)$$

was written in canonical form, following a procedure analogous to that adopted for the example with two factors in § **11·53**.

Determination of the centre of the system

11·731. The position of S, the centre of the system of contours represented by Equation $(11·91)$, is found by differentiating the right-hand side with respect to each of the variables x_1, x_2, and x_3 in turn and equating the results to zero. This gives a set of equations of the form

$$2b_{11}x_1 + b_{12}x_2 + b_{13}x_3 = -b_1$$
$$b_{12}x_1 + 2b_{22}x_2 + b_{23}x_3 = -b_2$$
$$b_{13}x_1 + b_{23}x_2 + 2b_{33}x_3 = -b_3$$

The values x_{1S}, x_{2S}, and x_{3S} which satisfy these equations are the co-ordinates of S. For k variables the equations will be exactly of the same type; on the left-hand side of the equations the diagonal coefficients equal twice the quadratic effects and the off-diagonal term coefficients equal the interaction effects, while the elements on the right-hand side equal minus the first-order effects. In the present example these equations are

$$3·078x_1 + 3·088x_2 + 2·188x_3 = 1·944$$
$$3·088x_1 + 0·528x_2 + 1·212x_3 = 0·906$$
$$2·188x_1 + 1·212x_2 + 1·352x_3 = 1·069$$

in which the signs have been changed on both sides to avoid repetition of minus signs.

These equations may be solved by straightforward elimination, but a more convenient and rapid method, especially when the number of factors is greater than three, is given in § **11A·2** of Appendix 11A, where the solution of the above equations is given as an example. In this way the co-ordinates of the stationary point S are found to be

$$x_{1S} = 0·060 \quad x_{2S} = 0·215 \quad x_{3S} = 0·501$$

and substituting these values in Equation $(11·91)$ the yield Y_S predicted at this point can be found. An equivalent but simpler formula for Y_S for k factors is

$$Y_S = b_0 + \tfrac{1}{2}b_1x_{1S} + \tfrac{1}{2}b_2x_{2S} + \ldots + \tfrac{1}{2}b_kx_{kS} \quad \ldots\ldots(11·92)$$

For the present example this formula gives $Y_S = 68·14$. Using Formula $(11·9)$, the co-ordinates* of the stationary point S in terms of the original variables are

$$T_S = 147·3° \text{ C.} \quad c_S = 38·04\% \quad t_S = 9·25 \text{ hours}$$

* The properties of confidence intervals for a stationary point calculated in this way are given in [11·6].

N2

The canonical form of the second-degree equation. Determination of the coefficients

11·732. Equation $(11·91)$ is now reduced to the canonical form

$$Y - Y_S = B_{11}X_1{}^2 + B_{22}X_2{}^2 + B_{33}X_3{}^2 \dots \dots \dots (11·93)$$

To find the coefficients B_{11}, B_{22}, and B_{33} the following characteristic equation must be solved:

$$f(B) = \begin{vmatrix} b_{11} - B & \tfrac{1}{2}b_{12} & \tfrac{1}{2}b_{13} \\ \tfrac{1}{2}b_{12} & b_{22} - B & \tfrac{1}{2}b_{23} \\ \tfrac{1}{2}b_{13} & \tfrac{1}{2}b_{23} & b_{33} - B \end{vmatrix} = 0 \dots \dots (11·94)$$

In general there will be three values of B which when subtracted from the diagonal terms in the manner shown above will cause the determinant to vanish. These three values will be B_{11}, B_{22}, and B_{33}. If the determinant were multiplied out it would be found that a cubic equation in B resulted:

$$f(B) = B^3 + \alpha B^2 + \beta B + \gamma = 0$$

where α, β, and γ are constants calculated from the known values b_{11}, b_{12}, etc.

In general, for k variables the characteristic equation will be a polynomial of degree k, the k roots of which will give the k values B_{11}, B_{22}, ..., B_{kk}. One method of procedure is to calculate the polynomial equation and determine the roots. This method was used in the example of § **11·532**, when $k = 2$, and it can be adopted also when $k = 3$ without undue labour; standard methods for the solution of the resulting cubic equation will be found in any good algebra book. The experimenter may frequently have to deal with examples in which k is greater than 3 however, when the method of direct solution becomes laborious.

For this reason a method is given in Appendix 11A which may be used conveniently for any value of k. This method is there illustrated for the present example, where k is only 3, in which particular case it is probably no quicker than the direct calculation and solution of the polynomial equation.

The roots are thus found to be

$$B_{11} = -3·190 \qquad B_{22} = -0·069 \qquad B_{33} = 0·780$$

Determination of the axes of the fitted second-degree surface

11·733. The orthogonal transformation which changes Equation $(11·91)$ to its canonical form is found using a procedure precisely similar to that used for the example with two variables in § **11·533**.

For example, the coefficients m_{11}, m_{12}, and m_{13} in the equation

$$X_1 = m_{11}(x_1 - x_{1S}) + m_{12}(x_2 - x_{2S}) + m_{13}(x_3 - x_{3S})$$

are provided by the solutions of the following equations:

$$- 1\!\cdot\!651m_{11} + 1\!\cdot\!544m_{12} + 1\!\cdot\!094m_{13} = 0$$
$$1\!\cdot\!544m_{11} - 2\!\cdot\!926m_{12} + 0\!\cdot\!606m_{13} = 0$$
$$1\!\cdot\!094m_{11} + 0\!\cdot\!606m_{12} - 2\!\cdot\!512m_{13} = 0$$

where the coefficients on the left-hand side are the elements of the determinant in *(11·94)* with $B_{11} = -3\!\cdot\!190$ substituted for B. These equations form a consistent set, and values for the m's may be obtained by substituting an arbitrary value for any one of them and then solving any two of the equations. The m's are then proportional to these values, the factor of proportionality being so chosen as to make the sum of squares of the coefficients unity. Thus, substituting $m_{13} = 1$ and solving the first two equations, m_{11}, m_{12}, and m_{13} are found to be proportional to 1·6906, 1·0992, and 1·0000. Dividing these values by the square root of their sum of squares, the required values are

$$m_{11} = 0\!\cdot\!7511 \qquad m_{12} = 0\!\cdot\!4884 \qquad m_{13} = 0\!\cdot\!4443$$

The solution of equations in which the coefficients are symmetrical about the diagonal can be accomplished more rapidly than the solution for non-symmetrical equations. Symmetry in the coefficients is ensured by omitting the equation in which the m given an arbitrary value occupies a position in the leading diagonal. Thus if $m_{13} = 1$ was substituted, the third equation would be omitted and the first two solved; or if $m_{12} = 1$ was substituted, the second equation would be omitted and the remaining two solved. The solution of only two equations in two unknowns is trivial, but when k is greater than three the corresponding set of symmetrical equations can be most conveniently solved by the method given in § **11A·2**.

Returning to the present example, the coefficients of the equations expressing X_2 and X_3 in terms of x_1, x_2, and x_3 are found by substituting the values of B_{22} and B_{33} respectively for B in the determinant of *(11·93)* and proceeding as above in the case of X_1. In this way the orthogonal transformation was found to be

$$\left. \begin{aligned} X_1 &= 0\!\cdot\!7511(x_1 - x_{1S}) + 0\!\cdot\!4884(x_2 - x_{2S}) + 0\!\cdot\!4443(x_3 - x_{3S}) \\ X_2 &= 0\!\cdot\!3066(x_1 - x_{1S}) + 0\!\cdot\!3383(x_2 - x_{2S}) - 0\!\cdot\!8897(x_3 - x_{3S}) \\ X_3 &= 0\!\cdot\!5848(x_1 - x_{1S}) - 0\!\cdot\!8044(x_2 - x_{2S}) - 0\!\cdot\!1044(x_3 - x_{3S}) \end{aligned} \right\} \quad ..(11\!\cdot\!95)$$

An important property of orthogonal transformations is that the reciprocal transformation by means of which the x's may be expressed in terms of the

X's is of exactly similar form with rows substituted for columns. Thus for the present example the reciprocal transformation is given by

$$
\left.\begin{aligned}
x_1 - x_{1S} &= 0{\cdot}7511X_1 + 0{\cdot}3066X_2 + 0{\cdot}5848X_3 \\
x_2 - x_{2S} &= 0{\cdot}4884X_1 + 0{\cdot}3383X_2 - 0{\cdot}8044X_3 \\
x_3 - x_{3S} &= 0{\cdot}4443X_1 - 0{\cdot}8897X_2 - 0{\cdot}1044X_3
\end{aligned}\right\}
\quad\ldots\ldots(11{\cdot}951)
$$

Interpretation of the results

11·74. The canonical form of Equation (*11·91*) is

$$
Y - 68{\cdot}14 = -3{\cdot}190X_1{}^2 - 0{\cdot}069X_2{}^2 + 0{\cdot}780X_3{}^2
$$

The coefficient B_{22} is negligible compared with the coefficient B_{11}, and B_{33} is not large and is probably not significantly different from zero. However B_{33} is positive and, if it were real, would indicate that increases would occur by moving away from S in either direction along the X_3-axis. A series of experiments along the X_3-axis, however, failed to show any such increase, in fact the yield was remarkably constant and near its maximum value. The information from these extra points was now included in the calculation, using a technique outside the scope of the present volume but described fully in [11·1] and [11·3]. This recalculation showed* (as was to be expected from the experimental results) that not only B_{22} but also B_{33} was negligibly small compared with B_{11}, which was not greatly affected in magnitude by the addition of the extra information.

Approximately therefore, assuming B_{22} and B_{33} to be negligibly small, the canonical form of the equation is

$$
Y - 68{\cdot}14 = -3{\cdot}190X_1{}^2
$$

$$
\text{or}\qquad X_1 = \pm\sqrt{\left(\frac{Y - 68{\cdot}14}{-3{\cdot}190}\right)}
$$

This equation defines pairs of parallel planes on which the yield is Y. Putting in the value $Y_S = 68{\cdot}14$ it is seen that there is a plane $X_1 = 0$ on which the yield is maximal at approximately 68%. From the first equation of the set (*11·95*) the equation of this plane referred to the x-co-ordinates is therefore

$$
0{\cdot}7511(x_1 - x_{1S}) + 0{\cdot}4884(x_2 - x_{2S}) + 0{\cdot}4443(x_3 - x_{3S}) = 0
$$

or using (*11·9*) it is given in the original co-ordinates by

$$
0{\cdot}1502T + 0{\cdot}1954c + 0{\cdot}2962t = 32{\cdot}30 \ldots\ldots\ldots(11{\cdot}96)
$$

Equation (*11·96*) defines approximately the sets of alternative conditions giving the same maximum yield. It should be remembered that only locally to the experimental design can this approximation be expected to apply. In

---

* This example is discussed more fully in [11·7].

Figure 11·9 are shown this maximal plane and the corresponding planes for
$Y = 60$. From the figure the nature of the dependence between the variables
is apparent. This example is a situation in which a change in any one or two
of the variables, temperature, concentration, or time, can be compensated by
a suitable change in level of the other variables.*

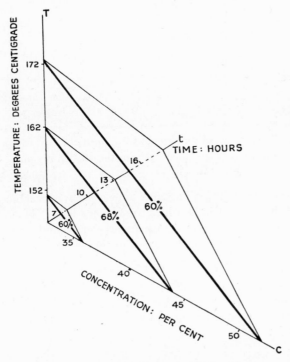

Fig. 11·9. Near-stationary plane (yield about 68%) with accompanying 60%
contour planes

The alternative sets of conditions giving about the same yield can be shown
most conveniently by Figure 11·91. This diagram represents the plane of
maximum yield, and the straight lines ruled across it are the lines of inter-
section of the planes $T = 147°$ C., $T = 152°$ C., $c = 37·5\%$, $c = 40\%$, etc.

Choice of conditions
11·741. As stated at the beginning of § **11·7**, the object of the experiment was
to obtain the maximum yield of C, subject to the condition that the yield of

* A discussion of how the characteristics of this surface are linked to the possible
physical mechanism of this reaction is given in [11·8].

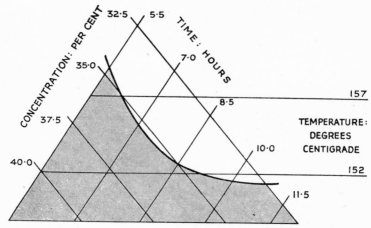

Fig. 11·91. Plane of maximum yield of C (approximately 68%). The yield of D is greater than 20% in the shaded region.

D should not exceed 20%. Therefore an analysis was next undertaken for the yield of the by-product D, which was denoted by z. The main purpose here was to find the region of the maximum plane found for y on which Z was less than 20%. The second-degree equation fitted was

$$Z = 18{\cdot}379 + 5{\cdot}150x_1 + 2{\cdot}362x_2 + 2{\cdot}188x_3 + 0{\cdot}728x_1{}^2 + 0{\cdot}103x_2{}^2$$
$$+ 1{\cdot}303x_3{}^2 + 2{\cdot}175x_1x_2 + 2{\cdot}075x_1x_3 + 1{\cdot}300x_2x_3$$

This equation was expressed in terms of the X-variables, using the transformation (11·951); then putting $X_1 = 0$ and $Z = 20$, the resulting equation was

$$- 0{\cdot}855 = - 0{\cdot}319X_2 + 0{\cdot}972X_3 + 0{\cdot}380X_2{}^2 - 0{\cdot}712X_3{}^2 + 0{\cdot}079X_2X_3$$

This equation defines the boundary of the "20% or more" region for Z on the maximum plane for y, and this boundary is drawn in Figure 11·91.

Conditions of the variables could then be chosen for which a maximum yield of approximately 68% was obtained for y, while the yield of z was kept less than 20%.

Discussion of the example
11·75. Using a modest number of experimental points it has been possible to obtain a great deal of information about a time, temperature, concentration system.

The conclusions drawn were not expected to be exact, and it was necessary to confirm them with further experiments performed about the predicted ridge; in particular to ensure that the ridge found was really stationary and not slowly rising. So far as the experimental region of interest was concerned, these experiments showed this to be approximately true although, as might have been expected, the surface on which the yield was nearly stationary had some slight curvature.

General conclusions

11·8. In investigations of the sort discussed here, methods of sequential experimentation are required in which the results from one set of experiments lead to decisions as to what experiments should be performed next.

Having performed a set of experiments in a given sub-region, it may appear:

(i) That the effects are not determined with sufficient accuracy for reliable conclusions to be drawn.

In such a situation the experimenter may replicate (or if the design is a fractional replicate he may perform a second fraction of the whole); alternatively it may be advisable to choose wider ranges for the factors, arranging the design so that higher-order effects, necessary in this larger region, can be determined.

(ii) That the effects are determined with sufficient accuracy and that first-order effects are dominant in the sub-region considered.

In this event the method of steepest ascent may be used to decide in which direction to perform the next set of experiments.

(iii) That the effects are determined with sufficient accuracy and that first-order effects are probably not large in comparison with those of second order.

Here the experimenter should if necessary add further points to the basic design so that all effects of second order may be determined, and subsequent action will be decided by considering the canonical equation of the fitted surface.

When as a result of (iii) additional experiments are performed close to the main design, a recalculation of the constants including this information can most conveniently be made by the method of [11·3].

For information on the latter topics the reader is referred to the original papers.

REFERENCES

[11·1] Box, G. E. P., and WILSON, K. B. "On the Experimental Attainment of Optimum Conditions." *J. Roy. Stat. Soc.*, B, **13**, 1 (1951).

[11·2] Box, G. E. P. "Multi-factor Designs of First Order." *Biometrika*, **39**, 49 (1952).

[11·3] PLACKETT, R. L. "Some Theorems in Least Squares." *Ibid.*, **37**, 149 (1950).

[11·4] Box, G. E. P., and HUNTER, J. S. "Multifactor Designs." Report prepared under Office of Ordnance Contract No. DA-36-034-ORD-1177 (RD) (1954).

(*Continued on page* 578)

SOLUTION OF LINEAR EQUATIONS. INVERSION OF MATRICES. CALCULATION OF DETERMINANTS

Introduction

11A·1. In order to concentrate attention on the principles of the experimental methods, the discussion of details of calculations have been avoided in the chapter as far as possible. For the same reason only examples with not more than three variables were considered. The reader who has mastered the examples given should find no difficulty in extending the procedures to additional variables. When dealing with linear equations and determinants for more than three variables it is an advantage to follow the set schemes devised for this purpose. The reader should note particularly the arrangement of the letters in the scheme as this assists in the use of the schemes for fewer variables and their extension to a larger number.

Solution of linear equations

11A·2. To apply the methods described in Chapter 11 it is necessary to solve sets of linear equations of the form

$$\left.\begin{array}{l} az_1 + bz_2 + dz_3 + gz_4 = A \\ bz_1 + cz_2 + ez_3 + hz_4 = C \\ dz_1 + ez_2 + fz_3 + iz_4 = F \\ gz_1 + hz_2 + iz_3 + jz_4 = \mathcal{J} \end{array}\right\} \quad \ldots\ldots\ldots\ldots(11A\cdot1)$$

where $a, b, c, \ldots, j$ and A, C, F, and $\mathcal{J}$ are known quantities and z_1, z_2, z_3, and z_4 are the unknowns to be determined. The methods will be illustrated in terms of the four equations $(11A\cdot1)$, but no difficulty will be experienced in extending the methods to p equations in p unknowns.

It will be noted that the coefficients on the left-hand sides of the equations are symmetrical about the diagonal elements a, c, f, and j, and advantage is taken of this property in the computation. Equations of this type occur

(i) In the estimation of the effects by the method of Least Squares (see Appendix 11B). Here the coefficients $a, b, \ldots, j$ are the sums of squares and products of the independent variables, while A, C, F, and $\mathcal{J}$ are the sums of products of the independent variables and the observed response. The unknowns (z's) are b_0, b_1, b_2, etc., the estimates of the effects.

(ii) In the calculation of the position of the centre S of the contours generated by the second degree equation (for example § **11·731**).

Here a, b, etc., are the quantities $2b_{11}$, b_{12}, etc., A, C, F, and $\mathcal{J}$ are the quantities $- b_1$, $- b_2$, etc., and the unknowns (z's) are the co-ordinates x_1, x_2, etc., of the centre S.

(iii) In the calculation of the transformation giving the new co-ordinates (X's) in terms of the old (x's). Here the unknowns (z's) are the coefficients m_{11}, m_{12}, etc., while the coefficients $a, b, \ldots, j$ are obtained from the second-order estimates and the quantities B_{11}, B_{22}, etc., in the manner described in § 11·733.

When there are only two equations they can be solved by the straight-forward elimination method. For a large number of equations this method is extremely laborious, and for three or more equations the following routine should be followed. It is an elimination method reduced to its most compact form. It can be made completely self-checking, and it is particularly valuable when used with a calculating machine.

The form of the computation is set out below, followed by an explanation.

Table 11A·1

SOLUTION OF LINEAR EQUATIONS

						S	
a	b	d	g	A	(A)	s_1	
b	c	e	h	C	(C)	s_2	
d	e	f	i	F	(F)	s_3	
g	h	i	j	$\mathcal{J}$	$(\mathcal{J})$	s_4	
						S	
a	**b**	**d**	**g**	**A**		s_1	a^{-1}
	c	**e**	**h**	**C**		s_2	c^{-1}
		f	**i**	**F**		s_3	f^{-1}
			j	**J**		s_4	j^{-1}
z_1	z_2	z_3	z_4				

The quantities $a, b, \ldots, j$ and A, C, F, and $\mathcal{J}$ are first written out in a rectangular array and an "S check" column is added on the right. The elements in this column are simply the sums of the successive rows of coefficients, e.g.

$$s_1 = a + b + d + g + A$$

and are included solely to provide a running check on the computation. A second array of numbers denoted by bold sans-serif type is now calculated row by row from the first array in accordance with the following scheme.

Row 1*

Enter, in the positions shown, $\boldsymbol{a} = \sqrt{a}$ and $\boldsymbol{a}^{-1}$, then calculate and enter $\boldsymbol{b} = b\boldsymbol{a}^{-1}$, $\boldsymbol{d} = d\boldsymbol{a}^{-1}$, $\boldsymbol{g} = g\boldsymbol{a}^{-1}$, $\boldsymbol{A} = A\boldsymbol{a}^{-1}$, and $\boldsymbol{s_1} = s_1\boldsymbol{a}^{-1}$ in succession.
Confirm S check:

$$\boldsymbol{a} + \boldsymbol{b} + \boldsymbol{d} + \boldsymbol{g} + \boldsymbol{A} = \boldsymbol{s_1}$$

Row 2

Enter $\boldsymbol{c} = \sqrt{(c - b^2)}$, then $\boldsymbol{c}^{-1}$, followed by $\boldsymbol{e} = (e - bd)\boldsymbol{c}^{-1}$, $\boldsymbol{h} = (h - bg)\boldsymbol{c}^{-1}$, $\boldsymbol{C} = (C - bA)\boldsymbol{c}^{-1}$, and $\boldsymbol{s_2} = (s_2 - bs_1)\boldsymbol{c}^{-1}$ in succession.
Confirm S check:

$$\boldsymbol{c} + \boldsymbol{e} + \boldsymbol{h} + \boldsymbol{C} = \boldsymbol{s_2}$$

Row 3

Enter $\boldsymbol{f} = \sqrt{(f - d^2 - e^2)}$, then $\boldsymbol{f}^{-1}$, followed by $\boldsymbol{i} = (i - dg - eh)\boldsymbol{f}^{-1}$, $\boldsymbol{F} = (F - dA - eC)\boldsymbol{f}^{-1}$, and $\boldsymbol{s_3} = (s_3 - ds_1 - es_2)\boldsymbol{f}^{-1}$
Confirm S check:

$$\boldsymbol{f} + \boldsymbol{i} + \boldsymbol{F} = \boldsymbol{s_3}$$

Row 4

Enter $\boldsymbol{j} = \sqrt{(j - g^2 - h^2 - i^2)}$, then $\boldsymbol{j}^{-1}$, followed by $\boldsymbol{J} = (\mathcal{J} - gA - hC - iF)\boldsymbol{j}^{-1}$, and $\boldsymbol{s_4} = (s_4 - gs_1 - hs_2 - is_3)\boldsymbol{j}^{-1}$
Confirm S check:

$$\boldsymbol{j} + \boldsymbol{J} = \boldsymbol{s_4}$$

The unknown z's are now obtained in succession as follows:

$$z_4 = \boldsymbol{J}\boldsymbol{j}^{-1}$$
$$z_3 = (\boldsymbol{F} - \boldsymbol{i}z_4)\boldsymbol{f}^{-1}$$
$$z_2 = (\boldsymbol{C} - \boldsymbol{h}z_4 - \boldsymbol{e}z_3)\boldsymbol{c}^{-1}$$
$$z_1 = (\boldsymbol{A} - \boldsymbol{g}z_4 - \boldsymbol{d}z_3 - \boldsymbol{b}z_2)\boldsymbol{a}^{-1}$$

The z's are entered in the positions indicated and a final check is obtained by substituting them in the equations. The calculated values A, C, F, and $\mathcal{J}$ of the right-hand sides of the equations should agree closely with the actual values A, C, F, and $\mathcal{J}$.

In practice it will be found that the above routine is much simpler than it at first appears, since it follows a regular and easily remembered pattern. The method is illustrated in the following example, taken from § **11·731**. The co-ordinates of the centre S are the solutions of the following equations:

$$\left.\begin{array}{l} 3{\cdot}078x_1 + 3{\cdot}088x_2 + 2{\cdot}188x_3 = 1{\cdot}944 \\ 3{\cdot}088x_1 + 0{\cdot}528x_2 + 1{\cdot}212x_3 = 0{\cdot}906 \\ 2{\cdot}188x_1 + 1{\cdot}212x_2 + 1{\cdot}352x_3 = 1{\cdot}069 \end{array}\right\} \quad \dots\dots\dots(11A{\cdot}2)$$

---

* For convenience in printing the symbol $\boldsymbol{a}^{-1}$ will be used for $1/\boldsymbol{a}$ throughout.

The calculation is set out as follows.

Table 11A·2

SOLUTION OF EQUATIONS *11A·2*

					S	
3·078	3·088	2·188	1·944	(1·9440)	10·298	
3·088	0·528	1·212	0·906	(0·9060)	5·734	
2·188	1·212	1·352	1·069	(1·0690)	5·821	
					S	
1·75442	1·76013	1·24714	1·10806		5·86976	0·56999
	1·60314*i*	0·61326*i*	0·65143*i*		2·86785*i*	−0·62378*i*
		0·41561	0·20834		0·62397	2·40610
0·05995	0·21459	0·50129				

The solutions of Equations (*11A·2*) are thus found to be

$$x_1 = 0{\cdot}0599; \quad x_2 = 0{\cdot}2146; \quad x_3 = 0{\cdot}5013 \quad \ldots \ldots (11A{\cdot}3)$$

to four-decimal accuracy.

It will be noticed in the above example that at one stage in the calculation it was required to take the square root of a negative number, and this was made possible by introducing the symbol i, which satisfies the relation $i^2 = -1$, or $i = \sqrt{-1}$, and $1/i = -i$. The calculation then proceeded as before, replacing i^2 by -1 wherever it occurred. This is the procedure to be adopted in general.

Inversion of matrices

11A·3. If all that is required is the solution of a single set of equations, the method described above is most rapid and convenient. However, as was mentioned in § **11·622**, it is sometimes convenient to solve equations indirectly by first calculating from the matrix of coefficients on the left-hand sides of the equations a second matrix, called the reciprocal matrix. This reciprocal matrix may be defined as follows.

Suppose that instead of solving the set of equations (*11A·1*) the following four sets of equations are solved.

$$\begin{matrix} & (1) & (2) & (3) & (4) \end{matrix}$$

$$\left. \begin{aligned} aZ_1 + bZ_2 + dZ_3 + gZ_4 &= 1 \quad 0 \quad 0 \quad 0 \\ bZ_1 + cZ_2 + eZ_3 + hZ_4 &= 0 \quad 1 \quad 0 \quad 0 \\ dZ_1 + eZ_2 + fZ_3 + iZ_4 &= 0 \quad 0 \quad 1 \quad 0 \\ gZ_1 + hZ_2 + iZ_3 + jZ_4 &= 0 \quad 0 \quad 0 \quad 1 \end{aligned} \right\} \ \ldots \ldots (11A{\cdot}4)$$

These sets of equations have the same coefficients on the left-hand side as (*11A·1*), but the elements $A, C, F,$ and $\mathcal{J}$ on the right-hand side are replaced for the first set by $1, 0, 0, 0$ (the elements of column (1)), for the second set by $0, 1, 0, 0$ (the elements of column (2)), and so on for the third and fourth sets.

It will be found that if the solutions of the first set of equations are denoted by $Z_1 = A'$, $Z_2 = B'$, $Z_3 = D'$, and $Z_4 = G'$, then the solutions of the second set can be written $Z_1 = B'$, $Z_2 = C'$, $Z_3 = E'$, and $Z_4 = H'$, where Z_1 of the second set is the same as Z_2 of the first set, and so on. The four sets of solutions may be arranged in a table as follows:

	Z_1	Z_2	Z_3	Z_4
(i)	A'	B'	D'	G'
(ii)	B'	C'	E'	H'
(iii)	D'	E'	F'	I'
(iv)	G'	H'	I'	$\mathcal{J}'$

The matrix

$$\begin{matrix} A' & B' & D' & G' \\ B' & C' & E' & H' \\ D' & E' & F' & I' \\ G' & H' & I' & \mathcal{J}' \end{matrix}$$

is called the reciprocal (or inverse) of the matrix

$$\begin{matrix} a & b & d & g \\ b & c & e & h \\ d & e & f & i \\ g & h & i & j \end{matrix}$$

and the process of calculating one from the other is referred to as matrix inversion. If, as is the case for Equations $(11A \cdot 1)$, the matrix of coefficients for the left-hand side of the equations is symmetrical, then so will be its reciprocal matrix. The solution of any set of equations like $(11A \cdot 1)$ with elements A, C, F, and $\mathcal{J}$ on the right-hand side can be obtained immediately from the reciprocal matrix as follows:

$$\left. \begin{aligned} z_1 &= A'A + B'C + D'F + G'\mathcal{J} \\ z_2 &= B'A + C'C + E'F + H'\mathcal{J} \\ z_3 &= D'A + E'C + F'F + I'\mathcal{J} \\ z_4 &= G'A + H'C + I'F + \mathcal{J}'\mathcal{J} \end{aligned} \right\} \quad \cdots\cdots\cdots (11A \cdot 5)$$

If it is required to solve several sets of equations like $(11A \cdot 1)$ which have identical coefficients on the left but different values for A, C, F, and $\mathcal{J}$ on the right, this is best done by first calculating the reciprocal matrix of the matrix of coefficients on the left of the equations and then using Equations $(11A \cdot 5)$ to give the various sets of solutions. The calculation of the reciprocal matrix is particularly useful in the solution of the Normal equations (see Appendix 11B) which arise in the methods of Least Squares, for in this case the elements of the matrix are proportional to the variances and covariances of the estimates which are usually required in any case. Thus by solving the Normal equations using the reciprocal matrix, quantities required to give the standard errors and degree of correlation between the estimates are also obtained.

A rapid self-checking method similar to that used above in § **11A·2** for obtaining single solutions of linear equations is described later whereby the reciprocal matrix can be found without explicitly solving Equations (*11A·4*). This is usually the best method to employ. Occasionally, however, the coefficients are such that the equations readily simplify, and the reciprocal matrix can be most easily found from first principles.

An example occurs in § **11·72**, where it is required to find the reciprocal of the matrix of coefficients

$$
\begin{array}{cccc}
15 & 16 & 16 & 16 \\
16 & 40 & 8 & 8 \\
16 & 8 & 40 & 8 \\
16 & 8 & 8 & 40
\end{array}
$$

The sets of equations corresponding to (*11A·4*) are

$$
\begin{array}{cccc}
 & (1) & (2) & (3) & (4)
\end{array}
$$

$$
\begin{aligned}
15Z_1 + 16Z_2 + 16Z_3 + 16Z_4 &= 1 & 0 & 0 & 0 \\
16Z_1 + 40Z_2 + 8Z_3 + 8Z_4 &= 0 & 1 & 0 & 0 \\
16Z_1 + 8Z_2 + 40Z_3 + 8Z_4 &= 0 & 0 & 1 & 0 \\
16Z_1 + 8Z_2 + 8Z_3 + 40Z_4 &= 0 & 0 & 0 & 1
\end{aligned}
$$

If half the first equation is subtracted from each of the others, the new sets of equations obtained are

$$
\begin{array}{cccc}
 & (1) & (2) & (3) & (4)
\end{array}
$$

$$
\begin{aligned}
\text{(i)} \quad & 15Z_1 + 16Z_2 + 16Z_3 + 16Z_4 & = & \;\;1 & 0 & 0 & 0 \\
\text{(ii)} \quad & 8{\cdot}5Z_1 + 32Z_2 & = & -\tfrac{1}{2} & 1 & 0 & 0 \\
\text{(iii)} \quad & 8{\cdot}5Z_1 \qquad\quad + 32Z_3 & = & -\tfrac{1}{2} & 0 & 1 & 0 \\
\text{(iv)} \quad & 8{\cdot}5Z_1 \qquad\qquad\quad + 32Z_4 & = & -\tfrac{1}{2} & 0 & 0 & 1
\end{aligned}
$$

Consider the set of equations obtained by taking column (1) on the right-hand side. It is evident from Equations (ii), (iii), and (iv) that for this set of solutions $Z_2 = Z_3 = Z_4$. Consequently $B' = D' = G'$ and Equations (i) and (ii) may be rewritten:

$$
\begin{aligned}
15A' + 48B' &= 1 \\
8{\cdot}5A' + 32B' &= -\tfrac{1}{2}
\end{aligned}
$$

from which $A' = 7/9$, $B' = D' = G' = -2/9$.

From the set of equations obtained by taking column (2) on the right-hand side it will be seen that Equations (ii), (iii), and (iv) may be rewritten as

$$
\begin{aligned}
8{\cdot}5B' + 32C' &= 1 \\
8{\cdot}5B' + 32E' &= 0 \\
8{\cdot}5B' + 32H' &= 0
\end{aligned}
$$

Since $B' = -2/9$, then $C' = 13/144$, and $E' = H' = 17/288$. On considering the two sets of equations obtained by taking columns (3) and (4) on the right-hand side it is seen that the coefficients and hence the solutions of the equations are the same as those obtained with column (2) except that the order is changed, so that finally the reciprocal matrix is

$$\frac{1}{288}\begin{bmatrix} 224 & -64 & -64 & -64 \\ -64 & 26 & 17 & 17 \\ -64 & 17 & 26 & 17 \\ -64 & 17 & 17 & 26 \end{bmatrix}$$

The notation used here implies that each number within the brackets is to be divided by 288, and then the resulting array of numbers is the reciprocal matrix.

In the general case, in which the equations do not simplify, a routine is used which follows closely the computation already described in § **11A·2** for obtaining single solutions of linear equations. This calculation of the reciprocal matrix can best be set out as follows.

Table 11A·3

CALCULATION OF RECIPROCAL MATRIX

					S
	a	b	d	g	s_1
	b	c	e	h	s_2
	d	e	f	i	s_3
	g	h	i	j	s_4
					S
s_8	$A'a$	$B'b$	$D'd$	$G'g$	s_1	a^{-1}
s_7	B'	$C'c$	$E'e$	$H'h$	s_2	c^{-1}
s_6	D'	E'	$F'f$	$I'i$	s_3	f^{-1}
s_5	G'	H'	I'	$J'j$	s_4	j^{-1}
	s_1	s_2	s_3	s_4		

The matrix to be inverted is written down together with the sums s_1, s_2, s_3 and s_4 of the rows, which are entered on the right of the matrix in the column marked S. For a reason to be explained later, the same values s_1, s_2, s_3, and s_4 are copied immediately below where the last row G', H', I', J' of the reciprocal matrix is due to appear. The triangular array a, b, d, etc., is next written down, following exactly the procedure already described in § **11A·2** for the solution of linear equations. In fact, this first stage in the calculation is identical with that in § **11A·2** but with the elements A, C, F, and J omitted. The S check is applied as each row is computed, exactly as before. From the elements of this triangular array the elements of the reciprocal matrix may be obtained immediately. These are calculated in order from right to left, starting at the bottom row. As each row is completed it is checked by calculating the sum of products of the elements of the row with s_1, s_2, s_3, and s_4, which have been placed below the matrix for this purpose. It will be seen from Equations (11A·4), which define the reciprocal matrix, that the sum of products between any row or column of the original matrix and the corresponding row or column of the reciprocal matrix must be unity, while the sum of products of any row or column in the original matrix with any other row or column in the reciprocal matrix must be zero. It follows that the sum of products of any row of the reciprocal matrix with the row of elements s_1, s_2, s_3, and s_4 must be equal to unity if the calculation is correct. Therefore as each row of the reciprocal matrix is derived this check is carried out. The sums of products of the check are entered as s_5, s_6, s_7, and s_8 in a column on the left. The calculation follows an easily remembered routine, as follows.

Row 4

Enter in turn the following elements:

$$J' = j^{-1}j^{-1}$$
$$I' = \quad (-J'i)f^{-1}$$
$$H' = \quad (-J'h - I'e)c^{-1}$$
$$G' = \quad (-J'g - I'd - H'b)a^{-1}$$

Check:

$$G's_1 + H's_2 + I's_3 + J's_4 = 1$$

Row 3

Copy I' in its other position, and then enter:

$$F' = (f^{-1} - I'i)f^{-1}$$
$$E' = \quad (-I'h - F'e)c^{-1}$$
$$D' = \quad (-I'g - F'd - E'b)a^{-1}$$

Check:

$$D's_1 + E's_2 + F's_3 + I's_4 = 1$$

Row 2

Copy E' and H' in their other positions, and then enter

$$C' = (c^{-1} - H'h - E'e)c^{-1}$$
$$B' = \quad (-H'g - E'd - C'b)a^{-1}$$

Check:

$$B's_1 + C's_2 + E's_3 + H's_4 = 1$$

Row 1

Copy B', D', and G' in their other positions, and then enter

$$A' = (a^{-1} - G'g - D'd - B'b)a^{-1}$$

Check:

$$A's_1 + B's_2 + D's_3 + G's_4 = 1$$

The reader will experience no difficulty in applying the method to matrices in which the number of rows or columns is greater or less than four. The following example shows the inversion of the 3×3 matrix of the left-hand side of the equations given in § 11A·2.

Table 11A·4

INVERSION OF MATRIX OF COEFFICIENTS OF EQUATIONS *11A·2*

							S	
3·078	3·088	2·188			2·188		8·354	
3·088	0·528	1·212			1·212		4·828	
2·188	1·212	1·352			1·352		4·752	

							S	
0·55258	1·75442	1·76013	—1·89353	1·24714			4·76170	0·56999
1·11471		1·60314i	—2·21464	0·61326i			2·21642i	—0·62378i
—1·89353			5·78932	0·41561			0·41563	2·40610

1·0000	1·11471		
1·0000	0·45809		
1·0000	—2·21464		

8·354   4·828   4·752

The reciprocal matrix is thus found to be

$$
\begin{array}{rrr}
0.5526 & 1.1147 & -1.8935 \\
1.1147 & 0.4581 & -2.2146 \\
-1.8935 & -2.2146 & 5.7893
\end{array}
$$

The check given confirms that the calculation has been completed satisfactorily.

Calculation of determinants

11A·4. In order to determine the coefficients B_{11}, B_{22}, etc., for the canonical form of the fitted equation it is necessary, as described in § 11·732, to solve a series of symmetrical determinants. Assuming the determinant to be

$$
\Delta =
\begin{vmatrix}
a & b & d & g \\
b & c & e & h \\
d & e & f & i \\
g & h & i & j
\end{vmatrix}
$$

its value can be most rapidly found by calculating, as described in § 11A·2, the derived triangular array $a, b, \ldots, j$ from the matrix formed from the elements $a, b, \ldots, j$ of the determinant. The value of the determinant is then given simply by the square of the product of the diagonal elements of this array. The calculation is set out as follows.

Table 11A·5

EVALUATION OF DETERMINANTS

				S	
a	b	d	g	s_1	
b	c	e	h	s_2	
d	e	f	i	s_3	
g	h	i	j	s_4	
				S	
a	b	d	g	s_1	a^{-1}
	c	e	h	s_2	c^{-1}
		f	i	s_3	f^{-1}
			j	s_4	j^{-1}

$$\Delta = (a\,c\,f\,j)^2$$

Thus the 3×3 determinant of the coefficients in the example discussed in § 11A·3 would be obtained as follows:

$$
\Delta = (1.75442 \times 1.60314i \times 0.41561)^2
$$
$$
= -1.3664
$$

It will be observed that when, as in the calculation of the canonical form of a second-degree equation, a series of calculations is performed on the

O2

same matrix of coefficients the derived triangular array may be used more than once, for example in solving the set of equations to find the co-ordinates of S, and in calculating the value of the determinant when $B = 0$.

Calculation of canonical form of the second degree equation

11A·5. In this method values of the determinant are calculated for $k + 1$ equally spaced values of B. Any polynomial of degree k is exactly defined by any $k + 1$ points through which it passes, and by using the successive differences of the $k + 1$ values any other value of the polynomial can be readily obtained without recalculating the determinant. Since it is now possible to rapidly determine the value of $f(B)$ for any desired value of B, the values of this constant which give zero value to the polynomial may be quickly obtained by successive approximation.

The method will be made clear by carrying out the calculation in the example of § **11·732**. The characteristic equation is

$$f(B) = \begin{vmatrix} 1{\cdot}539 + B & 1{\cdot}544 & 1{\cdot}094 \\ 1{\cdot}544 & 0{\cdot}264 + B & 0{\cdot}606 \\ 1{\cdot}094 & 0{\cdot}606 & 0{\cdot}676 + B \end{vmatrix} = 0 \quad \ldots(11A{\cdot}6)$$

where for convenience the signs of all the coefficients in the determinant have been reversed.

The value of the determinant is calculated for four values of B which for convenience are chosen to be equally spaced. The values taken were $B = 0$, $B = 1$, $B = 2$, and $B = 3$, but any other equally spaced values could have been used. Substituting these four values in $(11A{\cdot}6)$ and calculating the values of the four resulting determinants by the method given in § **11A·4**, the results were

$$f(0) = -0{\cdot}1708 \qquad f(1) = 0{\cdot}9853$$
$$f(2) = 13{\cdot}0994 \qquad f(3) = 42{\cdot}1716$$

It is clear by inspection of these values that one value of B satisfying $(11A{\cdot}6)$ lies between 0 and 1, since between these points the determinant has changed sign; also it seems likely, in view of the rapid increase in value of the determinant on the positive side, that the two remaining roots are negative.

To locate the remaining roots, other f values of $f(B)$ are required. No further recalculation of the determinant is necessary, however, since use may be made of the values of the third-order polynomial at four values of B to calculate its value at any other value of B. This is done by calculating the divided differences. In Table 11A·6 the results of these calculations are shown in bold type.

Table 11A·6

LOCATING THE ROOTS OF EQUATION (*11·93*), USING THE METHOD
OF DIVIDED DIFFERENCES

B	Value of determinant $f(B)$	First divided difference	Second divided difference	Third divided difference
− 4	− 15·2152	17·3241	− 6·5210	1·0000
− 3	2·1089	4·2821	− 3·5210	1·0000
− 2	6·3910	− 2·7599	− 0·5210	1·0000
− 1	3·6311	− 3·8019	2·4790	1·0000
0	− 0·1708	1·1561	5·4790	1·0000
1	0·9853	12·1141	8·4790	
2	13·0994	29·0722		
3	42·1716			

In the first column the values $B = 0$, 1, 2, and 3 are shown, and these are
followed in the second column by the values of the determinant calculated at
these points. The first divided difference shown in the third column is the
difference between successive values of $f(B)$ divided by the interval in B
(unity in this case). Thus the first divided difference corresponding to
$B = 0$ is

$$\{0·9853 − (− 0·1708)\}/1 = 1·1561$$

and that corresponding to $B = 1$ is

$$\{13·0994 − 0·9853\}/1 = 12·1141$$
$$\text{etc.}$$

The second divided differences shown in the fourth column are now similarly
obtained by taking differences between the elements of the third column
Thus that corresponding to $B = 0$ is

$$\{12·1141 − 1·1561\}/2 = 5·4790$$

The divisor is now 2; in general it is the value of the interval between the
extreme values of B involved. Finally, the third divided difference corresponding to $B = 0$ and given in the fifth column is

$$\{8·4790 − 5·4790\}/3 = 1·0000$$

Now it is true for any polynomial $f(B)$ of degree k that the kth divided difference is constant and equal to the coefficient of B_k in the polynomial (unity
in this case). This fact may be used to obtain other values of the polynomial
by a process exactly the reverse of that by which the differences were found.
For example, to obtain $f(− 1)$ from the line of differences corresponding to

$B = 0$, three times the third difference is subtracted from the second difference, then twice this second difference, which is that corresponding to $B = -1$, is subtracted from the first difference, and so on. The values of the determinant $f(B)$ at the points $B = -1, -2, -3$, and -4 calculated by this method are entered in Table 11A·6. The remaining two values of B which satisfy (11A·6) will evidently occur between 0 and -1 and between -3 and -4.

Having roughly located the roots, their precise positions are found by a process of successive approximation, using the following formula:

$$F(B_0 + h) = f(B_0) + d_1 h + d_2 h(h-1) + d_3 h(h-1)(h-2) + \ldots \quad (11A\cdot7)$$

where d_1, d_2, etc., are the successive divided differences corresponding to $B = B_0$. When there are k factors this expression finishes with a term in the kth divided difference d_k. Formula (11A·7) may be written in an alternative form, which is shown for $k = 3$.

$$f(B_0 + h) = f(B_0) + h[d_1 + (h-1)\{d_2 + (h-2)d_3\}] \quad ..(11A\cdot71)$$

This formula supplies a rapid method of calculating $f(B)$ for any value of B. The contents of the curly brackets are first calculated, then those of the square brackets, and so on.

A rough graph of $f(B)$ against B for the values given in Table 11A·6 indicates that a root is near $B = 0\cdot7$. The process of successive approximation using Formula (11A·71) is now illustrated for the location of this root. Substituting $B_0 = 0$, $h = 0\cdot7$, and the values of the divided differences corresponding to $B = 0$ given in Table 11A·6, it is found that $f(0\cdot7) = -0\cdot2391$. This value is obviously too low, since it gives a negative value for $f(B)$, and therefore the value $B = 0\cdot8$ is tried. The calculation thus proceeds as follows.

B	$f(B)$	
0·7	$-0\cdot2391$	Linear interpolation
0·8	$0\cdot0694$	gives $B = 0\cdot78$
0·78	$0\cdot0001$	

This gives a value for $f(B)$ of $0\cdot0001$ which is almost zero. It is clear that $B = 0\cdot780$ is accurate to three decimal places, which is sufficient.

The process of linear interpolation (interpolation by proportional parts) can be carried out conveniently on a calculating machine, using the formula:

Value of B for which $f(B) = 0$ is approximately $\dfrac{f(B_2)B_1 - f(B_1)B_2}{f(B_2) - f(B_1)}$

In calculating $f(B_2)B_1 - f(B_1)B_2$ the quantity $f(B_2) - f(B_1)$ is allowed to accumulate in the multiplication register of the machine, thus giving the required divisor.

The remaining roots may be located in a similar manner. Although Formula $(11A\cdot71)$ will apply whatever value is chosen for B_0, it is convenient to take B_0 fairly close to the expected location of the root. Thus for the root close to -3 it would be preferred to use Formula $(11A\cdot71)$ with $B_0 = -4$ and the divided differences corresponding to this value.

In practice, when $k-2$ roots have been located the remaining two can be found without recourse to the method described above, using the following two facts:

(i)   The product of all the roots, B_{11}, B_{22}, . . . , B_{kk}, is equal to $f(0)$, the value of the determinant when $B = 0$.

(ii) The sum of all the roots, $B_{11} + B_{22} + \ldots + B_{kk}$, is equal to the sum of the quadratic effects, $b_{11} + b_{22} + \ldots + b_{kk}$.

Suppose that all the roots except two, say B_{11} and B_{22}, are known. Then

$$B_{11}B_{22} = f(0)/B_{33}B_{44} \ldots B_{kk} = P$$
$$B_{11} + B_{22} = \overset{k}{\Sigma}b_{ii} - B_{33} - B_{44} - \ldots - B_{kk} = Q$$

and it is easy to show that B_{11} and B_{22} are given by the roots of the equation

$$B^2 - QB + P = 0$$

In the present example $k = 3$ and one root, $B_{33} = 0\cdot780$, has been found; therefore the remaining two roots, B_{11} and B_{22}, may be determined by the above process. Remembering that the signs of the effects in the determinant of $(11A\cdot6)$ were changed:

$$P = B_{11}B_{22} \qquad = \qquad 0\cdot219$$
$$Q = B_{11} + B_{22} = -3\cdot259$$

and B_{11} and B_{22} are the roots of the equation

$$B^2 + 3\cdot259B + 0\cdot219 = 0$$

In this example, therefore, the location of all the roots by building up Table 11A·6 was not strictly necessary, but the process was illustrated here to demonstrate to the reader how to deal with examples in which more than three roots have to be located.

REFERENCES

[11A·1] WAUGH, F. V., and DWYER, P. S. "Compact Computation of the Inverse of a Matrix." *Ann. Math. Stat.*, **16**, 259 (1945).

[11A·2] Fox, L., and HAYES, J. G. "More Practical Methods for the Inversion of Matrices." *J. Roy. Stat. Soc.*, B, **13**, 83 (1951).

[11A·3] DWYER, P. S. *Linear Computations.* John Wiley (1951).

APPENDIX 11B

THE USE OF THE METHOD OF LEAST SQUARES IN THE
FITTING OF RESPONSE SURFACES

Introduction

11B·1. The method of Least Squares is applicable whenever it may be assumed that a response (or dependent variable) η is related to the known levels of a set of constants (or independent variables) $a_1, a_2, \ldots, a_p$ by an equation:

$$\eta = \theta_1 a_1 + \theta_2 a_2 + \ldots + \theta_p a_p \quad\ldots\ldots\ldots\ldots(11B\cdot1)$$

and the problem is to estimate the parameters $\theta_1, \theta_2, \ldots, \theta_p$. The field of problems thus included is very wide, but the present discussion is confined to the use of the method in fitting surfaces to sets of experimentally observed values. In the applications discussed in this chapter, η is represented by a polynomial in the factor levels $x_1, x_2, \ldots, x_k$. Thus in fitting an equation of second degree with two factors it is assumed that

$$\eta = \beta_0 x_0 + \beta_1 x_1 + \beta_2 x_2 + \beta_{11} x_1{}^2 + \beta_{22} x_2{}^2 + \beta_{12} x_1 x_2 \ldots(11B\cdot2)$$

This is the same form of expression as $(11B\cdot1)$ with the unknown parameters $\theta_1 = \beta_0$, $\theta_2 = \beta_1$, $\theta_3 = \beta_2$, $\theta_4 = \beta_{11}$, $\theta_5 = \beta_{22}$, $\theta_6 = \beta_{12}$ and the known independent variables $a_1 = x_0 = 1$, $a_2 = x_1$, $a_3 = x_2$, $a_4 = x_1{}^2$, $a_5 = x_2{}^2$, $a_6 = x_1 x_2$. Here the a's are powers and products of the x's, but if it were more appropriate, any other functions of the x's involving, for example, logarithms and reciprocals could be used.

Least Squares results in general

11B·2. The general Least Squares results due to GAUSS will now be explained. For clarity it will be supposed that four parameters, $\theta_1, \theta_2, \theta_3$, and θ_4, are to be estimated. Thus it is assumed that

$$\eta = \theta_1 a_1 + \theta_2 a_2 + \theta_3 a_3 + \theta_4 a_4 \quad\ldots\ldots\ldots\ldots(11B\cdot3)$$

The reader will find no difficulty in extending these results to any number of parameters. Suppose that as a result of performing n trials, n observed values $y_1, y_2, \ldots, y_n$ of the response are available, corresponding to n sets of values of the independent variables, and these observed responses differ from the true responses $\eta_1, \eta_2, \ldots, \eta_n$ on account of experimental error. A table of the values of the independent variables and the observed responses could then be made out as Table 11B·1.

Table 11B·1

LEVELS OF THE INDEPENDENT VARIABLES FOR EQUATION (*11B·3*)
AND THE OBSERVED RESPONSES FOR n TRIALS

Trial	Level of independent variable				Observed response
	a_1	a_2	a_3	a_4	y
I	a_{11}	a_{21}	a_{31}	a_{41}	y_1
2	a_{12}	a_{22}	a_{32}	a_{42}	y_2
.	.	.	.	.	.
i	a_{1i}	a_{2i}	a_{3i}	a_{4i}	y_i
.	.	.	.	.	.
n	a_{1n}	a_{2n}	a_{3n}	a_{4n}	y_n

This rectangular array of the exactly known independent variables (the a's) is called the matrix of independent variables.

The necessity for independence between the a's—Other assumptions

11B·21. The stipulation will be introduced that the columns of the a's in the matrix of independent variables are linearly independent; that is to say, the elements of one column cannot be obtained as a weighted sum of the corresponding elements in the others. For example, the columns of the a's would not be linearly independent if for every row of a's it were true that

$$a_1 + 2a_2 - 3a_3 = a_4$$

In such a case, however, the original equation (*11B·3*) could be written

$$\eta = \theta_1 a_1 + \theta_2 a_2 + \theta_3 a_3 + \theta_4(a_1 + 2a_2 - 3a_3)$$

i.e.
$$\eta = (\theta_1 + \theta_4)a_1 + (\theta_2 + 2\theta_4)a_2 + (\theta_3 - 3\theta_4)a_3$$

Provided that the values of a_1, a_2, and a_3 are linearly independent, therefore, estimates of the quantities $\theta_1 + \theta_4$, $\theta_2 + 2\theta_4$, and $\theta_3 - 3\theta_4$ could be calculated, but not individual estimates of θ_1, θ_2, θ_3, and θ_4. Regarded as estimates of θ_1, θ_2, and θ_3 these calculated quantities would be biased estimates, or to look at it another way, θ_4 would be an alias of θ_1, θ_2, and θ_3. It is precisely in this way that the biases and aliases discussed in Chapters 10 and 11 arise. A further consequence of the necessity for linear independence is that there must always be at least as many observations as there are quantities to be estimated.

The necessity for linear independence of the a's does not mean that these independent variables must be entirely unrelated. For instance, in the example of fitting a second-degree equation (*11B·2*) mentioned above $a_2 = x_1$ and $a_4 = x_1{}^2$, thus a_2 and a_4 are related, but for most sets of values of x_1 the levels corresponding to a_2 and a_4 would still be linearly independent.

If the n values of the response observed under the various experimental conditions were known exactly, that is to say the y's were the same as the η's and if the assumption that an equation like (*11B·3*) fitted the data were strictly true, then the values of θ_1, θ_2, θ_3, and θ_4 could be obtained exactly by solving any four independent equations among

$$\eta_1 = \theta_1 a_{11} + \theta_2 a_{21} + \theta_3 a_{31} + \theta_4 a_{41}$$

$$\eta_i = \theta_1 a_{1i} + \theta_2 a_{2i} + \theta_3 a_{3i} + \theta_4 a_{4i}$$

$$\eta_n = \theta_1 a_{1n} + \theta_2 a_{2n} + \theta_3 a_{3n} + \theta_4 a_{4n}$$

relating the response and the corresponding levels of the independent variables.

In fact, the observed responses $y_1, \ldots, y_n$ are subject to experimental error. It is assumed that the error variance is constant from one observation to the next and that the error in one observation is not related to the error in any other, but nothing else is assumed about the form of the distribution of the errors; in particular it is not assumed that the errors are Normally distributed.

The principle of Least Squares

11B·22. Estimates of θ_1, θ_2, θ_3, and θ_4 are denoted by T_1, T_2, T_3, and T_4 respectively. GAUSS considered estimates which were linear functions of the observations, that is to say, estimates which were of the form

$$T = u_1 y_1 + u_2 y_2 + \ldots + u_n y_n$$

where $u_1, u_2, \ldots, u_n$ were constants. He showed that of all such estimates those having the smallest variances were those supplied by the method of Least Squares, and this is the justification for the use of the method.

Suppose that a set of estimates T_1, T_2, T_3, and T_4 has been obtained by some method. Then it is possible to calculate from them n predicted values $Y_1, Y_2, \ldots, Y_i, \ldots, Y_n$, where $Y_i = T_1 a_{1i} + T_2 a_{2i} + T_3 a_{3i} + T_4 a_{4i}$, and the goodness of the estimates may be judged by how nearly the observed values (the y's) agree with the predicted values (the Y's). The method of Least Squares consists in choosing those estimates which make the sum of squares of the discrepancies between observed and predicted values $S = \sum\limits_{i}^{n}(y_i - Y_i)^2$ a minimum.

Calculation of the estimates and their standard errors

11B·23. It is easy to show that S is a minimum when the estimates T_1, T_2, T_3, and T_4 are chosen so that the following equations (called the Normal equations) are satisfied:

$$\left.\begin{aligned}
C_{11}T_1 + C_{12}T_2 + C_{13}T_3 + C_{14}T_4 = C_{y1} \\
C_{12}T_1 + C_{22}T_2 + C_{23}T_3 + C_{24}T_4 = C_{y2} \\
C_{13}T_1 + C_{23}T_2 + C_{33}T_3 + C_{34}T_4 = C_{y3} \\
C_{14}T_1 + C_{24}T_2 + C_{34}T_3 + C_{44}T_4 = C_{y4}
\end{aligned}\right\} \dots\dots(11B\cdot4)$$

where the coefficients C_{11}, C_{12}, etc., are the sums of squares and products between the elements in the columns of the matrix of independent variables. Thus $C_{11} = \sum_i^n a_{1i}^2$, the sum of squares of the elements of the first independent variable, $C_{12} = \sum_i^n a_{1i}a_{2i}$, the sum of products between corresponding elements of the first and second independent variables, and so on. The quantities C_{y1}, C_{y2}, etc., on the right-hand side of the equations are the sums of products between the observed response and the independent variables; thus $C_{y1} = \sum_i^n y_i a_{1i}$.

The symmetrical array of coefficients

$$\begin{matrix}
C_{11} & C_{12} & C_{13} & C_{14} \\
C_{12} & C_{22} & C_{23} & C_{24} \\
C_{13} & C_{23} & C_{33} & C_{34} \\
C_{14} & C_{24} & C_{34} & C_{44}
\end{matrix}$$

is called the C-matrix and the Equations (*11B·4*) are best solved by first calculating the reciprocal of the C-matrix, the elements of which are denoted by C^{11}, C^{12}, etc. It will be noted that since the elements of the C-matrix are functions of the a's only and not of the observed responses, the reciprocal matrix C^{-1} for a particular experimental design when once worked out can be used again and again for different sets of observations. Following the general method of solution of equations using the reciprocal matrix of the coefficients as described in § **11A·3**, the estimates T_1, T_2, T_3, and T_4 are obtained as the sums of products of the successive rows of the matrix C^{-1} with the elements C_{y1}, C_{y2}, C_{y3}, and C_{y4}; thus

$$T_1 = C^{11}C_{y1} + C^{12}C_{y2} + C^{13}C_{y3} + C^{14}C_{y4}, \text{ etc.}$$

The elements of the matrix C^{-1} also give the variances and covariances of the estimates in terms of the experimental error variance σ^2. Thus for example

$$V(T_1) = C^{11}\sigma^2, \ V(T_2) = C^{22}\sigma^2, \ \text{Cov}(T_1T_2) = C^{12}\sigma^2$$

and the coefficient of correlation between the two estimates T_1 and T_2 is given by

$$\rho(T_1 T_2) = \frac{C^{12}}{\sqrt{(C^{11} C^{22})}}$$

If estimates are positively correlated it will mean that a positive error in one is likely to be accompanied by a positive error in the other, and if they are negatively correlated a positive error in one is likely to be accompanied by a negative error in the other. There is, of course, no objection to the use of correlated estimates. It will generally be found, however, that if the correlation is large then so are the variances of the estimates.

Estimates of linear functions of the parameters

11B·24. GAUSS proved not only that the estimates provided by Least Squares had the smallest variance but also that if an estimate of some linear function of the parameters θ_1, θ_2, θ_3, and θ_4 were required, say

$$\theta_0 = \gamma_1 \theta_1 + \gamma_2 \theta_2 + \gamma_3 \theta_3 + \gamma_4 \theta_4$$

where γ_1, γ_2, γ_3, and γ_4 were known constants, then the estimate of θ_0 having smallest variance was supplied by

$$T_0 = \gamma_1 T_1 + \gamma_2 T_2 + \gamma_3 T_3 + \gamma_4 T_4$$

where T_1, T_2, T_3, and T_4 are the Least Square estimates of θ_1, θ_2, θ_3 and θ_4.

The transformation of observations to estimates

11B·25. It was mentioned in § 11B·22 that the Least Square estimates T_1, T_2, T_3, and T_4 are linear functions of the observations

$$T_1 = u_{11} y_1 + u_{12} y_2 + \ldots + u_{1n} y_n$$
$$T_2 = u_{21} y_1 + u_{22} y_2 + \ldots + u_{2n} y_n$$
$$\text{etc.}$$

If desired the values of the constants, the u's, which transform the observations to the estimates may be obtained explicitly. The u's are in fact weighted sums of the elements in the rows of the matrix of independent variables, and the weights are the elements of the reciprocal matrix C^{-1}. Thus

$$u_{11} = C^{11} a_{11} + C^{12} a_{21} + C^{13} a_{31} + C^{14} a_{41}$$
$$u_{12} = C^{11} a_{12} + C^{12} a_{22} + C^{13} a_{32} + C^{14} a_{42}$$
$$\cdot \qquad \cdot \qquad \cdot \qquad \cdot \qquad \cdot$$
$$u_{1n} = C^{11} a_{1n} + C^{12} a_{2n} + C^{13} a_{3n} + C^{14} a_{4n}$$

The transforming constants $u_{21}, u_{22}, \ldots, u_{2n}$ for the second estimate T_2 are obtained similarly but using the second row of elements, $C^{12}, C^{22}, C^{23}, C^{24}$, of the matrix C^{-1} as weights. The array of elements

$$
\begin{array}{cccc}
u_{11} & u_{21} & u_{31} & u_{41} \\
u_{12} & u_{22} & u_{32} & u_{42} \\
. & . & . & . \\
u_{1n} & u_{2n} & u_{3n} & u_{4n}
\end{array}
$$

is called the transforming matrix, and since it depends only on the a's it may be calculated for a given set of a's once and for all. The estimates T_1, T_2, T_3, and T_4 are then obtained simply by placing the n observed responses $y_1, \ldots, y_n$ in a column adjacent to the columns of the transforming matrix and calculating the sums of products between the u's and the y's.

Estimate of the experimental error variance σ^2

11B·26. In § 11B·23 the variances and covariances of the estimates were given in terms of the experimental error variance σ^2. To determine estimates of these variances and covariances explicitly it is necessary to have some estimate of σ^2. In work in which the object is merely to give a rough indication of the accuracy of these estimates it may be sufficient to give upper limits for the standard errors. This can be done if an upper limit for the experimental error variance can be given. For example:

$$ \text{S.E.}(T_1) \text{ max} = \sqrt{\{C^{11}(\sigma^2 \text{ max})\}} $$

In investigations in which errors are large it may be necessary to repeat each trial r times in order to obtain the necessary precision. In such a case the mean result for the repeat trials would be taken as the observation y, it being remembered then that y has experimental error variance σ^2/r. The variation within replications would then allow an independent estimate of σ^2 and hence of σ^2/r to be obtained in the usual way. If there is no replication but more observations than parameters, and the mathematical model

$$ \eta = \theta_1 a_1 + \theta_2 a_2 + \theta_3 a_3 + \theta_4 a_4 $$

can be assumed to provide a perfect fit, then σ^2 can be estimated from the residual sum of squares, that is to say the sum of squares, $S = \overset{n}{\underset{i}{\Sigma}}(y_i - Y_i)^2$, of the discrepancies between the observed and the predicted values. In fact it may be shown that $s^2 = S/(n - p)$ provides an unbiased estimate of σ^2, where n is the number of observations and p the number of parameters in the fitted equation. In practice it is unnecessary to calculate the value of the sum of squares S from the values of y and Y, for it is given more quickly by the relation

$$S = C_{yy} - T_1 C_{y1} - T_2 C_{y2} - \ldots - T_p C_{yp} \quad \ldots\ldots (11B\cdot 5)$$

where $C_{yy} = \Sigma y^2$

So far no assumption has been made concerning the distribution of the experimental errors; if it is supposed that the errors are Normally distributed, a test whether T_i is significantly different from some theoretical value θ_i (for example, zero) can be made by calculating the ratio of $T_i - \theta_i$ to its standard error $s\sqrt{C^{ii}}$ and referring it to tables of the t-distribution with the same number of degrees of freedom as the error estimate. Also a confidence interval for θ_i is given by $T_i \pm ts\sqrt{C^{ii}}$.

Analysis of variance tests

11B·3. Tests on the net effect of a number of parameters may be made using analysis of variance. The assumption is made that the experimental error is Normally distributed.

Overall test for p parameters

11B·31. A test of whether or not the p parameters of Equation ($11B\cdot 1$) are all zero is provided by referring to the F-table the ratio of the mean squares for "due to fitted parameters" and "residual" given in the following analysis of variance.

Source of variation	Degrees of freedom	Sum of squares
Due to fitted parameters	p	$T_1 C_{y1} + T_2 C_{y2} + \ldots + T_p C_{yp}$
Residual..	$n - p$	$C_{yy} - T_1 C_{y1} - T_2 C_{y2} - \ldots - T_p C_{yp}$
Total	n	C_{yy}

Test for necessity of extra q parameters

11B·32. To test whether or not q parameters $\theta_1, \theta_2, \ldots, \theta_q$ out of the p parameters of Equation ($11B\cdot 1$) are zero, an analysis is first performed including the q parameters and then a similar analysis omitting these parameters. The analysis of variance table is given below. This type of analysis is required, for example, when terms up to second order (p in all) have been fitted but the necessity for the second-order terms (q in all) is in doubt.

Source of variation	Degrees of freedom	Sum of squares
Due to p parameters .. .. (e.g. all terms up to second order)	p	(1)
Due to $p - q$ parameters .. (e.g. all terms up to first order)	$p - q$	(2)
Extra due to q parameters .. (e.g. extra due to second-order terms)	q	(3) = (1) - (2)
Residual	$n - p$	(4) = Total - (1)

The ratio of the mean squares for "extra due to q parameters" and "residual" may then be referred to the F-table. It should be noted that when the first q parameters are omitted the values obtained for the estimates of the parameters $T_{q+1}, \ldots, T_p$ will in general be different from the values obtained when the first q parameters are included. The extra sum of squares due to the q parameters will not be given in general, therefore, by $T_1 C_{y1} + T_2 C_{y2} + \ldots + T_q C_{yq}$. The exception to this otherwise general rule occurs when the q estimates are orthogonal to the remaining estimates. This is explained in detail in § 11B·4.

Elimination of the mean

11B·33. An important special case of the above occurs in the elimination of the mean. In many examples, particularly in the fitting of surfaces, the observations vary not about zero but about some other general level. To take account of this the constant a_1 (that is x_0) accompanying θ_1 (that is β_0) is put equal to unity in each of the trials. The sum of squares accounted for by θ_1 will then usually be very large, but it will normally be desired to test whether or not the other parameters $\theta_2, \ldots, \theta_p$ are really different from zero. Following the general method given in § 11B·32 above, the analysis is of the following form.

Source of variation	Degrees of freedom	Sum of squares
Due to $\theta_1, \ldots, \theta_p$	p	(1)
Due to θ_1 alone	1	(2)
Extra due to $\theta_2, \ldots, \theta_p$.. ..	$p - 1$	(3) = (1) - (2)
Residual	$n - p$	(4) = Total - (1)

The sum of squares "due to θ_1" is easily seen to be what is usually called the "correction due to the mean" $= n\bar{y}^2$ and the analysis may be written in the alternative form shown.

Source of variation	Degrees of freedom	Sum of squares
Due to $\theta_2, \ldots, \theta_p$	$p - 1$	(1)
Residual	$n - p$	(2)
Total (after elimination of mean)	$n - 1$	

In deciding on the efficacy of the fitted equation in accounting for the significant part of the variation, the mean, which is usually of little interest in itself, should first be eliminated in this way. The elimination of the mean is simplified by employing a device discussed in § 11B·4.

Test for a single parameter

11B·34. A second important special case occurs when it is desired to test whether or not a single parameter is really zero. The analysis of variance then becomes:

Source of variation	Degrees of freedom	Sum of squares
Due to p parameters	p	(1)
Due to $p - 1$ parameters ..	$p - 1$	(2)
Extra due to the single parameter	1	(3) = (1) − (2)
Residual	$n - p$	(4) = Total − (1)

It can be shown that the mean square corresponding to the "extra due to the single parameter" is equal to T_1^2/C^{11}. Hence the F-ratio is

$$F = \frac{\text{M.S. (Extra due to the single parameter)}}{\text{M.S. (Residual)}}$$

$$= T_1^2/C^{11}s^2$$

$$= (T_1/\text{S.E.}T_1)^2 = t^2$$

The analysis of variance test is thus equivalent to comparing the estimate T_1 with its standard error by means of the t-test as described in § 11B·26.

Orthogonality

11B·4. Suppose that the columns of the matrix of independent variables can be divided into groups such that any two columns taken from different groups have zero sums of products. For example, suppose a_1 and a_3 are in one group and a_2 and a_4 in the other. Then C_{12}, C_{14}, C_{23}, and C_{34} will all be zero and the C-matrix will be of the form

$$
\begin{matrix}
C_{11} & 0 & C_{13} & 0 \\
0 & C_{22} & 0 & C_{24} \\
C_{13} & 0 & C_{33} & 0 \\
0 & C_{24} & 0 & C_{44}
\end{matrix}
$$

or if the order of the terms in Equation (*11B·3*) is changed:

$$
\begin{matrix}
C_{11} & C_{13} & 0 & 0 \\
C_{13} & C_{33} & 0 & 0 \\
0 & 0 & C_{22} & C_{24} \\
0 & 0 & C_{24} & C_{44}
\end{matrix}
$$

The Normal equations then reduce to two sets:

$$
\left.\begin{array}{l} C_{11}T_1 + C_{13}T_3 = C_{y1} \\ C_{13}T_1 + C_{33}T_3 = C_{y3} \end{array}\right\} \quad \text{and} \quad \left\{\begin{array}{l} C_{22}T_2 + C_{24}T_4 = C_{y2} \\ C_{24}T_2 + C_{44}T_4 = C_{y4} \end{array}\right.
$$

It will be observed that the first set involves the independent variables a_1 and a_3 only and the second set involves a_2 and a_4 only. It follows that the reciprocal matrix is of the form

$$
\begin{matrix}
C^{11} & C^{13} & 0 & 0 \\
C^{13} & C^{33} & 0 & 0 \\
0 & 0 & C^{22} & C^{24} \\
0 & 0 & C^{24} & C^{44}
\end{matrix}
$$

and C^{11}, C^{33}, and C^{13} are entirely functions of a_1 and a_3, while C^{22}, C^{44}, and C^{24} are entirely functions of a_2 and a_4. Consequently the estimates of T_1 and T_3 and their standard errors may be calculated from the y's and the constants a_1 and a_3, entirely ignoring the values of a_2 and a_4, and the estimates of T_2 and T_4, and their standard errors may be calculated from the y's and the constants a_2 and a_4, entirely ignoring the values of a_1 and a_3. Also from the form of the reciprocal matrix it is seen that the two sets of estimates are un-correlated. The group of independent variables (a_1, a_3) and the corresponding estimates (T_1, T_3) are then said to be orthogonal to the group of independent variables (a_2, a_4) and the estimates (T_2, T_4). The analysis of variance will be as follows.

Source of variation	Degrees of freedom	Sum of squares
Due to θ_1 and θ_3 ..	2	$T_1 C_{y1} + T_3 C_{y3}$
Due to θ_2 and θ_4 ..	2	$T_2 C_{y2} + T_4 C_{y4}$
Residual	$n - 4$	$C_{yy} - T_1 C_{y1} - T_2 C_{y2} - T_3 C_{y3} - T_4 C_{y4}$
Total	n	C_{yy}

It will be seen that when the independent variables can be separated into orthogonal groups in this way there is a very considerable simplification in the calculation. For instance, if there are p independent variables which can be divided into q orthogonal groups containing p_1, p_2, . . . , p_q of them respectively, then the estimates and their standard errors may be obtained by inverting the q small matrices instead of the large $p \times p$ matrix, which is a considerably less laborious task. The analysis of variance can be split into q separate additive sums of squares.

In particular, suppose that one of the orthogonal groups contains only one independent variable and for convenience assume it to be a_1. Then C_{12}, C_{13}, etc., are all zero and the first of the Normal equations simplifies to

$$C_{11} T_1 = C_{y1}$$

Also from the definition of the reciprocal matrix

$$C^{11} = 1/C_{11}$$

Consequently

$$T_1 = C_{y1}/C_{11}, \quad V(T_1) = \sigma^2/C_{11}$$

and the covariance of T_1 and each of the other estimates is zero. Thus T_1 is entirely independent of all the other estimates, and it may be calculated as if θ_1 had been the only parameter to be estimated. The calculation is therefore greatly simplified.

More important, however, is the fact that orthogonal estimates have greater efficiency than other estimates (i.e. under comparable conditions the variance of such an estimate is less than the variance of other estimates). When it is possible to choose the a's so that each one is orthogonal to all the others, each of the θ's may be estimated with maximum efficiency and may be calculated very simply. For example, if there are two factors whose levels are denoted by x_1 and x_2 and it may be assumed that the response surface is locally planar, then the following equation can be fitted:

$$\eta = \beta_0 x_0 + \beta_1 x_1 + \beta_2 x_2 \dots\dots\dots\dots\dots(11B\cdot6)$$

Suppose that four trials are performed at the points in a two-level factorial design using levels -1 and $+1$. Then the matrix of independent variables corresponding to ($11B \cdot 6$) is

$$
\begin{array}{ccc}
a_1 = x_0 & a_2 = x_1 & a_3 = x_2 \\
1 & -1 & -1 \\
1 & 1 & -1 \\
1 & -1 & 1 \\
1 & 1 & 1
\end{array}
$$

and the C-matrix and its reciprocal C^{-1} are

$$
\begin{array}{ccc}
& C & \\
4 & 0 & 0 \\
0 & 4 & 0 \\
0 & 0 & 4
\end{array}
\qquad
\begin{array}{ccc}
& C^{-1} & \\
\frac{1}{4} & 0 & 0 \\
0 & \frac{1}{4} & 0 \\
0 & 0 & \frac{1}{4}
\end{array}
$$

from which the estimates are

$$
b_0 = \Sigma y x_0 / 4 \qquad b_1 = \Sigma y x_1 / 4 \qquad b_2 = \Sigma y x_2 / 4
$$

each having variance $\sigma^2 / 4$.

When there are a large number of variables, the gain in simplicity which occurs from the use of orthogonal designs is even more important. Most of the designs discussed in this book result in orthogonality of the independent variables, either separately or in groups. This is the reason for the high efficiency of these designs and the simplicity with which the effects can be calculated.

Elimination of the mean

11B·41. When, as frequently happens, the first independent variable a_1 consists of a column of 1's it is a simple matter and often convenient to rearrange the equation so that the remaining columns of independent variables $a_2, a_3, \ldots, a_p$ are all orthogonal to a_1. This is done by using the alternative form of the equation

$$
\eta = \bar{\eta} + \theta_2(a_2 - \bar{a}_2) + \theta_3(a_3 - \bar{a}_3) + \theta_4(a_4 - \bar{a}_4) \ldots \ldots (11B \cdot 7)
$$

where

$$
\bar{\eta} = \theta_1 \bar{a}_1 + \theta_2 \bar{a}_2 + \theta_3 \bar{a}_3 + \theta_4 \bar{a}_4 \ldots \ldots \ldots \ldots (11B \cdot 71)
$$

The estimate of $\bar{\eta}$ is $\bar{y}$, which is orthogonal to all the remaining estimates so that by this device the number of variables which have to be dealt with is effectively reduced by one. This device is used in §§ **11·51** and **11·621**. The value of T_1 is found explicitly from ($11B \cdot 71$) using the information of § **11B·24**, thus:

$$
T_1 = \bar{y} - T_2 \bar{a}_2 - T_3 \bar{a}_3 - T_4 \bar{a}_4
$$

P2

The analysis of variance can then be written in the following form.

Source of variation	Degrees of freedom	Sum of squares
Due to mean ($\bar{\eta}$)	I	(1)
Extra due to other parameters ..	$p - 1$	(2)
Residual	$n - p$	(3)
Total	n	

Alternatively, the mean is often assumed to have been eliminated, and the "total" sum of squares is equal to (total — due to mean), that is to say, (total — correction due to mean) and has $n - 1$ degrees of freedom.

REFERENCES

[11B·1] GAUSS, C. F. Werke, 4, Göttingen (1821).
[11B·2] FISHER, R. A. *Statistical Methods for Research Workers*. 12th edition. Oliver and Boyd (Edinburgh and London, 1954).
[11B·3] MARKOFF, A. A. *Wahrscheinlichkeitrechnung*. Teubner (Leipzig, 1912).
[11B·4] KOLODZIEJCZYK, ST. "On an Important Class of Statistical Hypotheses." *Biometrika*, **27**, 161 (1935).

REFERENCES (*continued from page 551*)

[11·5] BOX, G. E. P., and HUNTER, J. S. "Multifactor Experimental Designs for exploring Response Surfaces." *Ann. Math. Statist.*, **28** (1957).
[11·6] *Idem.* "A Confidence Region for the Solution of a Set of Simultaneous Equations with an Application to Experimental Design." *Biometrika*, **41**, 190 (1954).
[11·7] BOX, G. E. P. "The Exploration and Exploitation of Response Surfaces; some General Considerations and Examples." *Biometrics*, **10**, 16 (1954).
[11·8] BOX, G. E. P., and YOULE, P. U. "The Exploration and Exploitation of Response Surfaces; an Example of the Link between the Fitted Surface and the Basic Mechanism of the System." *Ibid.*, **11**, 287 (1955).

GLOSSARY OF TECHNICAL TERMS

In order to avoid the frequent use of cross-reference symbols the convention has been adopted throughout this glossary of giving initial capital letters to technical terms which are explained elsewhere in it, though such terms do not generally appear with capital letters in the text of the book.

Alias

In a complete Factorial Design all the Main Effects and Interactions are estimated independently. In a Fractional Factorial Design, in which only part of the complete factorial design is carried out, the number of effects which can be estimated independently is correspondingly smaller. It then happens that a comparison which estimates a required effect also estimates one or more other effects. These effects are then confounded and may be said to be Aliases of one another. By careful choice of the design it may be possible to ensure that the important effects which we require to estimate are not confounded with one another.

The above considerations apply to any type of experimental design. In general, if two effects which we require to estimate are given by the same comparison, then one effect is an Alias of the other and cannot be independently determined. Aliases cannot be avoided when the number of comparative effects likely to exist equals or exceeds the number of observations.

Average, Mean

The Arithmetic Average or Mean of a series of items is obtained by dividing their total by the number of items.

Balanced Incomplete Block

Experiments may be encountered in which the practicable block size is too small to accommodate all the treatments which are required to be compared. Balanced designs are possible in which every pair of treatments appears together in a block the same number of times, and such arrangements are called Balanced Incomplete Block Designs. If a block is sufficient only for three of four treatments, T_1, T_2, T_3, T_4, the following is a suitable balanced incomplete block design.

1st block	2nd block	3rd block	4th block
T_1	T_1	T_1	T_2
T_2	T_2	T_3	T_3
T_3	T_4	T_4	T_4

T_1 and T_3 appear in blocks 1 and 3, T_1 and T_4 in blocks 2 and 3, etc.

The advantages of the balanced incomplete block designs are (i) that maximum precision is obtained, (ii) that all treatments are compared with the same precision, and (iii) that the calculations are simple and can be systematised.

Bias

A Bias is a persistent or systematic error as opposed to a random error. A method of measurement is biased if the average of a long series of measurements tends to a value other than the true value as the number of measurements increases. Similarly, one method of measurement is said to be biased relatively to another if averages of long series of Observations by the two methods tend to different values.

Block, Lot

A Block is a part of the experimental material which is likely to be more homogeneous than the whole. Observations within blocks can therefore be compared with greater precision than observations distributed over the whole experimental material. For example, observations made within a short period of time, on a single unit of plant, on a single sheet of a textile or a plastic material, or on the produce grown on a relatively small area of ground, are frequently subject to less variation than observations made on random samples from the whole material. In certain industrial experiments, the word Lot appears more appropriate than Block, and it has sometimes been used in this book.

In general, the Treatment Combinations within a block should be applied in a Random order, giving what is called a Randomised Block design.

(See also *Latin Square, Balanced Incomplete Block, Confounding*.)

Chi-squared Test (χ^2 Test)

Technically, χ^2 (chi squared) denotes a quantity which has the same probability distribution as has the sum of the squares of a number of independent variates from a Normal Universe with zero Mean and unit Standard Deviation. The probability distribution depends upon the number of independent variates, which number is called the number of Degrees of Freedom associated with χ^2. The probability of obtaining any particular value of χ^2 can be calculated, and Table B contains the results of such a calculation in a form convenient for practical use.

Table B can be used to decide whether the estimate of Variance from a sample of Normally distributed observations is consistent with their having been drawn from a universe of specified standard deviation, and also to test whether the numbers of observations found in different classes agree (within the limits of random error) with the numbers expected in those classes.

Confidence Limits, Fiducial Limits, Confidence Coefficient

Suppose that the mean of a sample of observations drawn from a Normally distributed universe is $\bar{x}$ and that s^2 is the estimate of variance calculated from the data. To test the hypothesis that the true universe mean is μ the quantity $\dfrac{\bar{x} - \mu}{s/\sqrt{n}}$ is referred to the table of the t-distribution, and it is known that if the true mean is μ then with probability $1 - a$

$$- t_{\frac{1}{2}a} < \frac{\bar{x} - \mu}{s/\sqrt{n}} < t_{\frac{1}{2}a}$$

where $t_{\frac{1}{2}a}$ is the positive deviate of the t-distribution which is exceeded with probability $\frac{1}{2}a$. Rearranging the inequality, we have

$$\bar{x} - \frac{st_{\frac{1}{2}a}}{\sqrt{n}} < \mu < \bar{x} + \frac{st_{\frac{1}{2}a}}{\sqrt{n}}$$

That is to say, the probability is $1 - a$ that μ will be included in the limits

$$\bar{x} \pm \frac{st_{\frac{1}{2}a}}{\sqrt{n}}$$

These limits are called the $100(1 - a)\%$ Confidence Limits or Fiducial Limits for μ, and $1 - a$ is called the Confidence Coefficient.

An alternative way of regarding the limits is to say that the hypothesis that the value of the true mean is μ is contradicted by the data for all values of μ lying outside these limits at the $100a\%$ level of probability.

Confidence limits of this sort can be formed for all the commonly used parameters. For example:

$$\chi^2_{1 - \frac{1}{2}a} < \frac{\phi s^2}{\sigma^2} < \chi^2_{\frac{1}{2}a}$$

and

$$\frac{\phi s^2}{\chi^2_{\frac{1}{2}a}} < \sigma^2 < \frac{\phi s^2}{\chi^2_{1 - \frac{1}{2}a}}$$

Confounding, Double Confounding, Partial Confounding

The size of the Block available for a Factorial Experiment may be too small to accommodate the whole experiment, so that the various Treatment Combinations must be applied to material from several blocks. Application of treatment combinations in a haphazard manner inflates the experimental error, because of the differences between blocks. It is possible, however, by suitable allotment of the treatment combinations to the different blocks, to make the difference between blocks correspond to Effects of small importance (usually high-order Interactions) while the important effects are retained as within-block comparisons. The experimental error of such comparisons is thus not inflated by the differences between blocks. The comparisons between treatments which become indistinguishable from differences between blocks are said to be confounded with these block differences, and designs involving this feature are Confounded Factorial Designs [Chapter 9].

Sometimes the experimental material can be divided into blocks in two ways; for instance, each of four units of plant might represent a block, while also, owing to trends with time, each day's make on any unit might be more homogeneous than material made on successive days, so that each day's make should be regarded as a block. It may be desirable to confound some unimportant comparisons with one type of block differences and others of another type with another set. This process is called Double Confounding.

When an experiment involves several Replications, it is possible to design it so that different treatment comparisons are confounded in the different replicates. In this way any treatment comparison is a within-block comparison in at least some of the replicates, and so can be estimated without confusion with differences between blocks. This is Partial Confounding, and a comparison which is confounded in one replicate and not in another is said to be Partially Confounded [Chapter 9].

Defining Contrasts

The set of treatment comparisons confounded in any particular Confounded Factorial Experiment is called the set of Defining Contrasts of the experimental design (see Appendix 9D). Since a Fractional Replicate is a block in a factorial design involving confounding, the defining contrasts of this design determine a set of fractional replicates. The defining contrasts are used to determine the treatment combinations assigned to each block in a confounded design, and in a fractional factorial design they enable the aliases of the effects to be determined [Chapter 10].

Degrees of Freedom

Degrees of Freedom correspond to terms in a sum of squares which can be assigned arbitrarily. For example, the sum of squares of deviations from the mean in a sample of n observations

$$\Sigma(x - \bar{x})^2 = (x_1 - \bar{x})^2 + (x_2 - \bar{x})^2 + \ldots + (x_n - \bar{x})^2$$

has $n - 1$ degrees of freedom, because when any $n - 1$ deviations are known the nth can be obtained from the identity

$$(x_1 - \bar{x}) + (x_2 - \bar{x}) + \ldots + (x_n - \bar{x}) = 0$$

This is obvious from the definition of the mean, $\bar{x}$.

The $n - 1$ degrees of freedom thus correspond to the $n - 1$ independent comparisons which can be made within the n observations. Similarly, in

Factorial Experiments which are designed to enable comparisons to be made between the responses to the different treatment combinations, these comparisons can be associated with the degrees of freedom occurring in the analysis of variance.

Double Confounding
See *Confounding*.

Double-tail Test, Double-sided Test
See *Significance*.

Effect
See *Factor*.

Error of the First Kind, Error of the Second Kind
See *Significance*.

Expectation, Expected Value
If q is any quantity calculated from a Sample of observations, the Expectation or Expected Value of q is the average value which would be obtained for q if it were calculated from an infinite number of samples of the same size drawn from the same Universe. It is frequently denoted by $E(q)$.

Experiment, Trial, Observation
For the purpose of this book the word Experiment means a planned set of operations (Trials) which lead to a corresponding set of Observations, these being the results of the individual trials constituting the experiment.

F-test, Variance Ratio Test
The distribution of the ratio of two estimates of Variance obtained from two independent samples drawn from a Normal universe is called the F-distribution. The distribution depends only on ϕ_1 and ϕ_2, the numbers of Degrees of Freedom associated with the two estimates of variance.

The F-distribution is used, for instance, to decide whether two independent estimates of variance can reasonably be accepted as being two estimates of the variance of a single Normally distributed universe. The probability that two such independent estimates of the variance of a single Normal universe shall have any particular ratio can be calculated, and Table D shows the ratios which will be equalled or exceeded by chance, with probabilities 0·1, 0·05 and 0·01, in relation to the numbers of degrees of freedom on which the two estimates are based.

These probabilities correspond to the use of the F-distribution for a Single-sided Test, as this is what is needed in testing significance in an analysis of variance. Sometimes, however, it is appropriate to use a Double-sided Test, for instance when comparing the variability of two processes or two analysts, and this can be obtained by regarding the tabulated values of F as corresponding to twice the probabilities in the left-hand column of Table D.

Factor, Factorial Experiment Design, Complete Factorial Design, Level, Effect, Interaction, Response, Treatment Combination

A Factorial Experiment studies the effect on some observable quantity (e.g. the yield of a process) of varying two or more Factors, such as temperature, pressure, source of raw materials, etc. A series of values or Levels of each factor is chosen, and certain combinations of the levels of the factors are tested, these being the Treatments or Treatment Combinations. The particular combinations of the factor levels chosen and the order in time in which they are tested are referred to as the Design of the experiment. More generally, the Design is the configuration of points in the factor space and in time. In a Complete Factorial Design all combinations of all the Levels of all the Factors are tested. The numerical result of an observation made with a particular treatment combination is called the Response corresponding to that treatment. The differences between the means of the observed quantity for levels of one factor, averaged over all levels of the other factors, constitute the Effect of that factor, or more specifically its Main Effect.

Sometimes the effect of one factor is different at different levels of one or more of the other factors. As an hypothetical example, the yield of a chemical reaction might depend on two factors, A and B, in the following way:

			Level of A	
			Lower	Higher
Level of B	Lower ..		77%	85%
	Higher ..		84%	83%

so that with B at the lower level a change in the level of A increases the yield appreciably, whereas with B at the higher level the effect of A is different. In such a case there is said to be an Interaction between the two factors. The Main Effect of A in this case would be measured by the difference between the mean yields at its two levels, i.e. $84\% - 80.5\%$, and the main effect of B

similarly would be measured by $83.5\% - 81\%$. The interaction of A and B is measured by

$$\{\tfrac{1}{2}(77 + 83) - \tfrac{1}{2}(84 + 85)\}\%, \text{ i.e. } - 4.5\%$$

The above is an example of a two-factor interaction. Sometimes the value of a two-factor interaction is different at different levels of a third factor, and in such a case there is said to be a three-factor interaction, and so on.

Factorial Experiment
See *Factor*.

Fiducial Limits
See *Confidence Limits*.

Fractional Factorial Experiment, Fractional Replicate
It often happens that some of the comparisons which can be made in a factorial experiment measure Effects which may be expected to be negligible, e.g. certain Interactions may be unlikely, on physical grounds, to have any real existence. In certain circumstances these comparisons may be used to measure the effects of additional factors. Experimental designs based on this principle are called Fractional Factorial designs, since they are fractions of the complete Factorial Experiment which would measure all the effects and interactions of all the factors. By an extension of the idea of a replicate, they may also be regarded as Fractional Replicates of the complete factorial experiment.

Interaction
See *Factor*.

Latin Square
A Latin Square is a square array of elements such that each element appears once and only once in each row and each column. For instance, denoting four elements by A, B, C, and D, the following is one of the possible Latin Squares:

$$\begin{array}{cccc} B & A & C & D \\ A & C & D & B \\ D & B & A & C \\ C & D & B & A \end{array}$$

If the treatments to be investigated are regarded as the elements of a Latin Square, and the rows and columns of the square correspond to two different subdivisions of the experimental material into blocks, the Latin Square design thus obtained eliminates the effects of differences between the blocks. For example, if four treatments are to be tested, using four blends of material, in an experiment extending over four weeks, then each blend could be identified with a row, and each week with a column, of the Latin Square design; and since each treatment is tested in each week, and also in each blend of material, the comparison of the four treatments can be made independently of the differences between blends of material, and independently of systematic week-to-week effects, provided there are no appreciable interactions between rows, columns and treatments.

Lattice Square

A Lattice Square is a special design of the Incomplete Block type which is specially suitable when the number of treatments to be compared is large. It enables p^2 treatments to be compared in $2p$ blocks of p treatments. Additional replication may be used if desired [§ **6·5**].

Level

1. In a factorial experiment, see *Factor*.
2. In a test of significance, see *Significance*.

Likelihood, Likelihood Ratio

Suppose n independent observations x_1, x_2, . . . , x_n are drawn from a universe which is such that the probability of an observation in the range x to $x + dx$ is $f(x, \theta)dx$, where θ represents one or more parameters of the universe. Then $f(x_r, \theta)$ is called the Likelihood of the observation x_r, and the function

$$f(x, \theta) \; f(x_2, \theta) \ldots f(x_n, \theta)$$

denotes the likelihood of the whole sample of observations.

If θ may on two different hypotheses have values θ_1, θ_2, then the Likelihood Ratio is

$$\frac{f(x_1, \theta_1) \; f(x_2, \theta_1) \ldots f(x_n, \theta_1)}{f(x_1, \theta_2) \; f(x_2, \theta_2) \ldots f(x_n, \theta_2)}$$

If this ratio is large it is clearly an indication that the observations support the hypothesis that $\theta = \theta_1$, and conversely the hypothesis that $\theta = \theta_2$ receives support if the ratio is small. Consequently the likelihood ratio affords a criterion for establishing a preference for one of the two hypotheses. If we calculate the frequency with which different values of the likelihood ratio will occur in random sampling, a Significance Test can be obtained for deciding between the hypotheses. Significance tests derived in this way can be shown to have certain optimum properties compared with other possible significance tests.

Lot

See *Block*.

Mean

See *Average*.

Normal Universe, Normal Distribution

In a Normal Universe the probability of obtaining an observation in the interval x to $x + dx$ is

$$\frac{1}{\sigma\sqrt{(2\pi)}} \exp\left\{\frac{-(x-\mu)^2}{2\sigma^2}\right\} dx$$

where $\exp\{\ldots\}$ denotes the exponential function. This distribution is specified by two parameters, μ the Mean, and σ the Standard Deviation.

Null Hypothesis

See *Significance*.

Observation

See *Experiment*.

Orthogonality

Orthogonality is that property of the design of an experiment which ensures that the different classes of Effects shall be capable of direct and separate estimation without any entanglement. The sums of squares of all the effects are then independent and additive.

Consider an experiment to observe the effect of varying two factors, say temperature (tested at the four levels 40°, 60°, 80°, and 100° C.) and pressure (tested at three levels, say 1 atm., 2 atm., and 3 atm.). Then if the twelve treatment combinations obtainable by taking each temperature with all the levels of pressure are applied, the comparison between the averages of the three observations obtained at any two temperatures will be purely a measure of the effect of temperature. If, however, one of these six observations were not obtained, two of the averages would be based on observations obtained at three pressure levels and the other on observations obtained at two, and the difference between the averages would be influenced by the effect of pressure. In this case the experiment would not be orthogonal.

The precise mathematical definition is as follows:

If $x_1, x_2, \ldots, x_n$ are n observations, any two linear functions

$$a_1x_1 + a_2x_2 + \ldots + a_nx_n$$

and

$$b_1x_1 + b_2x_2 + \ldots + b_nx_n$$

are orthogonal if

$$a_1b_1 + a_2b_2 + \ldots + a_nb_n = 0$$

This is equivalent to absence of correlation between the functions, which is a condition of independence.

Parameter

See *Universe.*

Partial Confounding

See *Confounding.*

Partial Replicate

See *Fractional Factorial Experiment.*

Population

See *Universe.*

Power of a Statistical Test

See *Significance.*

Randomised Block

See *Block.*

Randomising

In an experiment, the order of application of the different Treatment Combinations should be a random one, in so far as this is not restricted by the design used. For example, if n levels of a single factor are being tried, they should be tried in a random order. The effect of this will be to avoid possible bias due to the influence of systematic disturbances, known or unknown. If a number of duplicate samples are to be analysed they should be numbered in a random order without reference to their being duplicates; if a Latin Square design is to be used the square should be selected at random from all possible Latin Squares of the given size.

Randomising should be done by some chance process such as spinning a coin, dealing from a shuffled pack of cards, or using a table of random numbers.

Regression, Regression Equation, Regression Coefficient

A Regression Equation is an equation relating the expectation of one variable to the values of others when one or more of the variables are subject to random errors. Suppose a quantity y is believed to be dependent upon the values of the variables $x_1, x_2, \ldots$, so that

$$E(y) = \beta_0 + \beta_1 f_1(x_1, x_2, \ldots, x_n) + \beta_2 f_2(x_1, x_2, \ldots, x_n) + \cdots$$

where $f_1, f_2, \ldots$ denote known functions of the variables $x_1, x_2, \ldots, x_n$, then this is known as a Regression Equation and $\beta_0, \beta_1, \beta_2, \ldots$ are called Regression Coefficients.

Replicate

An experiment in which each Treatment or Treatment Combination is applied once is a single Replicate of the experiment. If each treatment or treatment combination is applied n times, the experiment is said to be replicated n times or to involve n replicates.

Response

See *Factor*.

Sample

See *Universe*.

Sequential Tests

The classical method of comparing two treatments is to apply each a number of times and to use a Significance Test to decide whether the differences between the observations obtained under the two treatments amount to more than random variations. The number of observations to be made is determined before the experiment is performed, and is such that the chances of errors of the first and second kinds are acceptably small, i.e. so that the conclusion from the experiment would have only a small chance of being wrong. When the treatments have, in fact, markedly different effects, this procedure may be wasteful, because the difference would be conclusively revealed by fewer observations than the number decided upon.

A more economical procedure is obtained by deciding the number of observations in the course of the experiment instead of beforehand, and by stopping when a conclusive decision can be made from the differences already recorded. An experiment performed in this way is called a Sequential Experiment, since an assessment is made after each member of a sequence of groups of observations. The ordinary significance tests used in the classical method are based on the assumption of a determinate number of observations and so do not apply to sequential experiments; suitable alternative significance tests have however been devised.

Significance, Level of Significance, Significance Test, Double-sided Test, Single-sided Test, Single-tail Test, Null Hypothesis, Error of the First Kind, Error of the Second Kind, Power of a Statistical Test

A Significance Test is a procedure adopted to assess whether some quantity which is subject to random variation differs from a postulated figure by an amount greater than that attributable to random variation alone. For this purpose the probabilities of obtaining different values of the quantity are calculated on the hypothesis (the Null Hypothesis) that only random variation is occurring, and in the case of those tests usually needed (like the t-test, F-test, and chi-squared test) the results of such calculations have been tabulated in a convenient form.

If the observed value of the quantity has only a small probability α of being attained or exceeded if the Null Hypothesis were true, it is concluded that this hypothesis is untrue. α is called the Level of Significance used in the significance test, and the conclusion is usually expressed in some such form as "A statistical test indicates a significant departure from the given Null Hypothesis at the 100α % level (e.g. 5% level)." This procedure implies that there is a chance of concluding erroneously that there is a departure from the Null Hypothesis, namely a 100α % chance. The procedure is useful because α can (and should) be chosen before the observations are made, to have a value corresponding to whatever chance of error may be tolerable in the particular experiment. The error of asserting a departure from the Null Hypothesis when it is actually true is called the Error of the First Kind.

The fact that a significance test is performed implies that there is at least one Alternative Hypothesis, which if true would lead to a different expected value for the quantity. Owing to the existence of random variation, actual values of the quantity will be distributed about this expected value with a certain probability distribution when this Alternative Hypothesis is true. Thus, just as above, there will be a certain chance β of rejecting the Alternative Hypothesis when it is true and consequently of accepting the Null Hypothesis erroneously. This error is called the Error of the Second Kind. The chance of committing it depends upon (a) the magnitude of the random variations, (b) the difference between the expected values of the quantity on the Null Hypothesis and on the Alternative Hypothesis, (c) the level of significance α which is used, and (d) the number of observations from which the quantity is calculated. In principle, only the last of these can be determined by the experimenter, and in a number of cases [Chapter 2] methods are now available whereby he can determine this number.

The Power of a statistical test is the chance which it affords of accepting the Alternative Hypothesis when it is true; the power is thus the complement of the chance of the error of the second kind (power $= 1 - \beta$), and so depends upon the same factors as this chance.

In some cases we are interested in departures from the Null Hypothesis in a single direction; for instance, we may be interested in adopting a modified process only if it results in an improvement in the product. In such cases the test of significance used should be a Single-sided Test, which would result in rejecting the Null Hypothesis (that the modification made no difference) only if the product were improved, and not if it were adversely affected, by the modification. In other cases we are interested in any departure from the Null Hypothesis; for instance, if a modified process significantly depreciates the product this may be useful information, because it may suggest another modification which might improve it. In this case a Double-sided Test is needed capable of indicating a significant departure in either direction from the expected value of the quantity on the Null Hypothesis. Tables appropriate for both single-sided and double-sided tests for commonly used tests of significance are given at the end of the volume.

Single-sided Test, Single-tail Test

See *Significance*.

Standard Deviation, Standard Error

These terms are synonymous and denote the square root of the Variance. The term Standard Error is usually used to denote the Standard Deviation of a Statistic.

Statistic

See *Universe*.

t-test, t-distribution

The ratio of a Normally distributed variate with zero mean to its estimated standard error is denoted by t, and the probability distribution of t is known. Tables derived from this distribution (such as Table C) make it possible to determine whether the mean of a set of observations is consistent with their having been drawn from a Universe having some specified mean, whether the means of two sets of observations are consistent with the two sets having been drawn from a single Normal Universe, or whether a Regression Coefficient is consistent with some assigned value, etc.

Treatment, Treatment Combination

See *Factor*.

Trial

See *Experiment*.

Universe, Population, Parameter, Sample, Statistic

Population and Universe are synonymous.

Statistical reasoning employs the concept of a Sample of individuals or observations drawn at random from a population or universe of possible observations. When a number of determinations of the same physical or chemical quantity are made, the values obtained are regarded as a random sample of all the determinations which might have been made in indefinite repetition of the test actually performed. The population or universe thus has no real existence, only a notional one. The term Population derives from the field of vital statistics in which the population may have a real existence, and in this book the term Universe has generally been preferred so as not to imply this.

A universe is generally characterised by one or more Parameters, such as its mean and its standard deviation. Any finite sample can only give estimates of these parameters. An estimate of a parameter, obtained from a sample, is called a Statistic.

Variance

The Variance is the mean value of the squares of the deviations of an infinite set of observations from their mean. Symbolically, the Variance of a variate x is the mean of $(x - \mu)^2$ in the universe, where μ is the mean of x in the universe of possible values of x. From a finite sample of n observations the variance is estimated by $\Sigma(x - \bar{x})^2/(n - 1)$, where $\bar{x}$ is the mean of the sample.

Variance Ratio Test

See *F-test*.

χ^2-test

See *Chi-squared Test*.

Youden Square

A YOUDEN Square is an experimental design of the Balanced Incomplete Block type, in which possible effects of position in the block are eliminated from the averaged comparisons between the treatments. A YOUDEN square resembles a Latin Square with one or more rows missing, and retains the property of a Latin Square of eliminating some trends which would otherwise inflate the estimate of experimental error [§ **6·4**].

TABLES OF STATISTICAL FUNCTIONS

A. Normal Distribution (single-sided)

A·1. Probability points of the Normal distribution (single-sided test)

A·2. Probability points of the Normal distribution (double-sided test)

B. Probability points of the χ^2 distribution

C·1. Probability points of the t-distribution (single-sided test)

C·2. Probability points of the t-distribution (double-sided test)

D. Probability points of the variance ratio (F-distribution)

E. Number of observations for t-test of mean

E·1. Number of observations for t-test of difference between two means

F. Table of $x = \arc \sin \sqrt{p}$

G. Number of observations required for the comparison of a population variance with a standard value using the χ^2-test

H. Number of observations required for the comparison of two population variances using the F-test

K. Values of $\begin{Bmatrix} a \\ b \end{Bmatrix}$ for various values of α and β

L. BARNARD's sequential t-test.

M. Main effects and interactions in 2^2, 2^3, 2^4, 2^5, and 2^6 factorial designs

N. Table of random numbers.

ACKNOWLEDGMENTS

Table A. Condensed and adapted from *The Biometrika Tables for Statisticians*, 1, Table 4, with permission of the Trustees of *Biometrika*.

Table A·1. Condensed and adapted by permission from *Statistical Tables for Biological, Agricultural and Medical Research*, by R. A. Fisher and F. Yates (copyright 1948, Oliver and Boyd).

Table B. Condensed and adapted from *The Biometrika Tables for Statisticians*, 1, Table 8, with permission of the Trustees of *Biometrika*, and from *Statistical Tables for Biological, Agricultural and Medical Research*, by R. A Fisher and F. Yates (copyright 1948, Oliver and Boyd).

Table C. Compiled by permission from *Statistical Methods in Research and Production*, edited by O. L. Davies (copyright 1947, Oliver and Boyd), and from *Statistical Tables for Biological, Agricultural and Medical Research*, by R. A. Fisher and F. Yates (copyright 1948, Oliver and Boyd).

Table D. Condensed and adapted from *The Biometrika Tables for Statisticians*, 1, Table 18, with permission of the Trustees of *Biometrika*, and from *Statistical Tables for Biological, Agricultural and Medical Research*, by R. A. Fisher and F. Yates (copyright 1948, Oliver and Boyd).

Tables E and E·1. Adapted by permission from *Research*, 1 (1948), 520–5.

Tables G and H. Condensed and adapted, with independent additions, from *Selected Techniques of Statistical Analysis*, by the Statistical Research Group, Columbia University (editors C. Eisenhart, M. W. Hastay, and W. A. Wallis) (copyright 1947, McGraw-Hill Book Company Inc.).

Table L. Designed and computed by Dr. S. Rushton, Imperial College of Science and Technology, under the direction of Professor G. A. Barnard and with financial assistance from Imperial Chemical Industries Ltd.

Table N. Extracted from *Tables of Random Sampling Numbers*, by M. G. Kendall and B. Babington Smith, and *Tracts for Computers*, XXIV, with permission of University College, London. Table N consists of pp. 40 and 41 from these tables.

DESIGN AND ANALYSIS

Table A

NORMAL DISTRIBUTION (SINGLE-SIDED)

Proportion (A) of whole area lying to right of ordinate through

$$u = (x - \mu)/\sigma$$

Deviate (u)	Prefix	0·00	0·01	0·02	0·03	0·04	0·05	0·06	0·07	0·08	0·09	Prefix	Deviate (u)
0·0	0·5	000	960	920	880	840	801	761	721	681	641	0·4	0·0
0·1	0·4	602	562	522	483	443	404	364	325	286	247	0·4	0·1
0·2	0·4	207	168	129	090	052	013	974	936	897	859	0·3	0·2
0·3	0·3	821	783	745	707	669	632	594	557	520	483		0·3
0·4		446	409	372	336	300	264	228	192	156	121	0·3	0·4
0·5	0·3	085	050	015	981	946	912	877	843	810	776	0·2	0·5
0·6	0·2	743	709	676	643	611	578	546	514	483	451		0·6
0·7		420	389	358	327	296	266	236	206	177	148	0·2	0·7
0·8	0·2	119	090	061	033	005	977	949	922	894	867	0·1	0·8
0·9	0·1	841	814	788	762	736	711	685	660	635	611		0·9
1·0		587	562	539	515	492	469	446	423	401	379		1·0
1·1		357	335	314	292	271	251	230	210	190	170	0·1	1·1
1·2	0·1	151	131	112	093	075	056	038	020	003	985	0·0	1·2
1·3	0·0	968	951	934	918	901	885	869	853	838	823		1·3
1·4		808	793	778	764	749	735	721	708	694	681		1·4
1·5		668	655	643	630	618	606	594	582	571	559		1·5
1·6		548	537	526	516	505	495	485	475	465	455		1·6
1·7		446	436	427	418	409	401	392	384	375	367		1·7
1·8		359	351	344	336	329	322	314	307	301	294		1·8
1·9		287	281	274	268	262	256	250	244	239	233		1·9
2·0		228	222	217	212	207	202	197	192	188	183		2·0
2·1		179	174	170	166	162	158	154	150	146	143		2·1
2·2		139	136	132	129	125	122	119	116	113	110	0·0	2·2
2·3	0·0	107	104	102	990	964	939	914	889	866	842	0·00	2·3
2·4	0·00	820	798	776	755	734	714	695	676	657	639		2·4
2·5		621	604	587	570	554	539	523	508	494	480		2·5
2·6		466	453	440	427	415	402	391	379	368	357		2·6
2·7		347	336	326	317	307	298	289	280	272	264		2·7
2·8		256	248	240	233	226	219	212	205	199	193		2·8
2·9	0·00	187	181	175	169	164	159	154	149	144	139	0·00	2·9

Table A (*continued*)

EXTENSION FOR HIGHER VALUES OF THE DEVIATE

Deviate (u)	Proportion of whole area (A)	Deviate (u)	Proportion of whole area (A)	Deviate (u)	Proportion of whole area (A)	Deviate (u)	Proportion of whole area (A)
3·0	·00 135	3·5	·000 233	4·0	·0^{4}317	4·5	·0^{5}340
3·1	·000 968	3·6	·000 159	4·1	·0^{4}207	4·6	·0^{5}211
3·2	·000 687	3·7	·000 108	4·2	·0^{4}133	4·7	·0^{5}130
3·3	·000 483	3·8	·0^{4}723	4·3	·0^{5}854	4·8	·0^{6}793
3·4	·000 337	3·9	·0^{4}481	4·4	·0^{5}541	4·9	·0^{6}479
						5·0	·0^{6}287

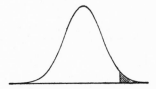

The illustration shows the Normal Curve. The shaded portion is the area (*A*), which is given in the table.

The entries refer to positive values of the argument (*u*). For negative values of *u* write down the complements of the entries.

EXAMPLES

Let u = + 1·96. The prefix = 0·0 and the entry = 250, together 0·0250 = area to right. Area to left = 1 − 0·0250 = 0·9750.

Let u = − 3·00. The tabulated value = 0·00135. Since *u* is negative, this represents the area to the *left*. Area to right = 1 − 0·00135 = 0·99865.

Let u = + 4·50. Tabulated value = 0·00000340. Area to left = 0·99999660.

To find the value of *u* corresponding to a given *A* we use the table in reverse, thus:

Let area to right (i.e. A) = 0·10. The two adjacent tabulated values are $A = 0·1003$ for $u = 1·28$, and $A = 0·0985$ for $u = 1·29$. We interpolate linearly to obtain the required value of *u*. Thus $u = 1·28 + (3)(0·01)/18 = 1·2817$.

Tables A·1 and A·2

PROBABILITY POINTS OF THE NORMAL DISTRIBUTION

Table A·1 $u = (x - \mu)/\sigma$ Table A·2

SINGLE-SIDED TEST   DOUBLE-SIDED TEST

P	u
0·001	3·0902
0·005	2·5758
0·01	2·3263
0·02	2·0537
0·025	1·9600
0·05	1·6449
0·1	1·2816
0·2	0·8416
0·3	0·5244
0·4	0·2533
0·5	0·0000

P	u
0·001	3·2905
0·005	2·8070
0·01	2·5758
0·02	2·3263
0·025	2·2414
0·05	1·9600
0·1	1·6449
0·2	1·2816
0·3	1·0364
0·4	0·8416
0·5	0·6745

Normal   Normal

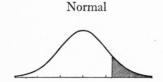 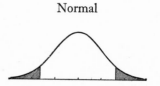

The illustrations show the Normal Curve. The shaded area expressed as a proportion of the total area under the curve is the argument in Tables A·1 and A·2.

EXAMPLES

The deviate of the Normal Curve which cuts off a single tail equivalent to $\alpha = 0.05$ is given by $u = 1.6449$. Alternatively, the chance that an item taken at random from a Normal population specified by mean μ and standard deviation σ will not exceed in the algebraic sense $\mu + 1.6449\sigma$ is 0.95, or 95%.

The deviates of the Normal Curve which jointly cut off a double tail equivalent to $\alpha = 0.05$ are given by $u \pm 1.9600\sigma$. Alternatively, the chance that an item taken at random from a Normal population specified by mean μ and standard deviation σ will not deviate from μ in the absolute sense by more than 1.9600σ is 0.95, or 95%.

Table B

PROBABILITY POINTS OF THE χ^2 DISTRIBUTION

ϕ	0·001	0·005	0·01	0·025	0·05	0·1	0·25	0·5	0·75	0·9	0·95	0·975	0·99	0·995	ϕ
1	10·8	7·88	6·63	5·02	3·84	2·71	1·32	·455	·102	·016	—	—	—	—	1
2	13·8	10·6	9·21	7·38	5·99	4·61	2·77	1·39	·575	·211	·103	·051	·020	·010	2
3	16·3	12·8	11·3	9·35	7·81	6·25	4·11	2·37	1·21	·584	·352	·216	·115	·072	3
4	18·5	14·9	13·3	11·1	9·49	7·78	5·39	3·36	1·92	1·06	·711	·484	·297	·207	4
5	20·5	16·7	15·1	12·8	11·1	9·24	6·63	4·35	2·67	1·61	1·15	·831	·554	·412	5
6	22·5	18·5	16·8	14·4	12·6	10·6	7·84	5·35	3·45	2·20	1·64	1·24	·872	·676	6
7	24·3	20·3	18·5	16·0	14·1	12·0	9·04	6·35	4·25	2·83	2·17	1·69	1·24	·989	7
8	26·1	22·0	20·1	17·5	15·5	13·4	10·2	7·34	5·07	3·49	2·73	2·18	1·65	1·34	8
9	27·9	23·6	21·7	19·0	16·9	14·7	11·4	8·34	5·90	4·17	3·33	2·70	2·09	1·73	9
10	29·6	25·2	23·2	20·5	18·3	16·0	12·5	9·34	6·74	4·87	3·94	3·25	2·56	2·16	10
11	31·3	26·8	24·7	21·9	19·7	17·3	13·7	10·3	7·58	5·58	4·57	3·82	3·05	2·60	11
12	32·9	28·3	26·2	23·3	21·0	18·5	14·8	11·3	8·44	6·30	5·23	4·40	3·57	3·07	12
13	34·5	29·8	27·7	24·7	22·4	19·8	16·0	12·3	9·30	7·04	5·89	5·01	4·11	3·57	13
14	36·1	31·3	29·1	26·1	23·7	21·1	17·1	13·3	10·2	7·79	6·57	5·63	4·66	4·07	14
15	37·7	32·8	30·6	27·5	25·0	22·3	18·2	14·3	11·0	8·55	7·26	6·26	5·23	4·60	15
16	39·3	34·3	32·0	28·8	26·3	23·5	19·4	15·3	11·9	9·31	7·96	6·91	5·81	5·14	16
17	40·8	35·7	33·4	30·2	27·6	24·8	20·5	16·3	12·8	10·1	8·67	7·56	6·41	5·70	17
18	42·3	37·2	34·8	31·5	28·9	26·0	21·6	17·3	13·7	10·9	9·39	8·23	7·01	6·26	18
19	43·8	38·6	36·2	32·9	30·1	27·2	22·7	18·3	14·6	11·7	10·1	8·91	7·63	6·84	19
20	45·3	40·0	37·6	34·2	31·4	28·4	23·8	19·3	15·5	12·4	10·9	9·59	8·26	7·43	20
21	46·8	41·4	38·9	35·5	32·7	29·6	24·9	20·3	16·3	13·2	11·6	10·3	8·90	8·03	21
22	48·3	42·8	40·3	36·8	33·9	30·8	26·0	21·3	17·2	14·0	12·3	11·0	9·54	8·64	22
23	49·7	44·2	41·6	38·1	35·2	32·0	27·1	22·3	18·1	14·8	13·1	11·7	10·2	9·26	23
24	51·2	45·6	43·0	39·4	36·4	33·2	28·2	23·3	19·0	15·7	13·8	12·4	10·9	9·89	24
25	52·6	46·9	44·3	40·6	37·7	34·4	29·3	24·3	19·9	16·5	14·6	13·1	11·5	10·5	25
26	54·1	48·3	45·6	41·9	38·9	35·6	30·4	25·3	20·8	17·3	15·4	13·8	12·2	11·2	26
27	55·5	49·6	47·0	43·2	40·1	36·7	31·5	26·3	21·7	18·1	16·2	14·6	12·9	11·8	27
28	56·9	51·0	48·3	44·5	41·3	37·9	32·6	27·3	22·7	18·9	16·9	15·3	13·6	12·5	28
29	58·3	52·3	49·6	45·7	42·6	39·1	33·7	28·3	23·6	19·8	17·7	16·0	14·3	13·1	29
30	59·7	53·7	50·9	47·0	43·8	40·3	34·8	29·3	24·5	20·6	18·5	16·8	15·0	13·8	30

P

ϕ is the number of degrees of freedom.

Table B (*continued*)

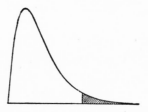

The illustration shows the χ^2 curve for $\phi = 3$. The shaded area expressed as a proportion of the total area under the curve corresponds to the columnar heading in the table.

EXAMPLES

Let $\chi^2 = 3.80$, $\phi = 3$. This is between the 50% and 25% points, and is therefore not significant.

Let $\chi^2 = 20.1$, $\phi = 9$. This is between the 2.5% and 1% points, and is therefore significant.

VALUES OF χ^2 FOR $\phi > 30$

For values of $\phi > 30$ the expression $\sqrt{(2\chi^2)} - \sqrt{(2\phi - 1)}$ may be used as a Normal deviate with unit variance, remembering that the probability for χ^2 corresponds to that of a single tail of the Normal Curve.

EXAMPLE

Let $\chi^2 = 124.3$, $\phi = 100$. Then $u = \sqrt{248.6} - \sqrt{199} = 1.66$.

For $u = 1.66$, the value of $P = 0.0485 = 4.85\%$. χ^2 is therefore just significant.

Table C
PROBABILITY POINTS OF THE t-DISTRIBUTION

Table C·1	Table C·2
Single-sided test	Double-sided test

ϕ	P				ϕ	P			
	0·005	0·01	0·05	0·1		0·005	0·01	0·05	0·1
1	63·7	31·8	6·31	3·08	1	127	63·7	12·7	6·31
2	9·92	6·96	2·92	1·89	2	14·1	9·92	4·30	2·92
3	5·84	4·54	2·35	1·64	3	7·45	5·84	3·18	2·35
4	4·60	3·75	2·13	1·53	4	5·60	4·60	2·78	2·13
5	4·03	3·36	2·01	1·48	5	4·77	4·03	2·57	2·01
6	3·71	3·14	1·94	1·44	6	4·32	3·71	2·45	1·94
7	3·50	3·00	1·89	1·42	7	4·03	3·50	2·36	1·89
8	3·36	2·90	1·86	1·40	8	3·83	3·36	2·31	1·86
9	3·25	2·82	1·83	1·38	9	3·69	3·25	2·26	1·83
10	3·17	2·76	1·81	1·37	10	3·58	3·17	2·23	1·81
11	3·11	2·72	1·80	1·36	11	3·50	3·11	2·20	1·80
12	3·05	2·68	1·78	1·36	12	3·43	3·05	2·18	1·78
13	3·01	2·65	1·77	1·35	13	3·37	3·01	2·16	1·77
14	2·98	2·62	1·76	1·34	14	3·33	2·98	2·14	1·76
15	2·95	2·60	1·75	1·34	15	3·29	2·95	2·13	1·75
16	2·92	2·58	1·75	1·34	16	3·25	2·92	2·12	1·75
17	2·90	2·57	1·74	1·33	17	3·22	2·90	2·11	1·74
18	2·88	2·55	1·73	1·33	18	3·20	2·88	2·10	1·73
19	2·86	2·54	1·73	1·33	19	3·17	2·86	2·09	1·73
20	2·85	2·53	1·72	1·32	20	3·15	2·85	2·09	1·72
21	2·83	2·52	1·72	1·32	21	3·14	2·83	2·08	1·72
22	2·82	2·51	1·72	1·32	22	3·12	2·82	2·07	1·72
23	2·81	2·50	1·71	1·32	23	3·10	2·81	2·07	1·71
24	2·80	2·49	1·71	1·32	24	3·09	2·80	2·06	1·71
25	2·79	2·48	1·71	1·32	25	3·08	2·79	2·06	1·71
26	2·78	2·48	1·71	1·32	26	3·07	2·78	2·06	1·71
27	2·77	2·47	1·70	1·31	27	3·06	2·77	2·05	1·70
28	2·76	2·47	1·70	1·31	28	3·05	2·76	2·05	1·70
29	2·76	2·46	1·70	1·31	29	3·04	2·76	2·05	1·70
30	2·75	2·46	1·70	1·31	30	3·03	2·75	2·04	1·70
40	2·70	2·42	1·68	1·30	40	2·97	2·70	2·02	1·68
60	2·66	2·39	1·67	1·30	60	2·91	2·66	2·00	1·67
120	2·62	2·36	1·66	1·29	120	2·86	2·62	1·98	1·66
∞	2·58	2·33	1·64	1·28	∞	2·81	2·58	1·96	1·64

The illustrations show the *t*-curve for $\phi = 3$. The shaded areas correspond to the columnar headings of the table and the unshaded areas to their complements.

EXAMPLES

Single-sided test. For $\phi = 10$ the deviate of the *t*-curve which cuts off a single tail equivalent to $\alpha = 0\cdot05$ is given by $t = 1\cdot81$. For the Normal Curve the corresponding value of u is $1\cdot64$.

Double-sided test. For $\phi = 10$ the deviates of the *t*-curve which jointly cut off a double tail equivalent to $\alpha = 0\cdot05$ are given by $t = 2\cdot23$. For the Normal Curve the corresponding value of u is $1\cdot96$.

TABLE OF THE VARIANCE RATIO (*F*-DISTRIBUTION)
(*See next page.*)

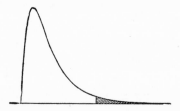

The illustration shows the distribution of the variance ratio for 4 and 16 degrees of freedom. The shaded area, expressed as a proportion of the total area under the curve, is the argument in the first column of Table D.

The variance ratio is always calculated with the *larger* estimate of variance in the *numerator*, and ϕ_1 and ϕ_2 are the numbers of degrees of freedom in the numerator and denominator respectively.

EXAMPLE

Let $F = 4 \cdot 60$, $\phi_1 = 5$, $\phi_2 = 24$. The 5% and 1% points are $2 \cdot 62$ and $3 \cdot 90$, and the result is significant.

In calculating confidence limits for the variance ratio we require the upper and lower tail areas of the F-distribution. The levels actually tabled refer to the single upper tail area $F_a(\phi_1\phi_2)$.

However, the value $F_{1-a}(\phi_1\phi_2)$ (i.e. the value of F *below which* a proportion a of the whole curve lies) is given by

$$F_{1-a}(\phi_1\phi_2) = \frac{1}{F_a(\phi_2\phi_1)}$$

EXAMPLE

To obtain the 90% confidence limits for the variance ratio we require the values $F_{0 \cdot 95}$ $(\phi_1\phi_2)$ and $F_{0 \cdot 05}$ $(\phi_1\phi_2)$.
If $\phi_1 = 4$ and $\phi_2 = 20$, then

$$F_{0 \cdot 95} (4, 20) = \frac{1}{F_{0 \cdot 05} (20, 4)} = \frac{1}{5 \cdot 80} \text{ and } F_{0 \cdot 05} (4, 20) = 2 \cdot 87$$

The required values are thus $0 \cdot 172$ and $2 \cdot 87$.

Table D
PROBABILITY POINTS OF THE VARIANCE RATIO (*F*-DISTRIBUTION)

φ₁ (corresponding to greater mean square)

ϕ_2	Probability point	1	2	3	4	5	6	7	8	9	10	12	15	20	24	30	40	60	120	∞
1	0·1	39·9	49·5	53·6	55·8	57·2	58·2	58·9	59·4	59·9	60·2	60·7	61·2	61·7	62·0	62·3	62·5	62·8	63·1	63·3
	0·05	161	199	216	225	230	234	237	239	241	242	244	246	248	249	250	251	252	253	254
	0·01	4052	4999	5403	5625	5764	5859	5928	5982	6022	6056	6106	6157	6209	6235	6261	6287	6313	6339	6366
2	0·1	8·53	9·00	9·16	9·24	9·29	9·33	9·35	9·37	9·38	9·39	9·41	9·42	9·44	9·45	9·46	9·47	9·47	9·48	9·49
	0·05	18·5	19·0	19·2	19·2	19·3	19·3	19·4	19·4	19·4	19·4	19·4	19·4	19·4	19·5	19·5	19·5	19·5	19·5	19·5
	0·01	98·5	99·0	99·2	99·2	99·3	99·3	99·4	99·4	99·4	99·4	99·4	99·4	99·4	99·5	99·5	99·5	99·5	99·5	99·5
3	0·1	5·54	5·46	5·39	5·34	5·31	5·28	5·27	5·25	5·24	5·23	5·22	5·20	5·18	5·18	5·17	5·16	5·15	5·14	5·13
	0·05	10·1	9·55	9·28	9·12	9·01	8·94	8·89	8·85	8·81	8·79	8·74	8·70	8·66	8·64	8·62	8·59	8·57	8·55	8·53
	0·01	34·1	30·8	29·5	28·7	28·2	27·9	27·7	27·5	27·3	27·2	27·1	26·9	26·7	26·6	26·5	26·4	26·3	26·2	26·1
4	0·1	4·54	4·32	4·19	4·11	4·05	4·01	3·98	3·95	3·94	3·92	3·90	3·87	3·84	3·83	3·82	3·80	3·79	3·78	3·76
	0·05	7·71	6·94	6·59	6·39	6·26	6·16	6·09	6·04	6·00	5·96	5·91	5·86	5·80	5·77	5·75	5·72	5·69	5·66	5·63
	0·01	21·2	18·0	16·7	16·0	15·5	15·2	15·0	14·8	14·7	14·5	14·4	14·2	14·0	13·9	13·8	13·7	13·7	13·6	13·5
5	0·1	4·06	3·78	3·62	3·52	3·45	3·40	3·37	3·34	3·32	3·30	3·27	3·24	3·21	3·19	3·17	3·16	3·14	3·12	3·10
	0·05	6·61	5·79	5·41	5·19	5·05	4·95	4·88	4·82	4·77	4·74	4·68	4·62	4·56	4·53	4·50	4·46	4·43	4·40	4·36
	0·01	16·3	13·3	12·1	11·4	11·0	10·7	10·5	10·3	10·2	10·1	9·89	9·72	9·55	9·47	9·38	9·29	9·20	9·11	9·02
6	0·1	3·78	3·46	3·29	3·18	3·11	3·05	3·01	2·98	2·96	2·94	2·90	2·87	2·84	2·82	2·80	2·78	2·76	2·74	2·72
	0·05	5·99	5·14	4·76	4·53	4·39	4·28	4·21	4·15	4·10	4·06	4·00	3·94	3·87	3·84	3·81	3·77	3·74	3·70	3·67
	0·01	13·7	10·9	9·78	9·15	8·75	8·47	8·26	8·10	7·98	7·87	7·72	7·56	7·40	7·31	7·23	7·14	7·06	6·97	6·88
7	0·1	3·59	3·26	3·07	2·96	2·88	2·83	2·78	2·75	2·72	2·70	2·67	2·63	2·59	2·58	2·56	2·54	2·51	2·49	2·47
	0·05	5·59	4·74	4·35	4·12	3·97	3·87	3·79	3·73	3·68	3·64	3·57	3·51	3·44	3·41	3·38	3·34	3·30	3·27	3·23
	0·01	12·2	9·55	8·45	7·85	7·46	7·19	6·99	6·84	6·72	6·62	6·47	6·31	6·16	6·07	5·99	5·91	5·82	5·74	5·65
8	0·1	3·46	3·11	2·92	2·81	2·73	2·67	2·62	2·59	2·56	2·54	2·50	2·46	2·42	2·40	2·38	2·36	2·34	2·32	2·29
	0·05	5·32	4·46	4·07	3·84	3·69	3·58	3·50	3·44	3·39	3·35	3·28	3·22	3·15	3·12	3·08	3·04	3·01	2·97	2·93
	0·01	11·3	8·65	7·59	7·01	6·63	6·37	6·18	6·03	5·91	5·81	5·67	5·52	5·36	5·28	5·20	5·12	5·03	4·95	4·86
9	0·1	3·36	3·01	2·81	2·69	2·61	2·55	2·51	2·47	2·44	2·42	2·38	2·34	2·30	2·28	2·25	2·23	2·21	2·18	2·16
	0·05	5·12	4·26	3·86	3·63	3·48	3·37	3·29	3·23	3·18	3·14	3·07	3·01	2·94	2·90	2·86	2·83	2·79	2·75	2·71
	0·01	10·6	8·02	6·99	6·42	6·06	5·80	5·61	5·47	5·35	5·26	5·11	4·96	4·81	4·73	4·65	4·57	4·48	4·40	4·31

Table D (continued)

ϕ_1 (corresponding to greater mean square)

ϕ_2	Probability point	1	2	3	4	5	6	7	8	9	10	12	15	20	24	30	40	60	120	∞
10	0·1	3·28	2·92	2·73	2·61	2·52	2·46	2·41	2·38	2·35	2·32	2·28	2·24	2·20	2·18	2·16	2·13	2·11	2·08	2·06
	0·05	4·96	4·10	3·71	3·48	3·33	3·22	3·14	3·07	3·02	2·98	2·91	2·84	2·77	2·74	2·70	2·66	2·62	2·58	2·54
	0·01	10·0	7·56	6·55	5·99	5·64	5·39	5·20	5·06	4·94	4·85	4·71	4·56	4·41	4·33	4·25	4·17	4·08	4·00	3·91
11	0·1	3·23	2·86	2·66	2·54	2·45	2·39	2·34	2·30	2·27	2·25	2·21	2·17	2·12	2·10	2·08	2·05	2·03	2·00	1·97
	0·05	4·84	3·98	3·59	3·36	3·20	3·09	3·01	2·95	2·90	2·85	2·79	2·72	2·65	2·61	2·57	2·53	2·49	2·45	2·40
	0·01	9·65	7·21	6·22	5·67	5·32	5·07	4·89	4·74	4·63	4·54	4·40	4·25	4·10	4·02	3·94	3·86	3·78	3·69	3·60
12	0·1	3·18	2·81	2·61	2·48	2·39	2·33	2·28	2·24	2·21	2·19	2·15	2·10	2·06	2·04	2·01	1·99	1·96	1·93	1·90
	0·05	4·75	3·89	3·49	3·26	3·11	3·00	2·91	2·85	2·80	2·75	2·69	2·62	2·54	2·51	2·47	2·43	2·38	2·34	2·30
	0·01	9·33	6·93	5·95	5·41	5·06	4·82	4·64	4·50	4·39	4·30	4·16	4·01	3·86	3·78	3·70	3·62	3·54	3·45	3·36
13	0·1	3·14	2·76	2·56	2·43	2·35	2·28	2·23	2·20	2·16	2·14	2·10	2·05	2·01	1·98	1·96	1·93	1·90	1·88	1·85
	0·05	4·67	3·81	3·41	3·18	3·03	2·92	2·83	2·77	2·71	2·67	2·60	2·53	2·46	2·42	2·38	2·34	2·30	2·25	2·21
	0·01	9·07	6·70	5·74	5·21	4·86	4·62	4·44	4·30	4·19	4·10	3·96	3·82	3·66	3·59	3·51	3·43	3·34	3·25	3·17
14	0·1	3·10	2·73	2·52	2·39	2·31	2·24	2·19	2·15	2·12	2·10	2·05	2·01	1·96	1·94	1·91	1·89	1·86	1·83	1·80
	0·05	4·60	3·74	3·34	3·11	2·96	2·85	2·76	2·70	2·65	2·60	2·53	2·46	2·39	2·35	2·31	2·27	2·22	2·18	2·13
	0·01	8·86	6·51	5·56	5·04	4·69	4·46	4·28	4·14	4·03	3·94	3·80	3·66	3·51	3·43	3·35	3·27	3·18	3·09	3·00
15	0·1	3·07	2·70	2·49	2·36	2·27	2·21	2·16	2·12	2·09	2·06	2·02	1·97	1·92	1·90	1·87	1·85	1·82	1·79	1·76
	0·05	4·54	3·68	3·29	3·06	2·90	2·79	2·71	2·64	2·59	2·54	2·48	2·40	2·33	2·29	2·25	2·20	2·16	2·11	2·07
	0·01	8·68	6·36	5·42	4·89	4·56	4·32	4·14	4·00	3·89	3·80	3·67	3·52	3·37	3·29	3·21	3·13	3·05	2·96	2·87
16	0·1	3·05	2·67	2·46	2·33	2·24	2·18	2·13	2·09	2·06	2·03	1·99	1·94	1·89	1·87	1·84	1·81	1·78	1·75	1·72
	0·05	4·49	3·63	3·24	3·01	2·85	2·74	2·66	2·59	2·54	2·49	2·42	2·35	2·28	2·24	2·19	2·15	2·11	2·06	2·01
	0·01	8·53	6·23	5·29	4·77	4·44	4·20	4·03	3·89	3·78	3·69	3·55	3·41	3·26	3·18	3·10	3·02	2·93	2·84	2·75
17	0·1	3·03	2·64	2·44	2·31	2·22	2·15	2·10	2·06	2·03	2·00	1·96	1·91	1·86	1·84	1·81	1·78	1·75	1·72	1·69
	0·05	4·45	3·59	3·20	2·96	2·81	2·70	2·61	2·55	2·49	2·45	2·38	2·31	2·23	2·19	2·15	2·10	2·06	2·01	1·96
	0·01	8·40	6·11	5·18	4·67	4·34	4·10	3·93	3·79	3·68	3·59	3·46	3·31	3·16	3·08	3·00	2·92	2·83	2·75	2·65
18	0·1	3·01	2·62	2·42	2·29	2·20	2·13	2·08	2·04	2·00	1·98	1·93	1·89	1·84	1·81	1·78	1·75	1·72	1·69	1·66
	0·05	4·41	3·55	3·16	2·93	2·77	2·66	2·58	2·51	2·46	2·41	2·34	2·27	2·19	2·15	2·11	2·06	2·02	1·97	1·92
	0·01	8·29	6·01	5·09	4·58	4·25	4·01	3·84	3·71	3·60	3·51	3·37	3·23	3·08	3·00	2·92	2·84	2·75	2·66	2·57

For explanation and examples see p. 601

Table D (continued)

Probability point	φ₂	φ₁ (corresponding to greater mean square) 1	2	3	4	5	6	7	8	9	10	12	15	20	24	30	40	60	120	∞	φ₂	Probability point
0.1	19	2.99	2.61	2.40	2.27	2.18	2.11	2.06	2.02	1.98	1.96	1.91	1.86	1.81	1.79	1.76	1.73	1.70	1.67	1.63	19	0.1
0.05		4.38	3.52	3.13	2.90	2.74	2.63	2.54	2.48	2.42	2.38	2.31	2.23	2.16	2.11	2.07	2.03	1.98	1.93	1.88		0.05
0.01		8.18	5.93	5.01	4.50	4.17	3.94	3.77	3.63	3.52	3.43	3.30	3.15	3.00	2.92	2.84	2.76	2.67	2.58	2.49		0.01
0.1	20	2.97	2.59	2.38	2.25	2.16	2.09	2.04	2.00	1.96	1.94	1.89	1.84	1.79	1.77	1.74	1.71	1.68	1.64	1.61	20	0.1
0.05		4.35	3.49	3.10	2.87	2.71	2.60	2.51	2.45	2.39	2.35	2.28	2.20	2.12	2.08	2.04	1.99	1.95	1.90	1.84		0.05
0.01		8.10	5.85	4.94	4.43	4.10	3.87	3.70	3.56	3.46	3.37	3.23	3.09	2.94	2.86	2.78	2.69	2.61	2.52	2.42		0.01
0.1	21	2.96	2.57	2.36	2.23	2.14	2.08	2.02	1.98	1.95	1.92	1.87	1.83	1.78	1.75	1.72	1.69	1.66	1.62	1.59	21	0.1
0.05		4.32	3.47	3.07	2.84	2.68	2.57	2.49	2.42	2.37	2.32	2.25	2.18	2.10	2.05	2.01	1.96	1.92	1.87	1.81		0.05
0.01		8.02	5.78	4.87	4.37	4.04	3.81	3.64	3.51	3.40	3.31	3.17	3.03	2.88	2.80	2.72	2.64	2.55	2.46	2.36		0.01
0.1	22	2.95	2.56	2.35	2.22	2.13	2.06	2.01	1.97	1.93	1.90	1.86	1.81	1.76	1.73	1.70	1.67	1.64	1.60	1.57	22	0.1
0.05		4.30	3.44	3.05	2.82	2.66	2.55	2.46	2.40	2.34	2.30	2.23	2.15	2.07	2.03	1.98	1.94	1.89	1.84	1.78		0.05
0.01		7.95	5.72	4.82	4.31	3.99	3.76	3.59	3.45	3.35	3.26	3.12	2.98	2.83	2.75	2.67	2.58	2.50	2.40	2.31		0.01
0.1	23	2.94	2.55	2.34	2.21	2.11	2.05	1.99	1.95	1.92	1.89	1.85	1.80	1.74	1.72	1.69	1.66	1.62	1.59	1.55	23	0.1
0.05		4.28	3.42	3.03	2.80	2.64	2.53	2.44	2.37	2.32	2.27	2.20	2.13	2.05	2.00	1.96	1.91	1.86	1.81	1.76		0.05
0.01		7.88	5.66	4.76	4.26	3.94	3.71	3.54	3.41	3.30	3.21	3.07	2.93	2.78	2.70	2.62	2.54	2.45	2.35	2.26		0.01
0.1	24	2.93	2.54	2.33	2.19	2.10	2.04	1.98	1.94	1.91	1.88	1.83	1.78	1.73	1.70	1.67	1.64	1.61	1.57	1.53	24	0.1
0.05		4.26	3.40	3.01	2.78	2.62	2.51	2.42	2.36	2.30	2.25	2.18	2.11	2.03	1.98	1.94	1.89	1.84	1.79	1.73		0.05
0.01		7.82	5.61	4.72	4.22	3.90	3.67	3.50	3.36	3.26	3.17	3.03	2.89	2.74	2.66	2.58	2.49	2.40	2.31	2.21		0.01
0.1	25	2.92	2.53	2.32	2.18	2.09	2.02	1.97	1.93	1.89	1.87	1.82	1.77	1.72	1.69	1.66	1.63	1.59	1.56	1.52	25	0.1
0.05		4.24	3.39	2.99	2.76	2.60	2.49	2.40	2.34	2.28	2.24	2.16	2.09	2.01	1.96	1.92	1.87	1.82	1.77	1.71		0.05
0.01		7.77	5.57	4.68	4.18	3.86	3.63	3.46	3.32	3.22	3.13	2.99	2.85	2.70	2.62	2.54	2.45	2.36	2.27	2.17		0.01
0.1	26	2.91	2.52	2.31	2.17	2.08	2.01	1.96	1.92	1.88	1.86	1.81	1.76	1.71	1.68	1.65	1.61	1.58	1.54	1.50	26	0.1
0.05		4.23	3.37	2.98	2.74	2.59	2.47	2.39	2.32	2.27	2.22	2.15	2.07	1.99	1.95	1.90	1.85	1.80	1.75	1.69		0.05
0.01		7.72	5.53	4.64	4.14	3.82	3.59	3.42	3.29	3.18	3.09	2.96	2.82	2.66	2.58	2.50	2.42	2.33	2.23	2.13		0.01

For explanation and examples see p. 601

Table D (continued)

ϕ_1 (corresponding to greater mean square)

Probability point	ϕ_2	1	2	3	4	5	6	7	8	9	10	12	15	20	24	30	40	60	120	∞
0·1	27	2·90	2·51	2·30	2·17	2·07	2·00	1·95	1·91	1·87	1·85	1·80	1·75	1·70	1·67	1·64	1·60	1·57	1·53	1·49
0·05		4·21	3·35	2·96	2·73	2·57	2·46	2·37	2·31	2·25	2·20	2·13	2·06	1·97	1·93	1·88	1·84	1·79	1·73	1·67
0·01		7·68	5·49	4·60	4·11	3·78	3·56	3·39	3·26	3·15	3·06	2·93	2·78	2·63	2·55	2·47	2·38	2·29	2·20	2·10
0·1	28	2·89	2·50	2·29	2·16	2·06	2·00	1·94	1·90	1·87	1·84	1·79	1·74	1·69	1·66	1·63	1·59	1·56	1·52	1·48
0·05		4·20	3·34	2·95	2·71	2·56	2·45	2·36	2·29	2·24	2·19	2·12	2·04	1·96	1·91	1·87	1·82	1·77	1·71	1·65
0·01		7·64	5·45	4·57	4·07	3·75	3·53	3·36	3·23	3·12	3·03	2·90	2·75	2·60	2·52	2·44	2·35	2·26	2·17	2·06
0·1	29	2·89	2·50	2·28	2·15	2·06	1·99	1·93	1·89	1·86	1·83	1·78	1·73	1·68	1·65	1·62	1·58	1·55	1·51	1·47
0·05		4·18	3·33	2·93	2·70	2·55	2·43	2·35	2·28	2·22	2·18	2·10	2·03	1·94	1·90	1·85	1·81	1·75	1·70	1·64
0·01		7·60	5·42	4·54	4·04	3·73	3·50	3·33	3·20	3·09	3·00	2·87	2·73	2·57	2·49	2·41	2·33	2·23	2·14	2·03
0·1	30	2·88	2·49	2·28	2·14	2·05	1·98	1·93	1·88	1·85	1·82	1·77	1·72	1·67	1·64	1·61	1·57	1·54	1·50	1·46
0·05		4·17	3·32	2·92	2·69	2·53	2·42	2·33	2·27	2·21	2·16	2·09	2·01	1·93	1·89	1·84	1·79	1·74	1·68	1·62
0·01		7·56	5·39	4·51	4·02	3·70	3·47	3·30	3·17	3·07	2·98	2·84	2·70	2·55	2·47	2·39	2·30	2·21	2·11	2·01
0·1	40	2·84	2·44	2·23	2·09	2·00	1·93	1·87	1·83	1·79	1·76	1·71	1·66	1·61	1·57	1·54	1·51	1·47	1·42	1·38
0·05		4·08	3·23	2·84	2·61	2·45	2·34	2·25	2·18	2·12	2·08	2·00	1·92	1·84	1·79	1·74	1·69	1·64	1·58	1·51
0·01		7·31	5·18	4·31	3·83	3·51	3·29	3·12	2·99	2·89	2·80	2·66	2·52	2·37	2·29	2·20	2·11	2·02	1·92	1·80
0·1	60	2·79	2·39	2·18	2·04	1·95	1·87	1·82	1·77	1·74	1·71	1·66	1·60	1·54	1·51	1·48	1·44	1·40	1·35	1·29
0·05		4·00	3·15	2·76	2·53	2·37	2·25	2·17	2·10	2·04	1·99	1·92	1·84	1·75	1·70	1·65	1·59	1·53	1·47	1·39
0·01		7·08	4·98	4·13	3·65	3·34	3·12	2·95	2·82	2·72	2·63	2·50	2·35	2·20	2·12	2·03	1·94	1·84	1·73	1·60
0·1	120	2·75	2·35	2·13	1·99	1·90	1·82	1·77	1·72	1·68	1·65	1·60	1·54	1·48	1·45	1·41	1·37	1·32	1·26	1·19
0·05		3·92	3·07	2·68	2·45	2·29	2·18	2·09	2·02	1·96	1·91	1·83	1·75	1·66	1·61	1·55	1·50	1·43	1·35	1·25
0·01		6·85	4·79	3·95	3·48	3·17	2·96	2·79	2·66	2·56	2·47	2·34	2·19	2·03	1·95	1·86	1·76	1·66	1·53	1·38
0·1	∞	2·71	2·30	2·08	1·94	1·85	1·77	1·72	1·67	1·63	1·60	1·55	1·49	1·42	1·38	1·34	1·30	1·24	1·17	1·00
0·05		3·84	3·00	2·60	2·37	2·21	2·10	2·01	1·94	1·88	1·83	1·75	1·67	1·57	1·52	1·46	1·39	1·32	1·22	1·00
0·01		6·63	4·61	3·78	3·32	3·02	2·80	2·64	2·51	2·41	2·32	2·18	2·04	1·88	1·79	1·70	1·59	1·47	1·32	1·00

For explanation and examples see p. 601

Table E

NUMBER OF OBSERVATIONS FOR t-TEST OF MEAN

The entries in this table show the numbers of observations needed in a t-test of the significance of a mean in order to control the probabilities of errors of the first and second kinds at α and β respectively.

Level of t-test

Value of $D = \dfrac{\delta}{\sigma}$	0·01					0·02					0·05					0·1				
Single-sided test	α = 0·005					α = 0·01					α = 0·025					α = 0·05				
Double-sided test	α = 0·01					α = 0·02					α = 0·05					α = 0·1				
β =	0·01	0·05	0·1	0·2	0·5	0·01	0·05	0·1	0·2	0·5	0·01	0·05	0·1	0·2	0·5	0·01	0·05	0·1	0·2	0·5
0·05																				
0·10																				
0·15																					122
0·20										139					99					70
0·25					110					90				128	64			139	101	45
0·30				134	78				115	63			119	90	45		122	97	71	32
0·35			125	99	58			109	85	47		109	88	67	34		90	72	52	24
0·40		115	97	77	45		101	85	66	37	117	84	68	51	26	101	70	55	40	19
0·45		92	77	62	37	110	81	68	53	30	93	67	54	41	21	80	55	44	33	15
0·50	100	75	63	51	30	90	66	55	43	25	76	54	44	34	18	65	45	36	27	13
0·55	83	63	53	42	26	75	55	46	36	21	63	45	37	28	15	54	38	30	22	11
0·60	71	53	45	36	22	63	47	39	31	18	53	38	32	24	13	46	32	26	19	9
0·65	61	46	39	31	20	55	41	34	27	16	46	33	27	21	12	39	28	22	17	8
0·70	53	40	34	28	17	47	35	30	24	14	40	29	24	19	10	34	24	19	15	8
0·75	47	36	30	25	16	42	31	27	21	13	35	26	21	16	9	30	21	17	13	7
0·80	41	32	27	22	14	37	28	24	19	12	31	22	19	15	9	27	19	15	12	6
0·85	37	29	24	20	13	33	25	21	17	11	28	21	17	13	8	24	17	14	11	6
0·90	34	26	22	18	12	29	23	19	16	10	25	19	16	12	7	21	15	13	10	5
0·95	31	24	20	17	11	27	21	18	14	9	23	17	14	11	7	19	14	11	9	5

NUMBER OF OBSERVATIONS FOR t-TEST OF MEAN

The entries in this table show the numbers of observations needed in a t-test of the significance of a mean in order to control the probabilities of errors of the first and second kinds at α and β respectively.

Level of t-test column groups:

Level of t-test	Single-sided test (α)	Double-sided test (α)
0.01	0.005	0.01
0.02	0.01	0.02
0.05	0.025	0.05
0.1	0.05	0.1

$D=\dfrac{\delta}{\sigma}$	0.01: β=0.01	0.05	0.1	0.2	0.5	0.02: β=0.01	0.05	0.1	0.2	0.5	0.05: β=0.01	0.05	0.1	0.2	0.5	0.1: β=0.01	0.05	0.1	0.2	0.5
1.1	24	19	16	14	9	21	16	14	12	8	18	13	11	9	6	15	11	9	7	
1.2	21	16	14	12	8	18	14	12	10	7	15	12	10	8	5	13	10	8	6	
1.3	18	15	13	11	8	16	13	11	9	6	14	10	9	7		11	8	7	6	
1.4	16	13	12	10	7	14	11	10	9	6	12	9	8	7		10	8	7	5	
1.5	15	12	11	9	7	13	10	9	8	6	11	8	7	6		9	7	6		
1.6	13	11	10	8	6	12	10	9	7	5	10	8	7	6		8	6	6		
1.7	12	10	9	8	6	11	9	8	7		9	7	6	5		8	6	5		
1.8	12	10	9	8	6	10	8	7	7		8	7	6			7	6			
1.9	11	9	8	7	6	10	8	7	6		8	6	6			7	5			
2.0	10	8	8	7	5	9	7	7	6		7	6	5			6				
2.1	10	8	7	7		8	7	6	6		7	6				6				
2.2	9	8	7	6		8	7	6	6		7	6				6				
2.3	9	7	7	6		8	6	6	6		6	5				5				
2.4	8	7	7	6		7	6	6	6		6									
2.5	8	7	6	6		7	6	6	6		6									
3.0	7	6	6	5		6	5	5	5		5									
3.5	6	5	5			5														
4.0	6																			

EXAMPLES

Single-sided Test. Let $\delta = 1 \cdot 2$, $\alpha = 0 \cdot 05$, $\beta = 0 \cdot 1$, and an estimate of σ be $0 \cdot 8$. Thus $D = 1 \cdot 2 / 0 \cdot 8 = 1 \cdot 5$. Entering the table with these values it is found that $n = 6$. Six observations should be taken therefore and a t-test made at the $0 \cdot 05$ level.

Double-sided Test. Let $\delta = 0 \cdot 9$, $\alpha = 0 \cdot 02$, $\beta = 0 \cdot 05$, and an estimate of σ be $1 \cdot 2$. Thus $D = 0 \cdot 9 / 1 \cdot 2 = 0 \cdot 75$. Entering the table with these values it is found that $n = 31$. Thirty-one observations should be taken therefore and a t-test made at the $0 \cdot 02$ level.

NUMBER OF OBSERVATIONS FOR t-TEST OF DIFFERENCE BETWEEN TWO MEANS

The entries in this table show the number of observations needed in a t-test of the significance of the difference between two means in order to control the probabilities of the errors of the first and second kinds at α and β respectively.

Level of t-test

Value of D = δ/σ	0·01					0·02					0·05					0·1					β =
Single-sided test	α = 0·005					α = 0·01					α = 0·025					α = 0·05					
Double-sided test	α = 0·01					α = 0·02					α = 0·05					α = 0·1					
β =	0·01	0·05	0·1	0·2	0·5	0·01	0·05	0·1	0·2	0·5	0·01	0·05	0·1	0·2	0·5	0·01	0·05	0·1	0·2	0·5	
0·05																					0·05
0·10																					0·10
0·15																					0·15
0·20																				137	0·20
0·25															124					88	0·25
0·30										123					87					61	0·30
0·35					110					90					64				102	45	0·35
0·40					85					70				100	50			108	78	35	0·40
0·45				118	68				101	55			105	79	39		108	86	62	28	0·45
0·50				96	55			106	82	45		106	86	64	32		88	70	51	23	0·50
0·55			101	79	46		104	88	68	38		87	71	53	27	112	73	58	42	19	0·55
0·60		101	85	67	39		90	74	58	32	104	74	60	45	23	89	61	49	36	16	0·60
0·65		87	73	57	34	104	77	64	49	27	88	63	51	39	20	76	52	42	30	14	0·65
0·70	100	75	63	50	29	90	66	55	43	24	76	55	44	34	17	66	45	36	26	12	0·70
0·75	88	66	55	44	26	79	58	48	38	21	67	48	39	29	15	57	40	32	23	11	0·75
0·80	77	58	49	39	23	70	51	43	33	19	59	42	34	26	14	50	35	28	21	10	0·80
0·85	69	51	43	35	21	62	46	38	30	17	52	37	31	23	12	45	31	25	18	9	0·85
0·90	62	46	39	31	19	55	41	34	27	15	47	34	27	21	11	40	28	22	16	8	0·90
0·95	55	42	35	28	17	50	37	31	24	14	42	30	25	19	10	36	25	20	15	7	0·95
1·00	50	38	32	26	15	45	33	28	22	13	38	27	23	17	9	33	23	18	14	7	1·00

R2

Table E·1 (continued)

NUMBER OF OBSERVATIONS FOR t-TEST OF DIFFERENCE BETWEEN TWO MEANS

The entries in this table show the number of observations needed in a t-test of the significance of the difference between two means in order to control the probabilities of the errors of the first and second kinds at α and β respectively.

	Level of t-test																				
	0·01					0·02					0·05					0·1					
Single-sided test	α = 0·005					α = 0·01					α = 0·025					α = 0·05					
Double-sided test	α = 0·01					α = 0·02					α = 0·05					α = 0·1					
β =	0·01	0·05	0·1	0·2	0·5	0·01	0·05	0·1	0·2	0·5	0·01	0·05	0·1	0·2	0·5	0·01	0·05	0·1	0·2	0·5	Value of $D = \dfrac{\delta}{\sigma}$
1·1	42	32	27	22	13	38	28	23	19	11	32	23	19	14	8	27	19	15	12	6	1·1
1·2	36	27	23	18	11	32	24	20	16	9	27	20	16	12	7	23	16	13	10	5	1·2
1·3	31	23	20	16	10	28	21	17	14	8	23	17	14	11	6	20	14	11	9	5	1·3
1·4	27	20	17	14	9	24	18	15	12	8	20	15	12	10	6	17	12	10	8	4	1·4
1·5	24	18	15	13	8	21	16	14	11	7	18	13	11	9	5	15	11	9	7	4	1·5
1·6	21	16	14	11	7	19	14	12	10	6	16	12	10	8	5	14	10	8	6	4	1·6
1·7	19	15	13	10	7	17	13	11	9	6	14	11	9	7	4	12	9	7	6	3	1·7
1·8	17	13	11	10	6	15	12	10	8	5	13	10	8	6	4	11	8	7	5		1·8
1·9	16	12	10	9	6	14	11	9	8	5	12	9	7	6	4	10	7	6	5		1·9
2·0	14	11	10	8	6	13	10	9	7	5	11	8	7	6	4	9	7	6	4		2·0
2·1	13	10	9	8	5	12	9	8	7	5	10	8	6	5	3	8	6	5	4		2·1
2·2	12	10	8	7	5	11	9	7	6	4	9	7	6	5		8	6	5	4		2·2
2·3	11	9	8	7	5	10	8	7	6	4	9	7	6	5		7	5	5	4		2·3
2·4	11	9	8	6	5	10	8	7	6	4	8	6	5	4		7	5	4	4		2·4
2·5	10	8	7	6	4	9	7	6	5	4	8	6	5	4		6	5	4	3		2·5
3·0	8	6	6	5	4	7	6	5	4	3	6	5	4	4		5	4	3			3·0
3·5	6	5	5	4	3	6	5	4	4		5	4	4	3		4	3				3·5
4·0	6	5	5	4		5	4	4	3		4	4	4			4					4·0

Examples

Single-sided Test. Let $\delta = 1.6$, $\alpha = 0.025$, $\beta = 0.01$, and an estimate of σ be 1.0. Thus $D = 1.6/1.0 = 1.6$. Entering the table with these values it is found that $n = 16$. Sixteen observations should be taken therefore in each group and a t-test made at the 0.025 level.

Double-sided Test. Let $\delta = 1.8$, $\alpha = 0.01$, $\beta = 0.05$, and an estimate of σ be 1.5. Thus $D = 1.8/1.5 = 1.2$. Entering the table with these values it is found that $n = 27$. Twenty-seven observations should be taken therefore in each group and a t-test made at the 0.01 level.

Table F

$$x = \text{arc sin } \sqrt{p}$$

(x measured in radians)

	0.00	0.01	0.02	0.03	0.04	0.05	0.06	0.07	0.08	0.09
0.0	0.0000	0.1002	0.1419	0.1741	0.2014	0.2255	0.2475	0.2678	0.2868	0.3047
0.1	0.3218	0.3381	0.3537	0.3689	0.3835	0.3977	0.4115	0.4250	0.4381	0.4510
0.2	0.4636	0.4760	0.4882	0.5002	0.5120	0.5236	0.5351	0.5464	0.5576	0.5687
0.3	0.5796	0.5905	0.6013	0.6119	0.6225	0.6331	0.6435	0.6539	0.6642	0.6745
0.4	0.6847	0.6949	0.7051	0.7152	0.7253	0.7353	0.7454	0.7554	0.7654	0.7754
0.5	0.7854	0.7954	0.8054	0.8154	0.8254	0.8355	0.8455	0.8556	0.8657	0.8759
0.6	0.8861	0.8963	0.9066	0.9169	0.9273	0.9377	0.9483	0.9589	0.9695	0.9803
0.7	0.9912	1.0021	1.0132	1.0244	1.0357	1.0472	1.0588	1.0706	1.0826	1.0948
0.8	1.1071	1.1198	1.1326	1.1458	1.1593	1.1731	1.1873	1.2019	1.2171	1.2327
0.9	1.2490	1.2661	1.2840	1.3030	1.3233	1.3453	1.3694	1.3967	1.4289	1.4706
1.0	1.5708									

The score x corresponding to the proportion p is given in the body of the table for the values of p given by the sum of the two marginal numbers. Thus arc sin $\sqrt{0.27} = 0.5464$.

Table G

NUMBER OF OBSERVATIONS REQUIRED FOR THE COMPARISON OF A POPULATION VARIANCE WITH A STANDARD VALUE USING THE χ^2-TEST.

The entries in this table show the value of the ratio R of the population variance σ_1^2 to a standard variance σ_0^2 which is undetected with frequency β in a χ^2 test at significance level α of an estimate s_1^2 of σ_1^2 based on ϕ degrees of freedom.

ϕ	$\alpha = 0.01$				$\alpha = 0.05$			
	$\beta=0.01$	$\beta=0.05$	$\beta=0.1$	$\beta=0.5$	$\beta=0.01$	$\beta=0.05$	$\beta=0.1$	$\beta=0.5$
1	42,240	1,687	420.2	14.58	24,450	977.0	243.3	8.444
2	458.2	89.78	43.71	6.644	298.1	58.40	28.43	4.322
3	98.79	32.24	19.41	4.795	68.05	22.21	13.37	3.303
4	44.69	18.68	12.48	3.955	31.93	13.35	8.920	2.826
5	27.22	13.17	9.369	3.467	19.97	9.665	6.875	2.544
6	19.28	10.28	7.628	3.144	14.44	7.699	5.713	2.354
7	14.91	8.524	6.521	2.911	11.35	6.491	4.965	2.217
8	12.20	7.352	5.757	2.736	9.418	5.675	4.444	2.112
9	10.38	6.516	5.198	2.597	8.103	5.088	4.059	2.028
10	9.072	5.890	4.770	2.484	7.156	4.646	3.763	1.960
12	7.343	5.017	4.159	2.312	5.889	4.023	3.335	1.854
15	5.847	4.211	3.578	2.132	4.780	3.442	2.925	1.743
20	4.548	3.462	3.019	1.943	3.802	2.895	2.524	1.624
24	3.959	3.104	2.745	1.842	3.354	2.630	2.326	1.560
30	3.403	2.752	2.471	1.735	2.927	2.367	2.125	1.492
40	2.874	2.403	2.192	1.619	2.516	2.103	1.919	1.418
60	2.358	2.046	1.902	1.490	2.110	1.831	1.702	1.333
120	1.829	1.661	1.580	1.332	1.686	1.532	1.457	1.228
∞	1.000	1.000	1.000	1.000	1.000	1.000	1.000	1.000

EXAMPLES

Testing for an increase in variance. Let $\alpha = 0.05$, $\beta = 0.01$, and $R = 4$. Entering the table with these values it is found that the value 4 occurs between the rows corresponding to $n = 15$ and $n = 20$. Using rough interpolation it is indicated that the estimate of variance should be based on nineteen degrees of freedom.

Testing for a decrease in variance. Let $\alpha = 0.05$, $\beta = 0.01$, and $R = 0.33$. The table is entered with $\alpha' = \beta = 0.01$, $\beta' = \alpha = 0.05$, and $R' = 1/R = 3$. It is found that the value 3 occurs between the rows corresponding to $n = 24$ and $n = 30$. Using rough interpolation it is indicated that the estimate of variance should be based on 26 degrees of freedom.

Table H

NUMBER OF OBSERVATIONS REQUIRED FOR THE COMPARISON OF TWO POPULATION VARIANCES USING THE F-TEST

The entries in this table show the value of the ratio R of two population variances σ_2^2/σ_1^2 which remains undetected with frequency β in a variance ratio test at significance level α of the ratio s_2^2/s_1^2 of estimates of the two variances, both being based on ϕ degrees of freedom.

ϕ	$\alpha = 0.01$				$\alpha = 0.05$				$\alpha = 0.5$			
	$\beta=0.01$	$\beta=0.05$	$\beta=0.1$	$\beta=0.5$	$\beta=0.01$	$\beta=0.05$	$\beta=0.1$	$\beta=0.5$	$\beta=0.01$	$\beta=0.05$	$\beta=0.1$	$\beta=0.5$
1	16,420,000	654,200	161,500	4052	654,200	26,070	6,436	161·5	4,052	161·5	39·85	1·000
2	9,801	1,881	891·0	99·00	1,881	361·0	171·0	19·00	99·00	19·00	9·000	1·000
3	867·7	273·3	158·8	29·46	273·3	86·06	50·01	9·277	29·46	9·277	5·391	1·000
4	255·3	102·1	65·62	15·98	102·1	40·81	26·24	6·388	15·98	6·388	4·108	1·000
5	120·3	55·39	37·87	10·97	55·39	25·51	17·44	5·050	10·97	5·050	3·453	1·000
6	71·67	36·27	25·86	8·466	36·27	18·35	13·09	4·284	8·466	4·284	3·056	1·000
7	48·90	26·48	19·47	6·993	26·48	14·34	10·55	3·787	6·993	3·787	2·786	1·000
8	36·35	20·73	15·61	6·029	20·73	11·82	8·902	3·438	6·029	3·438	2·589	1·000
9	28·63	17·01	13·06	5·351	17·01	10·11	7·757	3·179	5·351	3·179	2·440	1·000
10	23·51	14·44	11·26	4·849	14·44	8·870	6·917	2·978	4·849	2·978	2·323	1·000
12	17·27	11·16	8·923	4·155	11·16	7·218	5·769	2·687	4·155	2·687	2·147	1·000
15	12·41	8·466	6·946	3·522	8·466	5·777	4·740	2·404	3·522	2·404	1·972	1·000
20	8·630	6·240	5·270	2·938	6·240	4·512	3·810	2·124	2·938	2·124	1·794	1·000
24	7·071	5·275	4·526	2·659	5·275	3·935	3·376	1·984	2·659	1·984	1·702	1·000
30	5·693	4·392	3·833	2·386	4·392	3·389	2·957	1·841	2·386	1·841	1·606	1·000
40	4·470	3·579	3·183	2·114	3·579	2·866	2·549	1·693	2·114	1·693	1·506	1·000
60	3·372	2·817	2·562	1·836	2·817	2·354	2·141	1·534	1·836	1·534	1·396	1·000
120	2·350	2·072	1·939	1·533	2·072	1·828	1·710	1·352	1·533	1·352	1·265	1·000
∞	1·000	1·000	1·000	1·000	1·000	1·000	1·000	1·000	1·000	1·000	1·000	1·000

EXAMPLE

Let $\alpha = 0{\cdot}05$, $\beta = 0{\cdot}01$, and $R = 4$. Entering the table with these values it is found that the value 4 occurs between the rows corresponding to $n = 30$ and $n = 40$. Using rough interpolation it is indicated that each estimate of variance should be based on thirty-four degrees of freedom.

Table K

VALUES OF $\{^a_b\}$ FOR VARIOUS VALUES OF α AND β

$$a = \ln\frac{1-\beta}{\alpha} \qquad b = \ln\frac{1-\alpha}{\beta}$$

β \ α	0·0005	0·001	0·005	0·01	0·02	0·025	0·04	0·05	0·10	0·20	0·25	0·40	0·50
0·0005	7·600 / 7·600	6·907 / 7·600	5·298 / 7·596	4·605 / 7·591	3·911 / 7·581	3·688 / 7·576	3·218 / 7·560	2·995 / 7·550	2·302 / 7·496	1·609 / 7·378	1·386 / 7·313	0·916 / 7·090	0·693 / 6·908
0·001	7·600 / 6·907	6·907 / 6·907	5·297 / 6·903	4·604 / 6·898	3·911 / 6·888	3·688 / 6·882	3·218 / 6·867	2·995 / 6·856	2·302 / 6·802	1·608 / 6·685	1·385 / 6·620	0·915 / 6·397	0·692 / 6·215
0·005	7·596 / 5·298	6·903 / 5·297	5·293 / 5·293	4·600 / 5·288	3·907 / 5·278	3·684 / 5·273	3·214 / 5·257	2·991 / 5·247	2·298 / 5·193	1·604 / 5·075	1·381 / 5·011	0·911 / 4·787	0·688 / 4·605
0·01	7·591 / 4·605	6·898 / 4·604	5·288 / 4·600	4·595 / 4·595	3·902 / 4·585	3·679 / 4·580	3·209 / 4·564	2·986 / 4·554	2·293 / 4·500	1·599 / 4·382	1·376 / 4·317	0·906 / 4·094	0·683 / 3·912
0·02	7·581 / 3·911	6·888 / 3·911	5·278 / 3·907	4·585 / 3·902	3·892 / 3·892	3·669 / 3·887	3·199 / 3·871	2·976 / 3·861	2·282 / 3·807	1·589 / 3·689	1·366 / 3·624	0·896 / 3·401	0·673 / 3·219
0·025	7·576 / 3·688	6·882 / 3·688	5·273 / 3·684	4·580 / 3·679	3·887 / 3·669	3·664 / 3·664	3·194 / 3·648	2·970 / 3·638	2·277 / 3·583	1·584 / 3·466	1·361 / 3·401	0·891 / 3·178	0·668 / 2·996
0·04	7·560 / 3·218	6·867 / 3·218	5·257 / 3·214	4·564 / 3·209	3·871 / 3·199	3·648 / 3·194	3·178 / 3·178	2·955 / 3·168	2·262 / 3·114	1·569 / 2·996	1·345 / 2·931	0·875 / 2·708	0·652 / 2·526
0·05	7·550 / 2·995	6·856 / 2·995	5·247 / 2·991	4·554 / 2·986	3·861 / 2·976	3·638 / 2·970	3·168 / 2·955	2·944 / 2·944	2·251 / 2·890	1·558 / 2·773	1·335 / 2·708	0·865 / 2·485	0·642 / 2·303
0·10	7·496 / 2·302	6·802 / 2·302	5·193 / 2·298	4·500 / 2·293	3·807 / 2·282	3·583 / 2·277	3·114 / 2·262	2·890 / 2·251	2·197 / 2·197	1·504 / 2·079	1·281 / 2·015	0·811 / 1·792	0·588 / 1·609
0·20	7·378 / 1·609	6·685 / 1·608	5·075 / 1·604	4·382 / 1·599	3·689 / 1·589	3·466 / 1·584	2·996 / 1·569	2·773 / 1·558	2·079 / 1·504	1·386 / 1·386	1·163 / 1·322	0·693 / 1·099	0·470 / 0·916
0·25	7·313 / 1·386	6·620 / 1·385	5·011 / 1·381	4·317 / 1·376	3·624 / 1·366	3·401 / 1·361	2·931 / 1·345	2·708 / 1·335	2·015 / 1·281	1·322 / 1·163	1·099 / 1·099	0·629 / 0·875	0·405 / 0·693
0·40	7·090 / 0·916	6·397 / 0·915	4·787 / 0·911	4·094 / 0·906	3·401 / 0·896	3·178 / 0·891	2·708 / 0·875	2·485 / 0·865	1·792 / 0·811	1·099 / 0·693	0·875 / 0·629	0·405 / 0·405	0·182 / 0·223
0·50	6·908 / 0·693	6·215 / 0·692	4·605 / 0·688	3·912 / 0·683	3·219 / 0·673	2·996 / 0·668	2·526 / 0·652	2·303 / 0·642	1·609 / 0·588	0·916 / 0·470	0·693 / 0·405	0·223 / 0·182	0·000 / 0·000

EXAMPLES

Let $\alpha = 0 \cdot 005$, $\beta = 0 \cdot 10$. The...

BARNARD'S SEQUENTIAL t-TEST
Boundary Values U_0 and U_1
$D = 0\cdot10$

n	$\alpha=0\cdot20$ $\beta=0\cdot20$ U_0	U_1	$\alpha=0\cdot20$ $\beta=0\cdot05$ U_0	U_1	$\alpha=0\cdot20$ $\beta=0\cdot01$ U_0	U_1	$\alpha=0\cdot05$ $\beta=0\cdot20$ U_0	U_1	$\alpha=0\cdot05$ $\beta=0\cdot05$ U_0	U_1	$\alpha=0\cdot05$ $\beta=0\cdot01$ U_0	U_1	$\alpha=0\cdot01$ $\beta=0\cdot20$ U_0	U_1	$\alpha=0\cdot01$ $\beta=0\cdot05$ U_0	U_1	$\alpha=0\cdot01$ $\beta=0\cdot01$ U_0	U_1
2																		
4																		
6																		
8	[−5·14]	[4·97]																
10	[−4·49]	[4·49]		[5·01]		[5·13]	[−5·09]						[−5·24]					
15	−3·53	3·75		[4·17]		[4·27]	[−4·00]	[6·28]					[−4·11]	[7·09]				
20	−2·96	3·31	[−6·27]	3·68		3·77	−3·36	[5·67]	[−6·68]				−3·46	[6·73]	[−6·79]			
25	−2·58	3·00	[−5·50]	3·34		3·42	−2·94	5·25	[−5·87]	[6·00]		[6·07]	−3·02	6·44	[−5·96]			
30	−2·30	2·79	−4·94	3·10		3·18	−2·63	4·91	−5·27	[5·55]		[5·62]	−2·70	5·93	−5·36	[7·35]		
35	−2·08	2·63	−4·51	2·92	[−7·39]	2·98	−2·38	4·64	−4·81	5·19	[−7·70]	5·26	−2·45	5·57	−4·89	6·98		
40	−1·90	2·50	−4·16	2·77	−6·84	2·83	−2·18	4·42	−4·44	4·91	−7·13	4·97	−2·25	5·27	−4·51	6·67	[−7·20]	[7·41]
45	−1·76	2·39	−3·88	2·65	−6·38	2·71	−2·01	4·23	−4·14	4·67	−6·65	4·73	−2·08	5·03	−4·20	6·15	[−6·71]	[7·04]
50	−1·63	2·31	−3·63	2·55	−6·02	2·60	−1·87	3·93	−3·88	4·47	−6·27	4·53	−1·93	4·83	−3·94	5·77	−6·33	6·72
60	−1·42	2·17	−3·25	2·39	−5·36	2·44	−1·64	3·70	−3·47	4·15	−5·59	4·20	−1·69	4·16	−3·51	5·46	−5·64	6·19
70	−1·26	2·06	−2·95	2·26	−4·89	2·31	−1·47	3·51	−3·16	3·90	−5·10	3·95	−1·52	3·78	−3·21	5·21	−5·15	5·81
80	−1·12	1·98	−2·69	2·17	−4·51	2·21	−1·31	3·37	−2·88	3·70	−4·71	3·75	−1·36		−2·93	5·00	−4·76	5·50
90	−1·00	1·92	−2·48	2·10	−4·20	2·14	−1·18	3·24	−2·66	3·55	−4·38	3·59	−1·23		−2·71	4·30	−4·43	5·25
100	−0·90	1·87	−2·30	2·04	−3·92	2·08	−1·07	2·85	−2·47	3·41	−4·10	3·46	−1·11		−2·52	3·90	−4·14	5·04
150	−0·52	1·73	−1·64	1·87	−2·98	1·90	−0·66	2·65	−1·80	2·99	−3·12	3·03	−0·69		−1·84		−3·16	4·33
200	−0·27	1·68	−1·25	1·80	−2·40	1·83	−0·40		−1·38	2·77	−2·53	2·80	−0·42		−1·42		−2·56	3·93
n_0, n_1	14	15	28	17	44	17	16	29	29	31	45	31	16	46	30	47	46	48
$\bar n_0$, $\bar n_1$	200	200	400	300	700	300	300	400	600	600	900	600	400	700	600	900	1000	1000

n_0 and n_1 refer to the smallest number of observations for which a decision is possible when $\mu = \mu_0$ and $\mu = \mu_0 + D\sigma$ respectively.

$\bar n_0$ and $\bar n_1$ are the approximate average sample numbers when $\mu = \mu_0$ and $\mu = \mu_0 + D\sigma$ respectively.

Values of U shown in square brackets are included to assist interpolation and the drawing of boundaries and must not be used in making the test.

Table L.2
BARNARD'S SEQUENTIAL t-TEST
Boundary Values U_0 and U_1
$$D = 0.25$$

n	$\alpha=0.01$, $\beta=0.01$ U_0	U_1	$\alpha=0.01$, $\beta=0.05$ U_0	U_1	$\alpha=0.01$, $\beta=0.20$ U_0	U_1	$\alpha=0.05$, $\beta=0.01$ U_0	U_1	$\alpha=0.05$, $\beta=0.05$ U_0	U_1	$\alpha=0.05$, $\beta=0.20$ U_0	U_1	$\alpha=0.20$, $\beta=0.01$ U_0	U_1	$\alpha=0.20$, $\beta=0.05$ U_0	U_1	$\alpha=0.20$, $\beta=0.20$ U_0	U_1
2					[−3.48]												[−5.20]	[2.93]
4					[−2.56]	[4.72]					[−3.37]	[4.03]			[−4.02]	[3.23]	[−2.94]	[2.51]
6	[−6.26]	[5.68]			−2.06	[5.46]	[−6.20]	[4.29]	[−4.32]	[4.24]	[−2.48]	[3.71]		[3.30]	[−3.41]	[2.77]	−2.16	2.27
8			[−4.39]	[4.87]	−1.73	4.29	[−4.62]	[3.95]	[−3.67]	[3.91]	−1.99	3.23		[2.83]	−2.52	2.49	−1.76	2.11
10			[−3.73]	[5.64]	−1.20	3.97					−1.67	2.95	[−5.91]	2.55	−2.00	2.32	−1.43	
15	−4.67	4.91	−2.76	4.41	−0.89	3.75	−3.75	3.43	−2.72	3.39	−1.16	2.77	−4.41	2.36	−1.64	2.06	−0.98	1.89
20	−3.79	4.44	−2.21	4.09	−0.67	3.59	−3.17	3.13	−2.17	3.10	−0.85	2.65	−3.58	2.10	−1.37	1.92	−0.70	1.78
25	−3.21	4.12	−1.82	3.87	−0.49	3.46	−2.75	2.93	−1.77	2.90	−0.63	2.56	−3.02	1.96	−1.16	1.85	−0.49	1.71
30	−2.78	3.90	−1.54	3.70	−0.35	3.36	−2.42	2.80	−1.50	2.77	−0.46	2.50	−2.61	1.88	−0.98	1.80	−0.33	1.68
35	−2.45	3.72	−1.31	3.57	−0.22	3.28	−2.15	2.70	−1.28	2.67	−0.32	2.45	−2.30	1.83	−0.83	1.77	−0.20	1.66
40	−2.18	3.59	−1.12	3.46	−0.12	3.15	−1.92	2.63	−1.09	2.60	−0.20	2.41	−2.03	1.80	−0.69	1.76	−0.09	1.65
45	−1.95	3.48	−0.96	3.37	−0.02	3.07	−1.73	2.57	−0.93	2.55	−0.09	2.36	−1.81	1.78	−0.47	1.75	0.01	1.65
50	−1.75	3.40	−0.81	3.24	0.14	3.01	−1.41	2.53	−0.79	2.51	0.00	2.33	−1.63	1.77	−0.28	1.75	0.10	1.65
60	−1.43	3.26	−0.58	3.15	0.28	2.97	−1.15	2.46	−0.56	2.44	0.16	2.32	−1.32	1.77	−0.12	1.75	0.25	1.67
70	−1.17	3.17	−0.39	3.09	0.40	2.95	−0.93	2.43	−0.37	2.41	0.30	2.32	−1.07	1.78	0.02	1.77	0.38	1.69
80	−0.95	3.11	−0.22	3.04	0.51	2.92	−0.74	2.41	−0.20	2.39	0.42	2.32	−0.85	1.79	0.14	1.80	0.49	1.72
90	−0.76	3.06	−0.07	3.01	0.60	2.97	−0.58	2.41	−0.06	2.39	0.52	2.41	−0.67	1.81	0.62	1.83	0.60	1.76
100	−0.59	3.03	0.05	2.97	1.00		−0.48	2.41	0.07	2.39	0.62	2.52	−0.51	1.84	0.98	1.86	0.69	1.79
150	0.03	2.98	0.55	3.01	1.31		0.04	2.47	0.57	2.46	1.01		0.10	1.87		2.02	1.07	1.97
200	0.46	3.03	0.92				0.48	2.58	0.93	2.57	1.32		0.52	2.20		2.19	1.37	2.14
	n_0 18	n_1 20	n_0 12	n_1 20	n_0 7	n_1 20	n_0 18	n_1 14	n_0 12	n_1 13	n_0 7	n_1 13	n_0 17	n_1 8	n_0 11	n_1 7	n_0 6	n_1 7
	$\bar{n}_0$ 150	$\bar{n}_1$ 150	$\bar{n}_0$ 100	$\bar{n}_1$ 150	$\bar{n}_0$ 50	$\bar{n}_1$ 125	$\bar{n}_0$ 150	$\bar{n}_1$ 100	$\bar{n}_0$ 100	$\bar{n}_1$ 100	$\bar{n}_0$ 50	$\bar{n}_1$ 75	$\bar{n}_0$ 125	$\bar{n}_1$ 50	$\bar{n}_0$ 75	$\bar{n}_1$ 50	$\bar{n}_0$ 50	$\bar{n}_1$ 50

n_0 and n_1 refer to the smallest number of observations for which a decision is possible when $\mu = \mu_0$ and $\mu = \mu_0 + D\sigma$ respectively.

$\bar{n}_0$ and $\bar{n}_1$ are the approximate average sample numbers when $\mu = \mu_0$ and $\mu = \mu_0 + D\sigma$ respectively.

BARNARD'S SEQUENTIAL t-TEST
Boundary Values U_0 and U_1
$D = 0.50$

n	$\alpha = 0.01$						$\alpha = 0.05$						$\alpha = 0.20$					
	$\beta = 0.01$		$\beta = 0.05$		$\beta = 0.20$		$\beta = 0.01$		$\beta = 0.05$		$\beta = 0.20$		$\beta = 0.01$		$\beta = 0.05$		$\beta = 0.20$	
	U_0	U_1	U_0	U_1	U_0	U_1	U_0	U_1	U_0	U_1	U_0	U_1	U_0	U_1	U_0	U_1	U_0	U_1
2	[−3·96]	[3·49]	[−7·14]		[−2·66]		[−3·91]		[−6·96]		[−2·56]	[2·89]	[−5·65]	[2·38]	[−6·28]	[2·34]	[−2·16]	[2·15]
4	[−2·98]	[3·32]	[−3·19]		−1·24		[−2·94]		[−3·13]		−1·20	[2·62]	[−3·70]	1·99	[−2·86]	1·94	−1·00	1·79
6			−2·11	[3·46]	−0·75	[3·37]	−2·35	[3·03]	−2·07	[3·01]	−0·71	2·47	−2·78	1·82	−1·89	1·79	−0·56	1·67
8			−1·55	[3·30]	−0·45	[3·21]		[2·75]	−1·51	[2·73]	−0·41	2·37	−2·21	1·75	−1·37	1·73	−0·29	1·62
10			−1·18		−0·23			2·49	−1·15	2·46	−0·20			1·73	−1·03	1·70	−0·09	1·60
15	−1·50	3·07	−0·59	3·05	0·14	2·97	−1·47	2·36	−0·57	2·34	0·17	2·27	−1·38	1·73	−0·48	1·70	0·25	1·62
20	−0·98	2·96	−0·22	2·94	0·40	2·87	−0·96	2·33	−0·21	2·31	0·42	2·24	−0·87	1·77	−0·12	1·75	0·50	1·68
25	−0·60	2·87	0·06	2·86	0·61	2·80	−0·59	2·31	0·07	2·30	0·62	2·24	−0·51	1·82	0·14	1·81	0·69	1·74
30	−0·31	2·85	0·28	2·84	0·78	2·79	−0·30	2·34	0·29	2·32	0·79	2·27	−0·23	1·89	0·36	1·87	0·85	1·81
35	−0·07	2·85	0·47	2·84	0·93	2·79	−0·06	2·37	0·48	2·36	0·94	2·31	0·00	1·95	0·54	1·94	0·99	1·88
40	0·13	2·86	0·64	2·85	1·06	2·80	0·14	2·41	0·65	2·40	1·07	2·35	0·19	2·02	0·70	2·00	1·12	1·95
45	0·31	2·88	0·78	2·87	1·18	2·83	0·32	2·45	0·79	2·44	1·19	2·39	0·37	2·08	0·84	2·07	1·24	2·02
50	0·47	2·91	0·91	2·90	1·29	2·85	0·48	2·50	0·92	2·49	1·30	2·44	0·53	2·14	0·97	2·13	1·35	2·09
60	0·74	2·97	1·15	2·96	1·49	2·92	0·75	2·59	1·16	2·58	1·50	2·54	0·80	2·27	1·20	2·26	1·54	2·22
70	0·98	3·04	1·35	3·03	1·67	3·00	0·99	2·69	1·36	2·68	1·68	2·64	1·03	2·39	1·40	2·38	1·72	2·34
80	1·19	3·12	1·53	3·11	1·83	3·07	1·20	2·79	1·54	2·78	1·84	2·74	1·23	2·50	1·58	2·49	1·88	2·46
90	1·38	3·20	1·70	3·19	1·99	3·16	1·39	2·88	1·71	2·88	2·00	2·84	1·42	2·61	1·75	2·60	2·03	2·57
100	1·55	3·28	1·86	3·27	2·12	3·24	1·56	2·98	1·87	2·97	2·13	2·94	1·59	2·72	1·90	2·71	2·16	2·68
150	2·26	3·67	2·51	3·67	2·71	3·64	2·26	3·42	2·51	3·42	2·72	3·39	2·29	3·21	2·54	3·20	2·75	3·18
200	2·81	4·04	3·03	4·04	3·21	4·01	2·81	3·83	3·03	3·83	3·22	3·80	2·84	3·64	3·05	3·63	3·24	3·61
n_0, n_1	9	11	6	11	4	11	9	8	6	7	4	7	8	4	6	4	3	4
$\bar{n}_0$, $\bar{n}_1$	45	45	30	45	15	35	45	30	30	30	15	20	35	15	20	15	10	10

n_0 and n_1 refer to the smallest number of observations for which a decision is possible when $\mu = \mu_0$ and $\mu = \mu_0 + D\sigma$ respectively.

$\bar{n}_0$ and $\bar{n}_1$ are the approximate average sample numbers when $\mu = \mu_0$ and $\mu = \mu_0 + D\sigma$ respectively.

Values of U shown in square brackets are included to assist interpolation and the drawing of boundaries and must not be used in making the test.

Table L·4
BARNARD'S SEQUENTIAL t-TEST
Boundary Values U_0 and U_1
$D = 0.75$

n	$\alpha = 0.01$						$\alpha = 0.05$						$\alpha = 0.20$					
	$\beta = 0.01$		$\beta = 0.05$		$\beta = 0.20$		$\beta = 0.01$		$\beta = 0.05$		$\beta = 0.20$		$\beta = 0.01$		$\beta = 0.05$		$\beta = 0.20$	
	U_0	U_1	U_0	U_1	U_0	U_1	U_0	U_1	U_0	U_1	U_0	U_1	U_0	U_1	U_0	U_1	U_0	U_1
2	[−3.28]	[2.99]	[−3.96]	[2.97]	−1.29	[2.91]	[−3.21]	[2.61]	[−3.90]	[2.60]	−1.23	[2.50]	[−3.01]	[1.77]	[−3.48]	[1.73]	−0.99	[1.62]
4	−1.93	[2.83]	−1.53	[2.82]	−0.35	[2.74]	−1.90	[2.31]	−1.49	[2.30]	−0.32	[2.22]	−1.76	1.63	−1.32	1.61	−0.19	1.52
6	−1.24	2.73	−0.78	2.72	0.05	2.66	−1.21	2.22	−0.76	2.20	0.07	2.13	−1.11	1.62	−0.63	1.61	0.17	1.53
8	−0.81	2.69	−0.37	2.68	0.30	2.62	−0.79	2.18	−0.35	2.16	0.32	2.10	−0.71	1.65	−0.27	1.63	0.40	1.56
10	−0.52	2.67	−0.08	2.66	0.50	2.61	−0.51	2.17	−0.07	2.16	0.51	2.11	−0.42	1.70	0.02	1.69	0.58	1.63
15	−0.14	2.68	0.42	2.68	0.87	2.63	−0.12	2.24	0.44	2.23	0.88	2.18	−0.05	1.84	0.48	1.83	0.93	1.78
20	0.31	2.73	0.77	2.72	1.15	2.68	0.33	2.34	0.78	2.33	1.16	2.29	0.38	1.99	0.82	1.98	1.20	1.93
25	0.64	2.81	1.04	2.80	1.38	2.76	0.65	2.45	1.05	2.44	1.39	2.40	0.69	2.13	1.09	2.12	1.43	2.08
30	0.91	2.89	1.27	2.88	1.58	2.85	0.92	2.56	1.28	2.55	1.59	2.51	0.96	2.27	1.32	2.26	1.63	2.22
35	1.14	2.97	1.48	2.97	1.76	2.93	1.15	2.66	1.49	2.66	1.77	2.63	1.19	2.39	1.52	2.39	1.80	2.35
40	1.35	3.06	1.66	3.05	1.92	3.02	1.36	2.77	1.67	2.76	1.92	2.73	1.39	2.52	1.70	2.51	1.96	2.48
45	1.54	3.15	1.83	3.14	2.08	3.12	1.54	2.88	1.84	2.87	2.09	2.84	1.58	2.64	1.87	2.63	2.12	2.60
50	1.71	3.24	1.98	3.24	2.22	3.21	1.71	2.98	1.99	2.97	2.22	2.95	1.74	2.75	2.02	2.75	2.26	2.72
60	2.02	3.41	2.27	3.41	2.48	3.38	2.02	3.17	2.27	3.17	2.48	3.14	2.05	2.97	2.30	2.97	2.51	2.93
70	2.29	3.58	2.52	3.58	2.72	3.55	2.29	3.36	2.52	3.35	2.72	3.33	2.32	3.17	2.55	3.16	2.75	3.14
80	2.53	3.75	2.75	3.74	2.94	3.72	2.54	3.54	2.76	3.53	2.94	3.51	2.57	3.36	2.78	3.35	2.97	3.33
90	2.75	3.90	2.96	3.89	3.13	3.87	2.77	3.71	2.97	3.71	3.13	3.68	2.79	3.52	2.99	3.53	3.17	3.51
100	2.97	4.05	3.15	4.05	3.33	4.03	2.98	3.87	3.17	3.87	3.33	3.84	3.00	3.71	3.20	3.70	3.36	3.68
150	3.87	4.75	4.00	4.75	4.16	4.72	3.87	4.59	4.00	4.59	4.16	4.56	3.87	4.45	4.03	4.45	4.19	4.43
200	4.61	5.33	4.75	5.33	4.85	5.33	4.61	5.23	4.75	5.23	4.85	5.20	4.61	5.12	4.78	5.12	4.88	5.10
n_0 / n_1	6	8	4	8	2	8	6	5	4	5	2	5	6	3	4	3	2	3
$\bar{n}_0$ / $\bar{n}_1$	25	25	20	25	15	20	25	20	20	20	10	15	20	10	15	10	10	10

n_0 and n_1 refer to the smallest number of observations for which a decision is possible when $\mu = \mu_0$ and $\mu = \mu_0 + D\sigma$ respectively.

$\bar{n}_0$ and $\bar{n}_1$ are the approximate average sample numbers when $\mu = \mu_0$ and $\mu = \mu_0 + D\sigma$ respectively.

BARNARD'S SEQUENTIAL t-TEST

Boundary Values U_0 and U_1

$$D = 1.00$$

$\alpha = 0.01$

n	$\beta = 0.01$ U_0	U_1	$\beta = 0.05$ U_0	U_1	$\beta = 0.20$ U_0	U_1
2	[−5·80]	[2·53]	[−2·21]	[2·52]	−0·52	[2·64]
4	−1·68	[2·49]	−0·55	[2·48]	0·21	[2·48]
6	−0·73	2·50	0·01	2·49	0·56	2·44
8	−0·23	2·53	0·35	2·49	0·81	2·45
10	0·13	2·53	0·62	2·52	1·02	2·49
15	0·73	2·66	1·10	2·65	1·41	2·62
20	1·15	2·80	1·46	2·79	1·72	2·76
25	1·47	2·96	1·75	2·95	1·99	2·93
30	1·76	3·12	2·01	3·11	2·22	3·09
35	2·01	3·27	2·24	3·26	2·43	3·24
40	2·23	3·41	2·44	3·40	2·62	3·38
45	2·43	3·54	2·63	3·54	2·81	3·52
50	2·62	3·68	2·82	3·67	2·98	3·65
60	2·98	3·94	3·16	3·94	3·30	3·92
70	3·30	4·18	3·45	4·18	3·59	4·16
80	3·58	4·41	3·73	4·41	3·86	4·39
90	3·85	4·62	3·99	4·62	4·11	4·61
100	4·10	4·83	4·23	4·82	4·34	4·81
150	5·16	5·76	5·26	5·76	5·35	5·75
200	6·05	6·57	6·15	6·57	6·23	6·56
n_0 / n_1	4	7	3	7	2	6
$\bar{n}_0$ / $\bar{n}_1$	15	15	10	15	5	10

$\alpha = 0.05$

n	$\beta = 0.01$ U_0	U_1	$\beta = 0.05$ U_0	U_1	$\beta = 0.20$ U_0	U_1
2	[−5·66]	[2·15]	[−2·14]	[2·13]	−0·49	[2·06]
4	−1·65	[2·04]	−0·53	2·03	0·23	1·97
6	−0·71	2·05	0·03	2·04	0·58	1·99
8	−0·22	2·10	0·37	2·09	0·82	2·05
10	0·14	2·17	0·63	2·16	1·03	2·12
15	0·74	2·35	1·11	2·34	1·42	2·31
20	1·16	2·53	1·47	2·52	1·73	2·49
25	1·48	2·71	1·76	2·70	2·00	2·67
30	1·76	2·88	2·02	2·88	2·22	2·85
35	2·02	3·05	2·24	3·05	2·43	3·02
40	2·24	3·21	2·45	3·21	2·63	3·19
45	2·44	3·36	2·64	3·36	2·81	3·34
50	2·63	3·50	2·82	3·50	2·99	3·48
60	2·99	3·77	3·16	3·77	3·30	3·75
70	3·30	4·03	3·45	4·03	3·59	4·01
80	3·59	4·27	3·73	4·27	3·86	4·25
90	3·86	4·50	3·99	4·49	4·11	4·48
100	4·11	4·70	4·24	4·70	4·35	4·69
150	5·16	5·66	5·27	5·65	5·36	5·64
200	6·05	6·49	6·15	6·48	6·23	6·47
n_0 / n_1	4	5	3	5	2	4
$\bar{n}_0$ / $\bar{n}_1$	10	10	10	10	5	7

$\alpha = 0.20$

n	$\beta = 0.01$ U_0	U_1	$\beta = 0.05$ U_0	U_1	$\beta = 0.20$ U_0	U_1
2	[−5·16]	[1·56]	[−1·89]	[1·54]	−0·33	[1·46]
4	−1·51	1·54	−0·43	1·53	0·31	1·49
6	−0·62	1·65	0·10	1·64	0·64	1·58
8	−0·15	1·74	0·43	1·73	0·88	1·68
10	0·20	1·84	0·68	1·83	1·07	1·79
15	0·78	2·08	1·15	2·07	1·46	2·04
20	1·19	2·30	1·50	2·30	1·76	2·27
25	1·51	2·49	1·79	2·48	2·02	2·46
30	1·79	2·68	2·05	2·68	2·25	2·65
35	2·04	2·86	2·26	2·86	2·45	2·83
40	2·26	3·04	2·47	3·03	2·65	3·01
45	2·46	3·20	2·66	3·19	2·83	3·17
50	2·65	3·35	2·84	3·34	3·01	3·32
60	3·01	3·63	3·18	3·63	3·32	3·61
70	3·32	3·90	3·47	3·89	3·61	3·88
80	3·60	4·15	3·75	4·14	3·87	4·13
90	3·87	4·38	4·01	4·38	4·13	4·36
100	4·12	4·60	4·25	4·59	4·36	4·58
150	5·17	5·56	5·28	5·56	5·37	5·55
200	6·06	6·41	6·16	6·41	6·24	6·40
n_0 / n_1	4	3	3	3	2	3
$\bar{n}_0$ / $\bar{n}_1$	10	5	5	5	5	5

n_0 and n_1 refer to the smallest number of observations for which a decision is possible when $\mu = \mu_0$ and $\mu = \mu_0 + D\sigma$ respectively.

$\bar{n}_0$ and $\bar{n}_1$ are the approximate average sample numbers when $\mu = \mu_0$ and $\mu = \mu_0 + D\sigma$ respectively.

Values of U shown in square brackets are included to assist interpolation and the drawing of boundaries and must not be used in making the test.

Table L.6
BARNARD'S SEQUENTIAL t-TEST
Boundary Values U_0 and U_1
$D = 1.50$

n	$\alpha=0.01$ $\beta=0.01$ U_0	U_1	$\beta=0.05$ U_0	U_1	$\beta=0.20$ U_0	U_1	$\alpha=0.05$ $\beta=0.01$ U_0	U_1	$\beta=0.05$ U_0	U_1	$\beta=0.20$ U_0	U_1	$\alpha=0.20$ $\beta=0.01$ U_0	U_1	$\beta=0.05$ U_0	U_1	$\beta=0.20$ U_0	U_1
2	[−1·89]	[2·06]	−0·44	[2·05]	0·32	[2·02]	[−1·88]	[1·70]	−0·47	[1·69]	0·33	[1·64]	[−1·65]	1·35	−0·39	1·33	0·40	1·28
4	[−0·03]	[2·13]	0·49	[2·12]	0·85	[2·09]	−0·02	1·85	0·51	1·84	0·86	1·81	0·04	1·56	0·55	1·56	0·90	1·53
6	0·56	2·26	0·90	2·25	1·19	2·22	0·57	2·02	0·91	2·01	1·20	1·99	0·61	1·78	0·95	1·77	1·24	1·75
8	0·93	2·39	1·22	2·38	1·46	2·36	0·94	2·19	1·23	2·18	1·47	2·16	0·98	1·97	1·26	1·97	1·50	1·95
10	1·23	2·53	1·48	2·52	1·70	2·50	1·24	2·35	1·49	2·34	1·70	2·32	1·27	2·15	1·52	2·15	1·73	2·13
15	1·80	2·87	2·00	2·86	2·17	2·84	1·81	2·71	2·01	2·70	2·18	2·68	1·84	2·55	2·03	2·55	2·20	2·53
20	2·24	3·18	2·42	3·17	2·56	3·15	2·25	3·03	2·42	3·02	2·57	3·01	2·28	2·89	2·44	2·89	2·59	2·87
25	2·62	3·46	2·78	3·46	2·91	3·44	2·63	3·32	2·78	3·32	2·91	3·30	2·66	3·19	2·80	3·19	2·92	3·18
30	2·95	3·72	3·09	3·72	3·21	3·70	2·96	3·59	3·09	3·59	3·21	3·57	2·99	3·47	3·11	3·47	3·23	3·46
35	3·25	3·96	3·38	3·96	3·49	3·94	3·26	3·84	3·38	3·84	3·49	3·82	3·29	3·73	3·40	3·73	3·50	3·72
40	3·52	4·19	3·64	4·19	3·74	4·17	3·53	4·07	3·64	4·07	3·75	4·06	3·56	3·97	3·66	3·97	3·76	3·96
45	3·78	4·40	3·89	4·40	3·99	4·38	3·78	4·30	3·89	4·29	3·99	4·28	3·81	4·20	3·90	4·20	4·00	4·19
50	4·02	4·61	4·12	4·61	4·21	4·60	4·02	4·51	4·12	4·50	4·21	4·49	4·05	4·42	4·14	4·42	4·23	4·41
	n_1 5		n_0 2	n_1 5	n_0 2	n_1 5	n_0 3	n_1 4	n_0 2	n_1 4	n_0 2	n_1 4	n_0 3	n_1 2	n_0 2	n_1 2	n_0 2	n_1 2

$\bar{n}_0$ and $\bar{n}_1$ are in each case less than 10.

n_0 and n_1 refer to the smallest number of observations for which a decision is possible when $\mu = \mu_0$ and $\mu = \mu_0 + D\sigma$ respectively.

$\bar{n}_0$ and $\bar{n}_1$ are the approximate average sample numbers when $\mu = \mu_0$ and $\mu = \mu_0 + D\sigma$ respectively.

Values of U shown in square brackets are included to assist interpolation and the drawing of boundaries and must not be used in making

BARNARD'S SEQUENTIAL t-TEST

Boundary Values U_0 and U_1

$D = 2.00$

n	$\alpha=0.01$ $\beta=0.01$ U_0	U_1	$\alpha=0.01$ $\beta=0.05$ U_0	U_1	$\alpha=0.01$ $\beta=0.20$ U_0	U_1	$\alpha=0.05$ $\beta=0.01$ U_0	U_1	$\alpha=0.05$ $\beta=0.05$ U_0	U_1	$\alpha=0.05$ $\beta=0.20$ U_0	U_1	$\alpha=0.20$ $\beta=0.01$ U_0	U_1	$\alpha=0.20$ $\beta=0.05$ U_0	U_1	$\alpha=0.20$ $\beta=0.20$ U_0	U_1
2	−0.26	[1.79]	0.36	[1.79]	0.73	[1.76]	−0.24	[1.57]	0.37	[1.56]	0.74	[1.54]	−0.16	1.36	0.42	1.35	0.78	1.32
4	0.75	2.00	1.02	2.00	1.23	1.98	0.74	1.83	1.03	1.82	1.23	1.80	0.77	1.66	1.06	1.66	1.27	1.64
6	1.22	2.22	1.42	2.22	1.59	2.20	1.22	2.07	1.43	2.06	1.59	2.05	1.25	1.93	1.45	1.93	1.61	1.91
8	1.56	2.42	1.73	2.42	1.87	2.41	1.56	2.29	1.74	2.29	1.87	2.27	1.59	2.17	1.75	2.16	1.89	2.15
10	1.85	2.62	2.00	2.61	2.12	2.60	1.85	2.49	2.00	2.49	2.12	2.48	1.87	2.38	2.01	2.38	2.14	2.36
15	2.42	3.03	2.54	3.03	2.64	3.02	2.42	2.94	2.54	2.94	2.64	2.93	2.44	2.85	2.55	2.84	2.65	2.83
20	2.87	3.41	2.97	3.41	3.06	3.40	2.87	3.32	2.97	3.32	3.06	3.31	2.88	3.25	2.98	3.24	3.07	3.23
25	3.28	3.76	3.36	3.75	3.43	3.74	3.28	3.67	3.36	3.67	3.43	3.66	3.29	3.60	3.37	3.60	3.44	3.59
30	3.63	4.07	3.71	4.07	3.78	4.06	3.63	3.99	3.71	3.99	3.78	3.98	3.64	3.93	3.72	3.93	3.79	3.92
35	3.96	4.36	4.03	4.36	4.09	4.35	3.96	4.29	4.03	4.29	4.09	4.28	3.97	4.23	4.04	4.23	4.10	4.22
40	4.25	4.63	4.32	4.63	4.38	4.62	4.25	4.57	4.32	4.57	4.38	4.56	4.26	4.51	4.33	4.51	4.39	4.50
45	4.54	4.89	4.60	4.89	4.65	4.88	4.54	4.83	4.60	4.83	4.65	4.82	4.54	4.78	4.61	4.77	4.66	4.77
50	4.80	5.14	4.86	5.14	4.91	5.13	4.80	5.08	4.86	5.08	4.91	5.07	4.80	5.03	4.87	5.03	4.92	5.02
	n_0 2	n_1 4	n_0 2	n_1 4	n_0 2	n_1 4	n_0 2	n_1 3	n_0 2	n_1 3	n_0 2	n_1 3	n_0 2	n_1 2	n_0 2	n_1 2	n_0 2	n_1 2

$\tilde{n}_0$ and $\tilde{n}_1$ are in each case less than 10.

n_0 and n_1 refer to the smallest number of observations for which a decision is possible when $\mu = \mu_0$ and $\mu = \mu_0 + D\sigma$ respectively.

$\tilde{n}_0$ and $\tilde{n}_1$ are the approximate average sample numbers when $\mu = \mu_0$ and $\mu = \mu_0 + D\sigma$ respectively.

Values of U shown in square brackets are included to assist interpolation and the drawing of boundaries and must not be used in making the test.

Table L.8

BARNARD'S SEQUENTIAL t-TEST

Boundary Values U_0 and U_1

$$D = 3.00$$

n	α = 0.01 $\beta = 0.01$ U_0	U_1	$\beta = 0.05$ U_0	U_1	$\beta = 0.20$ U_0	U_1	α = 0.05 $\beta = 0.01$ U_0	U_1	$\beta = 0.05$ U_0	U_1	$\beta = 0.20$ U_0	U_1	α = 0.20 $\beta = 0.01$ U_0	U_1	$\beta = 0.05$ U_0	U_1	$\beta = 0.20$ U_0	U_1
2	0.77	[1.57]	0.95	[1.57]	1.09	[1.56]	0.77	[1.46]	0.95	[1.46]	1.09	[1.44]	0.79	1.36	0.97	1.35	1.11	1.34
4	1.39	1.94	1.50	1.94	1.59	1.93	1.40	1.86	1.50	1.85	1.59	1.85	1.41	1.78	1.51	1.78	1.60	1.77
6	1.81	2.26	1.90	2.26	1.97	2.25	1.82	2.19	1.90	2.19	1.97	2.17	1.82	2.12	1.91	2.12	1.98	2.11
8	2.15	2.54	2.22	2.53	2.28	2.53	2.16	2.47	2.22	2.47	2.28	2.46	2.16	2.41	2.23	2.41	2.29	2.40
10	2.44	2.78	2.50	2.78	2.56	2.78	2.44	2.73	2.50	2.73	2.56	2.72	2.45	2.68	2.51	2.68	2.57	2.67
15	3.05	3.34	3.10	3.34	3.15	3.33	3.06	3.29	3.10	3.29	3.15	3.28	3.06	3.25	3.11	3.25	3.15	3.24
	n_0	n_1	n_0	n_1	n_0	n_1	n_0	n_1	n_0	n_1	n_0	n_1	n_0	n_1	n_0	n_1	n_0	n_1
	2	4	2	4	2	4	2	3	2	3	2	3	2	2	2	2	2	2

$\tilde{n}_0$ and $\tilde{n}_1$ are in each case less than 5.

n_0 and n_1 refer to the smallest number of observations for which a decision is possible when $\mu = \mu_0$ and $\mu = \mu_0 + D\sigma$ respectively.

$\tilde{n}_0$ and $\tilde{n}_1$ are the approximate average sample numbers when $\mu = \mu_0$ and $\mu = \mu_0 + D\sigma$ respectively.

Values of U shown in square brackets are included to assist interpolation and the drawing of boundaries and must not be used in making

EFFE... 2^6 ←

Combinations	CDF	ACDF	BCDF	ABCDF	EF	AEF	BEF	ABEF	CEF	ACEF	BCEF	ABCEF	DEF	ADEF	BDEF	ABDEF	CDEF	ACDEF	BCDEF	ABCDEF
(1)	−	+	+	−	+	−	−	+	−	+	+	−	−	+	+	−	+	−	−	+
a	−	−	+	+	+	+	−	−	−	−	+	+	−	−	+	+	+	+	−	−
b	−	+	−	+	+	−	+	−	−	+	−	+	−	+	−	+	+	−	+	−
ab	−	−	−	−	+	+	+	+	−	−	−	−	−	−	−	−	+	+	+	+
c	+	−	−	+	+	−	−	+	+	−	−	+	−	+	+	−	−	+	+	−
ac	+	+	−	−	+	+	−	−	+	+	−	−	−	−	+	+	−	−	+	+
bc	+	−	+	−	+	−	+	−	+	−	+	−	−	+	−	+	−	+	−	+
abc	+	+	+	+	+	+	+	+	+	+	+	+	−	−	−	−	−	−	−	−
d	+	−	−	+	+	−	−	+	−	+	+	−	+	−	−	+	−	+	+	−
ad	+	+	−	−	+	+	−	−	−	−	+	+	+	+	−	−	−	−	+	+
bd	+	−	+	−	+	−	+	−	−	+	−	+	+	−	+	−	−	+	−	+
abd	+	+	+	+	+	+	+	+	−	−	−	−	+	+	+	+	−	−	−	−
cd	−	+	+	−	+	−	−	+	+	−	−	+	+	−	−	+	+	−	−	+
acd	−	−	+	+	+	+	−	−	+	+	−	−	+	+	−	−	+	+	−	−
bcd	−	+	−	+	+	−	+	−	+	−	+	−	+	−	+	−	+	−	+	−
abcd	−	−	−	−	+	+	+	+	+	+	+	+	+	+	+	+	+	+	+	+

EXAMPLE

Let $\delta = 0.5$, $\alpha = 0.05$, $\beta = 0.05$ and an estimate of σ be 1.0. Thus $D = 0.5/1.0 = 0.5$ and the table appropriate for applying the test is Table L·3. In an experiment (see § **3·311**) the successive values obtained for $U = \Sigma(x - \mu_0)/\Sigma(x - \mu_0)^2$ were

n	1	2	3	4	5	6	7	8	9
U	—	0·92	1·35	1·65	1·85	1·97	1·36	1·43	1·35

n	10	11	12	13	14	15	16	17	
U	1·67	1·79	2·01	2·16	2·01	2·10	2·33	2·49	

The value of U remains within the corresponding values of the boundary limits U_0 and U_1 until the seventeenth observation, when it exceeds U_1. The hypothesis that a real difference has occurred is therefore accepted.

Table N
TABLE OF RANDOM NUMBERS

```
83 28   78 05   18 98   49 22   54 11   92 37   45 11   63 60   19 05   91 26
84 73   82 58   01 90   55 37   85 68   98 15   99 52   99 84   51 91   73 81
00 79   20 99   42 57   55 67   93 39   99 25   65 10   94 54   84 65   16 23
94 48   02 99   71 08   50 84   66 10   10 34   92 30   89 28   30 74   24 24
54 37   52 43   87 22   21 34   20 15   07 67   64 98   36 01   33 34   04 42

47 68   59 90   98 90   27 71   89 89   98 20   24 19   85 02   34 38   26 71
76 16   58 55   51 85   44 00   28 28   38 91   70 70   16 81   13 49   46 54
37 64   90 35   64 45   47 72   82 03   01 65   05 97   13 90   90 57   51 97
92 78   39 12   48 01   83 46   39 29   98 71   39 56   97 66   97 70   05 77
24 50   29 02   71 28   53 99   75 07   13 18   76 97   72 54   85 79   71 60

01 72   71 23   86 40   70 05   35 36   15 64   11 01   11 18   90 14   95 05
43 28   52 77   22 80   49 89   79 65   91 17   80 94   34 02   17 61   00 42
29 09   19 54   67 67   88 54   62 09   07 97   35 19   31 25   06 92   25 02
27 95   74 89   62 45   75 39   06 89   58 96   64 65   81 84   85 20   01 47
52 43   54 97   75 80   00 38   20 38   57 46   57 33   87 19   66 06   40 32

78 11   60 42   09 83   28 40   93 57   61 22   27 27   47 80   44 34   47 27
03 74   36 27   13 19   14 76   35 73   66 29   95 65   12 87   61 91   34 30
82 25   35 57   16 29   21 27   51 23   06 52   40 00   28 11   47 23   63 01
09 91   87 20   33 76   61 55   79 21   74 36   21 36   05 47   28 42   92 51
19 82   00 40   15 52   45 35   13 48   74 10   97 36   22 85   44 57   91 72

69 41   17 07   11 54   36 81   57 38   55 39   85 74   48 05   06 43   10 63
48 80   36 26   28 95   03 79   54 31   41 55   48 84   78 63   09 05   69 07
80 02   51 78   94 07   88 62   85 82   80 37   56 15   59 30   46 42   84 02
19 51   95 22   72 72   95 51   57 73   04 68   00 95   04 30   66 52   60 74
50 36   31 76   75 39   04 95   69 47   95 23   01 70   95 04   04 18   68 14

60 03   34 57   41 76   35 06   75 60   21 58   86 36   02 33   00 59   63 13
59 40   60 83   61 73   45 18   08 23   54 86   64 57   76 70   00 89   43 24
29 51   12 43   14 24   35 78   76 22   82 50   68 02   13 19   07 00   19 07
57 07   34 86   57 96   99 57   44 54   90 87   33 76   71 71   23 28   88 37
81 73   29 08   96 62   34 26   52 32   23 74   17 49   45 62   17 88   50 50

40 20   21 54   17 65   99 31   09 72   67 87   16 34   00 76   26 23   42 40
81 26   86 30   79 17   93 45   74 50   50 24   65 52   06 59   04 60   73 63
13 65   31 57   36 88   98 35   04 96   41 37   45 87   57 57   21 15   34 59
23 41   47 66   24 73   31 96   72 07   09 43   88 63   33 80   54 79   84 18
79 62   53 27   85 43   51 69   83 81   90 85   84 72   18 48   41 20   81 59

13 40   75 73   19 92   12 01   91 95   23 99   99 30   30 58   46 22   64 41
54 87   97 55   83 91   42 61   41 02   40 18   39 20   56 19   56 35   04 32
09 29   30 63   75 86   85 29   15 34   68 92   34 06   81 60   32 16   05 37
61 99   27 99   73 18   94 29   25 74   22 20   70 46   30 38   26 91   59 16
31 84   93 27   40 23   25 86   68 30   10 11   91 59   61 07   41 97   10 39

35 86   11 25   98 38   27 14   79 68   77 60   63 34   23 80   75 43   48 79
40 42   68 85   23 40   27 56   54 56   75 65   70 49   24 08   10 44   75 59
25 14   94 00   99 80   81 44   49 08   98 93   71 74   11 14   54 69   71 69
56 18   75 63   56 68   25 36   75 98   00 18   19 15   24 28   56 80   75 97
79 61   54 67   58 38   93 69   45 95   61 19   17 35   89 90   98 70   26 20

92 91   85 49   33 32   46 67   28 20   40 99   88 73   56 33   29 13   41 89
01 79   85 45   45 36   05 67   56 17   59 77   59 34   35 01   15 21   00 35
55 84   71 36   40 39   47 25   25 73   69 14   55 73   35 86   61 17   98 69
38 36   66 66   19 40   90 83   06 31   24 67   91 74   54 14   87 24   61 80
01 69   50 70   31 02   98 86   42 01   94 98   07 85   28 38   37 30   72 76
```

Table N (continued)
TABLE OF RANDOM NUMBERS

```
87 08   83 09   40 14   39 15   99 24   21 85   00 45   54 19   36 18   03 88
88 33   78 20   40 40   24 73   77 70   00 31   84 59   26 06   50 30   95 96
22 50   09 11   00 37   36 51   55 95   83 97   13 75   46 22   77 50   11 72
48 70   56 57   16 24   21 74   91 53   18 05   59 61   74 97   31 82   77 68
93 45   40 93   12 80   88 63   26 93   85 05   19 87   84 37   59 76   16 65

50 76   72 02   39 19   40 69   57 23   09 33   20 70   86 45   13 94   98 39
91 64   01 34   67 13   11 00   32 09   39 76   21 64   29 85   65 14   51 74
33 20   63 71   95 94   13 77   12 44   12 94   91 04   41 83   79 72   44 08
90 59   65 46   78 82   16 45   97 85   57 75   79 96   79 08   16 83   43 99
05 10   93 57   80 32   86 65   26 90   27 54   34 94   46 33   65 35   56 84

92 85   63 26   69 69   81 54   70 56   17 62   43 17   86 78   99 62   34 15
08 50   36 55   82 11   26 54   76 88   85 67   82 21   65 00   83 89   06 09
59 36   77 09   83 87   81 77   93 77   48 44   88 30   37 21   74 02   93 10
05 85   86 43   25 50   76 70   36 32   26 68   54 92   84 90   02 38   77 40
13 46   99 31   30 29   71 70   91 10   99 84   55 31   95 20   90 28   49 78

56 27   09 33   66 79   32 29   50 54   76 94   27 01   45 87   29 66   23 15
54 15   62 11   22 33   39 39   58 30   73 43   59 32   26 43   76 12   99 10
83 01   86 58   89 77   68 87   29 71   49 50   46 53   56 53   41 53   52 20
00 28   17 33   81 42   24 33   55 75   42 70   73 65   16 96   47 17   42 69
52 29   68 59   32 69   40 30   89 12   11 07   18 53   27 13   46 54   85 40

64 43   09 80   68 29   86 65   60 27   87 70   77 45   31 69   12 31   21 79
80 68   13 48   80 84   25 33   70 89   76 61   03 41   57 89   87 07   56 12
28 72   57 80   54 05   80 92   82 65   25 01   74 58   89 39   25 05   57 66
23 48   49 96   00 17   88 90   63 67   02 64   71 12   21 02   29 86   88 54
04 41   27 70   10 49   13 76   99 38   64 14   90 60   69 75   10 97   16 60

21 31   95 96   89 48   65 14   12 02   94 50   35 64   58 43   92 07   74 08
52 08   13 32   36 45   39 54   82 26   46 60   04 19   34 61   36 12   46 15
90 57   88 69   61 05   22 76   90 79   01 74   22 08   26 13   95 13   75 53
76 50   49 80   25 61   81 96   19 92   33 14   60 41   27 06   05 98   51 49
06 84   76 10   54 41   54 56   15 96   49 19   65 51   93 32   54 54   95 67

47 92   60 37   45 39   67 64   70 05   06 54   84 10   88 68   33 60   77 81
71 87   94 13   64 75   18 17   76 80   95 10   33 33   35 31   30 47   53 74
38 30   36 79   74 83   61 91   56 22   83 73   15 54   63 39   50 33   88 83
09 80   50 48   23 26   05 85   68 97   06 78   00 17   76 05   95 31   03 37
82 52   08 00   33 76   29 14   18 59   98 12   89 34   50 70   13 07   60 38

14 18   02 28   72 80   85 72   09 59   05 26   05 26   90 65   47 12   85 65
62 60   63 74   20 31   60 66   90 87   09 41   59 73   60 00   21 96   38 40
15 02   56 81   29 34   90 99   07 57   80 24   92 41   88 41   01 88   05 62
23 32   03 76   20 25   96 68   01 99   79 82   58 06   89 54   74 06   01 39
96 66   81 45   01 09   18 35   41 97   70 37   94 95   48 64   01 75   04 39

12 41   98 35   82 38   49 91   71 57   83 06   55 84   38 04   70 18   75 19
70 78   63 95   94 82   54 88   47 69   63 32   79 75   31 56   38 92   54 43
30 43   70 43   70 32   73 47   49 64   23 54   59 17   80 48   61 66   45 66
36 58   96 32   60 46   60 87   52 75   53 13   39 19   41 52   24 14   88 93
17 35   36 91   90 59   48 78   99 31   64 40   84 05   79 00   53 03   64 02

73 30   27 77   44 50   07 79   27 66   42 39   97 64   84 36   18 13   59 61
92 15   47 21   82 54   76 05   54 10   40 93   71 96   66 52   83 98   17 85
05 02   28 36   50 64   47 21   36 25   80 01   43 41   36 58   97 15   29 95
51 22   04 71   06 37   31 45   69 62   30 84   20 28   14 41   70 05   56 88
23 28   85 05   96 40   37 56   52 60   65 75   21 47   84 15   99 92   02 41
```

The commonest use in experimental work of a table of random numbers such as these (which are from a bigger set of tables by KENDALL and BABINGTON SMITH) is to enable a set of samples or treatment combinations to be arrayed in random order. If the number of items to be arrayed is N, and this is less than 11, the simplest way is to begin at random anywhere in the table, and working across (in either direction) or upwards or downwards to take the order of first occurrence of the numbers 1 to N as indicating the order to be adopted.

EXAMPLE

Place the seven items A, B, C, D, E, F, G in random order.

Make a random choice of a starting point in the table, say the entry in the 17th column and 33rd row in the first part of the table. Working down the column (again a random choice), the order of first occurrence of the figures 1 ... 7 is 7 4 1 2 6 5 3, so that a random order for the items is $G\ D\ A\ B\ F\ E\ C$.

If there are more than ten items it is generally laborious and time-consuming to adopt a similar method using the pairs of numbers in the table, and a better way is as follows. If the number of items is less than 100, choose a pair of numbers at random as a starting point, divide it by N, and use the remainder after division as indicating the item to be allocated to the first place in the random array. Score out this item. The next pair of numbers (upwards, downwards, or across) in the table is then divided by $N - 1$, the remainder taken as indicating the item to be allocated to the second place in the random array. Proceed in this way, scoring out each item allocated and reducing the divisor by unity at each stage.

EXAMPLE

Place the nineteen items $H, I, \mathcal{J}, K, L, M, N, O, P, Q, R, S, T, U, V, W$ X, Y, Z in random order. Beginning in the 3rd row from the bottom of the second part of the table and the 7–8th column, and working up the column, the places are obtained as follows:

Tabulated Random No.	.. 36	21	77	91	32	43	95	35	45	76	81	74	28	00	48	79	13	37
Divisor	.. 19	18	17	16	15	14	13	12	11	10	9	8	7	6	5	4	3	2
Remainder	17	3	9	11	2	1	4	11	1	6	0	2	0	0	3	3	1	1
Placing	..X	$\mathcal{J}$	Q	T	I	H	N	Y	K	S	Z	M	W	V	P	R	L	O U

GENERAL INDEX

INDEX OF PROPER NAMES

Printed in Great Britain at THE KYNOCH PRESS, Birmingham